Kinematics of spherical mechanisms

C. H. Chiang

KRIEGER PUBLISHING COMPANY
MALABAR, FLORIDA
2000

Original Edition 1988 (Cambridge University Press)
Corrected Edition 1996 (Mc-Graw Hill, Taiwan)
Reprinted Edition 2000 w/new preface (Krieger Publishing Company)

Printed and Published by
KRIEGER PUBLISHING COMPANY
KRIEGER DRIVE
MALABAR, FLORIDA 32950

Copyright © 1996 by Mc-Graw-Hill, Int'l Enterprises Inc. Taiwan
Transferred to Author 2000
Reprinted by Arrangement

Library of Congress Cataloging-in-Publication Data

Chiang, C. H.
    Kinematics of spherical mechanisms / C.H. Chiang.
        p. cm.
    Includes bibliographical references and index.
    ISBN 1-57524-155-2 (alk. paper)
    1. Machinery, Kinematics of. 2. Links and link-motion. 3. Spherical trigonometry. I. Title.

TJ175 .C43 2000
621.8'11—dc21
                                                    00-039067

10   9   8   7   6   5   4   3   2

CONTENTS

PREFACE

This book was first published by Cambridge University Press in 1988. It was then revised and reprinted by McGraw-Hill International Enterprises Inc. (Taiwan) in 1996. The present edition is reprinted from the revised book by Krieger Publishing Company, providing a service to the international kinematics community. The author is indebted to all three publishers for their effort in bringing this book to its finest style to the readers.

Taipei, 1999   C. H. Chiang

1

Introduction

The term Spherical Mechanism might make one think of a ball-and-socket joint or of a self-aligning spherical bearing. Although these machine elements are truly spherical joints, they are, however, not spherical mechanisms. A mechanism is, under any circumstances, a constrained kinematic chain or linkage with one link fixed. Thus, in general, a simple spherical mechanism consists of four links and four revolute pairs, while neither the links nor the pairs necessarily exhibit a spherical shape. One may even not have noticed the existence of spherical mechanisms although one might have encountered them frequently. For instance, the Hooke's universal joint is a spherical four-bar linkage and a pair of bevel gears is the spherical counterpart of a pair of spur gears.

As the names imply, in a plane mechanism any point in a moving body is confined to move within a plane, and all planes of motion are parallel to one another; similarly in a spherical mechanism any point in a moving body is confined to move within a spherical surface, and all spherical surfaces of motion are concentric. A moving body in a three dimensional space possesses six degrees of freedom, namely, translations in three mutually perpendicular directions and rotations about three mutually perpendicular axes. A body performing a plane motion has only three degrees of freedom: translations in two mutually perpendicular directions in the plane and rotation about an axis perpendicular to the plane of motion. Similarly a body performing a spherical motion has also only three degrees of freedom: rotations about three mutually perpendicular axes passing through the centre of the sphere. Hence any spherical motion is a rotation. The rotation may be one about a fixed axis, or about an instantaneous axis. No matter whether the axis is fixed or instantaneous, it must pass through the centre of the sphere. Even the axis of a relative spherical motion also passes through the sphere centre. This is why the axes of the four revolute pairs of a spherical four-bar linkage intersect in the sphere centre.

If a body performs a general spherical motion, the locus of the instantaneous axis of rotation in the fixed body is a cone, and is called the fixed polode cone. The locus of the instantaneous axis in the moving body is also a cone, and is called the moving polode cone. A general spherical motion can therefore be considered as a rolling motion of the moving polode cone on the fixed polode cone.

In a plane mechanism, or more specifically, in a plane four-bar linkage, most studies have been made on the kinematics of the connecting rod, or the coupler, because it is the only link which performs a general plane motion. Similarly, in a spherical four-bar linkage, the coupler is the only link which performs a general spherical motion, hence its motion demands more detailed study than those of the two links rotating about fixed axes. In fact, plane mechanisms are a special case of spherical mechanisms in which the radius of the sphere extends to infinity. Problems concerning kinematics of spherical motion may usually be treated by similar means to those used in kinematics of plane motion. The well-known Hartmann construction, Bobillier construction and Euler–Savary equation in plane kinematics have their respective counterparts in spherical kinematics. A comprehensive understanding of plane kinematics is therefore very helpful, though not essential, in the study of spherical mechanisms.

In spherical geometry a great circle arc corresponds to a straight line in plane geometry. Since any two great circles must intersect, therefore parallelism between two great circles does not exist, while it is quite correct to say that two great circles are perpendicular to each other. Consequently, in spite of some similarities between spherical and plane kinematics, theorems which are applicable to plane kinematics are in general not transferable to spherical kinematics. For instance, the spherical counterpart of the inflection circle is a rather complicated spherical inflection curve, and that of the Carter–Hall circle is no longer a spherical circle.

As shown by Dittrich, a comparison between plane, spherical and spatial mechanisms does not indicate that any one kind of mechanism has precedence over the other two kinds (Dittrich, 1970). The selection of a certain kind of mechanism should be determined rather by the kinematic efficiency in each individual case. However, we may say that in certain aspects spherical mechanisms have the following advantages. First of all, a spherical mechanism may take up the least space. It is possible by coupling two spherical four-bar linkages to obtain a variety of transmission characteristics (Uhing, 1957), and also by combining a spherical four-bar linkage with a pair of bevel gears easily to obtain a rotary dwell mechanism. In transmitting a rotary motion from one shaft to another shaft whose axis is intersecting at an angle with the axis of the first shaft, it seems that a spherical mechanism is rather a direct solution. It is even possible to obtain from a single spherical four-bar linkage the so-called proportional mechanism, i.e. a mechanism with approximately constant angular velocity ratio over a certain range of the input angle.

If we consider that the progress of mechanisms is from planar to spherical, and then from spherical to spatial, then spherical mechanisms are an intermediate stage between plane and spatial mechanisms. Just like the plane indicatrices of some spherical linkages, there are spherical indicatrices of spatial linkages (Dobrovolskii, 1952, 1947b, c; Keler, 1970). A thorough understanding of spherical mechanisms is helpful in the study of spatial mechanisms.

Articles published on analysis as well as on synthesis problems of spherical mechanisms during the past few decades are numerous, but are quite scattered, ranging from introductory papers (Crossley, 1955; Keator & Crossley, 1955) to papers dealing with specific problems. Early contributions of Dobrovolskii (1940, 1943, 1944, 1945, 1947a, b, c, 1952) can be considered as pioneer works in the kinematics of spherical mechanisms. In the following chapters we shall review some of the important knowledge and techniques so far developed in this branch of the theory of mechanisms.

2

Fundamental spherical mechanisms

2.1   **Spherical motion**

Spherical motion is defined as the motion of a rigid body, a unique point of which is permanently fixed in space. Let this point be denoted by O. Because the distance between any point in the body, say A, and the fixed point O is not changeable, the point A can only move within a spherical surface. The point O then becomes the centre of the spherical surface. The position of the rigid body will be completely determined if the positions of any two points A and B in the body are determined, provided that O, A and B are not collinear. In other words, if A and B are on the same spherical surface, the position of the whole body can be fully represented by the positions of A and B. It follows that, as far as kinematics of a rigid body is concerned, it is sufficient to consider the motion of two distinct points of the body, both lying on the same spherical surface. It is also sufficient, in the case of multiply moving bodies with a common sphere centre, to consider only the motion of such points of these bodies that lie on a unique spherical surface. Without loss of generality the radius of this unique sphere may be taken as unity and the sphere is called a unit sphere. Each body, however, may be considered as a spherical shell of negligible thickness, extending over the whole surface of the unit sphere.

Corresponding to the straight line on a plane, the shortest line on a curved surface connecting two points is called a *geodetic line*. The geodetic line on a spherical surface between two points is part of a great circle. The great circle is the intersection of the spherical surface with a plane passing through these two points and the sphere centre. It is well known that, in plane kinematics, a rigid body can be represented by a straight line passing through two points of the body. Similarly in spherical kinematics a rigid body can also be represented by a segment of a great circle passing through two points of the body, on the surface of the unit sphere. A spherical angle between two great circles is the dihedral angle made by the planes of the two great circles.

Let us consider the motion of a spherically moving body AB, represented by a piece of a spherical shell as shown in Fig. 2.1. Assume that the directions of the velocities $\mathbf{v}_A$ and $\mathbf{v}_B$ of the points A and B are known. $\mathbf{v}_A$ must be normal to OA. If we draw a great circle m passing through A and normal to the direction of $\mathbf{v}_A$, then, by the definition of a rigid body, the direction of the velocity of any point on the great circle m must be parallel to $\mathbf{v}_A$. Similarly the direction of the velocity of any point on the great circle n passing through B and normal to $\mathbf{v}_B$ must be parallel to $\mathbf{v}_B$. Let the intersection point of the two great circles m and n be denoted by P. If there existed a linear velocity $\mathbf{v}_P$ of the point P on the moving body, it must be parallel to both $\mathbf{v}_A$ and $\mathbf{v}_B$. Since this is not possible, $\mathbf{v}_P$ must vanish identically. P is thus called the velocity pole or pole of the moving body, and the body is rotating about the pole axis OP. Thus we see that any spherical motion is a rotation, i.e. an angular motion. OP can be either a fixed or an instantaneous axis of rotation.

Because the unit sphere is arbitrarily chosen, and all points on a straight radial line undergo the same angular movement with respect to the sphere centre O, the actual arc length along a great circle is meaningless. In spherical kinematics the distance between two points on the surface of the unit sphere is measured by the angle subtended by the arc of the great circle passing through these two points at the sphere centre.

Fig. 2.1. Velocity pole.

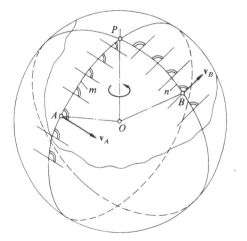

2.2   Spherical four-bar linkage

The spherical four-bar linkage, being analogous to the four-bar linkage in plane mechanisms, is the basic form of all spherical mechanisms. A typical spherical four-bar linkage A_0ABB_0 is shown in Fig. 2.2. Each link is represented by part of a great circle on the surface of the unit sphere. The joint between two adjacent links is, in general, a revolute pair whose axis passes through the sphere centre O. In earlier days the spherical four-bar linkage was termed a conic quadric chain, because the loci of all instantaneous axes are conical surfaces which have a common apex at O (Reuleaux, 1876). In Fig. 2.2 the *lengths* of the links A_0A, AB, B_0B and A_0B_0 are denoted by the central angles a, c, b and f respectively.[†] In the meantime let us restrict the lengths of the links so that the sum of any two link lengths is not greater than 180°. With the link A_0B_0 fixed, the two links A_0A and B_0B can only rotate about their respective fixed axes OA_0 and OB_0. Their position angles are then denoted respectively by ϕ and ψ. We shall arbitrarily assume that a counterclockwise angular displacement is considered as positive.

2.2.1   *The displacement equation and transmission function*

For given lengths f, a, b and position angles ϕ, ψ, the length c of the coupler AB is uniquely determined. For the sake of clarity the spherical four-bar is shown again in Fig. 2.3. Draw the diagonal great circle AB_0 dividing $\sphericalangle A_0B_0B$ into two parts ψ_s and ψ_u, and let the length AB_0 be denoted by h.

Fig. 2.2. Spherical four-bar linkage.

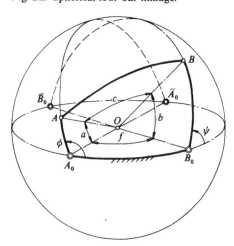

[†] In order to avoid confusion, the letter d will only be used as a differentiation symbol, and not for denoting a link length.

The angle ψ_s may be called the oscillating cylinder angle, and ψ_u the superposition angle (Meyer zur Capellen, Dittrich & Janssen, 1966), because $\measuredangle BB_0A_0$ may be represented by superposing ψ_u on ψ_s. According to the equation of the cosine law for sides (A1.9) we have for $\triangle ABB_0$:

$$\cos c = \cos h \cos b + \sin h \sin b \cos \psi_u \tag{2.1}$$

and for $\triangle AB_0A_0$:

$$\cos h = \cos a \cos f + \sin a \sin f \cos \phi \tag{2.2}$$

By the sine law, equation (A1.7), we have for $\triangle AB_0A_0$:

$$\sin h = \frac{\sin a}{\sin \psi_s} \sin \phi \tag{2.3}$$

For the superposition angle ψ_u we have then:

$$\cos \psi_u = -\cos(\psi_s + \psi)$$
$$= -\cos \psi_s \cos \psi + \sin \psi_s \sin \psi \tag{2.4}$$

Substituting equations (2.2), (2.3) and (2.4) into equation (2.1) yields finally the equation for the length c of the coupler AB:

$$\cos c = \cos a \cos b \cos f + (\sin a \cos b \cos \phi - \cos a \sin b \cos \psi) \sin f$$
$$+ \sin a \sin b (\sin \phi \sin \psi + \cos \phi \cos \psi \cos f) \tag{2.5}$$

In equation (2.5) the output angle ψ is expressed as an implicit function of

Fig. 2.3. Input angle ϕ, output angle ψ and coupler angle γ.

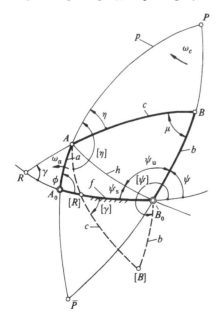

the input angle ϕ, hence it is called the displacement equation. It corresponds to Freudenstein's equation for a plane four-bar linkage (Freudenstein, 1955). However, in a spherical four-bar linkage the functional relationship $\psi = \psi(\phi)$ between ψ and ϕ depends on four independent parameters a, b, c and f, while in a plane four-bar it depends on only three independent bar ratios. If equation (2.5) is written in the form $F(\psi, \phi) = 0$, the function $F(\psi, \phi)$ is usually called the transmission function (Luck, 1975). The error caused in ψ due to geometrical inaccuracies is studied in (Tavkhelidze, Davitashvili & Demurishvili, 1979).

2.2.2   *Analytical expressions of kinematic quantities of output link*

In the previous section we have arbitrarily assumed ψ as the output angle and ϕ as the input angle, i.e. B_0B as the output link and A_0A the input link. It is sometimes desirable to have an explicit expression of ψ in terms of a, c, b, f and ϕ. Let

$$\left.\begin{aligned}
k_1 &= \cos a \cos b \cos f \\
k_2 &= \cos c \\
k_3 &= \sin a \cos b \sin f \\
k_4 &= \cos a \sin b \sin f \\
k_5 &= \sin a \sin b \cos f \\
k_6 &= \sin a \sin b
\end{aligned}\right\} \tag{2.6}$$

so that equation (2.5) can be written in the form

$$k_1 - k_2 + k_3 \cos \phi - k_4 \cos \psi + k_5 \cos \phi \cos \psi + k_6 \sin \phi \sin \psi = 0 \tag{2.5a}$$

and let

$$\left.\begin{aligned}
h_1 &= k_1 - k_2 + k_3 \cos \phi \\
h_2 &= -k_4 + k_5 \cos \phi \\
h_3 &= k_6 \sin \phi
\end{aligned}\right\} \tag{2.7}$$

Solving equation (2.5) for ψ gives

$$\tan \frac{\psi}{2} = \frac{-h_3 \pm (h_3^2 - h_1^2 + h_2^2)^{1/2}}{h_1 - h_2} \tag{2.8}$$

The double signs in equation (2.8) indicate two possible configurations A_0ABB_0 and $A_0A[B]B_0$ of the linkage, as shown in Fig. 2.3. The angle $[\psi]$ corresponds to the position angle of the link $B_0[B]$. $A[B]$, $[B]B_0$ and AB, BB_0 are symmetrically disposed about the great circle AB_0. These two positions of the linkage are called conjugate positions. The correct one which corresponds to a certain input angle ϕ will be discussed in Section 3.5.

Let the derivatives differentiated with respect to ϕ be denoted by the symbols $'$, $''$ etc., e.g. $\psi' = d\psi/d\phi$, $\psi'' = d^2\psi/d\phi^2$ etc. Just as in the case of a plane four-bar linkage, for a constant angular velocity $\omega_a = d\phi/dt$ of the input

crank A_0A, where t represents time, the angular velocity ω_b, angular acceleration α_b and angular jerk $\dot{\alpha}_b$ of the output link B_0B are, respectively:

$$\omega_b = \frac{d\psi}{dt} = \psi' \frac{d\phi}{dt} = \psi' \omega_a \tag{2.9}$$

$$\alpha_b = \frac{d\omega_b}{dt} = \frac{d\psi'}{dt} \omega_a = \psi'' \omega_a^2 \tag{2.10}$$

$$\dot{\alpha}_b = \frac{d\alpha_b}{dt} = \frac{d\psi''}{dt} \omega_a^2 = \psi''' \omega_a^3 \tag{2.11}$$

The symbol i is usually used for denoting the velocity ratio ω_b/ω_a, and from
equation (2.9) we have

$$i = \psi'$$

In other words, the symbols i and ψ' are identical.

We may differentiate equation (2.5) with respect to ϕ to obtain:

$$i = \psi' = (k_3 S_\phi + k_5 S_\phi C_\psi - k_6 C_\phi S_\psi)/\Phi \tag{2.12}$$

where

$$\left. \begin{aligned} S_\phi &= \sin \phi \\ C_\phi &= \cos \phi \\ S_\psi &= \sin \psi \\ C_\psi &= \cos \psi \end{aligned} \right\} \tag{2.13}$$

and

$$\Phi = k_4 S_\psi - k_5 C_\phi S_\psi + k_6 S_\phi C_\psi \tag{2.14}$$

It is understood that the output angle ψ has first to be determined by means
of equation (2.8).

Successive differentiation of equation (2.12) with respect to ϕ yields the
differential coefficients ψ'' and ψ''':

$$\begin{aligned} i' = \psi'' = [&\psi'^2(-k_4 C_\psi + k_5 C_\phi C_\psi + k_6 S_\phi S_\psi) \\ &+ 2\psi'(-k_5 S_\phi S_\psi - k_6 C_\phi C_\psi) + k_3 C_\phi + k_5 C_\phi C_\psi + k_6 S_\phi S_\psi]/\Phi \end{aligned} \tag{2.15}$$

$$\begin{aligned} i'' = \psi''' = [&3\psi'\psi''(-k_4 C_\psi + k_5 C_\phi C_\psi + k_6 S_\phi S_\psi) \\ &+ \psi'^3(k_4 S_\psi - k_5 C_\phi S_\psi + k_6 S_\phi C_\psi) \\ &+ 3\psi'^2(-k_5 S_\phi C_\psi + k_6 C_\phi S_\psi) + 3\psi''(-k_5 S_\phi S_\psi - k_6 C_\phi C_\psi) \\ &+ 3\psi'(-k_5 C_\phi S_\psi + k_6 S_\phi C_\psi) + (-k_3 S_\phi - k_5 S_\phi C_\psi + k_6 C_\phi S_\psi)]/\Phi \end{aligned} \tag{2.16}$$

The kinematic quantities ω_b, α_b and $\dot{\alpha}_b$ may then be obtained by multiplying
respectively ψ', ψ'' and ψ''' by the corresponding powers of ω_a according to
equations (2.9)–(2.11).

2.2.3 *The position angle and angular velocity of the coupler*

The position angle of the coupler c is denoted by the coupler angle γ,[†] the dihedral angle $\sphericalangle A_0 RA$ between the planes AB and $A_0 B_0$ (Fig. 2.3). Use has been made by some investigators of $\sphericalangle B_0 AB$, together with the oscillating cylinder angle ψ_s and the diagonal length h, to obtain an indirect expression of γ in terms of the independent variable ϕ (Meyer zur Capellen et al., 1966). An alternative procedure for finding γ is as follows.

From Fig. 2.3 we may observe that the relationship between η, the external angle of $\sphericalangle A_0 AB$, and ϕ is the same as that between ψ and ϕ, provided that we exchange the roles of a and f, and those of b and c. Let the values thus calculated according to equations (2.6) and (2.7) be denoted respectively by $k_1^*, k_2^*, \ldots$ and h_1^*, h_2^*, h_3^*, i.e.

$$\left. \begin{aligned} k_1^* &= \cos f \cos c \cos a \\ k_2^* &= \cos b \\ k_3^* &= \sin f \cos c \sin a \\ k_4^* &= \cos f \sin c \sin a \\ k_5^* &= \sin f \sin c \cos a \\ k_6^* &= \sin f \sin c \end{aligned} \right\} \tag{2.17}$$

$$\left. \begin{aligned} h_1^* &= k_1^* - k_2^* + k_3^* \cos \phi \\ h_2^* &= -k_4^* + k_5^* \cos \phi \\ h_3^* &= k_6^* \sin \phi \end{aligned} \right\} \tag{2.18}$$

Thus, by equation (2.8),

$$\tan \frac{\eta}{2} = \frac{-h_3^* \pm (h_3^{*2} - h_1^{*2} + h_2^{*2})^{1/2}}{h_1^* - h_2^*} \tag{2.19}$$

Again the double signs in equation (2.19) indicate two possible configurations of the linkage, as shown in Fig. 2.3. The angle $[\eta]$ corresponds to the position $A[B]$ of the coupler. The procedure for finding the correct value of η is similar to that for finding ψ described in Section 3.5.

Having found the angle η, the coupler angle γ can then be determined by applying the cosine law for angles, equation (A1.10), to $\triangle RA_0 A$:

$$\cos \gamma = -\cos \eta \cos (180° - \phi) + \sin \eta \sin (180° - \phi) \cos a$$
$$= \cos \eta \cos \phi + \sin \eta \sin \phi \cos a \tag{2.20}$$

Equation (2.20) applies equally well to $\triangle [R] A_0 A$ and the angle $[\gamma]$, where $[R]$ is the intersection of $A[B]$ and $A_0 B_0$. However, the angle $[\gamma]$, as shown in

---

[†] This notation is not to be confused with the angle of rotation γ of a spherically moving body mentioned in later sections.

Fig. 2.3, is negative, and it is to be noted that the sign of a negative angle cannot be detected from its cosine function.

The angular velocity and angular acceleration of the coupler are vector quantities in space, whose determination from the point of view of vector geometry will be treated later in Chapter 4. In the meantime, we shall only deal with the angular velocity ω_c of the coupler c. As will be shown later in Section 4.1.3, the axis perpendicular to the fixed plane $A_0 B_0$ is denoted by z. Suppose the angular velocity vector $\boldsymbol{\omega}_c$, or the axis OP, coincides instantaneously with the z-axis. It is obvious that, in this case, $\boldsymbol{\omega}_c$ does not affect the change of the coupler angle γ. In other words, in general, the component of the angular velocity $\boldsymbol{\omega}_c$ along the direction of the z-axis does not contribute to the variation of γ. Therefore ω_c is not represented by $\dot{\gamma}$. Meyer zur Capellen *et al.* (1966) have derived an expression for the velocity ratio ω_c/ω_a in terms of the rate of change of the angle η. However, we may derive this quantity from another point of view. As has been mentioned in Section 2.1 and shown in Fig. 2.1, the axis of rotation OP of a spherically moving body is uniquely determined by the directions of the velocities of two points A and B on the body. Referring again to Fig. 2.3, since the directions of the velocities of the points A and B are normal to $A_0 A$ and $B_0 B$ respectively, the point P of the instantaneous axis of rotation of the coupler c is therefore determined by the intersection of the extensions of $A_0 A$ and $B_0 B$. Because the point A is a common point of a and c, the angular velocities ω_c and ω_a are inversely proportional to the perpendicular distances from A to the respective axes. In other words,

$$\frac{\omega_c}{\omega_a} = -\frac{\sin A_0 A}{\sin AP} \tag{2.21}$$

Here we have to establish the sign convention of the great circle arcs. Imagine an observer on the sphere surface, tied to the sphere centre by an invisible but inextensible string. We say that AP and $A_0 A$ are of the same sign if the observer traces the arcs $A \to P$ and $A_0 \to A$ in the same sense, otherwise they are of opposite sign. Equation (2.21) may be rewritten as

$$\omega_c = -\frac{\sin a}{\sin p} \omega_a \tag{2.21a}$$

for the configuration as shown in Fig. 2.3, where p stands for AP, and is to be considered as positive. Equation (2.21a) indicates that, if an observer were viewing in the direction from P towards the sphere centre O, he would observe that the sense of ω_c is opposite to that of ω_a for a positive p. This means that if the pole $\bar{P}$, which is the antipode of P, were used in equation (2.21a), p would stand for $A\bar{P}$, which is negative and equal to $-(180° - AP)$. An observer viewing in the direction from $\bar{P}$ towards O would find that ω_c was of the same sense about $O\bar{P}$ as ω_a was about OA_0. More about the sign of an angular velocity will be discussed in Section 4.1.2.

In order to calculate p, applying the cotangent law (A1.11) to $\triangle A_0 B_0 P$, gives

$$\cos f \cos \phi = \sin f \cot (p + a) - \sin \phi \cot (180° - \psi)$$

or

$$\cot (p + a) = \frac{1}{\sin f}(\cos f \cos \phi - \sin \phi \cot \psi) \qquad (2.22)$$

Combining equations (2.22) and (2.21a), we may determine ω_c.

2.3   The crank–rocker and its special forms

2.3.1   *The crank–rocker*

In a crank–rocker mechanism, while one of the two rotating links, say $A_0 A$, makes complete revolutions, the other link $B_0 B$ can only swing between two extreme positions. $A_0 A$ is the *crank* and $B_0 B$ the *rocker*. Similarly to plane mechanisms, one of the necessary conditions for a four-bar linkage

Fig. 2.4. Variations of ψ, ψ', ψ'' and ψ''' for a crank–rocker with $a = 30°$, $b = 70°$, $c = 60°$ and $f = 90°$.

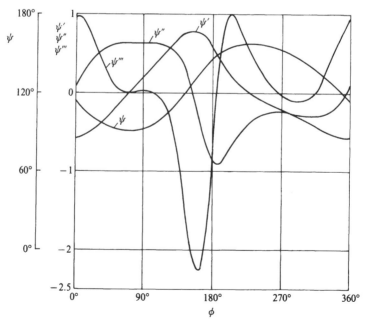

to become a crank–rocker is Grashof's rule (Grashof, 1883), namely, the sum of the lengths of the shortest and longest links should be less than the sum of the lengths of the other two links. In fact, with a, b, c and f denoting the respective lengths of the links as shown in Fig. 2.2, there are three independent necessary conditions to be satisfied for the existence of a crank–rocker:

$$\left.\begin{array}{l} a + b \leqslant c + f \\ a + c \leqslant b + f \\ a + f \leqslant b + c \end{array}\right\} \tag{2.23}$$

The derivation of these inequalities can be found from any textbook dealing with plane mechanisms (e.g. Dijksman, 1976, p. 225). However, a proof of these inequalities will be given later in Section 3.3. It will also be shown that these conditions are necessary and sufficient. From these it can be seen that the crank length a is the shortest of all four links. These conditions state that the sum of the length a of the crank and that of any other link should be less than the sum of the lengths of the two remaining links.

Fig. 2.4 shows the variations of ψ, ψ', ψ'' and ψ''' as functions of the input crank angle ϕ of a typical crank–rocker with $a = 30°$, $b = 70°$, $c = 60°$ and $f = 90°$. Fig. 2.5 shows the variations of γ and ω_c/ω_a as functions of ϕ of the same crank–rocker. These curves are computed by means of equations in Sections 2.2.2 and 2.2.3.

2.3.2 *Dead centre positions of a crank–rocker*

Just like the plane crank–rocker, a spherical crank–rocker mechanism has two dead centre positions. Fig. 2.6 shows the outer and inner dead

Fig. 2.5. Variations of γ and ω_c/ω_a for a crank–rocker with $a = 30°, b = 70°, c = 60°$ and $f = 90°$.

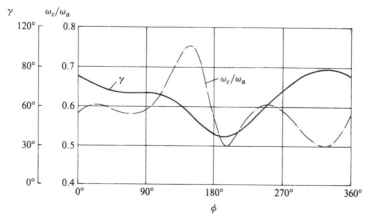

centre positions. In the outer dead centre position, the crank a and coupler c are aligned in the same great circle. The corresponding position angles ϕ and ψ are denoted by ϕ_a and ψ_a. From the known sides f, b and $a + c$ of the spherical triangle $\triangle A_0 B_0 B_a$, we have by the cosine law for sides (A1.9):

$$\cos b = \cos f \cos (a + c) + \sin f \sin (a + c) \cos \phi_a \qquad (2.24)$$

$$\cos (a + c) = \cos f \cos b + \sin f \sin b \cos (180° - \psi_a) \qquad (2.25)$$

Equations (2.24) and (2.25) can be rearranged for solving ϕ_a and ψ_a:

$$\cos \phi_a = \frac{- \cos f \cos (a + c) + \cos b}{\sin f \sin (a + c)} \qquad (2.24a)$$

$$\cos \psi_a = \frac{\cos f \cos b - \cos (a + c)}{\sin f \sin b} \qquad (2.25a)$$

Similarly for the inner dead centre position we have, with the position angles

Fig. 2.6. Dead centre positions of a crank–rocker.

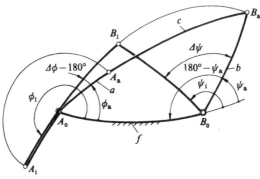

Fig. 2.7. Spherical central crank–rocker.

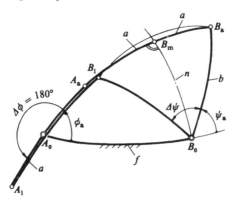

denoted by ϕ_i and ψ_i:

$$\cos b = \cos f \cos (c - a) + \sin f \sin (c - a) \cos (\phi_i - 180°) \qquad (2.26)$$

$$\cos (c - a) = \cos f \cos b + \sin f \sin b \cos (180° - \psi_i) \qquad (2.27)$$

$$\cos \phi_i = \frac{\cos f \cos (c - a) - \cos b}{\sin f \sin (c - a)} \qquad (2.26a)$$

$$\cos \psi_i = \frac{\cos f \cos b - \cos (c - a)}{\sin f \sin b} \qquad (2.27a)$$

The rocker b swings through the angle $\triangle \psi = \psi_i - \psi_a$ while the crank rotates through the angle $\triangle \phi = \phi_i - \phi_a$. Assuming that the crank a rotates with a uniform angular velocity, and that the angle $\triangle \phi = \phi_i - \phi_a \geqslant 180°$, we may make use of the crank–rocker to perform a quick return motion. The *time ratio*, i.e. the ratio of the time of working stroke to the time of return stroke, is then

$$\text{time ratio} = \frac{\phi_i - \phi_a}{360° - (\phi_i - \phi_a)} \qquad (2.28)$$

Similar to plane mechanisms, when the four points A_i, B_i; A_a, B_a lie on the same great circle, the mechanism is called a *spherical central crank–rocker* (Fig. 2.7), and $\triangle \phi = \phi_i - \phi_a = 180°$, or

$$\text{time ratio} = 1$$

If we draw, in Fig. 2.7, a great circle from B_0 perpendicular to $B_i B_a$, bisecting the latter in B_m, then $B_i B_m = B_m B_a = a$, and $A_0 B_m = A_i B_i = A_a B_a = c$. Let the great circle $B_0 B_m$ be denoted by n. From the right spherical triangle $\triangle B_i B_m B_0$ we have, by equation (A1.2),

$$\cos n = \frac{\cos b}{\cos a} \qquad (2.29)$$

Also from the right spherical triangle $\triangle A_0 B_m B_0$ we have

$$\cos n = \frac{\cos f}{\cos c} \qquad (2.30)$$

Comparing equation (2.30) with equation (2.29) yields

$$\cos b \cos c = \cos a \cos f \qquad (2.31)$$

We shall come back to equation (2.31) later in dealing with synthesis of spherical central crank–rockers (see Section 8.4.1).

The counterpart of equation (2.31) for a plane central crank–rocker mechanism is, if we denote the corresponding link lengths by a_p, b_p, c_p and f_p respectively, the well-known relation

$$b_p^2 + c_p^2 = a_p^2 + f_p^2 \qquad (2.31a)$$

2.3.3   Slider–crank mechanism

In plane kinematics, if the fixed centre of rotation B_0 of the rotating link B_0B of a crank–rocker mechanism A_0ABB_0 goes to infinity, the mechanism becomes a slider–crank and the joint B moves along a straight line perpendicular to the direction of $BB_{0\infty}$. The swinging motion of the rocker becomes a reciprocating motion of the slider. The slider is called *offset*, if the path of B, when extended, does not pass through the crank centre A_0, as shown in Fig. 2.8, otherwise it is called *central*, as shown in Fig. 2.9.

In spherical kinematics, however, there is in fact no rectilinear sliding motion. Spherical sliding is simply a rotation motion. The word *slider* is taken over from plane mechanisms for analogous purposes. Moreover, in spherical kinematics the movement of any point is restricted within the spherical surface and no point can go to infinity. If two great circles are perpendicular to a

Fig. 2.8. Plane offset slider–crank.

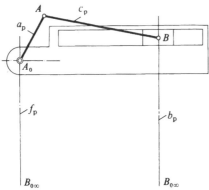

Fig. 2.9. Plane central slider–crank.

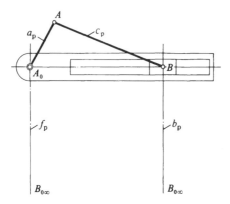

common third great circle, they are by no means parallel, but intersecting at two points, which are called the poles of the third great circle.[†] The *length* of each intersecting great circle, measured from the foot of perpendicularity, i.e. from the third circle, to each of the poles of the third circle, is 90°. Consequently a spherical link of *length* 90° corresponds to a plane link of infinite length. Fig. 2.10(*a*) shows an offset spherical slider–crank, and Fig. 2.11 shows a central spherical slider–crank, both being variations of the spherical crank–rocker mechanism.

It should be noted that, although a 90° spherical link corresponds to an infinitely long plane link, an infinitely long plane link does not necessarily correspond to a spherical link of 90°. This fact can be seen by comparing Fig. 2.10(*a*) with Fig. 2.8. In Fig. 2.8 the fixed link f_p is of infinite length, while in Fig. 2.10(*a*) the fixed link f is not 90°.

For the offset slider–crank, equations in previous sections apply. We have only to set $b = 90°$ in equations (2.6), thus obtaining $k_1 = k_3 = 0$. This will somewhat reduce the computation task in analysing the linkage.

For a central slider–crank, we have in addition to $k_1 = k_3 = 0$ the condition $k_5 = 0$ because $f = 90°$. Although the same analysis equations may be used, it is sometimes more convenient to count the input as well as the output angle from the outer dead centre position. In Fig. 2.11 the points A_1 and B_1 are the respective dead centre positions of A and B. Here θ is used in place of ϕ

Fig. 2.10. (*a*) Spherical offset slider–crank. (*b*) Offset oscillating cylinder.

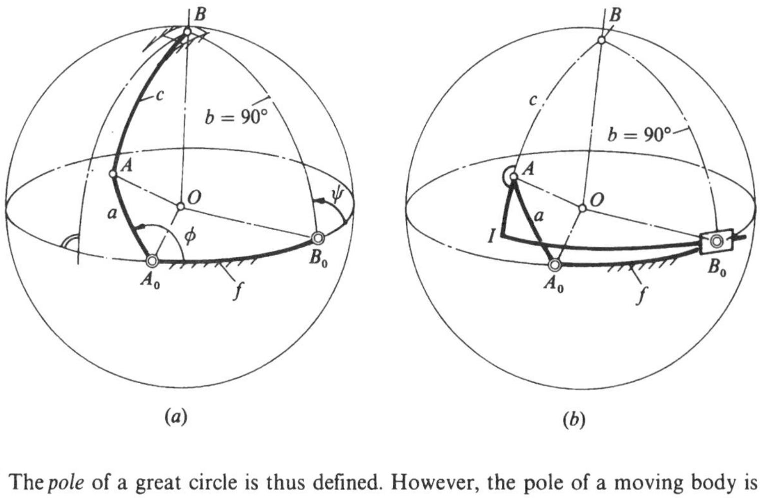

(*a*)   (*b*)

[†] The *pole* of a great circle is thus defined. However, the pole of a moving body is defined as in Section 2.1, and the pole of two finitely separated positions of a body is defined as in Section 6.1.1. In order to avoid confusion, unless the word *pole* is associated with a certain great circle, it always possesses a kinematical meaning.

and s or l is used in place of ψ. Note that

$$\phi = \theta + 90°$$

and

$$\psi = 180° - l$$

where

$$l = A_0 B = (a + c) - s$$

Equation (2.8) thus takes the form

$$\tan \frac{l}{2} = \frac{\cos a - \cos c}{-\sin a \, \cos\theta + (\cos^2 a - \cos^2 c + \sin^2 a \, \cos^2 \theta)^{1/2}}$$

(2.32)

Note that only the positive sign of the radical term in equation (2.8) is retained.
For simplification purposes the following notations will be used:

$$\left.\begin{array}{l} k_7 = \sin a \\ k_8 = \cos a \end{array}\right\}$$

(2.33)

$$\left.\begin{array}{l} S_\theta = \sin \theta \\ C_\theta = \cos \theta \\ S_l = \sin l \\ C_l = \cos l \end{array}\right\}$$

(2.34)

Equation (2.14) now reduces to

$$\Phi = k_8 S_l - k_7 C_l C_\theta$$

(2.35)

It is also understood here that l has first to be determined from equation

Fig. 2.11. Spherical central slider–crank.

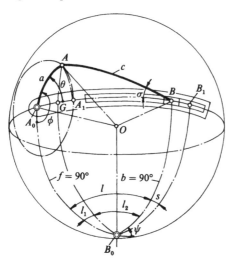

(2.32). Because $d\theta = d\phi$, and $ds = -dl = d\psi$, therefore $ds/d\theta = \psi'$, $d^2s/d\theta^2 = \psi''$, $d^3s/d\theta^3 = \psi'''$ etc. Equations (2.12), (2.15) and (2.16) become

$$i = \psi' = k_7 S_l S_\theta / \Phi \tag{2.36}$$

$$\psi'' = [\psi'^2(k_8 C_l + k_7 S_l C_\theta) - 2\psi' k_7 C_l S_\theta + k_7 S_l C_\theta]/\Phi \tag{2.37}$$

$$\psi''' = \{3\psi''\psi'(k_8 C_l + k_7 S_l C_\theta) + \psi'^3(k_8 S_l - k_7 C_l C_\theta) \\ - k_7[3\psi'^2 S_l S_\theta + 3\psi'' C_l S_\theta + 3\psi' C_l C_\theta + S_l S_\theta]\}/\Phi \tag{2.38}$$

An alternative expression for the velocity ratio i is given as follows (Meyer zur Capellen & Rath, 1960). In Fig. 2.11 a great circle is drawn from A perpendicular to $A_0 B$, dividing it into two parts: $l_1 = A_0 G$ and $l_2 = GB$. The angle $\sigma = \sphericalangle A_0 BA$ is determined by the sine law (A1.7) applied to $\triangle A_0 AB$:

$$\sin \sigma = \lambda S_\theta, \quad \text{where } \lambda = \frac{\sin a}{\sin c} \tag{2.39}$$

Hence

$$\cos \sigma = \sqrt{(1 - \lambda^2 S_\theta^2)} \tag{2.40}$$

For the right triangles $\triangle A_0 AG$ and $\triangle BAG$ we have, by equation (A1.6)

$$\tan l_1 = \cos \theta \tan a \tag{2.41}$$

$$\tan l_2 = \cos \sigma \tan c \tag{2.42}$$

Since

$$s = (a + c) - l = (a + c) - l_1 - l_2$$

therefore

$$i = \psi' = \frac{ds}{d\theta} = -\frac{dl_1}{d\theta} - \frac{dl_2}{d\theta} \tag{2.43}$$

Differentiating equations (2.41) and (2.42) gives

$$\psi' = -l_1'\left(1 + \frac{\cos c}{\cos a}\sigma'\right) \tag{2.44}$$

where

$$\sigma' = \frac{d\sigma}{d\theta} = \lambda \frac{\cos \theta}{\cos \sigma} \tag{2.45}$$

$$-l_1' = \frac{\tan a \cdot S_\theta}{1 + \tan^2 a \cdot C_\theta^2} \tag{2.46}$$

2.3.4 Dead centre positions of a slider–crank *(Dittrich, 1967)*

For an offset slider–crank we have $b = 90°$ in comparison with a general spherical crank–rocker. Equations (2.24a), (2.25a), (2.26a) and (2.27a) thus take respectively the following forms:

$$\cos \phi_a = -\cot f \cot(a + c) \tag{2.47}$$

$$\cos \psi_a = -\cos(a + c)/\sin f \tag{2.48}$$

$$\cos \phi_i = \cot f \cot (c - a) \tag{2.49}$$

$$\cos \psi_i = - \cos (c - a)/\sin f \tag{2.50}$$

For a central slider–crank we have in addition to $b = 90°$ the condition $f = 90°$. Equations (2.47) and (2.49) reduce respectively to $\phi_a = 90°$ and $\phi_i = 270°$, and from equations (2.48) and (2.50) we have

$$\psi_a = 180° - (a + c)$$

$$\psi_i = 180° - (c - a)$$

which yield the trivial result analogous to the plane central slider–crank

$$\psi_i - \psi_a = 2a$$

2.3.5   The wobble-plate

The Scotch yoke in plane mechanisms is a special case of the slider–crank in which the length c of the coupler is extended to infinity in a direction parallel to the path of the point B, as is shown in Fig. 2.12. As the crank $A_0 A$ rotates with a constant angular velocity, the slider performs a simple harmonic motion. The spherical counterpart of the plane Scotch yoke can thus be derived from Fig. 2.11 by assigning $c = 90°$ in addition to the conditions $b = 90°$ and $f = 90°$, as shown in Fig. 2.13. This mechanism is known as the wobble-plate, or the central cross-slider, in contrast with the offset cross-slider which is mentioned in Section 2.3.6. In German literature it is called a *Taumelscheibe* (Beyer, 1958) or a *Hookescher Schlüssel* (Uhing, 1957). Equation (2.32) now takes the form

$$\tan l = - \cot (a - s) = - \frac{k_8}{k_7 C_\theta} = - \frac{1}{\tan a \cdot C_\theta} \tag{2.51}$$

Fig. 2.12. Plane Scotch yoke.

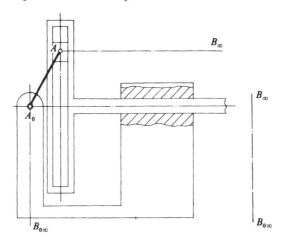

or

$$\tan(a - s) = \tan a \cdot C_\theta \qquad (2.51a)$$

Equation (2.51a) can be rewritten in the form

$$\tan s = \frac{\tan a(1 - C_\theta)}{1 + \tan^2 a \cdot C_\theta} \qquad (2.52)$$

Let

$$\Psi = 1 - k_7^2 S_\theta^2. \qquad (2.53)$$

Fig. 2.13. Wobble-plate or central cross-slider.

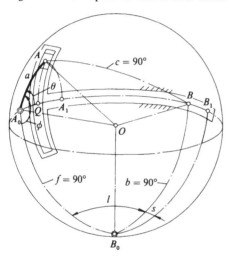

Fig. 2.14.

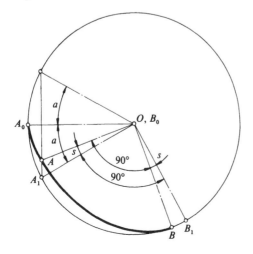

The differential coefficients ψ', ψ'' and ψ''' in the present case are:

$$i = \psi' = k_7 k_8 S_\theta / \Psi \tag{2.54}$$

$$\psi'' = [k_7 k_8 C_\theta (1 + k_7^2 S_\theta^2)] / \Psi^2 \tag{2.55}$$

$$\psi''' = [k_7^5 k_8 (1 + C_\theta^2) S_\theta^3 + 6 k_7^3 k_8 C_\theta^2 S_\theta - k_7 k_8 S_\theta] / \Psi^3 \tag{2.56}$$

It can be seen from equation (2.52) that the oscillatory motion of the output link $B_0 B$ is obviously not a simple harmonic motion if $\omega_a = \dot{\theta} = $ constant. This fact can easily be explained by observing a view parallel to the plane $A_0 O B_1$ as shown in Fig. 2.14, where B_1 is the outer dead centre position of the point B. In this view the projection of the point A performs a simple harmonic motion along a straight line perpendicular to $O A_0$. Because OB always lies on the plane $A_0 O B_1$, $\measuredangle A O B$ exhibited in this view is always 90°. Hence the oscillatory motion of the output link $B_0 B$ is the same as the oscillatory motion of the line joining A and O, which is by no means simple harmonic.

2.3.6   *The offset cross-slider and the oblique cross-slider*

In Fig. 2.12 the plane sliding yoke may be considered as being degenerated either from the slider of an offset slider–crank, Fig. 2.8, or from the slider of a central slider–crank, Fig. 2.9. As mentioned in Section 2.3.3, the sliding yoke results from the point B going to infinity in a direction parallel to the sliding direction of the slider. However, the spherical counterparts in the two corresponding cases are not identical. We may distinguish these two cases by inspecting whether the *path* of the point B, the great circle with pole B_0, passes through A_0. Fig. 2.15(a) shows the offset cross-slider in which the *path* of B does not pass through A_0. This mechanism is also called a *spherical slide oscillator* (Shigley & Uicker, 1980). It differs from the central cross-slider or the wobble-plate, Fig. 2.13, in which the *path* of B does pass through A_0. In fact the only difference between these two cases is that in the offset cross-slider $f \neq 90°$. In Figs. 2.13 and 2.15(a) let the intersection point of the two centre-line great circles of the *spherically sliding pairs* be denoted by Q, and these two centre-line great circles are perpendicular to each other at Q in both cases. Note that $Q B_0 = 90°$ in both cases, and in Fig. 2.15(a) the *path* of the point Q which coincides with the centre-line great circle of the *sliding pair b–f* also coincides with the *path* of B. It is advisable to bear in mind that *parallelism* between great circles does not exist but *perpendicularity* does. Thus in both cases it is false to say that AB is extended from A in a direction *parallel* to the direction of the centre-line great circle QB, but one may say that AB is extended from A in a direction perpendicular to the great circle AQ. In the case of the offset cross-slider we have in equations (2.6), because $b = 90°$ and $c = 90°$:

and

$$k_1 = 0, \quad k_2 = 0, \quad k_3 = 0$$

$$\left.\begin{array}{l} k_4 = \cos a \sin f \\ k_5 = \sin a \cos f \\ k_6 = \sin a \end{array}\right\} \tag{2.57}$$

and in equation (2.7) $h_1 = 0$. Equation (2.8) reduces to

$$\tan \psi = -\frac{h_2}{h_3} = \frac{k_4 - k_5 C_\phi}{k_6 S_\phi} \tag{2.58}$$

The radicand in equation (2.8) vanishes identically and the two possible configurations of the linkage become supplementary linkages. Supplementary linkages will be discussed in Section 3.2.

Fig. 2.15. (a) Offset cross-slider. (b),(c) Central oscillating cylinder.

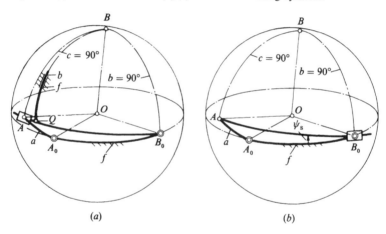

(a)   (b)

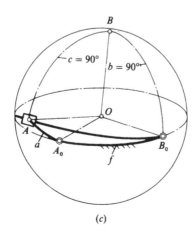

(c)

Comparing Fig. 2.15(a) with Fig. 2.3 shows that in the present case, because $\psi_u = 90°$,

$$\psi + \psi_s = 90°$$

or

$$\psi = 90° - \psi_s \tag{2.59}$$

It follows that

$$\left. \begin{array}{l} i = \psi' = -\psi'_s \\ \psi'' = -\psi''_s \\ \psi''' = -\psi'''_s \end{array} \right\} \tag{2.60}$$

Equation (2.58) can be further rewritten as

$$\tan \psi_s = \frac{\mu S_\phi}{1 - \nu C_\phi} \tag{2.61}$$

where the two constants are:

$$\mu = \frac{\tan a}{\sin f} \tag{2.62}$$

$$\nu = \frac{\tan a}{\tan f} \tag{2.63}$$

Equation (2.61) is a form preferred by some investigators (Meyer zur Capellen *et al.*, 1966). Note that because the form is explicit in nature, successive derivatives of ψ_s will not include the angle ψ_s itself and its lower derivatives. Let

$$r_s^2 = (\mu S_\phi)^2 + (1 - \nu C_\phi)^2 \tag{2.64}$$

Differentiating equation (2.61) successively with respect to ϕ gives

$$-r_s^2 i = r_s^2 \psi'_s = \mu(C_\phi - \nu) \tag{2.65}$$

$$-r_s^4 i' = r_s^4 \psi''_s = -\mu S_\phi p_1 \tag{2.66}$$

$$-r_s^6 i'' = r_s^6 \psi'''_s = -\mu(p_1 p_2 + p_3) \tag{2.67}$$

where

$$\left. \begin{array}{l} p_1 = (1 - \nu^2) + (\mu^2 - \nu^2)(1 - 2\nu C_\phi + C_\phi^2) \\ p_2 = r_s^2 C_\phi - 4S_\phi^2[\nu + (\mu^2 - \nu^2)C_\phi] \\ p_3 = 2(\mu^2 - \nu^2)r_s^2 S_\phi^2(\nu - C_\phi) \end{array} \right\} \tag{2.68}$$

The even more general case of plane cross-slider mechanisms is the oblique cross-slider, as shown in Fig. 2.16, in which the point B goes to infinity, but in a direction different from the sliding direction of the yoke. The corresponding spherical mechanism is shown in Fig. 2.17(a). Here the two centre-line great circles of the *spherically sliding pairs* are no longer perpendicular to each other at Q. However, the link length c is still extended from A in a direction perpendicular to the great circle AQ until $AB = 90°$. In this connection it should be noted that, while in plane mechanisms a slider performs a purely translatory motion so that all points on the slider have the same linear velocity, this is not the case with its spherical counterpart. As already mentioned in Section 2.1, any spherical motion is an angular motion, and consequently no two points on the same body can have the same linear velocity. In Figs. 2.10, 2.11, 2.13 and 2.15(a) the point B moves on a great circle because the link length $B_0 B = 90°$, but the paths of any other points on the great circle $B_0 B$ are only small circles. Thus in Fig. 2.17(a), although the point B lies indeed on and moves together with the *sliding* yoke, its path, however, is not necessarily a great circle because the link length $B_0 B$ is not necessarily equal to 90°. Note that here the path of the point Q as well as the centre-line great

Fig. 2.16. Plane oblique cross-slider.

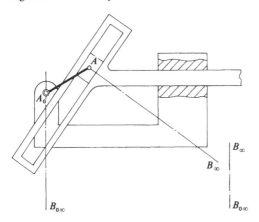

Fig. 2.17. (a) Spherical oblique cross-slider. (b) Offset oscillating cylinder.

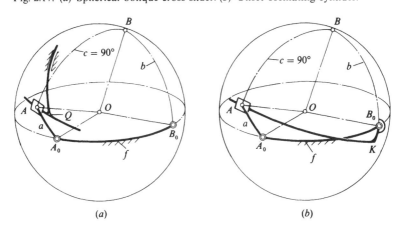

(a)   (b)

circle of the *sliding* member is a great circle with B_0 as its pole. In the present case we have only $c = 90°$ and this will not substantially reduce the task of applying equations in Section 2.2.2 to analysing the linkage.

2.3.7   *The oscillating cylinder and offset oscillating cylinder mechanisms*
It is well known in plane mechanisms that the oscillating cylinder is an inversion of the slider–crank mechanism. The two alternative constructions of the spherical oscillating cylinder mechanisms are shown in Figs. 2.15(*b*) and (*c*), both being in fact identical with the (square) offset cross-slider, Fig. 2.15(*a*), i.e. $b = 90°$ and $c = 90°$. As mentioned before, they are also identical with the partial mechanism A_0AB_0 of the spherical four-bar as shown in Fig. 2.3. Hence all these mechanisms can be analysed in the same way and equations in Section 2.3.6 apply. However, it should be noted that, in Fig. 2.15(*b*) the link passing through A and B_0 is part of the coupler c and the oscillating cylinder at B_0 is part of b, while in Fig. 2.15(*c*) the link passing through A and B_0 is part of b and the slider at A is part of c.

Fig. 2.10(*b*) shows a constructive form of an offset oscillating cylinder mechanism. The offset $AI = 90° - c$ with $BI = 90°$. It is identical with the offset slider–crank, Fig. 2.10(*a*), but differs from Fig. 2.15(*b*) in that $c \neq 90°$.

Fig. 2.17(*b*) shows a further constructive form of an offset oscillating cylinder mechanism. The offset $B_0K = 90° - b$ with $BK = 90°$. It is identical with the oblique cross-slider, Fig. 2.17(*a*), but differs from Fig. 2.15(*c*) in that $b \neq 90°$.

2.3.8   *Dead centre positions of oscillating cylinder mechanisms*
In the offset oscillating cylinder mechanism, Fig. 2.17(*b*), the linkage reaches its dead centre positions when the crank a is perpendicular to the circular rod AK which, being part of the output link b, passes through the oscillating block at A. In the outer dead centre position, we have, by substituting $c = 90°$ into equations (2.24*a*) and (2.25*a*),

$$\cos \phi_a = \frac{\cos f \sin a + \cos b}{\sin f \cos a} \tag{2.69}$$

$$\cos \psi_a = \frac{\sin a + \cos f \cos b}{\sin f \sin b} \tag{2.70}$$

Similarly, in the inner dead centre position, we have from equations (2.26*a*) and (2.27*a*) for $c = 90°$,

$$\cos \phi_i = \frac{\cos f \sin a - \cos b}{\sin f \cos a} \tag{2.71}$$

$$\cos \psi_i = \frac{\cos f \cos b - \sin a}{\sin f \sin b} \tag{2.72}$$

For a *central* oscillating cylinder, Fig. 2.15(c), we have in addition to $c = 90°$ the condition $b = 90°$. Equations (2.69) and (2.71) now take the following respective forms:

$$\cos \phi_a = \frac{\tan a}{\tan f} \tag{2.69a}$$

$$\cos \phi_i = \frac{\tan a}{\tan f} \tag{2.71a}$$

These two equations indicate that in both dead centre positions the crank and the circular rod AB_0 are symmetrically disposed about the fixed link f. In the dead centre positions $\sphericalangle A_0 AB_0 = 90°$ and $\triangle A_0 AB_0$ in Fig. 2.15(c) becomes a right spherical triangle. Either equation (2.69a) or (2.71a) could have been derived by applying equation (A1.6). This relation can also be derived from equation (2.65) by setting $\psi'_s = 0$.

The angular displacement of the crank between the two dead centre positions is

$$\phi_i - \phi_a = 360° - 2\phi_a = 360° - 2\cos^{-1}\frac{\tan a}{\tan f} \tag{2.73}$$

The upper limit of the angle ψ_s, Fig. 2.15(c), is given by

$$\sin \psi_{s\,max} = \frac{\sin a}{\sin f} \tag{2.74}$$

The range of oscillation of the output link b is then

$$\psi_i - \psi_a = 2\psi_{s\,max} = 2\sin^{-1}\frac{\sin a}{\sin f} \tag{2.75}$$

2.3.9 Summary of spherical crank–rockers

From the foregoing it can be concluded that as long as the input link rotates continuously and the output link swings, the spherical four-bar linkage is a crank–rocker. Table 2.1 is a general view of all spherical crank–rockers described in previous sections, the tabulation scheme of which is according to (Meyer zur Capellen *et al.*, 1966).

2.3.10 Applications of spherical crank–rockers

Fig. 2.18 shows a practical construction of the wobble-plate, namely, $b = 90°$, $f = 90°$ and $c = 90°$ as described in Section 2.3.5. Fig. 2.19 shows the actual application of such a mechanism to an overhead swivelling electric fan. In Fig. 2.20 the same mechanism is shown once more, but constructed in accordance with Fig. 2.13, with the *sliding* block in the slot of the yoke omitted.

Table 2.1 Spherical crank-rockers

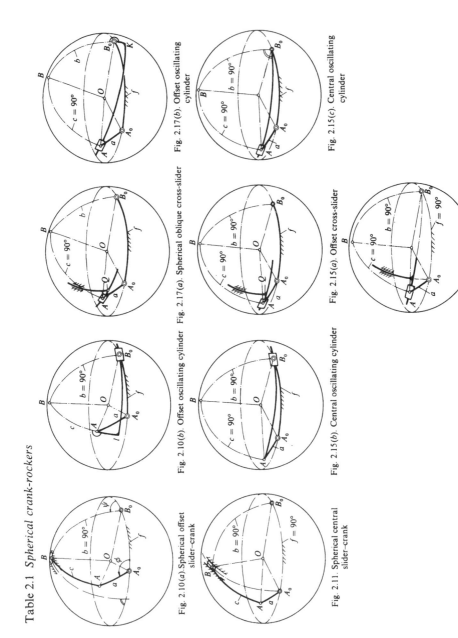

Fig. 2.10(a). Spherical offset slider–crank

Fig. 2.10(b). Offset oscillating cylinder

Fig. 2.17(a). Spherical oblique cross-slider

Fig. 2.17(b). Offset oscillating cylinder

Fig. 2.11. Spherical central slider–crank

Fig. 2.15(b). Central oscillating cylinder

Fig. 2.15(a). Offset cross-slider

Fig. 2.15(c). Central oscillating cylinder

Fig. 2.13. Spherical Scotch-yoke or

Fig. 2.18. Constructive form of a wobble-plate.

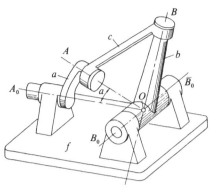

Fig. 2.19. Wobble-plate used in an overhead swivelling electric fan. (By permission of Harold Corporation, Taipei, Taiwan, China.)

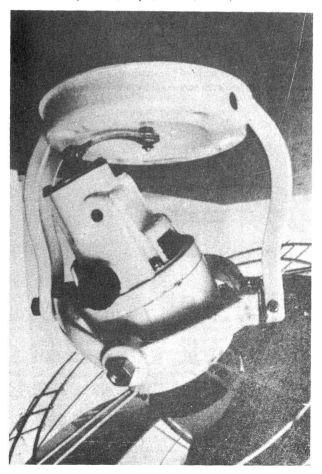

Fig. 2.20. Further constructive form of wobble-plate.

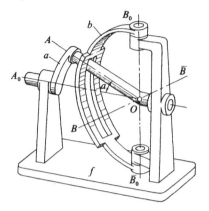

Fig. 2.21. Practical application of the wobble-plate as a driving mechanism for a washing machine. (By permission of Stephan–Werke GmbH & Co., Hameln, Germany.)

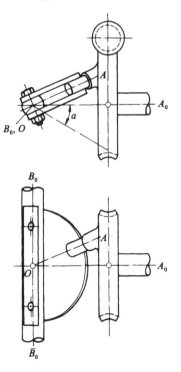

Fig. 2.21 shows the application of this kind of construction to the driving mechanism of a washing machine.

It should be pointed out here that because of design considerations the output link b is usually supported, in addition to at the axis OB_0, also at the axis $O\bar{B}_0$, where $\bar{B}_0$ is the antipode of B_0, as shown in Fig. 2.2. In fact the line $B_0O\bar{B}_0$ is a single axis, and the arc $B\bar{B}_0$ is the supplementary arc to the arc B_0B and the complete half circle $B_0B\bar{B}_0$ represents the single body of the link b. The same applies to the input link $A_0A\bar{A}_0$, which is supported at the axis $A_0O\bar{A}_0$.

2.4 The drag-link and its special forms

2.4.1 The drag-link

A drag-link, or double-crank mechanism, is a four-bar linkage, both rotating links of which are capable of making complete revolutions, as shown in Fig. 2.22. Again Grashof's rule must be fulfilled, but this time with the shortest link fixed. In fact a drag-link may be considered as an inversion of a crank–rocker, because in a crank–rocker the crank makes complete revolutions relative both to the fixed link and to the coupler. Replacing a, c, b and f by f, a, c and b cyclically in the inequalities (2.23) we get the necessary conditions to be satisfied for the existence of a drag-link:

$$\left.\begin{array}{l} f + c \leqslant a + b \\ f + a \leqslant c + b \\ f + b \leqslant c + a \end{array}\right\} \tag{2.76}$$

If we recall the inequalities to be satisfied by a plane drag-link, we shall find

Fig. 2.22. Spherical drag-link.

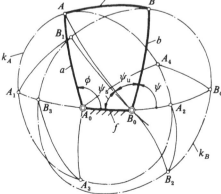

that those are analogous to the inequalities (2.76). In Fig. 2.22 let the small circles described by A and B be denoted respectively by k_A and k_B. Let the intersection points of k_A and the great circle $A_0 B_0$ be denoted by A_1 and A_2, and those of k_B and $A_0 B_0$ by B_3 and B_4. The last two inequalities in (2.76) claim that $c \geqslant A_1 B_3$ and $c \geqslant A_2 B_4$, and the first inequality claims that $c \leqslant B_3 A_2$. Since both $A_1 B_3$ and $A_2 B_4$ are generally much shorter than $B_3 A_2$, it is for this reason that the coupler length c is normally chosen shorter than a and b, although the inequalities (2.76) are symmetrical with respect to the three quantities a, b and c.

Equations derived in previous sections for a general spherical four-bar as well as those for a general crank–rocker can equally well be applied to drag-links. There are, however, no dead centre positions for a drag-link. Analytically this can be verified by considering equation (2.24), which was used for determining the position angle ϕ_a of the crank in the outer dead centre position of a crank–rocker. Equation (2.24) can be rewritten as

$$\cos b = \cos f \cos (a + c) + \sin f \sin (a + c) - \sin f \sin (a + c)$$
$$+ \sin f \sin (a + c) \cos \phi_a$$
$$= \cos [(a + c) - f] - \sin f \sin (a + c)(1 - \cos \phi_a) \qquad (2.24a)$$

Because of the third inequality in (2.76), i.e. $b \leqslant (a + c) - f$, we have $\cos b \geqslant \cos [(a + c) - f]$. It follows that, for the factor $\sin f \sin (a + c)$ is positive, $1 - \cos \phi_a$ must be negative, i.e. $\cos \phi_a \geqslant 1$. This proves that the angle ϕ_a does not exist for a drag-link. It must be pointed out that the inequality $f + b \leqslant c + a$ does not ensure the existence of a drag-link. The above proof shows only the nonexistence of the angle ϕ_a for a drag-link.

The partial mechanism $A_0 A B_0$ is no longer an oscillating cylinder mechanism, but becomes a spherical Whitworth mechanism. Because $a > f$, the small circle k_A described by the point A encircles the point B_0, and $\angle A_0 A B_0$ is always less than $90°$. There are as well no dead centre positions for this partial mechanism.

When $a = f, b = c$ and $a < b$, the linkage becomes a drag-link of particular property corresponding to the so-called Galloway rhomboid in plane kinematics. The input link a makes two complete revolutions to drive the output link b to complete one revolution (Tawchelidse, 1968).

2.4.2   The rotary slider–crank

One of the special forms of the spherical drag-link is the rotary slider–crank, the output link of which is of length $b = 90°$. This enables the point B to move on a great circle, as shown in Fig. 2.23(a). There is no counterpart of this mechanism in plane mechanisms, because the slider of a plane slider–crank can never move indefinitely in one direction. The linkage shown in Fig. 2.23(*a*) is an offset rotary slider–crank, i.e. the great circle of the path of *B* does not pass through A_0. There is no central rotary slider–crank, because in that case the length of the fixed link would be $f = 90°$, which is in contradiction to the prerequisite of a drag-link that f must be the shortest one of all four links.

2.4.3 Spherical Whitworth mechanisms

In plane mechanisms the inversion of a slider–crank with the shortest link fixed is usually called a Whitworth quick-return mechanism, or simply Whitworth mechanism. We shall call the spherical counterpart of this mechanism a spherical Whitworth mechanism. Corresponding to the two forms of offset oscillating cylinder mechanisms, Figs. 2.10(*b*) and 2.17(*b*), we

Fig. 2.23. (*a*) Rotary slider–crank. (*b*) Offset Whitworth mechanism.

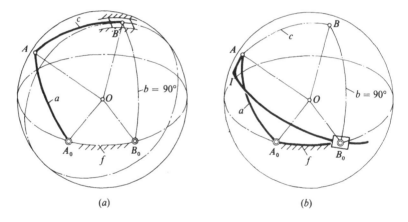

(*a*) (*b*)

Fig. 2.24. Offset Whitworth mechanism.

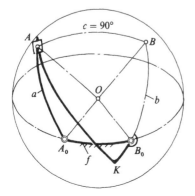

have, by setting $a > f$, the respective offset Whitworth mechanisms as shown in Figs. 2.23(b) and 2.24. In Fig. 2.23(b) the offset $AI = 90° - c$, and in Fig. 2.24 it is $B_0 K = 90° - b$. It should be noted that while the rotary slider–crank shown in Fig. 2.23(a) is identical with the spherical Whitworth mechanism of Fig. 2.23(b), it is different from the spherical Whitworth mechanism shown in Fig. 2.24.

If in Fig. 2.23(b) the offset of the coupler c is reduced to zero, i.e. the point A is chosen to coincide with the point I, the mechanism becomes that shown in Fig. 25(a). Similarly, if the offset of the output link b in Fig. 2.24 is reduced to zero, the mechanism then becomes that shown in Fig. 2.25(b). In fact both central Whitworth mechanisms shown in Figs. 2.25(a) and (b) are identical, and are equivalent to the partial mechanism $A_0 A B_0$ in Fig. 2.22. Equations (2.59)–(2.68) apply equally well for a central Whitworth mechanism. It is to

Fig. 2.25. (a),(b) Central Whitworth mechanisms.

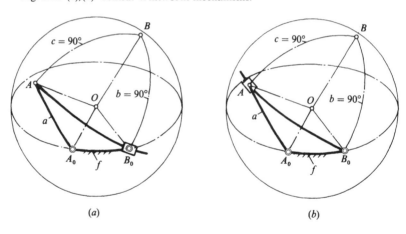

(a)   (b)

Fig. 2.26. $\psi–\phi$ diagram with a five-point contacting tangent, $\psi'' = \psi''' = \psi'''' = 0$.

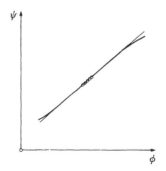

be noted, however, that ψ_s changes from $180°$ to $-180°$ as ϕ changes from $0°$ to $360°$.

The central Whitworth mechanism is useful in that it can be used as a proportional mechanism (Meyer zur Capellen & Dittrich, 1967), i.e. for a certain range of the input angle ϕ, the velocity ratio is approximately constant. If, in a certain position of the linkage, $\psi'' = \psi''' = \psi'''' = 0$, the ψ–ϕ diagram

Fig. 2.27. Relation (2.78).

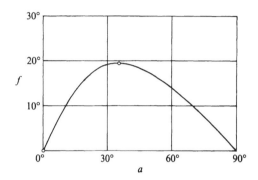

Fig. 2.28. (*a*), (*b*) Variations of ψ and ψ' of two central Whitworth mechanisms as proportional mechanisms.

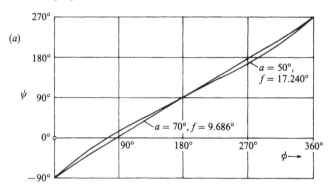

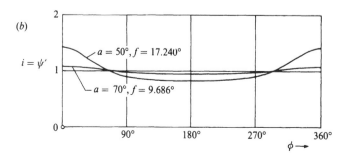

is said to have a five-point contacting tangent at this point, as shown in Fig. 2.26 (see also Section 8.2.1). This is just the case for a central Whitworth mechanism at $\phi = 180°$. It can be seen from equation (2.66) that $\psi'' = -\psi_s''$ vanishes identically for $\phi = 180°$. Also $\psi'''' = -\psi_s''''$ must vanish because of symmetry. It remains to set $\psi''' = -\psi_s''' = 0$ in equation (2.67). This leads to the following relation between μ and ν:

$$2(\mu^2 - \nu^2) - \nu + 1 = 0 \tag{2.77}$$

or a relation between a and f:

$$2\tan^2 a - \frac{1}{\tan f}\tan a + 1 = 0 \tag{2.78}$$

Equation (2.78) is a quadratic equation in $\tan a$ if f is given. This relation is shown in Fig. 2.27. Real roots exist only if $f \leqslant \tan^{-1}(1/2\sqrt{2}) = 19.471°$. It is therefore safer first to assume a value of a, and then compute f from equation (2.78). It can easily be seen from Fig. 2.27 that a is always larger than f, and hence the mechanism is always a drag-link. Figs. 2.28(a), (b) show, respectively, the variations of ψ and i ($= -\psi_s'$) of two central Whitworth mechanisms with $a = 50°$, $f = 17.240°$; and $a = 70°$, $f = 9.686°$.

At $\phi = 0°$, there are no positive values of a and f which can satisfy the condition $\psi''' = 0$, hence there exists no proportional mechanism at $\phi = 0°$.

2.4.4   The spherical rotary double-slider

Starting from the rotary slider–crank, Fig. 2.23(a), if we let the length of the input crank $a = 90°$, the linkage A_0ABB_0 becomes symmetrical to A_0A and B_0B. The point A, like the point B, moves along a great circle, hence the crank A_0A can also be replaced by a *slider* guided in a great circle slot. We have then a spherical double-slider, as shown in Fig. 2.29(a). Its counterpart in plane mechanisms is a double-slider mechanism with the two straight guides not perpendicular to each other. While in a plane double-slider the line A_0B_0 is at infinity, the length f of the fixed link A_0B_0 of the spherical double-slider is less than 90°.

Similarly the same linkage can also be considered as a variation from the offset Whitworth mechanism, Fig. 2.23(b). This variation is shown in Fig. 2.29(b). Here the crank A_0A is replaced by a rotary block at A_0 and a cross-shaped coupler c is sliding through the two blocks at A_0 and B_0. The coupler is so shaped that $BI = AJ = 90°$ with the two offsets $AI = BJ$, and the great circles A_0J and B_0I intersect in the point C. The two branches A_0C and B_0C of the coupler are rigidly connected at C. In other words, $\triangle CIJ$ is a rigid body representing the coupler c. This mechanism may be called a double-sliding bar mechanism. Let $\sphericalangle A_0CB_0$ be denoted by δ. The angle δ

Fig. 2.29. (a) Rotary double-slider. (b) Double-sliding bar. (c) Slider-sliding bar.

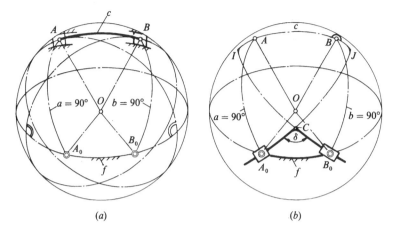

(a)   (b)

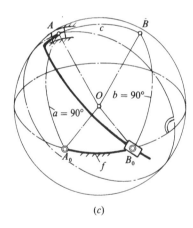

(c)

Fig. 2.30.

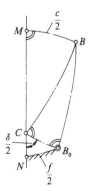

bears a certain relation to the coupler length c, as the following will show.

In the symmetrical position of the drag-link, Fig. 2.30, connect the middle point M of AB to the middle point N of A_0B_0 by a great circle MN. Then MN must pass through the point C. Because B is the pole of the great circle B_0C, therefore $BC = 90°$. In the right spherical triangle $\triangle CMB$, we have, by equation (A1.1),

$$\sin \measuredangle MCB = \frac{\sin \dfrac{c}{2}}{\sin BC} = \sin \frac{c}{2}$$

Hence

$$\measuredangle MCB = \frac{c}{2}$$

Fig. 2.31. (a), (b), (c) Forms of Hooke's universal joints corresponding to Fig. 2.29(a), (b), (c).

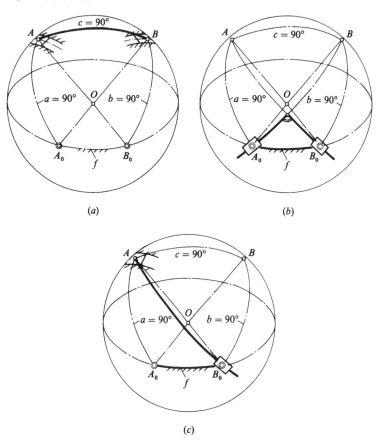

(a)

(b)

(c)

Therefore

$$\frac{\delta}{2} = 90° - \sphericalangle MCB = 90° - \frac{c}{2}$$

or

$$\delta = 180° - c \tag{2.79}$$

Equation (2.79) shows that δ is independent of f.

Fig. 2.29(c) shows once more the identical linkage, being a combination of Figs. 2.29(a) and (b), and may be called a slider-sliding bar mechanism.

2.4.5   The Hooke's universal joint

If, in addition to the conditions $a = 90°$, $b = 90°$ imposed on the double-slider, the length of the coupler is made $c = 90°$ too, the spherical drag-link becomes the well-known Hooke's universal joint, or simply Hooke's joint. The form of this mechanism which corresponds to Fig. 2.29(b) is shown in Fig. 2.31(b). According to equation (2.79) the rigid angle $\sphericalangle A_0CB_0$ in this case is $\delta = 90°$. The locus of the point C is a Thales ellipse, as mentioned in Appendix A1.3. The plane counterpart of this mechanism is the well-known Oldham coupling. Likewise the forms of the Hooke's joint corresponding to Figs. 2.29(a) and (c) are shown respectively in Figs. 2.31(a) and (c).

In the present case we have from equation (2.6) $k_1 = k_2 = k_3 = k_4 = 0$, $k_5 = \cos f$ and $k_6 = 1$, and from equation (2.7) $h_1 = 0$, $h_2 = \cos f \cos \phi$ and $h_3 = \sin \phi$. Equation (2.8) then becomes

$$\tan \psi = -\frac{\cos f}{\tan \phi} \tag{2.80}$$

Equation (2.80) can also be derived directly by applying equation (A1.5) to the right spherical triangle $\triangle A_0CB_0$:

$$\cos f = \cot \sphericalangle B_0A_0C \cot \sphericalangle A_0B_0C$$

and by noting that $\sphericalangle B_0A_0C = \phi - 90°$ and $\sphericalangle A_0B_0C = 90° - \psi$.

Fig. 2.32 shows the variation of ψ as a function of ϕ for a typical Hooke's universal joint with $f = 30°$.

From equations (2.12) and (2.14) we have the expression for the velocity ratio i:

$$i = \psi' = \frac{\cos f}{1 - \sin^2 f \cos^2 \phi} \tag{2.81}$$

or, by denoting

$$H = 1 - \sin^2 f \cos^2 \phi \tag{2.82}$$

we may rewrite equation (2.81) as

$$i = \psi' = \cos f / H \tag{2.81a}$$

Fig. 2.33 is a polar diagram showing the variation of i as a function of ϕ according to equation (2.81). It is of an elliptical shape and intersects a circle of unit radius in four points. This indicates that the angular velocity of the output link fluctuates above and below the angular velocity of the input link. The velocity ratio i reaches its maximum value of

$$i_{max} = \frac{1}{\cos f}$$

at $\phi = 0°$ and $180°$, and its minimum value of

$$i_{min} = \cos f$$

at $\phi = 90°$ and $270°$. The ratio

$$\frac{i_{max}}{i_{min}} = \frac{1}{\cos^2 f} \tag{2.83}$$

Fig. 2.32. $\psi-\phi$ diagram of a Hooke's universal joint with $f = 30°$.

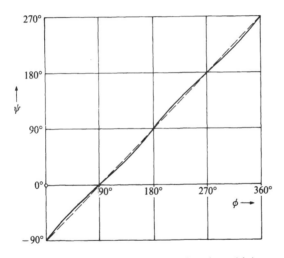

Fig. 2.33. Variation of i for a Hooke's universal joint as a function of ϕ.

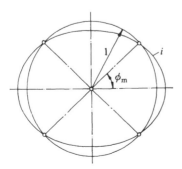

is an indication of the fluctuation of the velocity ratio i. For $f = 30°$ this ratio equals $4/3$. i becomes unity at the four intersection points as shown in Fig. 2.33, where the input crank angle $\phi = \pm \phi_m$ and $180° \pm \phi_m$. The value of ϕ_m is determined by equating the expression for i in equation (2.81) to 1 and solving for ϕ, i.e.

$$\phi_m = \tan^{-1} [\sqrt{(\cos f)}]$$

For $f = 30°$, $\phi_m = 42.94°$.

From successive differentiation of equation (2.81) with respect to ϕ, or from equations (2.15), (2.16) and (2.14), we may obtain

$$\psi'' = -2\sin^2 f \cos f\, S_\phi C_\phi / H^2 \tag{2.84}$$

$$\psi''' = \{2\sin^2 f \cos f[\sin^2 f\, C_\phi^2(1 + 2S_\phi^2) - (1 - 2S_\phi^2)]\}/H^3 \tag{2.85}$$

Fig. 2.34. Variations of ψ'' and ψ''' for a Hooke's universal joint with $f = 30°$.

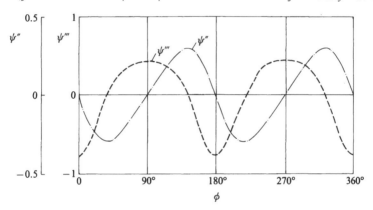

Fig. 2.35. Practical form of a Hooke's universal joint.

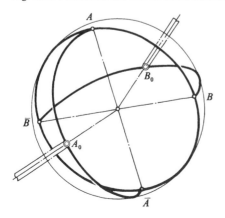

Fig. 2.34 shows the variations of ψ'' and ψ''' as functions of ϕ for a Hooke's joint with $f = 30°$.

The practical form of a Hooke's joint is shown in Fig. 2.35. The input crank extends from A_0 to $\bar{A}$, the antipode of A; and the output crank extends from B_0 to $\bar{B}$, the antipode of B, both cranks being of a 180° fork shape. The coupler body is then a ring with four 90° segments. The input and output cranks of commercially available Hooke's joints are usually made in a tubular form for easy mounting on the shafts, and the coupler is then usually in a form of a cross-piece.

2.4.6   Plane indicatrices of the spherical cross-slider and of the Hooke's universal joint

For the purposes of analysing a spherical cross-slider such as that shown in Fig. 2.15 or a Hooke's universal joint, there are two kinds of plane linkages whose kinematic rules of motion bear a certain resemblance to those of the corresponding spherical four-bars. The first kind is the elliptical oscillating cylinder, whose displacement equation is quite similar to that of a spherical cross-slider, with the Hooke's joint as a special case. The second kind is the ordinary oscillating cylinder, whose velocity ratio equation bears a certain resemblance to that of a Hooke's joint. Such plane linkages may be considered as coordinative linkages, or the so-called plane indicatrices, of the corresponding spherical linkages, as the following will show.

(1) Elliptical oscillating cylinder as the plane indicatrix of a spherical cross-slider (Meyer zur Capellen, 1958b)

Rewrite the displacement equation (2.61) of a spherical cross-slider as follows:

$$\tan \psi_s = \frac{\mu S_\phi}{1 - \nu C_\phi} = \frac{a_e S_\phi}{f_p - b_e C_\phi} \tag{2.86}$$

where $a_e = \mu f_p$ and $b_e = \nu f_p$, with f_p as an arbitrarily chosen convenient quantity. a_e, b_e and f_p are linear distances pertaining to a certain plane linkage.

Now consider a plane oscillating cylinder mechanism as shown in Fig. 2.36. A point C on the sliding rod is guided along an ellipse, whose major axis is $2a_e$ and minor axis is $2b_e$. From the well-known construction procedure of an ellipse by means of two concentric circles of radii a_e and b_e respectively, the parametric equations of the ellipse, or the locus of C, are

$$\left.\begin{array}{l} x = b_e C_\phi \\ y = a_e S_\phi \end{array}\right\} \tag{2.87}$$

where ϕ is the position angle of the radial line $A_0 A$. If the distance $A_0 B_0$ is made equal to f_p, we have then, for the orientation ψ_s of the oscillating cylinder, the equation

$$\tan \psi_s = \frac{y}{f_p - x} \qquad (2.88)$$

which is identical with equation (2.86). The plane linkage shown in Fig. 2.36 is therefore an analogue of the spherical cross-slider, the input angle ϕ and output angle ψ_s of both linkages being completely identical. Because the point C is guided along an ellipse, instead of a circle as in the case of an ordinary oscillating cylinder, this mechanism is termed the *elliptical oscillating cylinder*.

The ellipse can be generated by a Cardan circle-pair as shown in Fig. 2.36. The diameter of the smaller circle is $a_e + b_e$. The point C is a point on the body of the smaller circle, and the distance from the point C to the circle centre A of the smaller circle is $(a_e - b_e)/2$. The driving crank $A_0 A$ is a separate part from the body of the smaller circle.

When $a > f$, or $v > 1$ and $\mu > 1/\cos f$, the elliptical oscillating cylinder then becomes the plane analogue of a spherical Whitworth mechanism, Fig. 2.25.

Considering the Hooke's universal joint as a special case of the spherical cross-slider by setting $a = 90°$, we then have $\mu \to \infty$ and $v \to \infty$, and equation (2.61) becomes

$$\tan \psi_s = -\frac{\tan \phi}{\cos f} \qquad (2.89)$$

Equation (2.89) is in fact identical with equation (2.80) if we notice equation (2.59), or $\psi_s + \psi = 90°$. Now because $a = 90°$ the plane analogue of the Hooke's universal joint becomes an elliptical oscillating cylinder with $f_p = 0$,

Fig. 2.36. Plane elliptical oscillating cylinder.

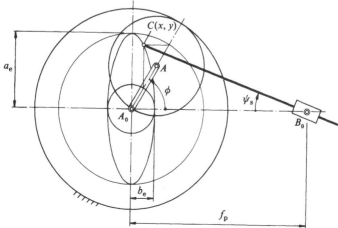

i.e. with a fixed link of zero length as shown in Fig. 2.37. Equation (2.88) then becomes

$$\tan \psi_s = -\frac{y}{x} = -\frac{a_e}{b_e} \tan \phi \tag{2.90}$$

where

$$\frac{a_e}{b_e} = \frac{\mu}{\nu} = \frac{1}{\cos f} \tag{2.91}$$

In other words, the size of the ellipse is immaterial, but the ratio of the semi-major axis to the semi-minor axis should be equal to $1/\cos f$.

(2) Ordinary oscillating cylinder as the plane indicatrix of a Hooke's universal joint (Meyer zur Capellen, 1958a)
Fig. 2.38 shows an ordinary plane oscillating cylinder mechanism, whose displacement equation, as can be found from any textbook on plane

Fig. 2.37. Plane elliptical oscillating cylinder with $f_p = 0$.

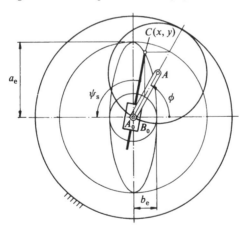

Fig. 2.38. Plane oscillating cylinder.

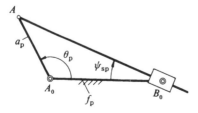

mechanisms, is

$$\tan \psi_{sp} = \frac{a_p \sin \theta_p}{f_p - a_p \cos \theta_p} = \frac{\lambda_p \sin \theta_p}{1 - \lambda_p \cos \theta_p} \tag{2.92}$$

where θ_p is the input angle and ψ_{sp} the output angle, a_p and f_p are the respective lengths of the crank and the fixed link, and $\lambda_p = a_p/f_p$. The angular velocity ratio i_p of this plane mechanism is then, considering a counterclockwise sense as positive,

$$\begin{aligned}
i_p &= -\frac{\dot{\psi}_{sp}}{\dot{\theta}} = -\frac{\lambda_p(\cos \theta_p - \lambda_p)}{1 - 2\lambda_p \cos \theta_p + \lambda_p^2} \\
&= \frac{1}{2} - \frac{1 - \lambda_p^2}{2(1 - 2\lambda_p \cos \theta_p + \lambda_p^2)}
\end{aligned} \tag{2.93}$$

Now the expression of the velocity ratio i of a Hooke's universal joint, equation (2.81), can be rewritten as:

$$i = \frac{\cos f}{1 - \sin^2 f \cos^2 \phi} = \frac{2 \cos f}{1 - \sin^2 f \cos 2\phi + \cos^2 f} \tag{2.94}$$

Comparing equation (2.94) with equation (2.93) shows that the velocity ratio i of a Hooke's universal joint can be expressed in terms of i_p of its plane indicatrix, provided that the bar ratio λ_p satisfies the relation

$$\frac{1 - \lambda_p}{1 + \lambda_p} = \cos f, \quad \text{or} \quad \lambda_p = \frac{1 - \cos f}{1 + \cos f} \tag{2.95}$$

In other words, substituting equation (2.95) into equation (2.94) reduces the latter to

$$i = \frac{1 - \lambda_p^2}{1 - 2\lambda_p \cos 2\phi + \lambda_p^2} \tag{2.96}$$

To summarize, the velocity ratio i of a Hooke's universal joint can be expressed in terms of the velocity ratio i_p of its coordinative plane oscillating cylinder by the relation

$$i = 1 - 2i_p \tag{2.97}$$

provided that the bar ratio of the oscillating cylinder satisfies equation (2.95) and that

$$\theta_p = 2\phi \tag{2.98}$$

which indicates that the crank of the oscillating cylinder should rotate with double the speed of that of the Hooke's joint.

Integration of equation (2.97) yields, taking the following boundary conditions into account: $\psi = -90°$ at $\phi = 0°$, and $\psi_{sp}(\theta_p) = 0°$ at $\theta_p = 2\phi = 0°$,

$$\psi = \phi + \psi_{sp}(2\phi) - 90° \tag{2.99}$$

2.4.7   *Coupling of two Hooke's universal joints – uniform velocity ratio*
From the foregoing it has been shown that the output shaft of a
Hooke's joint does not rotate with a constant speed if the input shaft rotates
uniformly. If, however, the output shaft is rigidly connected to the input shaft
of a second Hooke's joint, it is then possible, under certain circumstances, to
compensate for the nonuniformity of the transmission (Dittrich & Sommer,
1969). Fig. 2.39 shows such an arrangement. The input shaft of a first Hooke's
joint is I, and the output shaft of a second Hooke's joint is III. The input
crank C_0C of the second linkage C_0CDD_0 is rigidly connected to the output
crank B_0B of the first linkage A_0ABB_0 through an intermediate shaft II, both
cranks lying always in the same plane. The fixed links f_1 and f_2 of both
Hooke's joints are made equal and are in a plane containing the three shafts
I, II and III. It is evident that the output crank D_0D of the second linkage is
always parallel to the input crank A_0A of the first linkage, hence D_0D or $\bar{D}_0D$
rotates with the same angular velocity as A_0A.

Fig. 2.40 is a view of the plane containing the shafts I, II and III. Beside

Fig. 2.39. Coupling of two Hooke's universal joints, uniform velocity ratio.

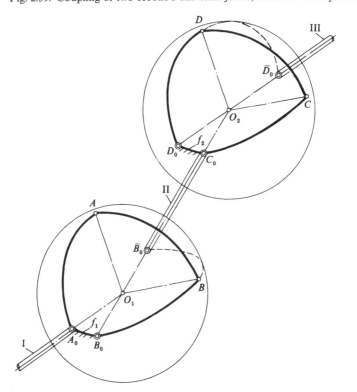

the linkage C_0CDD_0 another second Hooke's joint C_0CEE_0 is shown. The output shaft IV of this linkage makes with shaft II the same angle $f_2 = f_1$ as the angle between shafts III and II but in an opposite sense. It can be seen that the linkage $CE\bar{E}_0$ is symmetrically disposed to the linkage BAA_0 with respect to a middle plane perpendicular to the shaft II. Because the crank $\bar{E}_0E$ is always symmetrical to the crank A_0A, therefore $\bar{E}_0E$ rotates with the same speed as A_0A. The original spherical four-bar of this new second Hooke's joint is C_0CEE_0, which as shown is in a crossed position.

Fig. 2.40. Plane view of Fig. 2.39.

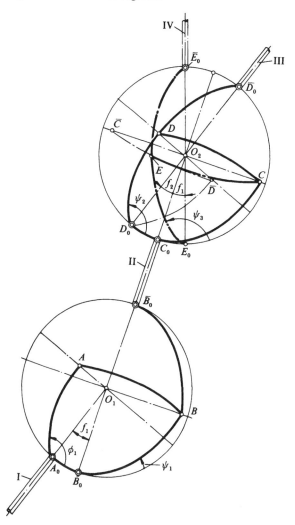

In fact it has already been shown in equation (2.80) that the two angles ϕ and ψ are interchangeable. This means that if the position angle of crank A_0A is ψ, then the position angle of crank B_0B is ϕ, or $\phi - 180°$. Thus in Fig. 2.40 the position angle ψ_2 of D_0D and the position angle ψ_3 of E_0E, both being output angles due to the input angle ψ_1 of crank C_0C, are equal, and are also equal to ϕ_1.

Imagine that in Fig. 2.39 we lock temporarily the linkage C_0CDD_0, then break the shaft II and twist the whole second Hooke's joint through an arbitrary angle and then rejoin the shaft II. After releasing the linkage C_0CDD_0 the crank D_0D still rotates with the same angular speed as A_0A, although the shafts I and III are non-parallel and non-intersecting. In fact the linkage CEE_0 in Fig. 2.40 may be considered as a position reached by twisting the linkage $\bar{C}\bar{D}\bar{D}_0$ about the axis of shaft II through an angle of 180°. Fig. 2.41 shows the relative position of two non-parallel and non-intersecting shafts I and III. If the common perpendicular between shafts I and III is h, the shaft angle is ε, and the distance between the two sphere centres is $O_1O_2 = e$, then the angle between the shafts II and I, or that between shafts III and II, which is the fixed link f_1 or f_2 of either Hooke's joint, is determined by

$$\cos f_1 = \cos f_2 = \frac{\sqrt{e^2 - h^2}}{e} \sin\frac{\varepsilon}{2} \qquad (2.100)$$

Fig. 2.41.

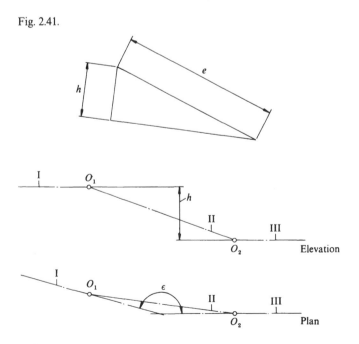

It can be shown that the angle of twist β, or the angle between the shaft planes (I, II) and (III, II), is determined by

$$\cos \beta = \frac{\alpha^2(1 - \cos \varepsilon) - (1 + \cos \varepsilon)}{\alpha^2(1 - \cos \varepsilon) + (1 + \cos \varepsilon)} \tag{2.101}$$

where $\alpha = h/e$.

The prerequisite for a uniform velocity ratio between shafts III and I is that when the input crank A_0A coincides with A_0B_0, the output crank D_0D should coincide with D_0C_0.

Some practical design data for a pair of coupled Hooke's joints can be found in (Schopke, 1968). The pair of coupled Hooke's joints, considered as a spatial mechanism, has been analyzed for its errors by means of the well-known Denavit-Hartenberg matrix-method (Austin, Denavit & Hartenberg, 1965).

2.4.8   *Coupling of two Hooke's universal joints – variable velocity ratio*

If the restriction of a uniform velocity ratio between shafts III and I is removed, changing f_2 and the position angle of the crank C_0C relative to B_0B may result in a variety of transmission characteristics of the whole coupling. As mentioned before, we may always temporarily lock the second Hooke's joint and reset it at any twisted angle relative to the first Hooke's joint. We may therefore, without loss of generality, assume that f_2 and f_1 are in the same plane. The relative position angle between the cranks C_0C and B_0B is characterized by the phase angle between these two crank planes. In other words, if ϕ_2 denotes at a certain instant the position angle of the input crank C_0C of the second Hooke's joint and ψ_1 the position angle of the output crank B_0B of the first Hooke's joint, the phase angle as shown in Fig. 2.42 is

$$\sigma = \phi_2 - \psi_1 \tag{2.102}$$

which is a constant, although both ϕ_2 and ψ_1 are variables. According to equation (2.80) we have for the first Hooke's joint the relation

$$\tan \psi_1 = -\frac{\cos f_1}{\tan \phi_1} = -\frac{m_1}{\tan \phi_1} \tag{2.103}$$

and for the second Hooke's joint the relation

$$\tan \psi_2 = -\frac{\cos f_2}{\tan \phi_2} = -\frac{m_2}{\tan \phi_2} \tag{2.104}$$

where ϕ_1 is the input angle of the first Hooke's joint; ψ_2 the output angle of the second Hooke's joint; and $m_1 = \cos f_1$ and $m_2 = \cos f_2$. Eliminating ψ_1 and ϕ_2 from equations (2.102), (2.103) and (2.104), we get the displacement equation for the whole coupling (Meyer zur Capellen, 1965a, b):

$$\tan \psi_2 = m_2 \frac{\tan \phi_1 + m_1 \tan \sigma}{m_1 - \tan \sigma \tan \phi_1} \tag{2.105}$$

Differentiating equation (2.105) with respect to ϕ_1, we get

$$i = \psi'_2 = \frac{d\psi_2}{d\phi_1} = \frac{m_1 m_2}{(m_1 \cos \sigma \cos \phi_1 - \sin \sigma \sin \phi_1)^2 + m_2^2 (\cos \sigma \sin \phi_1 + m_1 \sin \sigma \cos \phi_1)^2}$$

$$= \frac{4 m_1 m_2}{G + X \cos 2\phi_1 + Y \sin 2\phi_1} \tag{2.106}$$

where

$$\left. \begin{array}{l} G = (m_1^2 + 1)(m_2^2 + 1) - (m_1^2 - 1)(m_2^2 - 1) \cos 2\sigma \\ X = (m_1^2 - 1)(m_2^2 + 1) - (m_1^2 + 1)(m_2^2 - 1) \cos 2\sigma \\ Y = 2 m_1 (m_2^2 - 1) \sin 2\sigma \end{array} \right\} \tag{2.107}$$

Equation (2.106) can further be simplified in the following form:

$$i = \psi'_2 = \frac{4 m_1 m_2}{G + R \cos(2\phi_1 - \beta)} = \frac{4 m_1 m_2}{G + R \cos 2\phi_p} \tag{2.108}$$

Fig. 2.42. Coupling of two Hooke's universal joints, variable velocity ratio.

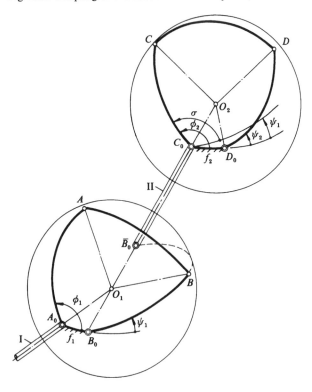

where

$$R^2 = X^2 + Y^2$$
$$\beta = \tan^{-1} \frac{Y}{X}$$ (2.109)

and

$$\phi_p = 2\phi_1 - \beta$$

Similar to a single Hooke's universal joint, for a coupled Hooke's universal joint pair there is also a plane indicatrix, or a coordinative plane linkage, as the following will show.

(1) The plane indicatrix of two coupled Hooke's universal joints is a mechanism consisting of two coupled elliptical oscillating cylinders, both with fixed links of zero length, as shown in Fig. 2.43. The first one is the same as that shown in Fig. 2.37. The output angle here as per equation (2.59) is $\psi_1 = 90° - \psi_{s1}$. The output motion of this elliptical oscillating cylinder is then transmitted to the input crank of a second elliptical oscillating cylinder. For the sake of clarity, this is done here by means of a parallel crank mechanism, although both oscillating cylinders could be coaxial. Because of the phase angle σ specified in equation (2.102), the input angle ϕ_2 of the second Cardan circle-pair should lag behind the first oscillating cylinder by an angle α, or

$$\phi_2 + \alpha = 180° - \psi_{s1}$$

Therefore

$$\alpha = 90° - \sigma$$ (2.110)

The output angle is $\psi_2 = 90° - \psi_{s2}$.

Fig. 2.43. Plane indicatrix of coupling of two Hooke's universal joints.

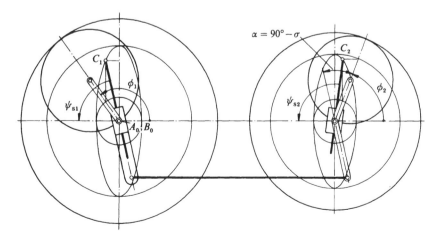

Table 2.2 Spherical drag-links

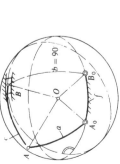

Fig. 2.23(a). Rotary slider–crank

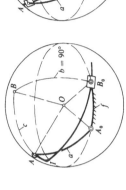

Fig. 2.23(b). Offset Whitworth mechanism

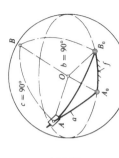

Fig. 2.24. Offset Whitworth mechanism

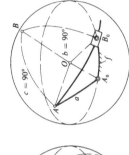

Fig. 2.25(a). Central Whitworth

Fig. 2.25(b). Central Whitworth mechanism

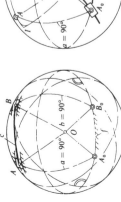

Fig. 2.29(b). Double sliding bar

Fig. 2.29(c). Slider-sliding bar

Fig. 2.31(b). Double sliding bar (Hooke's joint)

Fig. 2.31(c). Slider-sliding bar (Hooke's joint)

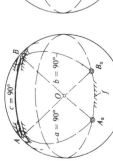

Fig. 2.31(a). Rotary double-slider (Hooke's joint)

(2) The similarity between equations (2.108) and (2.96) suggests that if equation (2.108) can be reduced to the form of equation (2.96), the whole coupling may be treated as a single Hooke's universal joint and analysed as a plane oscillating cylinder, Fig. 2.38, and equation (2.97) may then be applicable. To do this, let

$$\frac{4m_1 m_2}{G + R \cos 2\phi_p} = K \frac{1 - \lambda_p^2}{1 - 2\lambda_p \cos 2\phi_p + \lambda_p^2} \tag{2.111}$$

From equation (2.111) it can be found that

$$\lambda_p = \frac{\sqrt{(G - R)} - \sqrt{(G + R)}}{\sqrt{(G - R)} + \sqrt{(G + R)}} \tag{2.112}$$

and

$$K = -\frac{4m_1 m_2 \lambda_p}{R + G\lambda_p} \tag{2.113}$$

To summarize, the velocity ratio i of a coupled Hooke's universal joint pair may be expressed in terms of the velocity ratio i_p of its coordinative plane oscillating cylinder as shown in Fig. 2.38 by the relation

$$i = K(1 - 2i_p) \tag{2.114}$$

provided that the plane oscillating cylinder has a bar ratio λ_p specified as in equation (2.112), and the position angle θ_p of whose driving crank as shown in Fig. 2.38 equals ϕ_p as defined in equation (2.109).

More about Hooke's joints connected in series can be read from (Duditza, 1968a, 1969).

2.4.9 Summary of spherical drag-links

Table 2.2 shows a collection of all spherical drag-links described in previous sections. The tabulation scheme is in accordance with (Meyer zur Capellen, et al., 1966).

2.5 The double-rocker and its special forms

Just as in plane four-bars, a spherical four-bar is called a double-rocker if none of its rotating links is capable of making complete revolutions. There are Grashof and non-Grashof double-rockers, depending on whether Grashof's rule is satisfied, or whether the coupler can make full rotations.

2.5.1 Grashof double-rockers

An observation of the relative motion between the links of a four-bar which satisfies Grashof's rule, for example a typical crank-rocker such as that shown in Fig. 2.6, shows that the link opposite to the shortest link never makes complete revolutions relative to its neighbouring links. Hence fixing this link results in a double-rocker whose coupler is capable of making full rotations as shown in Fig. 2.44. Thus replacing a, c, b and f in the inequalities (2.23) by c, b, f and a cyclically we get the conditions to be satisfied for the existence of a Grashof double-rocker:

$$\left.\begin{array}{l} c + f \leqslant b + a \\ c + b \leqslant f + a \\ c + a \leqslant f + b \end{array}\right\} \tag{2.115}$$

Again equations derived previously for a general spherical four-bar apply equally well for a spherical double-rocker. There are, however, altogether four dead centre positions, two for each rocker. Denoting the four positions by $1, 3, 5$ and 7, the eight position angles are, applying the cosine law for sides as in Section 2.3.2, given by

$$\frac{\cos \phi_7}{\cos \phi_3} = \frac{-\cos f \cos a + \cos (b \mp c)}{\sin f \sin a} \tag{2.116}$$

$$\frac{\cos \psi_7}{\cos \psi_3} = \frac{\cos f \cos (b \mp c) - \cos a}{\sin f \sin (b \mp c)} \tag{2.117}$$

$$\frac{\cos \phi_1}{\cos \phi_5} = \frac{-\cos f \cos (a \pm c) + \cos b}{\sin f \sin (a \pm c)} \tag{2.118}$$

$$\frac{\cos \psi_1}{\cos \psi_5} = \frac{\cos f \cos b - \cos (a \pm c)}{\cdot \sin f \sin b} \tag{2.119}$$

It should be noted that the limiting position of one rocker does not correspond to the limiting position of the other rocker.

Fig. 2.44. Spherical double-rocker.

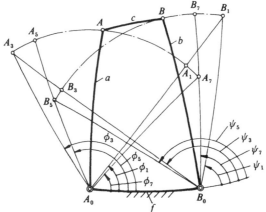

A special form of the Grashof double-rocker is obtained by setting one or more of the link lengths a, b or f equal to $90°$.

(1) The eccentric slider–rocker

Fig. 2.45 shows an eccentric slider–rocker, in which $b = 90°$ but $a \neq 90°$, $f \neq 90°$. The path of B, a great circle with pole B_0, does not pass through A_0. A double-rocker with $a = 90°$ but $b \neq 90°$ and $f \neq 90°$ is simply another eccentric slider–rocker in the opposite sense.

(2) The central slider–rocker

Fig. 2.46 shows a central slider–rocker, in which $b = 90°$, $f = 90°$ but $a \neq 90°$. The path of B, a great circle with pole B_0, passes through A_0. In the case $a = 90°$ but $b \neq 90°$, the double-rocker becomes another central slider–rocker with the path of A passing through B_0.

Fig. 2.45. Eccentric slider–rocker.

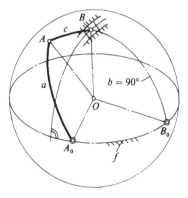

Fig. 2.46. Central slider–rocker.

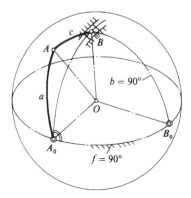

(3) The not right-angled double-rocker
This is a double-rocker with $a = 90°$, $b = 90°$ but $f \neq 90°$. The paths of A and B, both being great circles, do not intersect at a right angle, as shown in Fig. 2.47. It differs from the rotary double-slider, Fig. 2.29(a), in that $c < f$. Here a and b are not rotary, but only swinging.

(4) The right-angled double-rocker
A double-rocker with $a = 90°$, $b = 90°$, $f = 90°$ is a double-slider with the paths of points A and B perpendicular to each other, as shown in Fig. 2.48. A comparison of Fig. 2.48 with Fig. 2.31(a) shows that the right-angled double-rocker is an inversion of the Hooke's universal joint (Meyer zur Capellen, 1962).

Fig. 2.47. Not right-angled double-rocker.

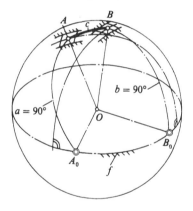

Fig. 2.48. Right-angled double-rocker.

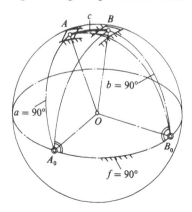

2.5.2 Non-Grashof double-rockers

Starting from the inequalities (2.23), the conditions to be fulfilled for the existence of a crank–rocker, if any one of the three conditions is violated the four-bar does not satisfy Grashof's rule, and hence cannot be a crank–rocker. We shall alter in turn each one of the inequalities, and see what kind of linkage the four-bar will be. There are altogether three cases, and in each case the rocker swings through a rocking angle symmetric with respect to the fixed link $A_0 B_0$.

(1) Non-Grashof double-rocker with internal rocking angles

Changing the sign of the third inequality of (2.23), we get

$$\left. \begin{array}{l} a + b \leqslant c + f \\ a + c \leqslant b + f \\ b + c \leqslant a + f \end{array} \right\} \tag{2.120}$$

These conditions imply that f is the longest link. Fig. 2.49 shows such a four-bar. Both rotating links $A_0 A$ and $B_0 B$ sweep through internal rocking angles.

Fig. 2.49. Non-Grashof double-rocker with internal rocking angles.

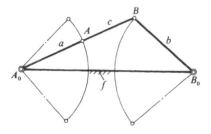

Fig. 2.50. Non-Grashof double-rocker with external rocking angles.

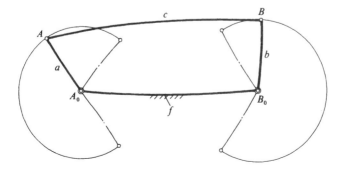

(2) Non-Grashof double-rocker with external rocking angles
Changing the sign of the middle inequality of (2.23) results in

$$\left.\begin{array}{l} a+b \leqslant c+f \\ b+f \leqslant a+c \\ a+f \leqslant b+c \end{array}\right\} \tag{2.121}$$

These conditions mean that the coupler c is the longest link. Fig. 2.50 shows such a four-bar. Both rotating links A_0A and B_0B sweep through external rocking angles. In fact this linkage is an inversion of the four-bar in Fig. 2.49, simply by exchanging the rôles of f and c.

(3) Non-Grashof double-rocker with overlapping rocking angles
Changing the sign of the first inequality of (2.23) yields

$$\left.\begin{array}{l} c+f \leqslant a+b \\ a+c \leqslant b+f \\ a+f \leqslant b+c \end{array}\right\} \tag{2.122}$$

These conditions mean that b is the longest link. Fig. 2.51 shows such a four-bar. The area swept by the rocker with the shorter length (here the link a) is overlapped by the area swept by the rocker with the longer length (here the link b).

Fig. 2.51. Non-Grashof double-rocker with overlapping rocking angles.

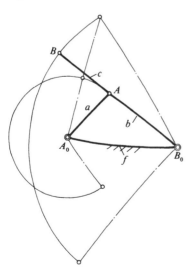

3

Classification of spherical four-bar linkages

3.1   **The meaning of classification of a**
spherical four-bar linkage
It has been pointed out in Section 2.3.10 that the crank $A_0 A$ of a
spherical four-bar linkage $A_0 ABB_0$, as shown in Fig. 2.2, may be replaced by
its supplementary arc $\bar{A}_0 A$, without affecting the motion of the original
four-bar. In doing so, the fixed link $A_0 B_0$ should then also be replaced either
by its supplementary arc $B_0 \bar{A}_0$, or even by the arc $360° - B_0 \bar{A}_0$. Thus we may
have spherical four-bar linkages with link lengths in the range from $0°$ to
$360°$. It is therefore necessary to classify, or identify, a given spherical four-bar.
The terms *classification* and *type determination* are synonymous. The problem
of type determination of a given spherical four-bar has been the subject of
study of a number of investigators during the past few decades (Bruewitsch,
1937; Dobrovolskii, 1947a, pp. 154–5; Freudenstein, 1965b; Duditza & Dittrich,
1969; Gilmartin & Duffy, 1972; Savage & Hall, 1970; Soni, 1970; Gupta, 1986).
Because of their contributions we now have a better understanding of the
classification problem (Chiang, 1984a).

First of all it has to be decided into what kind of catagories are we going
to classify spherical four-bar linkages. If we consider the crank–rocker, the
drag-link and the Grashof double-rocker as one class, and the non-Grashof
double-rockers as another class, then it makes sense to classify a spherical
four-bar linkage according to its rotatability. By rotatability is meant the
possibility of performing complete revolutions of one of the four links relative
to the other three links.[†]

[†] For the time being we shall exclude the case in which both opposite links are
equal and hence there are two links making complete revolutions relative to the
remaining two links.

3.2   Supplementary spherical four-bar linkages

Consider the spherical four-bar A_0ABB_0 as shown in Fig. 3.1. Each link is extended to become a full ring. Each pair of adjacent rings intersect at two points. There are altogether eight intersection points $A_0, A, B, B_0, \bar{A}_0, \bar{A}, \bar{B}$ and $\bar{B}_0$, dividing the rings into segments. These segments constitute, besides the original four-bar A_0ABB_0, 15 additional but kinematically equivalent four-bar linkages, namely:

$$A_0ABB_0$$
$$\bar{A}_0ABB_0, A_0\bar{A}BB_0, A_0A\bar{B}B_0, A_0AB\bar{B}_0$$
$$\bar{A}_0\bar{A}BB_0, \bar{A}_0A\bar{B}B_0, \bar{A}_0AB\bar{B}_0$$
$$A_0\bar{A}\bar{B}B_0, A_0\bar{A}B\bar{B}_0, A_0A\bar{B}\bar{B}_0$$
$$\bar{A}_0\bar{A}\bar{B}B_0, \bar{A}_0\bar{A}B\bar{B}_0, \bar{A}_0A\bar{B}\bar{B}_0, A_0\bar{A}\bar{B}\bar{B}_0$$
$$\bar{A}_0\bar{A}\bar{B}\bar{B}_0$$

It is understood that, in tracing a certain four-bar loop from one joint to the next joint, we always take a shorter route rather than a longer route. Although a link length, say AB, is kinematically equivalent to a link length of $360° - AB$ in motion transmission, only the shorter part of the full ring shall be considered in dealing with classification problems. Thus, for example, if the four-bar loop $A_0\bar{A}B\bar{B}_0A_0$ is to be traced, we trace first from A_0 downwards and then upwards to get to $\bar{A}$, instead of from A_0 passing through A and $\bar{A}_0$ to $\bar{A}$. The same principle applies to the routes $\bar{A}B$, $B\bar{B}_0$ and $\bar{B}_0A_0$. In other words, the link lengths $\bar{A}\bar{B}AB$, $BB_0\bar{B}\bar{B}_0$ and $\bar{B}_0\bar{A}_0B_0A_0$ shall not be considered. Hence none of the above listed 16 four-bars contains a link length longer than $180°$. Even

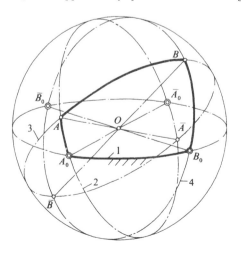

Fig. 3.1. Supplementary spherical four-bar linkages.

if a given spherical four-bar contains a link length longer than 180°, it can always be reduced to an equivalent four-bar which contains only link lengths less than or equal to 180°.

It seems that the 16 spherical four-bars are *cognate* linkages. In plane mechanisms two four-bar linkages are said to be cognate if the two couplers have a permanently common point. In other words, both linkages produce the same coupler curve at this particular common coupler point. This is, however, not the case with the spherical identical linkages, because the 16 spherical four-bars represent only four relatively moving bodies. The coupler is always the ring $AB\bar{A}\bar{B}$, and nothing else. Any point on the coupler will of course trace the same coupler curve by any one of the 16 linkages. In fact these 16 linkages are all identical and represent just one single linkage instead of 16 different linkages. The word *cognate* may sometimes be taken over from plane mechanisms to indicate these linkages, but a true spherical cognate such as the Roberts cognates in plane mechanisms does not exist because parallelism does not exist in spherical geometry. This fact may well be conceived by means of the gnomonic projection of the linkages as shown in Fig. 8.9. All 16 linkages are projected into a single plane four-bar linkage. This is also one of the reasons that gnomonic projection is adopted throughout this book. It seems to be adequate to term the linkages in Fig. 3.1 *supplementary linkages*.

Among the 16 linkages, eight of them are reflected ones of the other eight linkages. Thus, for example, $\bar{A}_0 A \bar{B} B_0$ is a reflection of $A_0 \bar{A} B \bar{B}_0$, and $\bar{A}_0 \bar{A} B \bar{B}_0$ is a reflection of $A_0 A B B_0$. As far as the link lengths are concerned, a reflected linkage possesses the same link lengths as those of the linkage before reflection and a symmetrical configuration. Thus, the configuration of $\bar{A}_0 \bar{A} B \bar{B}_0$ is not congruent, but symmetrical with that of $A_0 A B B_0$. Therefore, only eight linkages of different link lengths shall be considered (Freudenstein, 1965b; Soni & Harrisberger, 1967). These linkages, or, more precisely, eight four-bar loops are tabulated in Table 3.1. Here the symbols 1, 2, 3 and 4 are used to designate the four relatively moving bodies, as labelled in Fig. 3.1. From this table it can be seen that adjacent links remain adjacent, and opposite links remain opposite. It is also evident that any four-bar loop can be transformed into another four-bar loop by replacing *two* or *four* of its link lengths by their respective supplementary arc lengths. Therefore we may draw the following conclusions:

(1) If a given spherical four-bar linkage has an even number of link lengths which are $> 90°$, it is always possible to reduce it to a four-bar loop in which all link lengths are $< 90°$.

(2) If a given spherical four-bar linkage has an odd number of link

Table 3.1 *Supplementary spherical four-bar linkages*

Four-bar loop	Link length			
	Link 1	Link 2	Link 3	Link 4
$A_0ABB_0(\bar{A}_0)$	B_0A_0	A_0A	AB	BB_0
$A_0\bar{A}BB_0(\bar{A}_0)$	$180° - B_0A_0$	$180° - A_0A$	AB	BB_0
$A_0\bar{A}BB_0(A_0)$	B_0A_0	$180° - A_0A$	$180° - AB$	BB_0
$A_0A\bar{B}B_0(A_0)$	B_0A_0	A_0A	$180° - AB$	$180° - BB_0$
$A_0AB\bar{B}_0(A_0)$	$180° - B_0A_0$	A_0A	AB	$180° - BB_0$
$\bar{A}_0\bar{A}BB_0(\bar{A}_0)$	$180° - B_0A_0$	A_0A	$180° - AB$	BB_0
$\bar{A}_0A\bar{B}B_0(\bar{A}_0)$	$180° - B_0A_0$	$180° - A_0A$	$180° - AB$	$180° - BB_0$
$\bar{A}_0ABB_0(\bar{A}_0)$	B_0A_0	$180° - A_0A$	AB	$180° - BB_0$

lengths which are $> 90°$, it can always be reduced to a four-bar loop in which three link lengths are $< 90°$, and one link length is $> 90°$. Therefore, as long as there exists a single link length which is $= 90°$, it is always possible to reduce all link lengths to $\leqslant 90°$.

Consequently the following important conclusion can be drawn: any given spherical four-bar linkage can always be reduced to a four-bar loop in which the sum of any two link lengths is not greater than $180°$.

3.3   Criteria of classification

Let us study the conditions to be fulfilled by a crank-rocker. Denote as before the crank length by a, and the other three link lengths by c, b and f. We set forth a prerequisite that *the sum of any two link lengths is not greater than 180°*, which is always achievable according to the conclusion of the last paragraph.

There are four critical positions through which the crank must pass in order to ensure its rotatability. These positions are shown in Figs. 3.2(*a*), (*b*), (*c*) and (*d*), in which the crank a is in *line* with its adjacent links c and f respectively. The configuration Fig. 3.2(*a*) demands that

$$a + c \leqslant b + f \tag{3.1}$$

and Fig. 3.2(*b*) demands that

$$a + f \leqslant b + c \tag{3.2}$$

Fig. 3.2(*c*) demands either

$$c - a \geqslant f - b, \quad \text{if } f > b \tag{3.3}$$

or

$$c - a \geqslant b - f, \quad \text{if } b > f \tag{3.4}$$

Fig. 3.2(*d*) demands either

$$f - a \geqslant c - b, \quad \text{if } c > b \tag{3.5}$$

or

$$f - a \geqslant b - c, \quad \text{if } b > c \tag{3.6}$$

The inequality (3.3) leads again to (3.2), and (3.5) leads again to (3.1). The inequalities (3.4) and (3.6) are identical, leading to

$$a + b \leqslant c + f \tag{3.7}$$

Altogether we have therefore three independent conditions (3.1), (3.2) and (3.7), for the rotatability of the crank *a*. Setting them together gives the conditions mentioned before in Section 2.3.1:

Fig. 3.2. Four critical positions of a crank-rocker.

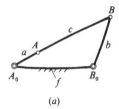

(*a*)

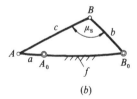

(*b*)

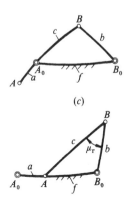

(*c*)

(*d*)

$$\left.\begin{array}{l} a + b \leqslant c + f \\ a + c \leqslant b + f \\ a + f \leqslant b + c \end{array}\right\} \qquad\qquad [(2.23)]$$

Because of the prerequisite already set forth, none of the sides of the four triangles in Fig. 3.2 is greater than 180°, hence each triangle is within a hemisphere. It is therefore evident that that prerequisite for a spherical four-bar loop is quite sufficient to ensure the validity of these conditions.

On the whole, the conditions (2.23) are sufficient, for any linkage which fulfils them ensures the existence of the four triangles shown in Fig. 3.2, hence the rotatability of the crank a. These conditions are also necessary, for if any one of the three inequalities is violated, the linkage becomes a double-rocker. The equal signs in (2.23) indicate the limiting cases in which the triangles in Fig. 3.2 degenerate into a single great circle. Let us now exclude these cases. As mentioned before, the conditions (2.23) claim that the sum of the length a of the crank and that of any other link should be less than the sum of the lengths of the two remaining links. Consequently, a is the shortest link length. In fact, Grashof's rule claiming that *the sum of the lengths of the shortest and longest links should be less than the sum of the lengths of the other two links* is quite a clever statement, for, no matter which one of b, c and f is the longest link, once one of the three inequalities is satisfied for the longest link, it automatically includes the other two inequalities.

There are therefore two classes of spherical four-bar linkages, and the following criteria may be established:

(1) Class 1 linkages are those which satisfy Grashof's rule. They may also be termed *Grashof linkages*. For this class of linkages, the shortest link is capable of making complete revolutions relative to the other three links, and (i) a crank-rocker exists if the link adjacent to the shortest link is fixed, (ii) a drag-link exists if the shortest link is fixed, and (iii) a double-rocker exists if the link opposite to the shortest link is fixed.

(2) Class 2 linkages are those which do not satisfy Grashof's rule. They may also be termed *non-Grashof linkages*. For this class of linkages, none of the links is capable of making complete revolutions relative to the other links, and a double-rocker exists whatever link is chosen as the frame. The linkage exhibits (i) internal rocking angles if the fixed link is the longest link, (ii) external rocking angles if the coupler is the longest link, and (iii) overlapping rocking angles if one of the two links adjacent to the fixed link is the longest link.

It should be noted that, before applying the above criteria, the four-bar

Table 3.2

	Link lengths				Result
	f	a	c	b	
Given:	80°	20°	60°	75°	Crank-rocker
Given:	30°	60°	60°	75°	Drag-link
Given:	80°	75°	25°	70°	Grashof double-rocker
Given:	85°	75°	65°	70°	Non-Grashof double-rocker with internal rocking angles
Given:	100°	160°	120°	105°	
Reduced to:	80°	20°	60°	75°	Crank-rocker
Given:	120°	25°	110°	100°	
Reduced to:	60°	25°	70°	100°	Crank-rocker
Given:	155°	60°	70°	80°	
Reduced to:	25°	60°	70°	100°	Drag-link
Given:	155°	50°	65°	80°	
Reduced to:	25°	50°	65°	100°	Non-Grashof double-rocker with overlapping rocking angles
Given:	60°	80°	25°	110°	
Reduced to:	60°	100°	25°	70°	Grashof double-rocker
Given:	100°	40°	90°	60°	
Reduced to:	80°	40°	90°	60°	Crank-rocker

loop should always be reduced to the one which satisfies the above mentioned prerequisite, namely, the sum of any two link lengths is not greater than 180°. The reduction is carried out, according to Table 3.1, by replacing each time the two longest link lengths by their respective supplementary arc lengths until none of the sums of two link lengths is greater than 180°. It is easy to conceive that the final four-bar loop is unique unless the sum of the two longest link lengths is just 180°, and that it is also the one having a minimum sum of all four link lengths. If the sum of the two longest link lengths is 180°, the type of Grashof linkage will not be altered, and the only effect is that one type of non-Grashof double-rocker will be changed to another type of

non-Grashof double-rocker. The procedure is quite straightforward, and will best be explained by the following illustrative examples:
In the following sections, particularly in numerical examples, the reduced four-bar loop only will be taken into consideration.
Examples: 10 miscellaneous examples are listed in Table 3.2. The given link lengths are reduced or not reduced according to the principle mentioned before. The results found by applying the criteria are listed in the right-hand column. Note that in the last two examples, the results could also be obtained without reducing the sum of link lengths to a minimum, although the reduction process is always recommended, in order to avoid any possible mistakes. Thus in the seventh example, without reduction a non-Grashof double-rocker would be mistaken for the drag-link.

3.4   Alternative criteria of classification

Another set of criteria of classification of spherical four-bar linkages, as given in (Duditza & Dittrich, 1969), is fundamentally the same as those in Section 3.3, but in a different representation. These are:

(I) A given spherical four-bar linkage with an even number $(0, 2, 4)$ of obtuse link lengths is rotatable if, after replacing all obtuse link lengths by their respective supplementary arc lengths, the sum of the shortest and longest link lengths is smaller than the sum of the other two link lengths, or smaller than half the sum of all link lengths.

(II) A given spherical four-bar linkage with an odd number $(1, 3)$ of obtuse link lengths is rotatable if, after replacing all obtuse link lengths by their respective supplementary arc lengths, the sum of the shortest link length and $90°$ is smaller than half the sum of all link lengths.

These two criteria can easily be verified on the basis of the criteria mentioned previously. It is evident that the former part of criterion (I) is identical with criterion (1) given in Section 3.3. Let the shortest and longest link lengths be represented respectively by l_{min} and l_{max}, and the lengths of the other two links be l_m and l_n. Grashof's rule states that

$$l_{min} + l_{max} \leqslant l_m + l_n$$

i.e.

$$2(l_{min} + l_{max}) \leqslant l_{min} + l_{max} + l_m + l_n$$

or

$$l_{min} + l_{max} \leqslant \frac{l_{min} + l_{max} + l_m + l_n}{2} \tag{3.8}$$

The inequality (3.8) represents the latter part of criterion (I).

To show the validity of criterion (II), let us start from criterion (2) of Section 3.3. Suppose the four-bar loop has been reduced to its minimum sum of four link lengths: l_1, l_2, l_3 and l_4. Without loss of generality we may assume that l_1 is the shortest one of all four link lengths, and that l_2 is the only one which is obtuse. Grashof's rule demands that

$$l_1 + l_2 \leqslant l_3 + l_4 \tag{3.9}$$

Now according to criterion (II), l_2 should also be reduced to an acute link length. Let

$$l_2 = 180° - l_x$$

Then (3.9) becomes

$$180° + (l_1 - l_x) \leqslant l_3 + l_4 \tag{3.10}$$

There are two possibilities, namely, either $l_x < l_1$ or $l_x \geqslant l_1$. If $l_x < l_1$, then the inequality (3.10) implies that $l_3 + l_4 > 180°$. But it has been assumed that neither l_3 nor l_4 is obtuse, therefore such an l_x does not exist. The only possibility is that $l_x \geqslant l_1$, hence $l_1 = l_{min}$ of the four quantities l_1, l_x, l_3 and l_4, and the inequality (3.10) can be written as

$$2l_{min} + 180° \leqslant l_1 + l_x + l_3 + l_4$$

or

$$l_{min} + 90° \leqslant \frac{l_1 + l_x + l_3 + l_4}{2} \tag{3.11}$$

which is a statement of criterion (II).

3.5 Conjugate positions of a spherical four-bar linkage

As has been shown in Fig. 2.3, and expressed by the double signs in equation (2.8), there are two positions of a linkage, hence two values of the output angle, i.e. ψ and $[\psi]$, corresponding to a single input angle ϕ. Similarly there are two input angles corresponding to a single output angle ψ. These two positions are termed *conjugate positions* or *branches* (Reinholtz, Sandor & Duffy, 1986) and have been used to synthesize linkages to produce coupler curves with cusps (Meyer zur Capellen & Werner, 1975). Let us confine our discussion to the conjugate positions represented in equation (2.8). The question is, which sign and which configuration are mutually correspondent? Consider first a crank-rocker A_0ABB_0, as shown in Fig. 2.3, which, according to the principle of Section 3.3, has already been reduced to a four-bar loop with minimum sum of link lengths.

An examination of Figs. 2.3, 2.22 and 2.44 together with Figs. 2.49, 2.50 and 2.51 shows that the two conjugate positions A_0ABB_0 and $A_0A[B]B_0$

cannot both exist for a given four-bar linkage, except when the linkage is a double-rocker. This means that, for a crank-rocker as shown in Fig. 2.3, if A_0ABB_0 is the given configuration, the conjugate configuration $A_0A[B]B_0$ can never be reached unless the joint at B is disassembled and reassembled at $[B]$. The same applies to a drag-link. This fact enables us to omit the computation of $[\psi]$ for a crank-rocker or for a drag-link. We shall assume in the following that, when the point A is on the *upper* side of A_0B_0, the angles ψ and $[\psi]$ correspond respectively to the two conjugate configurations as shown in Fig. 2.3.

For a given four-bar the analysis procedure in connection with equation (2.8) in computing ψ, or $[\psi]$, can be summarized as follows:

(1) If the four-bar is a crank-rocker or a drag-link, use the ' $+$ ' sign for all values of ϕ to compute ψ only.

(2) If the four-bar is a double-rocker, use the ' $+$ ' sign to compute ψ, and the ' $-$ ' sign to compute $[\psi]$.

4

Geometrical velocity and acceleration analyses of a spherical four-bar linkage

4.1 Velocity analysis

After the purely analytical derivation of the kinematic quantities of the output link given in Section 2.2.2, and those of the coupler given in Section 2.2.3, we shall now examine the velocity relations of a spherical four-bar linkage from a geometrical point of view.

4.1.1 Relative pole and Aronhold–Kennedy theorem

The pole of a spherically moving body as defined in Section 2.1 may be generalized for two cospherically moving shells. There exist between such two shells two instantaneously coincident points, each belonging to the respective shell, the linear velocities of which are identical. This common point is called the relative pole of the two shells. When one of the two shells is considered as fixed, the velocity of the relative pole is of course zero, and the other shell is rotating about the relative pole as illustrated in Fig. 2.1. In fact for two bodies moving about a common sphere centre, there are two relative poles located diametrically opposite to each other on the unit sphere, and the two bodies are said to rotate relative to each other about a relative pole axis which passes through the two relative poles and the sphere centre. However, in mentioning the relative pole between the cospherically moving shells, it is understood that only one of the two diametrically opposed points is taken into consideration.

The well-known Aronhold–Kennedy theorem in plane kinematics has its counterpart in spherical kinematics which may be stated as follows:

The three relative poles of three cospherically moving shells lie on a great circle.

This theorem can easily be proved by inspection. Let the three cospherically moving shells be denoted by f, a and b as shown in Fig. 4.1(a). The relative pole between a and f is denoted by P_{af} and that between b and f by P_{bf}. It is now required to prove that the relative pole P_{ab} between a and b lies on the great circle joining P_{af} and P_{bf}. Let us prove this by contradiction. Without loss of generality we shall consider only all motions relative to f. In other words, consider f as fixed. Suppose P_{ab} were located somewhere at P, not on the great circle $P_{af}P_{bf}$. Let the two coincident points on shells a and b be denoted by P_a and P_b respectively. As a point on a, P_a must have its velocity $\mathbf{v}_{P_a}$ in a direction normal to the plane $P_{af}P_a$. Similarly for point P_b, the velocity $\mathbf{v}_{P_b}$ must be in a direction normal to the plane $P_{bf}P_b$. $\mathbf{v}_{P_a}$ and $\mathbf{v}_{P_b}$ cannot be identical unless $P_{af}P_a$ and $P_{bf}P_b$ are the same plane, i.e. the plane $P_{af}P_{bf}$. This proves the theorem.

Although a rigorous mathematical proof of the theorem could be given (Müller, 1962, p. 12; Veldkamp, 1967b), we shall see that the theorem is self-evident. Using the usual right-hand convention for the angular velocity vectors, we notice that the three relative angular velocities ω_{af}, ω_{bf} and ω_{ba} of a relative to f, b relative to f and b relative to a respectively, are line vectors passing through the sphere centre O and the respective relative poles P_{af}, P_{bf} and P_{ba}. The corresponding angular velocity diagram is shown in Fig. 4.1(b). From the definition of relative angular velocities we have

$$\omega_{bf} = \omega_{ba} + \omega_{af} \tag{4.1}$$

Mathematically speaking, if three vectors in space are coplanar, they are linearly dependent, which means that any one vector can be expressed as a linear combination of the other two vectors. Conversely, if three vectors are linearly dependent, they are coplanar. Hence the three vectors ω_{af}, ω_{bf} and

Fig. 4.1. Aronhold–Kennedy theorem.

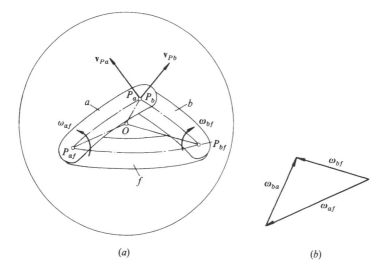

(a)   (b)

ω_{ba} are coplanar by definition. The statement of the Aronhold–Kennedy theorem in spherical kinematics is therefore trivial.

4.1.2   Angular velocity tetrahedron

Consider a spherical four-bar linkage A_0ABB_0 as shown in Fig. 4.2(a). Denote the four links as before: $a = A_0A$, $b = B_0B$, $c = AB$ and $f = A_0B_0$. Now A_0, A, B and B_0 are the four existing relative poles: $A_0 = P_{af}$, $A = P_{ca}$, $B = P_{cb}$ and $B_0 = P_{bf}$. Extend the great circles BA and B_0A_0 to intersect in R, and A_0A and B_0B to intersect in P. From the Aronhold–Kennedy theorem it is evident that R is the relative pole P_{ba} and P is the relative pole P_{cf}. Denote the arcs by: $p = AP$, $q = BP$, $e = RA_0$ and $g = RA$. Draw, from an arbitrary velocity pole $\mathbf{o}$ in space, the two angular velocity vectors $\mathbf{oa} = \omega_{af}$ and $\mathbf{ob} = \omega_{bf}$ in the directions OA_0 and OB_0 respectively, as shown in Fig. 4.2(b). The vector pointing from the terminal point $\mathbf{a}$ of ω_{af} to the terminal point $\mathbf{b}$ of ω_{bf} represents the relative angular velocity ω_{ba}, and must be parallel to RO, as described in the preceding section and illustrated in Fig. 4.1(b). Similarly the angular velocities $\mathbf{oc} = \omega_{cf}$, $\mathbf{ac} = \omega_{ca}$ and $\mathbf{bc} = \omega_{cb}$ must be in the directions PO, AO and BO respectively. There are altogether four sets of three relative angular velocities pertaining to three coplanar axes. The three angular velocities of each set form a triangle in the spatial velocity

Fig. 4.2. (a) Spherical four-bar linkage. (b) Angular velocity tetrahedron.

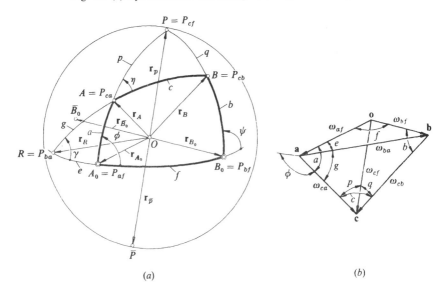

(a)   (b)

diagram. These are:

$$\omega_{ba} = \omega_{bf} - \omega_{af} \tag{4.1a}$$

$$\omega_{ba} = \omega_{ca} - \omega_{cb} \tag{4.2}$$

$$\omega_{ca} = \omega_{cf} - \omega_{af} \tag{4.3}$$

$$\omega_{cb} = \omega_{cf} - \omega_{bf} \tag{4.4}$$

The four triangles form a tetrahedron of angular velocities. The six edges of the tetrahedron are parallel respectively to the six pole axes of the spherical four-bar linkage. The apex angles of each triangle of the tetrahedron are equal to the corresponding great circle arcs. Thus,

$$\text{plane} \triangle \mathbf{oab} \parallel \text{plane } f: \measuredangle \mathbf{aob} = f, \measuredangle \mathbf{oab} = e \tag{4.5}$$

$$\text{plane} \triangle \mathbf{oac} \parallel \text{plane } a: \measuredangle \mathbf{oac} = a, \measuredangle \mathbf{oca} = p \tag{4.6}$$

$$\text{plane} \triangle \mathbf{obc} \parallel \textbf{plane } b: \measuredangle \mathbf{obc} = b, \measuredangle \mathbf{ocb} = q \tag{4.7}$$

$$\text{plane} \triangle \mathbf{abc} \parallel \text{plane } c: \measuredangle \mathbf{acb} = c, \measuredangle \mathbf{bac} = g \tag{4.8}$$

In the angular velocity tetrahedron, the four angles a, b, c and f are constants, and the angles e, g, p and q are variables. The only independent variable is ϕ, which is the input crank angle as shown in Fig. 4.2(a), or the external angle of the dihedral angle between the planes **oac** and **oab** in Fig. 4.2(b). We are now in a position to compute the angular velocities. Useful equations derived previously are reproduced here for easy reference. These are:

$$\psi = 2 \tan^{-1} \frac{- h_3 \pm (h_3^2 - h_1^2 + h_2^2)^{1/2}}{h_1 - h_2} \tag{2.8a}$$

$$\eta = 2 \tan^{-1} \frac{- h_3^* \pm (h_3^{*2} - h_1^{*2} + h_2^{*2})^{1/2}}{h_1^* - h_2^*} \tag{2.19a}$$

$$\gamma = \cos^{-1} (\cos \eta \cos \phi + \sin \eta \sin \phi \cos a) \tag{2.20a}$$

$$p = \tan^{-1} \left(\frac{\sin f}{\cos f \cos \phi - \sin \phi \cot \psi} \right) - a \tag{2.22a}$$

Applying the cotangent law (A1.11) to $\triangle A_0 R A$ gives

$$e = \tan^{-1} \left(\frac{\sin a}{\sin \phi \cot \eta - \cos a \cos \phi} \right) \tag{4.9}$$

and applying the cosine law for sides (A1.9) to the same triangle gives

$$g = \cos^{-1} (\cos a \cos e - \sin a \cos \phi \sin e) \tag{4.10}$$

Magnitudes of the relative angular velocities, expressed in terms of the input angular velocity ω_{af} according to the sine law for a plane triangle, as well as the positive direction of the corresponding unit vectors, are listed in Table 4.1.

Table 4.1 *Relative angular velocities in a spherical four-bar*

Magnitude of angular velocity	Positive direction of unit vector	Positive sense of great circle arc	
ω_{af}	$\mathbf{r}_{A_0} = \overrightarrow{OA_0}$		
$\omega_{bf} = \dfrac{\sin e}{\sin(e+f)}\,\omega_{af}$	$\mathbf{r}_{B_0} = \overrightarrow{OB_0}$	$e = \widehat{A_0 R}$, positive if in the same sense as $f = \widehat{B_0 A_0}$	(4.11)
$\omega_{cf} = -\dfrac{\sin a}{\sin p}\,\omega_{af}$	$\mathbf{r}_P = \overrightarrow{OP}$	$p = \widehat{AP}$, positive if in the same sense as $a = \widehat{A_0 A}$	(4.12)
$\omega_{ba} = -\dfrac{\sin f}{\sin(e+f)}\,\omega_{af}$	$\mathbf{r}_R = \overrightarrow{OR}$	$e = \widehat{A_0 R}$, positive if in the same sense as $f = \widehat{B_0 A_0}$	(4.13)
$\omega_{ca} = -\dfrac{\sin(a+p)}{\sin p}\,\omega_{af}$	$\mathbf{r}_A = \overrightarrow{OA}$	$p = \widehat{AP}$, positive if in the same sense as $a = \widehat{A_0 A}$	(4.14)
$\omega_{cb} = \dfrac{\sin g}{\sin c}\,\omega_{ba}$			
$\quad = -\dfrac{\sin g \sin f}{\sin c \sin(e+f)}\,\omega_{af}$	$\mathbf{r}_B = \overrightarrow{OB}$	$g = \widehat{AR}$, positive if in the same sense as $c = \widehat{BA}$	(4.15)

Note that if f is fixed, $\omega_{bf}/\omega_{af} = i = \psi'$, and equation (4.11) yields the same result as that given by equation (2.12). In other words,

$$i = \psi' = \frac{\sin e}{\sin(e+f)} \tag{4.16}$$

Also, equation (4.12) is identical with equation (2.21a).

As indicated in Table 4.1, the positive direction of each angular velocity is given as a radial axis originating from the sphere centre O. As has already been described in Section 2.2.3, although a diametral line, say, for instance, $B_0 O \bar{B}_0$, is the whole axis of rotation of the body b relative to f, as far as the angular velocity ω_{bf} is concerned, it is always to be considered as two axes, namely, OB_0 and $O\bar{B}_0$, directed in opposite senses. Thus, if the computed value of e happens to be negative and $e + f$ is positive, ω_{bf} is then negative about the axis OB_0 according to equation (4.11). However, the same ω_{bf} is positive about the axis $O\bar{B}_0$. As another example, a unit vector in the direction OP is denoted by $\mathbf{r}_P$ as listed in Table 4.1. The antipode of P is denoted as before by $\bar{P}$. A unit vector directed in the direction $O\bar{P}$ will be denoted by $\mathbf{r}_{\bar{P}}$.

According to equation (4.12) ω_{cf} is negative with respect to $\mathbf{r}_p$, but positive with respective to $\mathbf{r}_{\bar{p}}$, because $\mathbf{r}_{\bar{p}} = -\mathbf{r}_p$. With this kind of designation of two axes of a single moving body, all ambiguities will be excluded. In order to be consistent with the right-hand convention of an angular velocity vector, a simple rule is that, when we view in a direction normal to the spherical surface, a counterclockwise angular velocity is considered as positive, and a clockwise angular velocity is considered as negative. The same designation will also apply for other kinematic quantities such as angular displacements and angular accelerations.

The problem of synthesizing a spherical four-bar linkage to match prescribed ω_{af}, ω_{bf} and ω_{cf} has been solved analytically in (Di Benedetto, Francesco & Pennestri, 1983).

It seems that when $a + f = b + c$ at $\phi = 180°$, and when $c - b = f - a$ and $b - c = a - f$ at $\phi = 0°$, the location of the relative poles R ($= P_{ba}$) and P ($= P_{cf}$) as well as the velocity ratio i ($= \psi'$) would become indeterminate. For their determination the reader is referred to (Meyer zur Capellen, 1976).

4.1.3 Linear velocity of a coupler point

Let us examine the velocity relations of the coupler. Fig. 4.3(a) shows again a spherical four-bar linkage A_0ABB_0. The pole axis OP of the coupler c is located as before. If we view in the direction PO, the whole great circle of AB will appear in this view as an ellipse, as shown in Fig. 4.3(b). The velocity of any point on the coupler, e.g. $\mathbf{v}_A$ or $\mathbf{v}_B$, is parallel to this plane of view and appears as a true velocity. The velocity image of the great circle of AB in a velocity diagram as shown in Fig. 4.3(c) is also an ellipse, as in plane kinematics. Moreover, the velocity of any coupler point, say E, which does not lie on the great circle AB, or even does not lie on the unit sphere, is also parallel to the plane of view of Fig. 4.3(b), and can easily be determined in the velocity diagram Fig. 4.3(c) by means of the principle of similarity, shown here as the vector $\mathbf{OE}$, provided that the point E' can be located in the view of Fig. 4.3(b).

It has been shown in (Beyer, 1963, p. 126) that the end points of the velocity vectors in a velocity diagram of coplanar points of a link which makes a spatial screw motion are also coplanar. From the foregoing we can assert that this is true not only for coplanar link points, but also for all points of the link. This is because the velocity state of a body which makes an instantaneous spatial screw motion is a rotational velocity superposed by a translational velocity in the direction of the axis of rotation. Thus if the same translational velocity is added to all vectors in Fig. 4.3(c), the whole diagram will remain coplanar.

Fig. 4.3. (*a*) Spherical four-bar linkage. (*b*) View in direction *PO*. (*c*) Velocity diagram of coupler *AB*.

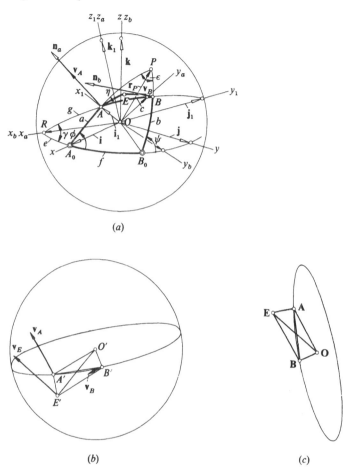

(*a*)

(*b*)   (*c*)

Fig. 4.4.

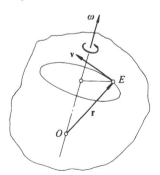

Graphical solutions for finding the linear velocity of a coupler point seem to be quite tedious and impracticable. We shall use vector algebra. Fig. 4.4 shows a body rotating with an angular velocity ω. The position vector of a point E on the body from an arbitrarily chosen origin O on the axis of rotation is $\mathbf{r}$. The linear velocity $\mathbf{v}$ of the point E is then the vector product of ω and $\mathbf{r}$, or

$$\mathbf{v} = \dot{\mathbf{r}} = \omega \times \mathbf{r}. \tag{4.17}$$

The following derivation of the angular velocity vector ω_c of the coupler is based directly on the geometrical concept of the linkage, although it might also be obtained by using standard formulas for Eulerian angles in theoretical mechanics (Tavkhelidze, 1971). Choose a right-handed coordinate system xyz fixed to the frame f, with the x-axis pointing in the direction OA_0 and the plane xOy coinciding with plane A_0OB_0, as shown in Fig. 4.3(a). The three unit vectors in the directions Ox, Oy and Oz are $\mathbf{i}, \mathbf{j}$ and $\mathbf{k}$ respectively. Let the unit vector normal to the plane A_0OA be denoted by $\mathbf{n}_a$, pointing in the increasing sense of ϕ. The direction cosines of $\mathbf{n}_a$ are: $(0, -\sin\phi, \cos\phi)$. We may write

$$\mathbf{n}_a = 0\mathbf{i} - \sin\phi\,\mathbf{j} + \cos\phi\,\mathbf{k} = \begin{bmatrix} 0 \\ -\sin\phi \\ \cos\phi \end{bmatrix} \begin{matrix} \text{(i)} \\ \text{(j)} \\ \text{(k)} \end{matrix} \tag{4.18}$$

In the following we shall be at liberty to use either form of the two alternative notations of a vector given in equation (4.18). However, when using the column matrix form the coordinate system to which the components are referred must be clearly marked, i.e. by $(\mathbf{i}),(\mathbf{j}),(\mathbf{k})$ as shown.

Similarly let the unit vector normal to the plane B_0OB be denoted by $\mathbf{n}_b$, pointing in the increasing sense of ψ. To find the direction cosines of $\mathbf{n}_b$ referred to the xyz-system, imagine that the link B_0B together with its normal were placed with B_0 at A_0. The direction cosines of this normal with respect to the $(\mathbf{i},\mathbf{j},\mathbf{k})$ system are then: $(0, -\sin\psi, \cos\psi)$. Now rotate this normal about the z-axis through an angle f to bring it to $\mathbf{n}_b$. The displacement matrix should be the one which corresponds to the inverse of the matrix in equation (A2.10). Hence we have

$$\mathbf{n}_b = \begin{bmatrix} \cos f & -\sin f & 0 \\ \sin f & \cos f & 0 \\ 0 & 0 & 1 \end{bmatrix} \begin{bmatrix} 0 \\ -\sin\psi \\ \cos\psi \end{bmatrix} = \begin{bmatrix} \sin f \sin\psi \\ -\cos f \sin\psi \\ \cos\psi \end{bmatrix} \begin{matrix} \text{(i)} \\ \text{(j)} \\ \text{(k)} \end{matrix} \tag{4.19}$$

Since OP is the intersection line of planes A_0OA and B_0OB, it is perpendicular to both $\mathbf{n}_a$ and $\mathbf{n}_b$, hence in the direction of $\mathbf{n}_a \times \mathbf{n}_b$. Denote the dihedral angle between the planes A_0OA and B_0OB by ε. Applying the cosine law for angles, equation (A1.10), to $\triangle A_0B_0P$ gives

$$\cos\varepsilon = \cos\phi\cos\psi + \sin\phi\sin\psi\cos f \tag{4.20}$$

The unit vector $\mathbf{r}_P$ in the direction OP is therefore, referred to the xyz-system,

$$\mathbf{r}_P = \frac{\mathbf{n}_a \times \mathbf{n}_b}{\sin \varepsilon} = \frac{1}{\sin \varepsilon} \begin{vmatrix} \mathbf{i} & \mathbf{j} & \mathbf{k} \\ 0 & -S_\phi & C_\phi \\ S_f S_\psi & -C_f S_\psi & C_\psi \end{vmatrix}$$

$$= \frac{1}{\sin \varepsilon} \begin{bmatrix} -S_\phi C_\psi + C_f C_\phi S_\psi \\ S_f C_\phi S_\psi \\ S_f S_\phi S_\psi \end{bmatrix} \begin{matrix} \text{(i)} \\ \text{(j)} \\ \text{(k)} \end{matrix} \qquad (4.21)$$

where S_ϕ, C_ϕ, S_ψ and C_ψ have been defined in equation (2.13), and $S_f = \sin f$, $C_f = \cos f$. The angular velocity vector $\boldsymbol{\omega}_c$ of the coupler is

$$\boldsymbol{\omega}_c = \omega_c \mathbf{r}_P = \omega_{cx} \mathbf{i} + \omega_{cy} \mathbf{j} + \omega_{cz} \mathbf{k} \qquad (4.22)$$

The next step is to find the position vector $\mathbf{r}_E$ of a coupler point E expressed in the xyz-system. Choose a right-handed coordinate system $x_1 y_1 z_1$ with the x_1-axis pointing in the direction OA and with the plane $x_1 y_1$ coinciding with the plane AB, Fig. 4.3(a). Suppose the position vector of E is expressed in the $x_1 y_1 z_1$-system with its three components x_{E1}, y_{E1}, z_{E1}. The $x_1 y_1 z_1$-system can be brought to the position of the xyz-system by rotating through three Eulerian angles, namely: (1) rotation about z_1-axis through angle $(-g)$ to $x_a y_a z_a$ such that x_a-axis $= OR$, (2) rotation about x_a-axis through angle $(-\gamma)$ to $x_b y_b z_b$ such that z_b-axis $\perp xy$-plane, and (3) rotation about z_b-axis through angle $(+e)$ to xyz-system. The transformation matrix is thus obtained by replacing ξ, η and ζ in the elements of the matrix $\mathbb{M}_{12}$ of equation (A2.17) respectively by $(-g)$, $(-\gamma)$ and $(+e)$. Therefore

$$\mathbf{r}_E = x_{E1} \mathbf{i}_1 + y_{E1} \mathbf{j}_1 + z_{E1} \mathbf{k}_1 = x_E \mathbf{i} + y_E \mathbf{j} + z_E \mathbf{k}$$

Fig. 4.5.

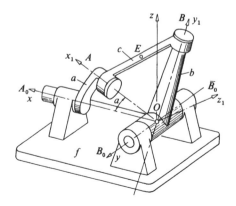

and

$$
\begin{bmatrix} x_E \\ y_E \\ z_E \end{bmatrix} = \begin{bmatrix} m_{11} & m_{12} & m_{13} \\ m_{21} & m_{22} & m_{23} \\ m_{31} & m_{32} & m_{33} \end{bmatrix} \begin{bmatrix} x_{E1} \\ y_{E1} \\ z_{E1} \end{bmatrix} = \mathbb{M}_{10} \begin{bmatrix} x_{E1} \\ y_{E1} \\ z_{E1} \end{bmatrix} \tag{4.23}
$$

where, according to equation (A2.17),

$$
\left.\begin{aligned}
m_{11} &= \cos g \cos e + \sin g \cos \gamma \sin e \\
m_{12} &= -\sin g \cos e + \cos g \cos \gamma \sin e \\
m_{13} &= -\sin \gamma \sin e \\
m_{21} &= -\cos g \sin e + \sin g \cos \gamma \cos e \\
m_{22} &= \sin g \sin e + \cos g \cos \gamma \cos e \\
m_{23} &= -\sin \gamma \cos e \\
m_{31} &= \sin g \sin \gamma \\
m_{32} &= \cos g \sin \gamma \\
m_{33} &= \cos \gamma
\end{aligned}\right\} \tag{4.24}
$$

A procedure for finding these elements without computing the values of η, e, g, γ will be given in Section 7.1.4. Finally, according to equation (4.17), the velocity vector $\mathbf{v}_E$ can be obtained from the vector product of $\boldsymbol{\omega}_c$ and $\mathbf{r}_E$:

$$
\mathbf{v}_E = \boldsymbol{\omega}_c \times \mathbf{r}_E = \begin{vmatrix} \mathbf{i} & \mathbf{j} & \mathbf{k} \\ \omega_{cx} & \omega_{cy} & \omega_{cz} \\ x_E & y_E & z_E \end{vmatrix}
$$
$$
= (\omega_{cy} z_E - \omega_{cz} y_E)\mathbf{i} + (\omega_{cz} x_E - \omega_{cx} z_E)\mathbf{j} + (\omega_{cx} y_E - \omega_{cy} x_E)\mathbf{k} \tag{4.25}
$$

Example: We take the wobble-plate shown in Fig. 2.18 to illustrate the computation procedure. This is reproduced in Fig. 4.5. Given: $a = 30°$, $b = 90°, c = 90°, f = 90°$. Let it be required to find the linear velocity of the midpoint E of the link AB in terms of the input crank velocity ω_a when $\phi = 135°$. The coordinates of the point E in millimetres in the $x_1 y_1 z_1$-system are: $x_{E1} = 50.0$, $y_{E1} = 50.0$, $z_{E1} = 0$.

For the sake of clarity the computed results are listed in Table 4.2 in sequential order.

4.1.4 Velocity matrix

In general, if a body rotates with an angular velocity $\boldsymbol{\omega} = \omega_x \mathbf{i} + \omega_y \mathbf{j} + \omega_z \mathbf{k}$, the velocity of a point on the body with position vector $\mathbf{r} = x\mathbf{i} + y\mathbf{j} + z\mathbf{k}$ is, as given by equation (4.25),

$$
\begin{aligned}
\dot{\mathbf{r}} = \mathbf{v} &= v_x \mathbf{i} + v_y \mathbf{j} + v_z \mathbf{k} \\
&= \dot{x}\mathbf{i} + \dot{y}\mathbf{j} + \dot{z}\mathbf{k} \\
&= (\omega_y z - \omega_z y)\mathbf{i} + (\omega_z x - \omega_x z)\mathbf{j} + (\omega_x y - \omega_y x)\mathbf{k}
\end{aligned} \tag{4.26}
$$

Table 4.2 *Example of computation of linear velocity of a coupler point*

Quantity	Result	Equation used for computation
l	112.208°	(2.51)
ψ	67.792°	$\psi = 180° - l$
p	76.102°	(2.22a)
ω_c	$-0.5151\omega_a$	(4.12)
ε	105.502°	(4.20)
ω_{cx} ω_{cy} ω_{cz}	$\left.\begin{array}{l} 0.143\omega_a \\ 0.350\omega_a \\ -0.350\omega_a \end{array}\right\}$	(4.22)
η	40.893°	(2.19a)
e	19.286°	(4.9)
g	20.901°	(4.10)
γ	97.680°	(2.20a)
Transformation Matrix $\mathbb{M}_{10}$	$\begin{bmatrix} 0.8660 & -0.3780 & -0.3273 \\ -0.3534 & 0 & -0.9354 \\ 0.3536 & 0.9258 & -0.1336 \end{bmatrix}$	(4.24)
x_E y_E z_E	$\left.\begin{array}{l} 24.40\,\text{mm} \\ -17.67\,\text{mm} \\ 63.97\,\text{mm} \end{array}\right\}$	(4.23)
v_{Ex} v_{Ey} v_{Ez}	$\left.\begin{array}{l} 16.21\omega_a \\ -17.68\omega_a \\ -11.07\omega_a \end{array}\right\}$	(4.25)

The unit of the linear velocity is mm/s if ω_a is given in rad/s.

Written in matrix form, equation (4.26) becomes

$$\begin{bmatrix} \dot{x} \\ \dot{y} \\ \dot{z} \end{bmatrix} = \begin{bmatrix} 0 & -\omega_z & \omega_y \\ \omega_z & 0 & -\omega_x \\ -\omega_y & \omega_x & 0 \end{bmatrix} \begin{bmatrix} x \\ y \\ z \end{bmatrix} \tag{4.27}$$

or simply

$$\mathbf{v} = \mathbb{V}_\omega \mathbf{r} \tag{4.28}$$

where $\mathbb{V}_\omega$ stands for the 3×3 matrix in equation (4.27), which is skew-symmetric, or antisymmetric, but no longer orthogonal. Equation (4.28) implies that, by applying $\mathbb{V}_\omega$ to $\mathbf{r}$, we get the velocity $\mathbf{v}$ of the point.

The matrix $\mathbb{V}_\omega$ may also be derived from the displacement matrix $\mathbb{D}_{12}$ in equation (A2.33). Suppose a body is rotating through an infinitesimal angle $d\delta$ about a given axis whose direction cosines l_x, l_y and l_z are known. The position vector $\mathbf{r}$ of a point on the body is rotated to a position $\mathbf{r} + d\mathbf{r}$, which is, taking $\sin d\delta \approx d\delta$ and $\cos d\delta \approx 1$ into account,

$$\mathbf{r} + d\mathbf{r} = \begin{bmatrix} x \\ y \\ z \end{bmatrix} + \begin{bmatrix} dx \\ dy \\ dz \end{bmatrix} = \begin{bmatrix} 1 & -l_z d\delta & l_y d\delta \\ l_z d\delta & 1 & -l_x d\delta \\ -l_y d\delta & l_x d\delta & 1 \end{bmatrix} \begin{bmatrix} x \\ y \\ z \end{bmatrix} \quad (4.29)$$

Rearranging terms, we get

$$\mathbf{v} = \dot{\mathbf{r}} = \begin{bmatrix} \dot{x} \\ \dot{y} \\ \dot{z} \end{bmatrix} = \begin{bmatrix} 1 & -l_z\omega & l_y\omega \\ l_z\omega & 1 & -l_x\omega \\ -l_y\omega & l_x\omega & 1 \end{bmatrix} \begin{bmatrix} x \\ y \\ z \end{bmatrix} - \begin{bmatrix} x \\ y \\ z \end{bmatrix} \quad (4.30)$$

which is identical with equation (4.27). Moreover, in fact the above procedure could have been bypassed if we had simply written

$$\mathbb{V}_\omega = \dot{\mathbb{D}}_{12} \quad (4.31)$$

for an infinitesimal angle of rotation δ.

4.2 Acceleration analysis

4.2.1 Acceleration analysis of the output link

The geometrical analysis of the acceleration of the output link of a spherical four-bar linkage can be carried out in a similar way to that of a plane four-bar (Chiang & Chen, 1983). We have already got the relation between the output angular velocity and the input angular velocity, equation (4.11):

$$\omega_{bf} = \frac{\sin e}{\sin(e+f)} \omega_{af}$$

Fig. 4.6 shows the corresponding geometrical relationship. Differentiating this

Fig. 4.6. Acceleration analysis of output link.

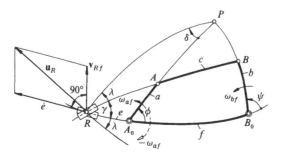

equation with respect to time results in

$$\alpha_{bf} = \dot{\omega}_{bf} = \frac{\sin f}{\sin^2 (e+f)} \dot{e} \omega_{af} + \frac{\sin e}{\sin (e+f)} \alpha_{af}$$

$$= \alpha_{bfn} + \alpha_{bft}$$

where

$$\alpha_{bfn} = \frac{\sin f}{\sin^2 (e+f)} \dot{e} \omega_{af} \tag{4.32}$$

is the part of α_{bf} due to ω_{af}, and

$$\alpha_{bft} = \frac{\sin e}{\sin (e+f)} \alpha_{af} \tag{4.33}$$

is the part of α_{bf} due to α_{af}, which is zero for a constant ω_{af}.

Imagine that a pair of *crossed sliders* were pivotally joined at the point R, the relative pole between cranks a and b, one slider being free to *slide on BA* and the other free on $B_0 A_0$. As the input crank a rotates with an angular velocity ω_{af} relative to the frame f, the point R *slides on $B_0 A_0$* with a linear velocity $\dot{e}$. The angular acceleration α_{bfn} can be obtained from equation (4.32) by substituting the value of $\dot{e}$. To determine $\dot{e}$, consider the inversion linkage by fixing a and rotating f with an angular velocity of $-\omega_{af}$ relative to a. According to the Bobillier theorem, the proof of which will be given later in Section 5.7, the relative pole R would trace a spherical polode whose tangent makes the same angle λ, but in the opposite sense, with link $A_0 B_0$ as the spherical *collineation great circle RP* makes with the link BA. Let the linear velocity of the pivot point R which is now the relative pole changing velocity, be denoted by $\mathbf{u}_R$. Then we have

$$\dot{e} = u_R \cos \lambda \tag{4.34}$$

The velocity $\mathbf{u}_R$ is produced by rotating f relative to a. Let the point on f but instantaneously coinciding with R be denoted by R_f. The velocity of R_f is obviously

$$v_{R_f} = \sin e \, \omega_{af} \tag{4.35}$$

Because v_{R_f} and $\dot{e}$ are two perpendicular components of $\mathbf{u}_R$, therefore we have

$$u_R = \frac{v_{R_f}}{\sin \lambda} = \frac{\sin e \, \omega_{af}}{\sin \lambda} \tag{4.36}$$

and from equation (4.34)

$$\dot{e} = \sin e \cot \lambda \, \omega_{af} \tag{4.37}$$

Substituting equation (4.37) into equation (4.32) gives finally

$$\alpha_{bfn} = \frac{\sin e \sin f}{\sin^2 (e+f)} \cot \lambda \, \omega_{af}^2 \tag{4.38}$$

Table 4.3

Quantity	Result	Equation used for computation
ψ	66.871°	(2.8a)
p	68.474°	(2.22a)
η	23.331°	(2.19a)
e	18.473°	(4.9)
$\gamma + \lambda$	70.606°	(4.40)
γ	47.278°	$\begin{cases} (2.20) \\ \text{or} \\ (4.41) \end{cases}$
λ	23.329°	
ψ''	0.691	(4.39)
α_b	$0.691\omega_a^2$	

Table 4.4

Quantity	Result	Equation used for computation
ψ	66.871°	(2.8a)
Φ	0.6360	(2.14)
ψ'	0.3170	(2.12)
ψ''	0.691	(2.15)
α_b	$0.691\omega_a^2$	

Comparing equation (4.38) with equation (2.10) we can conclude that

$$\psi'' = \frac{\sin e \sin f}{\sin^2(e+f)} \cot \lambda \tag{4.39}$$

The value of λ can be obtained by applying the cotangent law, equation (A1.11), first to $\triangle RA_0P$ to find $\gamma + \lambda$:

$$\cot(\gamma + \lambda) = \frac{\sin e \cot(p+a) + \cos e \cos \phi}{\sin \phi} \tag{4.40}$$

and then to $\triangle RA_0A$ to find γ:

$$\cot \gamma = \frac{\sin e \cot a + \cos e \cos \phi}{\sin \phi} \tag{4.41}$$

Note that γ could be found alternatively by equation (2.20) because η is already known at the stage of computing e.

The following example shows two different procedures for computing ψ'', or α_{bfn}.

Example: A spherical four-bar linkage with the following dimensions is given (see Fig. 4.11): $a = 36°, b = 50°, c = 60°$ and $f = 70°$, with f fixed. The input crank angle $\phi = 65°$. Find the angular acceleration $\alpha_b (= \alpha_{bfn})$ of the output crank b in terms of ω_a^2, where ω_a is the constant angular velocity of the input crank a.

(1) By equation (4.39). The results are listed in Table 4.3.
(2) By equation (2.15). The results are listed in Table 4.4.

The extremes of ψ'' have been dealt with in (Meyer zur Capellen *et al.*, 1970) from a geometrical point of view. However, as this would be beyond the scope of this book, we shall not go into details of this topic.

4.2.2   Extremes of angular velocity ratio

It is obvious from the preceding example that the procedure of finding α_b through the computation of λ is more involved than the other procedure of directly using equation (2.15). However, the significance of equation (4.38) lies in the fact that it provides a criterion for the occurrence of extremes of the velocity ratio $i = \psi'$. Equation (4.38) is analogous to a well-known relation for a plane four-bar linkage where in place of the sine functions are the respective linear lengths (Freudenstein, 1956). From equation (4.38) or (4.39) it is clear that ψ'' as well as α_{bfn} vanishes when λ becomes 90°. In other words, the velocity ratio $i = \psi' = \omega_b/\omega_a$ reaches its extreme whenever the spherical *collineation great circle RP* is perpendicular to the coupler AB, as has been otherwise proved in (Meyer zur Capellen, 1960; Pamidi & Soni, 1969; Meyer zur Capellen *et al.*, 1970). Fig. 4.7 shows such a configuration.

Consequently we may draw, without proof, the following corollaries which are analogous to those in plane kinematics (Freudenstein, 1956; Chiang, 1970). The value of the ratio ω_{cf}/ω_{af}, as well as that of ω_{ca}/ω_{af}, becomes an extreme whenever the collineation great circle is perpendicular to B_0B, and the ratio ω_{cf}/ω_{bf} becomes an extreme whenever the collineation great circle is perpendicular to A_0A. Also the ratio ω_{cb}/ω_{ca} becomes an extreme whenever the collineation great circle is perpendicular to A_0B_0. While these conditions are sufficient, they are not necessary. Thus, for instance, the ratio ω_{cf}/ω_{af} will also become an extreme when $p = 90°$.

The method of synthesizing a four-bar linkage to match a prescribed extreme value of $i = \psi'$ will be described later in Section 8.2.1.

The above consideration of the existence of an extreme velocity ratio is based on a geometrical concept. Algebraically, while equation (2.12) can be used to compute the extreme velocity ratios i when ψ'', as given by equation (2.15), vanishes, the latter equation does not, however, render the location or detection of the existence of an extreme velocity ratio in terms of the input angle ϕ. To this end, alternative formulations are necessary. It has been pointed out by Pamidi (Pamidi, 1976) that the possible extreme velocity ratios are in general among the real roots of a polynomial equation of the 10th degree. Let us see how this is derived. Equations (2.5a) and (2.12) can be rewritten in the following forms:

$$k_6 S_\phi S_\psi + (-k_4 + k_5 C_\phi)C_\psi = -k_1 + k_2 - k_3 C_\phi \tag{2.5b}$$

$$[(k_4 - k_5 C_\phi)i + k_6 C_\phi]S_\psi + (k_6 i - k_5)S_\phi C_\psi = k_3 S_\phi \tag{2.12a}$$

These two equations can be considered as two simultaneous equations in the unknowns S_ψ and C_ψ. Solving them for S_ψ and C_ψ gives

$$S_\psi = D_s/D \tag{4.42}$$

$$C_\psi = D_c/D \tag{4.43}$$

where

$$D_s = (-k_1 + k_2 - k_3 C_\phi)(k_6 i - k_5)S_\phi - (-k_4 + k_5 C_\phi)k_3 S_\phi$$

$$D_c = k_3 k_6 S_\phi^2 - [(k_4 - k_5 C_\phi)i + k_6 C_\phi](-k_1 + k_2 - k_3 C_\phi)$$

$$D = k_6(k_6 i - k_5)S_\phi^2 - [(k_4 - k_5 C_\phi)i + k_6 C_\phi](-k_4 + k_5 C_\phi)$$

It should be noted that the derivation of equations (4.42) and (4.43) is not valid in such cases as $S_\phi = 0$ or $b = c = 90°$. These cases will be dealt with later in this section.

(1) General case, equations (4.42) and (4.43) are valid
Substituting equations (4.42) and (4.43) into the condition $S_\psi^2 + C_\psi^2 = 1$ results

Fig. 4.7. Configuration at extreme of $i = \psi'$.

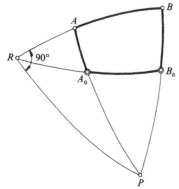

in the following quartic equation in the variable C_ϕ,

$$L(C_\phi, i) \equiv L_4(i)C_\phi^4 + L_3(i)C_\phi^3 + L_2(i)C_\phi^2 + L_1(i)C_\phi + L_0(i) = 0 \qquad (4.44)$$

where $L_4(i), \ldots, L_0(i)$ are all quadratic functions of i, namely,

$$\left.\begin{aligned}
L_4(i) &= L_{42}i^2 \\
L_3(i) &= L_{32}i^2 + L_{31}i \\
L_2(i) &= L_{22}i^2 + L_{21}i + L_{20} \\
L_1(i) &= L_{12}i^2 + L_{11}i + L_{10} \\
L_0(i) &= L_{02}i^2 + L_{01}i + L_{00}
\end{aligned}\right\} \qquad (4.45)$$

All coefficients in equations (4.45) are constants. They depend, similarly to those in equation (2.6), only on the *lengths* a, b, c and f of the four-bar. Because of the lengthiness of the expressions, they are listed in Appendix 5. Equation (4.44) can be considered as an expression of i, expressed as an implicit function of C_ϕ. For a certain value of the input angle ϕ, equation (4.44) becomes a quadratic equation in the unknown i. The two conjugate roots of this equation are the two velocity ratios of the respective conjugate linkages A_0ABB_0 and $A_0A[B]B_0$, for a certain value of the input angle ϕ as shown in Fig. 2.3. As equation (4.44) contains the input angle ϕ only in C_ϕ, its two roots are identical with the two roots for $-\phi$. This can also easily be observed from Fig. 2.3: if the input crank a takes a position $-\phi$, the two possible configurations of the linkage are those disposed symmetrically to A_0ABB_0 and $A_0A[B]B_0$, with respect to A_0B_0, hence the two points R and $[R]$ remain the same as those for $+\phi$.

For the occurrence of an extreme value of i, $di/d\phi$ must vanish. Differentiating equation (4.44) with respect to ϕ yields

$$\frac{\partial L}{\partial i}\frac{di}{d\phi} + \frac{\partial L}{\partial \phi} = 0 \qquad (4.46)$$

The condition $di/d\phi = 0$ leads to $\partial L/\partial\phi = 0$, or, by discarding the factor S_ϕ, which should not be zero, to

$$4L_4(i)C_\phi^3 + 3L_3(i)C_\phi^2 + 2L_2(i)C_\phi + L_1(i) = 0 \qquad (4.47)$$

Because the expression in equation (4.47) is exactly equal to $\partial L/\partial C_\phi$, its vanishing implies that equation (4.44), as a quartic equation in the unknown C_ϕ, possesses at least a double root, hence its discriminant must vanish, i.e.

$$4I^3(i) - J^2(i) = 0 \qquad (4.48)$$

where

$$I(i) = [12L_4(i)L_0(i) - 3L_3(i)L_1(i) + L_2^2(i)]/12$$

$$\begin{aligned}
J(i) = [&72L_4(i)L_2(i)L_0(i) + 9L_3(i)L_2(i)L_1(i) - 27L_4(i)L_1^2(i) \\
&- 27L_3^2(i)L_0(i) - 2L_2^3(i)]/432
\end{aligned}$$

Substituting the expressions for $L_4(i), L_3(i), L_2(i), L_1(i)$ and $L_0(i)$ into equation (4.48) results in the following polynomial equation of the 10th degree in the unknown i:

$$M_{10}i^{10} + M_9i^9 + M_8i^8 + M_7i^7 + M_6i^6 + M_5i^5 + M_4i^4 + M_3i^3$$
$$+ M_2i^2 + M_1i + M_0 = 0 \qquad (4.49)$$

Expressions for the $11M_n$'s are listed in Appendix 5. Corresponding to each root of equation (4.49) there is a double root of equation (4.44). Let a real root of equation (4.49) be denoted by i_r, and the corresponding double root of equation (4.44) be denoted by $C_{\phi r}$. Then $C_{\phi r}$ is given by

$$C_{\phi r} = \frac{L_4(i)G(i)I(i)}{H(i)[L_4^2(i)I(i) - 12H^2(i)] - 3G^2(i)} + \frac{L_3(i)}{4L_4(i)}, \quad i = i_r \qquad (4.50)$$

where

$$G(i) = [-8L_4^2(i)L_1(i) + 4L_4(i)L_3(i)L_2(i) - L_1^3(i)]/32$$
$$H(i) = [8L_4(i)L_2(i) - 3L_3^2(i)]/48$$

The thus calculated $C_{\phi r}$ should be within the limit

$$-1 \leqslant C_{\phi r} \leqslant 1 \qquad (4.51)$$

A further condition implemented to $C_{\phi r}$ is that, as can be seen from equation (4.46), in order that $di/d\phi$ be determinate, $\partial L/\partial i$ should not vanish, i.e.

$$2L_{42}iC_{\phi r}^4 + (2L_{32}i + L_{31})C_{\phi r}^3 + (2L_{22}i + L_{21})C_{\phi r}^2$$
$$+ (2L_{12}i + L_{11})C_{\phi r} + (2L_{02}i + L_{01}) \neq 0 \qquad (4.52)$$

Equations (4.49), (4.51) and (4.52) are the necessary and sufficient conditions for the existence of an extreme velocity ratio of a spherical four-bar. The procedure for finding the extreme velocity ratios of a given spherical four-bar may be summarized as follows:

(a) Compute the 11 coefficients M_n's of equation (4.49) and solve for i. Possible extreme values of i are among the real roots of this equation.

(b) For each real value of i thus computed, which will be denoted by i_r, find the corresponding $C_{\phi r}$ from equation (4.50), and see if this $C_{\phi r}$ satisfies both conditions (4.51) and (4.52). If it does, then the corresponding i_r is an extreme velocity ratio.

(c) The corresponding input angle is given by

$$\phi_r = \cos^{-1} C_{\phi r} \qquad (4.53)$$

As equation (4.53) yields in general two values of ϕ_r in two different quadrants, the correct one can be determined if it satisfies equation (4.49). Whether the extreme velocity ratio is a maximum or a minimum or even a point of inflection can be determined by using equation (2.16) to see whether the value of $\psi'''(= d^2 i/d\phi^2)$ is negative, positive, or zero.

(2) The case $S_\phi = 0$

As can be seen from equation (2.12a) in this section, if an extreme velocity ratio is to occur at $\phi = 0$, the condition $S_\phi = 0$ renders the first term on the left-hand side of this equation equal to zero. However, this does not mean that $S_\psi = 0$ is a solution of this equation as given by equation (4.42), rather it is

$$(k_4 \mp k_5)i \pm k_6 = 0 \tag{4.54}$$

in which the double signs correspond to $\phi = 0°$ and $180°$. For an extreme of i to occur, setting the expression for i' in equation (2.15) equal to zero and taking equation (4.54) into consideration gives

$$-ik_6 C_\psi + k_3 + k_5 C_\psi = 0 \tag{4.55}$$

Eliminating i from equations (4.54) and (4.55) yields

$$[\pm(k_5^2 - k_6^2) - k_4 k_5]C_\psi = k_3(k_4 \mp k_5) \tag{4.56}$$

Equation (2.5a) in this section now becomes

$$(k_4 \mp k_5)C_\psi = (k_1 - k_2) \pm k_3 \tag{4.57}$$

Combining the last two equations, we obtain the necessary condition to be satisfied by the link lengths of the four-bar if the linkage is to have an extreme value of i at $\phi = 0°$ or $180°$:

$$\cos c \cos(a \mp f) - \cos b = 0 \tag{4.58}$$

In addition to this condition, another necessary condition is that the coefficient of C_ψ in equation (4.57) should not vanish, or

$$\tan f \mp \tan a \neq 0 \tag{4.59}$$

Equations (4.58) and (4.59) are the necessary and sufficient conditions for the linkage to exhibit an extreme velocity ratio i at $\phi = 0°$ or $180°$. The value of this extreme velocity ratio can be easily obtained from equation (4.54).

(3) The case $b = 90°$ and $c = 90°$

This is the case of an offset cross-slider as mentioned in Section 2.3.6. In this case $k_1 = k_2 = k_3 = 0$, and the two equations (2.5a) and (2.12a) become a system of homogeneous linear equations in the unknowns S_ψ and C_ψ. It is well known that these equations will have nontrivial solutions provided that $D = 0$. The equations (4.42) and (4.43) are therefore not valid. Again setting the expression for i' in equation (2.15) equal to zero, setting $k_1 = k_2 = k_3 = 0$ in this and the two equations (2.5a) and (2.12a) and eliminating S_ψ, C_ψ and C_ϕ among these three equations results in the equation for the extreme value of velocity ratio

Table 4.5 *Examples of extreme angular velocity ratios*

No.	a	c	b	f	Type of linkage	φ (deg.)	ψ (deg.)	Extreme velocity ratio	
	(degrees)								
1	30	60	50	10	Drag-link	17.91	−86.19	1.5478 (max)	
						243.05	137.08	0.7074 (min)	
2	45	35	40	20	Drag-link	2.46	−58.51	1.6760 (max)	
						242.04	186.20	0.5223 (min)	
3	10	30	40	50	Crank-rocker	136.51	138.88	0.2919 (max)	
						345.40	136.59	−0.2836 (min)	
4	20	45	35	40	Crank-rocker	117.75	93.87	0.5982 (max)	
						346.48	86.60	−1.1892 (min)	
5	50	10	30	40	Grashof double-rocker	no extreme values			
6	40	20	45	35	Grashof double-rocker	no extreme values			Case (1)
7	30	10	40	70	Non-Grashof double-rocker with internal rocking angles	344.75	176.27	−0.7713 (max)	
						356.42	167.21	−0.7813 (min)	
8	45	30	35	60	Non-Grashof double-rocker with internal rocking angles	1.25	116.82	−2.7457 (min)	
						310.83	185.78	−0.7066 (max)	
9	70	55	73.334	10	Drag-link	228.90	169.67	0.9310 (min)	
10	45	50	71.253	15	Drag-link	342.28	−65.83	1.5082 (max)	
11	20	70	90	70	Crank-rocker	168.78	111.38	0.4640 (max)	
12	25	80	90	65	Crank-rocker	6.22	101.54	−0.6684 (min)	
13					Same as linkage no. 9	0	−58.77	1.0851 (max)	
14					Same as linkage no. 10	180	126.01	0.8165 (min)	
15					Same as linkage no. 11	0	110.00	−0.3420 (min)	
16					Same as linkage no. 12	180	100.00	0.4226 (max)	
17	40	90	90	20	Drag-link	0	−90	1.8794 (max)	
						180	90	0.7422 (min)	Case (2)
18	90	90	90	15	Drag-link (Hooke's universal joint)	0	−90	1.0353 (max)	
						180	90	1.0353 (max)	
19	25	90	90	50	Crank-rocker	0	90	−1 (min)	
						180	90	0.4375 (max)	
20	35	90	90	90	Crank-rocker	0	90	−0.7002 (min)	
						180	90	0.7002 (max)	
21					Same as linkage no. 17	180	90	0.7420 (min)	
						∓22.15	∓16.44		Case (3)
22					Same as linkage no. 18	90	0	0.9659 (min)	
						270	180	0.9659 (min)	

i, denoted here by i_e,

$$4i_e^2 - 4i_e \cos f + \cos^2 a = 0 \tag{4.60}$$

The roots of this equation are

$$i_e = [-\cos f \pm \sqrt{(\cos^2 f - \cos^2 a)}]/2 \tag{4.61}$$

The corresponding input angle, denoted by ϕ_e, for this i_e to occur, is given by solving C_ϕ from the above mentioned equation (2.5*a*) and the equation $i' = 0$,

$$C_\phi = C_{\phi_e} = \frac{1 - 2i \cos f}{2i \tan a \sin f} \tag{4.62}$$

The necessary conditions for a spherical four-bar with $b = 90°$ and $c = 90°$ to have an extreme velocity ratio (not in the position $\sin \phi = 0$) are:

$$\cos^2 f - \cos^2 a \geqslant 0$$

and

$$-1 \leqslant C_{\phi_e} \leqslant 1 \tag{4.63}$$

Examples: 22 miscellaneous examples taken from (Pamidi, 1976) are listed in Table 4.5 to show the extreme velocity ratios of spherical four-bar linkages in the three cases. The type of each linkage is determined by the classification criteria of Section 3.3.

4.2.3   *Angular velocity RCCC-linkage*

As has been mentioned in Section 4.1.2, in the angular velocity tetrahedron the four angles a, b, c and f are constants and the only independent variable is ϕ. We may devise, on the basis of the angular velocity tetrahedron, Fig. 4.2(*b*), a spatial four-link mechanism as shown in Fig. 4.8(*b*), the original spherical four-bar linkage being shown in Fig. 4.8(*a*). The angles a, b, c and f are all fixed link angles. Denote the links with link angles a, b, c, f by $a^\triangle, b^\triangle, c^\triangle, f^\triangle$ respectively. $f^\triangle$ is the fixed link. Because ω_{af} is constant, **oa** should be a constant, and the pair at **a** should be an R (= revolute)-pair. The other three pairs are all C (= cylindrical)-pairs to allow variations of the distances between apexes of the tetrahedron. The spatial linkage thus formed is a special RCCC-linkage with each two adjacent axes intersecting $a^\triangle$ is the driving link. Once the position angle ϕ of $a^\dashv$ is specified, the positions of the other two links $c^\triangle$ and $b^\triangle$ are determined accordingly. Because the plane **oac** is always parallel to the plane A_0OA of the original spherical four-bar, the position angle of $a^\triangle$ is also ϕ as mentioned before. The link $a^\triangle$ rotates therefore with the same angular velocity $\omega_a = \dot\phi$ as the driving link a of the spherical four-bar.

Analysis of the RCCC-linkage will produce some kinematic quantities of the original spherical four-bar linkage (Keler, 1970; Chiang, 1984*b*), although

Fig. 4.8. (*a*) Spherical four-bar linkage. (*b*) Angular velocity RCCC-linkage. (c) View of angular velocity tetrahedron in direction **ab**.

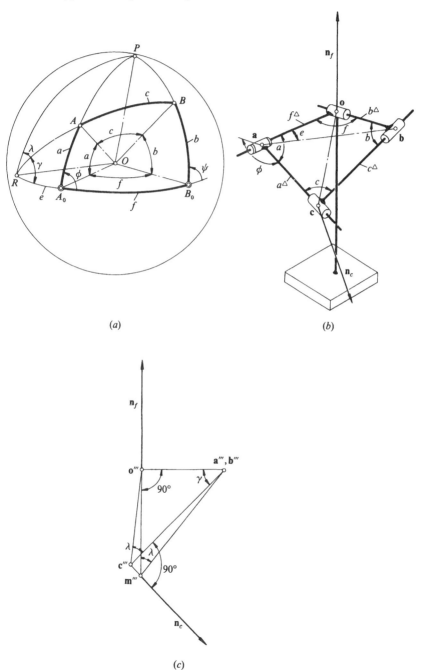

(*a*)   (*b*)

(*c*)

it may not be advantageous to analyse the spherical four-bar in this way. Thus, for instance, the sliding velocity of link $b^\triangle$ represents the angular acceleration of the output link b of the spherical four-bar, and the linear acceleration of $b^\triangle$ represents the angular jerk of b. Fig. 4.8(c) shows a view of the angular velocity tetrahedron in the viewing direction **ab**. In this view both planes **oab** and **abc** appear as straight lines. The normals $\mathbf{n}_f$ of the plane $f^\triangle$ and $\mathbf{n}_c$ of the plane $c^\triangle$ appear as their true lengths. $\mathbf{n}_f$ and $\mathbf{n}_c$ do not intersect, but their projections in this view intersect in a point $\mathbf{m}'''$. Comparing Fig. 4.8(c) with Fig. 4.8(a) shows that $\sphericalangle \mathbf{o}'''\mathbf{c}''\mathbf{a}''' = \lambda$ and $\sphericalangle \mathbf{o}'''\mathbf{a}''\mathbf{c}''' = \gamma$, and the distance $\mathbf{o}'''\mathbf{a}''' = \omega_{af}\sin e$. Because the four points $\mathbf{a}''', \mathbf{o}''', \mathbf{c}'''$ and $\mathbf{m}'''$ lie on a half circle, $\sphericalangle \mathbf{o}'''\mathbf{m}'''\mathbf{a}''' = \lambda$. Therefore we have

$$\mathbf{m}'''\mathbf{o}''' = \omega_{af}\sin e \cot \lambda \qquad (4.64)$$

Comparing equation (4.64) with equation (4.37) shows that the length $\mathbf{m}'''\mathbf{o}'''$ represents $\dot{e}$, the time rate of change of e. By substituting equation (4.64) into equation (4.32) we obtain

$$\alpha_{bfn} = \frac{\sin f}{\sin^2(e+f)}\mathbf{m}'''\mathbf{o}'''\omega_{af} \qquad (4.65)$$

We see that the length $\mathbf{m}'''\mathbf{o}'''$ serves as a variable factor in the computation of the angular acceleration α_{bfn} of the output link b; we did not even have to carry out the velocity analysis of the RCCC-linkage.

However, a velocity analysis of the RCCC-linkage will reveal some interesting relationships among the kinematic quantities. The relative velocity, in general, between two adjacent links $i^\triangle, k^\triangle$ of a cylindrical pair, consists of a relative angular velocity $\boldsymbol{\omega}_{i\triangle k\triangle}$ and a relative sliding velocity $\mathbf{v}_{i\triangle k\triangle}$. The axis of $\boldsymbol{\omega}_{i\triangle k\triangle}$, as well as the sliding direction of $\mathbf{v}_{i\triangle k\triangle}$, is the axis of the cylindrical pair $i^\triangle-k^\triangle$. The revolute R-pair may be considered as a special cylindrical pair of zero sliding velocity. For the four $\boldsymbol{\omega}_{i\triangle k\triangle}$'s we have, according to (Beyer, 1963, p. 153), the relation

$$\boldsymbol{\omega}_{a\triangle f\triangle} = \boldsymbol{\omega}_{a\triangle c\triangle} + \boldsymbol{\omega}_{c\triangle b\triangle} + \boldsymbol{\omega}_{b\triangle f\triangle} \qquad (4.66)$$

Equation (4.66) implies that, for a given $\boldsymbol{\omega}_{a\triangle f\triangle}$, all we have to do is simply resolve it into three components along the axes $a^\triangle c^\triangle, c^\triangle b^\triangle$ and $b^\triangle f^\triangle$. Thus if in the velocity tetrahedron, Fig. 4.8(b), **oa** represents $\boldsymbol{\omega}_{a\triangle f\triangle}$, the tetrahedron itself is its own angular velocity diagram, with $\mathbf{ca} = \boldsymbol{\omega}_{a\triangle c\triangle}$, $\mathbf{bc} = \boldsymbol{\omega}_{c\triangle b\triangle}$ and $\mathbf{ob} = \boldsymbol{\omega}_{b\triangle f\triangle}$.

To find the relative sliding velocities, we have again according to (Beyer, 1963, p. 155), the relation

$$\boldsymbol{\omega}_{a\triangle f\triangle} \times \mathbf{ob} + \boldsymbol{\omega}_{c\triangle a\triangle} \times \mathbf{cb} = \mathbf{v}_{a\triangle c\triangle} + \mathbf{v}_{c\triangle b\triangle} + \mathbf{v}_{b\triangle f\triangle} \qquad (4.67)$$

where the vector **ob** is the position vector of a point **b**, considered as a point belonging to the body $a^\triangle$, with respect to the axis oa of $\omega_{a\triangle f\triangle}$, and cb is the position vector of a point b, considered as a point belonging to the body $c^\triangle$, with respect to the axis ac of $\omega_{c\triangle a\triangle}$. The first vector product $\omega_{a\triangle f\triangle} \times ob$ is a linear velocity, of magnitude equal to twice the area of $\triangle$ **oab**, pointing in the direction n_f. The second vector product $\omega_{c\triangle a\triangle} \times cb$ is also a linear velocity, of magnitude equal to twice the area of $\triangle$ **acb**. Hence we may write

$$2(F_{\mathbf{oab}}\mathbf{n}_f + F_{\mathbf{acb}}\mathbf{n}_c) = \mathbf{v}_{a\triangle c\triangle} + \mathbf{v}_{c\triangle b\triangle} + \mathbf{v}_{b\triangle f\triangle} \tag{4.68}$$

where $F_{\mathbf{oab}}$ and $F_{\mathbf{acb}}$ are the areas of $\triangle$ **oab** and $\triangle$ **acb** respectively, or, if we write **v** for the sum of the two vector products on the left-hand side of equation (4.68),

$$\mathbf{v} = \mathbf{v}_{a\triangle c\triangle} + \mathbf{v}_{c\triangle b\triangle} + \mathbf{v}_{b\triangle f\triangle} \tag{4.68a}$$

Equation (4.68a) implies that all we have to do is to work out first the sum **v** of the two vector products, and then resolve it into three components along the axes $a^\triangle c^\triangle, c^\triangle b^\triangle$ and $b^\triangle f^\triangle$. The sum **v** of the two vector products is a vector in the plane of Fig. 4.8(c), while the directions of the three $\mathbf{v}_{i\triangle k\triangle}$'s are known. Equation (4.68) is equivalent to three scalar equations in three unknowns, i.e. the magnitudes of the three relative sliding velocities. It can be solved either analytically or graphically without difficulty.

We shall consider only the case when $\mathbf{v}_{b\triangle f\triangle}$ vanishes. Figs. 4.9(a), (b) and (c) show the three orthogonal views of the angular velocity tetrahedron, in first angle projection. If $\mathbf{v}_{b\triangle f\triangle}$ vanishes, **v** must be parallel to the plane **abc**. Therefore the scalar product of **v** and $\mathbf{n}_c$ must vanish.

$$(F_{\mathbf{oab}}\mathbf{n}_f + F_{\mathbf{acb}}\mathbf{n}_c)\cdot\mathbf{n}_c = 0$$

Fig. 4.9. Angular velocity tetrahedron in the case $\lambda = 90°$.

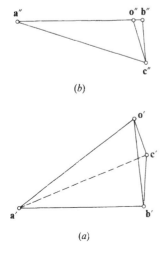

(a)

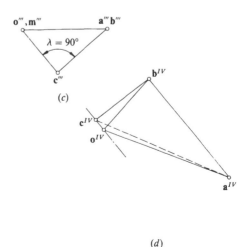

(b)   (c)   (d)

or

$$-F_{\text{oab}}\cos\gamma + F_{\text{acb}} = 0$$

$$F_{\text{acb}} = F_{\text{oab}}\cos\gamma \tag{4.69}$$

Equation (4.69) implies that the area of $\triangle\,\textbf{acb}$ should be equal to the area of $\triangle\,\textbf{oab}$ projected on the plane of $\textbf{acb}$. Fig. 4.9(d) shows a view of the tetrahedron in the viewing direction of $\mathbf{n}_c$. It is clear from this view that equation (4.69) is satisfied if $\mathbf{o}^{IV}\mathbf{c}^{IV}$ is parallel to $\mathbf{a}^{IV}\mathbf{b}^{IV}$, or in other words, the angle λ is equal to 90°. This is consistent with the result found in Section 4.2.2 that in the case when ω_b/ω_a reaches its extreme, λ equals 90°. Fig. 4.9(c) is also consistent with equation (4.64) that $\mathbf{o}'''\mathbf{m}''' = 0$ for $\lambda = 90°$.

4.2.4   Angular acceleration of the coupler

Graphical methods for finding the angular acceleration of the coupler, by means of descriptive geometry, are available (Beyer, 1963; Lowen, 1967). However, for readers who are not quite familiar with descriptive geometry such methods do not seem to be straightforward, especially a great deal of effort has to be made in carrying out the graphical work. We shall attack the problem in two different analytical ways.

(1) Acceleration of coupler determined directly as a change of coupler velocity

In Fig. 4.10, the angular velocity of the coupler c relative to the frame f, as given by equation (4.22), is

$$\boldsymbol{\omega}_c = \omega_c \mathbf{r}_P \tag{4.70}$$

Note that ω_c shown in Fig. 4.10 is negative. Differentiating equation (4.70)

Fig. 4.10. Pole changing velocity **u**.

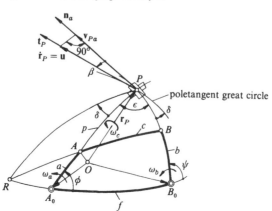

with respect to time gives

$$\boldsymbol{\alpha}_c = \dot{\boldsymbol{\omega}}_c = \dot{\omega}_c \mathbf{r}_P + \omega_c \dot{\mathbf{r}}_P$$
$$= \boldsymbol{\alpha}_{cr} + \boldsymbol{\alpha}_{ct} \tag{4.71}$$

where

$$\boldsymbol{\alpha}_{cr} = \dot{\omega}_c \mathbf{r}_P \tag{4.72}$$

is the part of $\boldsymbol{\alpha}_c$ due to the rate of change of the magnitude of $\boldsymbol{\omega}_c$, and

$$\boldsymbol{\alpha}_{ct} = \omega_c \dot{\mathbf{r}}_P \tag{4.73}$$

is the part of $\boldsymbol{\alpha}_c$ due to the rate of change of direction of the unit vector $\mathbf{r}_P$.

(1a) The part $\dot{\omega}_c \mathbf{r}_P$. The first step is to find $\dot{\omega}_c$. Differentiating equation (2.21a) with respect to time gives

$$\dot{\omega}_c = \frac{\sin a \cos p}{\sin^2 p} p' \omega_a^2 - \frac{\sin a}{\sin p} \alpha_a \tag{4.74}$$

where α_a is the angular acceleration of the input link a. The second term in equation (4.74) is similar to equation (2.21a), and is already known. It vanishes identically for an input link rotating with a constant velocity.

To find p', differentiating equation (2.22a) in Section 4.1.2 with respect to ϕ gives

$$p' = \frac{\sin^2 (p + a)}{\sin f} \left(\cos f \sin \phi + \cos \phi \cot \psi - \frac{\sin \phi}{\sin^2 \psi} \psi' \right) \tag{4.75}$$

The value of ψ' can be computed either from equation (2.12), or from equation (4.16).

(1b) *The part* $\omega_c \dot{\mathbf{r}}_P$. The vector $\dot{\mathbf{r}}_P$ is the rate of change of the unit vector $\mathbf{r}_P$, and is equal to the linear velocity of the point at the arrowhead of the vector $\mathbf{r}_P$. Because the radius of the unit sphere is unity, the vector $\dot{\mathbf{r}}_P$ is identical with the changing velocity $\mathbf{u}$ of the pole P, Fig. 4.10. Let the unit vector in the direction of $\mathbf{u}$ be denoted by $\mathbf{t}_P$. We have then

$$\dot{\mathbf{r}}_P = \mathbf{u} = u \mathbf{t}_P \tag{4.76}$$

the vector $\mathbf{t}_P$ is along the common tangent of the two spherical polodes, or for brevity, the poletangent at P. On the basis of the Bobillier theorem, the proof of which will be given later in Section 5.7, the poletangent great circle lies on a diametral plane, the dihedral angle between which and the plane $B_0 B$ is equal, but in the opposite sense, to the dihedral angle between the plane of the *collineation great circle* PR and the plane $A_0 A$. Denoting this angle by δ, we may compute δ by applying the cotangent law, equation (A1.11), to $\triangle A_0 PR$:

$$\cot \delta = \frac{\sin (p + a) \cot e + \cos (p + a) \cos \phi}{\sin \phi} \tag{4.77}$$

Denoting as before $\not\triangleleft A_0 P B_0$ by ε, we see that the angle between the normal $\mathbf{n}_a$ of the plane $A_0 O A$ and $\mathbf{t}_p$ is $(\varepsilon + \delta) - 90°$, which we shall denote by β:

$$\beta = (\varepsilon + \delta) - 90° \qquad (4.78)$$

The direction cosines of $\mathbf{t}_p$ can be found by rotating $\mathbf{n}_a$ about $\mathbf{r}_p$ through a positive angle β. Hence, the displacement matrix $\mathbb{D}_{12}$ as shown in equation (A2.33) can be worked out with the direction cosines l_x, l_y, l_z of the axis of rotation replaced by the direction cosines P_x, P_y, P_z of $\mathbf{r}_p$. Thus,

$$\mathbf{t}_p = \mathbb{D}_{12} \mathbf{n}_a \qquad (4.79)$$

Finally, the magnitude u of the pole changing velocity $\mathbf{u}$ can be obtained by imagining a pair of *crossed-sliders* mounted at P as shown in Fig. 4.10. One slider is free to *slide* on the great circle $A_0 A$, and the other on $B_0 B$, both being hinged at the point P. Let the point on a but instantaneously coinciding with P be denoted by P_a. The velocity of P_a is then

$$\mathbf{v}_{Pa} = \omega_a \sin(p + a) \mathbf{n}_a \qquad (4.80)$$

Because $\mathbf{v}_{Pa}$ is equal to the component of $\mathbf{u}$ in the direction of the pole tangent, therefore the magnitude of $\mathbf{u}$ is

$$u = \frac{\sin(p + a)}{\cos \beta} \omega_a = \frac{\sin(p + a)}{\sin(\varepsilon + \delta)} \omega_a \qquad (4.81)$$

The part $\boldsymbol{\alpha}_{ct}$ is therefore

$$\boldsymbol{\alpha}_{ct} = \omega_c u \mathbf{t}_p \qquad (4.82)$$

Having computed all the factors required in the determination of the angular acceleration of the coupler, the total angular acceleration $\boldsymbol{\alpha}_c$ can then be found by adding up the two parts $\boldsymbol{\alpha}_{cr}$ and $\boldsymbol{\alpha}_{ct}$. The procedure can best be illustrated by an example.

Example: A spherical four-bar linkage with the following dimensions is given

Fig. 4.11. Example.

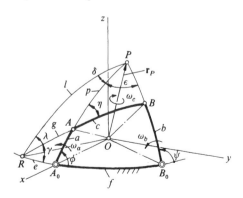

Table 4.6 Example of computation of angular acceleration of coupler

Quantity	Result	Equation used for computation
ψ	66.871°	(2.8a)
η	23.331°	(2.19a)
p	68.474°	(2.22a)
e	18.473°	(4.9)
ψ'	0.3170	(4.16)
p'	0.1504	(4.75)
$\dot\omega_c$	0.0375	(4.74) $\alpha_a = 0$
ε	63.188°	(4.20)
$\mathbf{r}_P$	$-0.2499\mathbf{i} + 0.4092\mathbf{j} + 0.8775\mathbf{k}$	(4.21)
$\boldsymbol{\alpha}_{cr} = \dot\omega_c\mathbf{r}_P$	$(-0.0094\mathbf{i} + 0.0153\mathbf{j} + 0.0329\mathbf{k})\omega_a^2$	
ω_c	$-0.6319\omega_a$	(4.12)
δ	17.980°	(4.77)
β	$-8.832°$	(4.78)
Displacement matrix $\mathbb{D}_{12}$	$\begin{bmatrix} 0.9889 & 0.1335 & -0.0654 \\ -0.1359 & 0.9901 & -0.0341 \\ 0.0602 & 0.0426 & 0.9973 \end{bmatrix}$	(A2.33)
$\mathbf{n}_a$	$0\mathbf{i} - 0.9063\mathbf{j} + 0.4226\mathbf{k}$	(4.18)
$\mathbf{t}_P = \mathbb{D}_{12}\mathbf{n}_a$	$-0.1487\mathbf{i} - 0.9118\mathbf{j} + 0.3828\mathbf{k}$	(4.79)
u	$0.9799\omega_a$	(4.81)
$\boldsymbol{\alpha}_{ct} = \omega_c u\mathbf{t}_P$	$(0.092\mathbf{i} + 0.565\mathbf{j} - 0.237\mathbf{k})\omega_a^2$	(4.82)
$\boldsymbol{\alpha}_c = \boldsymbol{\alpha}_{cr} + \boldsymbol{\alpha}_{ct}$	$(0.083\mathbf{i} + 0.580\mathbf{j} - 0.204\mathbf{k})\omega_a^2$	

as shown in Fig. 4.11: $a = 36°, b = 50°, c = 60°$ and $f = 70°$. The position angle of crank A_0A is $\phi = 65°$. Find the angular acceleration $\boldsymbol{\alpha}_c$ of the coupler c, in terms of its three components with respect to a right-handed coordinate system xyz, where the x-axis is in the direction OA_0 and the xy-plane coincides with the plane A_0OB_0.

The results are listed in Table 4.6 in sequential order.

(2) Acceleration of coupler determined from relative accelerations
In spite of the correctness of the preceding procedure for finding the angular acceleration $\boldsymbol{\alpha}_c$ of the coupler, it seems that it was rather involved. We

shall solve the same problem by an alternative method. Considering f as fixed, we may write equation (4.3) as

$$\boldsymbol{\omega}_c = \boldsymbol{\omega}_{ca} + \boldsymbol{\omega}_a \tag{4.83}$$

Differentiating equation (4.83) with respect to time yields

$$\boldsymbol{\alpha}_c = \boldsymbol{\alpha}_{ca} + \boldsymbol{\alpha}_a \tag{4.84}$$

On the right-hand side of equation (4.84), $\boldsymbol{\alpha}_a$ is given and it is only necessary to determine $\boldsymbol{\alpha}_{ca}$. As this is the time rate of change of $\boldsymbol{\omega}_{ca}$, we may write the latter as

$$\boldsymbol{\omega}_{ca} = \omega_{ca} \mathbf{r}_A \tag{4.85}$$

where $\mathbf{r}_A$ is the unit vector in the direction OA, Fig. 4.12. Differentiating equation (4.85) with respect to time gives

$$\begin{aligned}\boldsymbol{\alpha}_{ca} &= \dot{\omega}_{ca} \mathbf{r}_A + \omega_{ca} \dot{\mathbf{r}}_A \\ &= \boldsymbol{\alpha}_{car} + \boldsymbol{\alpha}_{cat},\end{aligned}$$

where

$$\boldsymbol{\alpha}_{car} = \dot{\omega}_{ca} \mathbf{r}_A \tag{4.86}$$

is the part of $\boldsymbol{\alpha}_{ca}$ due to the rate of change of the magnitude of $\boldsymbol{\omega}_{ca}$, and

$$\boldsymbol{\alpha}_{cat} = \omega_{ca} \dot{\mathbf{r}}_A \tag{4.87}$$

is the part of $\boldsymbol{\alpha}_{ca}$ due to the rate of change of direction of the unit vector $\mathbf{r}_A$.

(2a) *The part* $\dot{\omega}_{ca} \mathbf{r}_A$. The first step is to find $\dot{\omega}_{ca}$. Rewrite equation (4.14):

$$\omega_{ca} = -\frac{\sin(a + p)}{\sin p} \omega_a \tag{[(4.14)]}$$

The negative sign indicates that, for a positive value of p, as that shown in Fig. 4.2, ω_{ca} is negative, referred to the unit vector $\mathbf{r}_A$. Differentiating the above equation with respect to time gives

$$\dot{\omega}_{ca} = \frac{\sin a}{\sin^2 p} p' \omega_a^2 \tag{4.88}$$

Fig. 4.12.

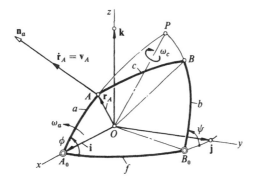

Table 4.7 *Alternative computation procedure for last example*

Quantity	Result	Equation used for computation
ψ	66.871°	(2.8a)
p	68.474°	(2.22a)
ψ'	0.3170	(2.12)
p'	0.1504	(4.75)
$\dot{\omega}_{ca}$	$0.1022\omega_a^2$	(4.88)
$\mathbf{r}_A$	$0.8090\mathbf{i} + 0.2484\mathbf{j} + 0.5327\mathbf{k}$	(4.89)
$\boldsymbol{\alpha}_{cr} = \dot{\omega}_{ca}\mathbf{r}_A$	$(0.0827\mathbf{i} + 0.0254\mathbf{j} + 0.0544\mathbf{k})\omega_a^2$	(4.86)
ω_{ca}	$-1.0409\omega_a$	(4.14)
$\mathbf{n}_a$	$0\mathbf{i} - 0.9063\mathbf{j} + 0.4226\mathbf{k}$	(4.18)
$\boldsymbol{\alpha}_{cat}$	$(0\mathbf{i} + 0.5545\mathbf{j} - 0.2586\mathbf{k})\omega_a^2$	(4.91)
$\boldsymbol{\alpha}_{ca} = \boldsymbol{\alpha}_{car} + \boldsymbol{\alpha}_{cat}$	$(0.083\mathbf{i} + 0.580\mathbf{j} - 0.204\mathbf{k})\omega_a^2$	

Values of p and p' can be found from equations (2.22a) in Section 4.12 and (4.75) respectively. The vector $\mathbf{r}_A$, as expressed in its three components in the xyz-system, can easily be found by rotating a unit vector $\cos a\,\mathbf{i} + \sin a\,\mathbf{j}$ about the x-axis through a positive angle ϕ by applying equation (A2.22):

$$\mathbf{r}_A = \cos a\,\mathbf{i} + \sin a \cos \phi\,\mathbf{j} + \sin a \sin \phi\,\mathbf{k} \qquad (4.89)$$

(2b) *The part* $\omega_{ca}\dot{\mathbf{r}}_A$. The vector $\dot{\mathbf{r}}_A$ is the rate of change of the unit vector $\mathbf{r}_A$, and is equal to the linear velocity of the point at the arrowhead of $\mathbf{r}_A$, or $\mathbf{v}_A$. Therefore

$$\dot{\mathbf{r}}_A = \mathbf{v}_A = \sin a\,\omega_a \mathbf{n}_a \qquad (4.90)$$

where $\mathbf{n}_a$ is the unit vector normal to the plane A_0OA, as defined in Section 4.1.3, and has already been given by equation (4.18):

$$\mathbf{n}_a = 0\mathbf{i} - \sin \phi\,\mathbf{j} + \cos \phi\,\mathbf{k}$$

Substituting equation (4.90) into equation (4.87) results finally in

$$\boldsymbol{\alpha}_{cat} = \omega_{ca} \sin a\,\omega_a \mathbf{n}_a \qquad (4.91)$$

Example: The preceding example shall be analysed by the present method. The results are listed in Table 4.7.

4.2.5 *Linear acceleration of a coupler point – the acceleration matrix*

Differentiating equation (4.17) with respect to time gives the linear acceleration of a point on a moving body,

$$\mathbf{a} = \dot{\mathbf{v}} = \ddot{\mathbf{r}} = \dot{\boldsymbol{\omega}} \times \mathbf{r} + \boldsymbol{\omega} \times \dot{\mathbf{r}}$$
$$= \boldsymbol{\alpha} \times \mathbf{r} + \boldsymbol{\omega} \times (\boldsymbol{\omega} \times \mathbf{r})$$
$$= \boldsymbol{\alpha} \times \mathbf{r} + (\boldsymbol{\omega} \cdot \mathbf{r})\boldsymbol{\omega} - \omega^2 \mathbf{r} \tag{4.92}$$

where $\boldsymbol{\alpha} = \alpha_x \mathbf{i} + \alpha_y \mathbf{j} + \alpha_z \mathbf{k}$ is the angular acceleration of the moving body. In order to facilitate computer operation, we shall write equation (4.92) in a matrix form. The first term on the right-hand side of equation (4.92) can be written in a form analogous to equation (4.27), and the other two terms expanded correspondingly. Thus,

$$\mathbf{a} = \begin{bmatrix} a_x \\ a_y \\ a_z \end{bmatrix} = \begin{bmatrix} 0 & -\alpha_z & \alpha_y \\ \alpha_z & 0 & -\alpha_x \\ -\alpha_y & \alpha_x & 0 \end{bmatrix} \begin{bmatrix} x \\ y \\ z \end{bmatrix}$$
$$+ \begin{bmatrix} \omega_x^2 - \omega^2 & \omega_x\omega_y & \omega_z\omega_x \\ \omega_x\omega_y & \omega_y^2 - \omega^2 & \omega_y\omega_z \\ \omega_z\omega_x & \omega_y\omega_z & \omega_z^2 - \omega^2 \end{bmatrix} \begin{bmatrix} x \\ y \\ z \end{bmatrix} \tag{4.93}$$

Similar to equation (4.28), the first 3×3 matrix on the right-hand side of equation (4.93) may be written as $\mathbb{A}_\alpha$. We may observe that $\mathbb{A}_\alpha = \dot{\mathbb{V}}_\omega$. The second 3×3 matrix in equation (4.93) is equal to $\mathbb{V}_\omega^2$. Thus equation (4.93) may be written as

$$\mathbf{a} = \mathbb{A}_\alpha \mathbf{r} + \mathbb{V}_\omega^2 \mathbf{r} = (\mathbb{A}_\alpha + \mathbb{V}_\omega^2)\mathbf{r} \tag{4.94}$$

The sum of the two matrices $\mathbb{A}_\alpha + \mathbb{V}_\omega^2$ is the acceleration matrix which, when applied to the position vector $\mathbf{r}$ of a point on the body, results in its linear acceleration. The symbols $\dot{\mathbb{V}}_\omega$ and $\mathbb{V}_\omega^2$, however, are used here just for the purpose of notation. The computation of the elements, for instance, of $\mathbb{A}_\alpha = \dot{\mathbb{V}}_\omega$ has to follow the procedure given in the preceding section, not by differentiating the elements of $\mathbb{V}_\omega$. It is to be noted that both matrices $\mathbb{A}_\alpha$ and $\mathbb{V}_\omega^2$ are not orthogonal.

To find the linear acceleration of a coupler point E, all we have to do is to find the three components $\omega_{cx}, \omega_{cy}, \omega_{cz}$ of the angular velocity $\boldsymbol{\omega}_c$ of the coupler and the three components $\alpha_{cx}, \alpha_{cy}, \alpha_{cz}$ of its angular acceleration $\boldsymbol{\alpha}_c$, and then substitute them into equation (4.93).

It should be noted that the axis of the angular acceleration $\boldsymbol{\alpha}$ is not the so-called *acceleration axis* of the moving body. It can be seen from equation (4.92) that, for any point on the axis of $\boldsymbol{\alpha}$, the vector $\boldsymbol{\alpha} \times \mathbf{r}$ indeed vanishes, but the vector $(\boldsymbol{\omega} \cdot \mathbf{r})\boldsymbol{\omega}$ which is in the direction of $\boldsymbol{\omega}$, possesses a component perpendicular to $\boldsymbol{\alpha}$, because $\boldsymbol{\omega}$ and $\boldsymbol{\alpha}$ are in general not parallel. We shall come back to this point later in Section 5.9.

Example: Suppose it is required to find the linear acceleration of the point E in the example at the end of Section 4.1.3, Fig. 4.5, in terms of ω_a^2 for a constant ω_a.

Table 4.8 *Example of computation of linear acceleration of a coupler point*

Quantity	Result				Equation used for computation
$\mathbb{A}_\alpha$	$\begin{bmatrix} 0 & 0.250 & 0.450 \\ 0.250 & 0 & 0.245 \\ -0.450 & -0.245 & 0 \end{bmatrix} \omega_a^2$				(4.93)
$\mathbb{V}_\omega^2$	$\begin{bmatrix} -0.245 & 0.050 & -0.050 \\ 0.050 & -0.143 & -0.123 \\ -0.050 & -0.123 & -0.143 \end{bmatrix} \omega_a^2$				(4.93)
$\mathbb{A}_\alpha + \mathbb{V}_\omega^2$	$\begin{bmatrix} -0.245 & -0.200 & 0.400 \\ 0.300 & -0.143 & 0.122 \\ -0.500 & -0.368 & -0.143 \end{bmatrix} \omega_a^2$				
$\mathbf{a}_E$	$(23.1\mathbf{i} + 17.7\mathbf{j} - 14.8\mathbf{k})\omega_a^2$				(4.94)

We have the coordinates of E in millimetres:

$$\mathbf{r}_E = \begin{bmatrix} 24.40 \\ -17.67 \\ 63.97 \end{bmatrix} \begin{matrix} (\mathbf{i}) \\ (\mathbf{j}) \\ (\mathbf{k}) \end{matrix},$$

and the angular velocity of the coupler found in that example:

$$\boldsymbol{\omega}_c = \begin{bmatrix} 0.143 \\ 0.350 \\ -0.350 \end{bmatrix} \begin{matrix} (\mathbf{i}) \\ (\mathbf{j}) \\ (\mathbf{k}) \end{matrix} \omega_a$$

Now we have to find the angular acceleration $\boldsymbol{\alpha}_c$ of the coupler. This is done by applying one of the two procedures mentioned in the preceding section, and the results are

$$\boldsymbol{\alpha}_c = \begin{bmatrix} -0.245 \\ 0.450 \\ 0.250 \end{bmatrix} \begin{matrix} (\mathbf{i}) \\ (\mathbf{j}) \\ (\mathbf{k}) \end{matrix} \omega_a^2$$

Substituting these data into equation (4.93), we obtain the numerical results as listed in Table 4.8.

5

On some topics regarding instantaneous motion of a spherically moving body

In this chapter we are going to deal with some topics on instantaneous kinematics of a spherically moving body. We shall derive first the spherical counterparts of the well-known theorems in plane kinematics such as the Hartmann construction, Euler–Savary equation, inflection circle and Bobillier theorem. These concepts in spherical kinematics have already been established by mathematicians (Garnier, 1956; Blaschke, 1948, 1950; Müller, 1962; Veldkamp, 1967b) as well as by kinematicians (Dittrich, 1964; Dittrich & Zakel, 1981; Bisshopp, 1969; Sasskii, 1960; Dittrich, 1965; Meyer zur Capellen & Dittrich, 1966; Meyer zur Capellen & Willkommen, 1974; Hein, 1959; Dobrovolskii, 1947a). The major concern of these topics is, as in plane kinematics, the relations between a point on the moving body and the centre of curvature of the spherical path of the moving point. The points $A, B, \ldots$ belong to a set of moving points on the moving body, or system, or shell, and the points $A_0, B_0, \ldots$, being the centres of curvature of the corresponding point paths, belong to a set of fixed points on the fixed body, or fixed shell. The points in these two sets exchange their rôles upon a kinematic inversion; the points $A_0, B_0, \ldots$ become the moving points and the points $A, B, \ldots$ become the centres of curvature of the corresponding paths described by $A_0, B_0, \ldots$

In the later sections we shall study the acceleration properties of a spherically moving shell.

Although in spherical kinematics the counterparts of circles and curves in plane kinematics are cones with apexes at the sphere centre O, and the counterpart of a point, e.g. a pole in plane kinematics, is an axis passing through O, for brevity we shall keep using the familiar terms from plane kinematics, as we have been doing so far. In other words, we shall use the terms *pole* and *curve* instead of *axis* and *cone*, except where they are specifically defined. However, since a cone with its apex at O intersects the unit sphere in two spherical curves which are mirror images to each other, it is understood that whenever we mention a point on a spherical curve, we mean a pair of points on the sphere diametrically opposite to each other.

5.1   Curvature and torsion of a spherical curve
The concept of curvature and torsion of a spherical curve may be found from any treatise on differential geometry or vector analysis. We shall derive these concepts in a simple way. A spherical curve may be considered as a path generated by a moving point E on the surface of a fixed unit sphere, as shown in Fig. 5.1(a). Let s be a curve parameter which specifies the curvilinear distance of a point E measured from a fiducial point on the curve. Associated with the point E is an orthogonal right-handed reference frame of three unit vectors $\mathbf{t}, \mathbf{n}, \mathbf{r}$. The vector $\mathbf{t}$ is tangent to the curve at E, in the sense of increasing s. The vector $\mathbf{n}$ is in the tangential plane of the sphere at E. The third vector is $\mathbf{r} = \mathbf{t} \times \mathbf{n}$, which is equal to the position vector $\overrightarrow{OE}$ of the point E on the unit sphere, but originating outwards from E. As the point E moves along the curve, the orthogonal frame moves with it. This orthogonal frame is therefore a kind of so-called *moving trihedron*. Suppose the point E moves through an infinitesimal distance ds. The moving trihedron thus experiences an infinitesimal translation and rotation. In fact, the trihedron performs an infinitesimal spherical motion about the sphere centre O, which

Fig. 5.1. Curvature and torsion of a spherical curve. (a) Moving trihedron. (b) View normal to plane EOE_0.

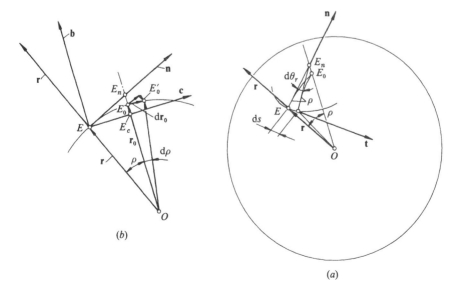

(b)

(a)

is a rotation only. Let this infinitesimal angle of rotation be denoted by $d\theta$, and its three components about the axes $\mathbf{t}$, $\mathbf{n}$, $\mathbf{r}$ be denoted respectively by $d\theta_t$, $d\theta_n$, $d\theta_r$. By analogy with an angular velocity vector, e.g. equation (4.22), the gradient of rotation can also be expressed as components along the three unit vectors, of the form

$$\Omega = \frac{\overrightarrow{d\theta}}{ds}$$

$$= \frac{d\theta_t}{ds}\mathbf{t} + \frac{d\theta_n}{ds}\mathbf{n} + \frac{d\theta_r}{ds}\mathbf{r} \tag{5.1}$$

where in place of the velocity components are the corresponding derivatives of the angles with respect to s. Denoting the three coefficients of the unit vectors $\mathbf{t}$, $\mathbf{n}$, $\mathbf{r}$ in equation (5.1) respectively by τ_g, κ_n, κ_g, we may write the vector Ω as

$$\Omega = \tau_g\mathbf{t} + \kappa_n\mathbf{n} + \kappa_g\mathbf{r} \tag{5.1a}$$

that is,

$$\tau_g\,ds = d\theta_t \tag{5.2}$$

$$\kappa_n\,ds = d\theta_n \tag{5.3}$$

$$\kappa_g\,ds = d\theta_r \tag{5.4}$$

The quantities τ_g, κ_n and κ_g for a general surface curve are called, respectively, the geodetic torsion, normal curvature and geodetic curvature of the surface curve (Wills, 1931). Now by analogy with the matrix in equation (4.27) we can form the following rotation matrix,

$$\mathbb{M}_{d\theta} = \begin{bmatrix} 0 & -\kappa_g & \kappa_n \\ \kappa_g & 0 & -\tau_g \\ -\kappa_n & \tau_g & 0 \end{bmatrix} \tag{5.5}$$

Applying the matrix $\mathbb{M}_{d\theta}$ to the unit vectors $\mathbf{t}$, $\mathbf{n}$, $\mathbf{r}$ in turn, we get, by analogy with equation (4.28),

$$\frac{d\mathbf{t}}{ds} = \mathbb{M}_{d\theta}\mathbf{t} = \qquad \kappa_g\mathbf{n} - \kappa_n\mathbf{r} \tag{5.6}$$

$$\frac{d\mathbf{n}}{ds} = \mathbb{M}_{d\theta}\mathbf{n} = -\kappa_g\mathbf{t} \qquad + \tau_g\mathbf{r} \tag{5.7}$$

$$\frac{d\mathbf{r}}{ds} = \mathbb{M}_{d\theta}\mathbf{r} = \qquad \kappa_n\mathbf{t} - \tau_g\mathbf{n} \tag{5.8}$$

The quantities τ_g, κ_n, κ_g can be obtained by forming scalar products by multiplying equations (5.6), (5.7), (5.8) respectively by $\mathbf{n}$, $\mathbf{r}$ and $\mathbf{t}$:

$$\kappa_g = \mathbf{n}\cdot\frac{d\mathbf{t}}{ds} \tag{5.9}$$

$$\tau_g = \mathbf{r} \cdot \frac{d\mathbf{n}}{ds} \tag{5.10}$$

$$\kappa_n = \mathbf{t} \cdot \frac{d\mathbf{r}}{ds} \tag{5.11}$$

The vector $\boldsymbol{\Omega}$ now takes the following form:

$$\boldsymbol{\Omega} = \left(\mathbf{r} \cdot \frac{d\mathbf{n}}{ds} \right) \mathbf{t} + \left(\mathbf{t} \cdot \frac{d\mathbf{r}}{ds} \right) \mathbf{n} + \left(\mathbf{n} \cdot \frac{d\mathbf{t}}{ds} \right) \mathbf{r} \tag{5.1b}$$

Equation (5.1b) is of a form which is analogous to the well-known Darboux rotation vector of a space curve (e.g. Wills, 1931).

Note that $\mathbf{t} = d\mathbf{r}/ds$ for a spherical curve. It follows from equation (5.8) that $\tau_g \equiv 0$ and $\kappa_n \equiv 1$. This means that the geodetic torsion of a spherical curve vanishes identically, and that the normal curvature of a spherical curve on the unit sphere is identically 1. This latter statement is trivial, for the radius of the unit sphere is equal to 1 by definition. We are therefore concerned about the geodetic curvature κ_g only. Hence for a spherical curve, equations (5.6), (5.7), (5.8) take the forms

$$d\mathbf{t} = \kappa_g \, ds \, \mathbf{n} - ds \, \mathbf{r} \tag{5.12}$$

$$d\mathbf{n} = -\kappa_g \, ds \, \mathbf{t} \tag{5.13}$$

$$d\mathbf{r} = ds \, \mathbf{t} \tag{5.14}$$

Suppose the spherical centre of curvature of the path of E is denoted by E_0, and the spherical *radius* of curvature of the spherical curve is denoted by ρ, i.e. $\rho = E_0 E$, as shown in Fig. 5.1(a). Let the vector $\overrightarrow{OE_0}$ be denoted by $\mathbf{r}_0$. Then

$$\mathbf{r}_0 = \cos \rho \, \mathbf{r} + \sin \rho \, \mathbf{n} \tag{5.15}$$

Differentiating equation (5.15) with respect to s gives

$$\frac{d\mathbf{r}_0}{ds} = \left(\cos \rho \, \frac{d\mathbf{r}}{ds} + \sin \rho \, \frac{d\mathbf{n}}{ds} \right) + (-\sin \rho \, \mathbf{r} + \cos \rho \, \mathbf{n}) \frac{d\rho}{ds} \tag{5.16}$$

Because $d\mathbf{r}_0$ is a vector representing $d\rho$, the extension of ρ, it is in a direction tangent to the spherical evolute of the spherical curve, hence lying in the plane EOE_0. It can be seen from Fig. 5.1(b), which shows a view of this plane, that $d\mathbf{r}_0/ds$ is represented by the two components included in the second bracket of equation (5.16). The first bracket of this equation must therefore vanish identically. Taking equations (5.13) and (5.14) into consideration, we have

$$\cos \rho - \kappa_g \sin \rho = 0$$

or

$$\kappa_g = \frac{1}{\tan \rho} \tag{5.17}$$

Equation (5.17) indicates that the geodetic curvature of a spherical curve is equal to the reciprocal of the tangent function of the spherical radius of curvature. For a spherical curve with a 90° radius of curvature, its geodetic curvature is zero.

Equation (5.17) can also be derived in an alternative way. Referring to Fig. 5.1(a), let the intersection point of OE_0 and n be denoted by E_n. In equation (5.4) the geodetic curvature has already been defined as

$$\kappa_g = \frac{d\theta_r}{ds} \tag{5.4a}$$

Comparing equation (5.4a) with equation (5.9), we note that $d\theta_r = \mathbf{n} \cdot d\mathbf{t}$. This means that $d\theta_r$ is the component of change of $\mathbf{t}$ in the direction $\mathbf{n}$. Therefore it is numerically equal to the infinitesimal angle of rotation of the normal vector $\mathbf{n}$, or

$$d\theta_r = \frac{ds}{EE_n} \tag{5.18}$$

as shown in Fig. 5.1(a). Substituting equation (5.18) into equation (5.4a) gives finally

$$\kappa_g = \frac{1}{EE_n} = \frac{1}{\tan \rho}$$

which is equation (5.17).

In Fig. 5.1(b) let $\mathbf{c}$ be the unit vector in the direction of $d\mathbf{t}$, and let $\mathbf{b}$ be the unit vector such that $\mathbf{b} = \mathbf{t} \times \mathbf{c}$. The curvature of a space curve is defined as $\kappa = \mathbf{c} \cdot (d\mathbf{t}/ds)$, or, on account of equations (5.12) and (5.17),

$$\kappa = \mathbf{c} \cdot (d\mathbf{t}/ds) = \kappa_g \cos \rho + \sin \rho = \frac{1}{\sin \rho} \tag{5.19}$$

Denoting the intersection point of $\mathbf{c}$ with OE_0 by E_c, we see that $EE_c = \sin \rho$ is exactly the linear radius of curvature of the curve.

The torsion of a space curve is defined as $\tau = -\mathbf{c} \cdot (d\mathbf{b}/ds)$. Because $\mathbf{c} \cdot \mathbf{b} = 0$, therefore

$$\frac{d\mathbf{c}}{ds} \cdot \mathbf{b} + \mathbf{c} \cdot \frac{d\mathbf{b}}{ds} = 0$$

hence

$$\tau = -\mathbf{c} \cdot \frac{d\mathbf{b}}{ds} = \frac{d\mathbf{c}}{ds} \cdot \mathbf{b} = \mathbf{b} \cdot \frac{d}{ds}(\cos \rho \, \mathbf{n} - \sin \rho \, \mathbf{r})$$

$$= -\frac{d\rho}{ds} \tag{5.20}$$

The geodetic curvature κ_g and torsion τ of a spherical curve can also be expressed in terms of the position vector $\mathbf{r}$ of the moving point and its derivatives with respect to time (Kreyszig, 1959; Struik, 1950; Dittrich & Zakel, 1981). Besides the resolution of the linear acceleration of a moving point into the three components, as expressed in equation (4.92), this linear acceleration can also be resolved into three components along the axes of the moving trihedron. The velocity of the moving point is

$$\mathbf{v} = \dot{\mathbf{r}} = v\mathbf{t} \tag{5.21}$$

Differentiating equation (5.21) with respect to time gives the linear acceleration of the moving point,

$$\mathbf{a} = \dot{\mathbf{v}} = \ddot{\mathbf{r}} = \dot{v}\mathbf{t} + v\dot{\mathbf{t}}$$

$$= \dot{v}\mathbf{t} + v^2 \frac{d\mathbf{t}}{ds} \tag{5.22}$$

Substituting equation (5.6) into equation (5.22) gives, noting that $\kappa_n \equiv 1$,

$$\mathbf{a} = \dot{v}\mathbf{t} + \kappa_g v^2 \mathbf{n} - v^2 \mathbf{r} \tag{5.23}$$

Vector multiplication of both sides of equation (5.23) by the two sides of equation (5.21) gives

$$\mathbf{v} \times \mathbf{a} = \kappa_g v^3 \mathbf{r} + v^3 \mathbf{n} \tag{5.24}$$

Forming the scalar product of equation (5.24) with $\mathbf{r}$ yields

$$\mathbf{r} \cdot (\mathbf{v} \times \mathbf{a}) = \kappa_g v^3$$

or

$$\kappa_g = \frac{\mathbf{r} \cdot (\mathbf{v} \times \mathbf{a})}{v^3} \tag{5.25}$$

Noting that $\mathbf{v} = \dot{\mathbf{r}}$ and $\mathbf{a} = \ddot{\mathbf{r}}$, and the magnitude $v = (\dot{\mathbf{r}} \times \dot{\mathbf{r}})^{1/2}$, equation (5.25) can be written as

$$\kappa_g = \frac{\mathbf{r} \cdot (\dot{\mathbf{r}} \times \ddot{\mathbf{r}})}{(\dot{\mathbf{r}} \cdot \dot{\mathbf{r}})^{3/2}} \tag{5.26}$$

Another expression for κ_g is derived as follows. Suppose the spherical polar coordinates of a point on the curve are (p, θ), and its rectangular coordinates with respect to an xyz-system are (x, y, z), as shown in Fig. A4.1. The transformation equations are, as given in Appendix 4,

$$\left. \begin{array}{l} x = \sin p \cos \theta \\ y = \sin p \sin \theta \\ z = \cos p \end{array} \right\} \tag{A4.2}$$

The position vector of the point is

$$\mathbf{r} = x\mathbf{i} + y\mathbf{j} + z\mathbf{k}$$

The velocity of the point is

$$\mathbf{v} = \dot{\mathbf{r}} = \dot{x}\mathbf{i} + \dot{y}\mathbf{j} + \dot{z}\mathbf{k}$$

and the acceleration of the point is

$$\mathbf{a} = \ddot{\mathbf{r}} = \ddot{x}\mathbf{i} + \ddot{y}\mathbf{j} + \ddot{z}\mathbf{k}$$

The vector $\mathbf{v} \times \mathbf{a}$ is then

$$\mathbf{v} \times \mathbf{a} = \begin{vmatrix} \mathbf{i} & \mathbf{j} & \mathbf{k} \\ \dot{x} & \dot{y} & \dot{z} \\ \ddot{x} & \ddot{y} & \ddot{x} \end{vmatrix} \tag{5.27}$$

Suppose the equation of the spherical curve is expressed as $p = p(\theta)$. We write $p' = dp/d\theta$, and $p'' = d^2p/d\theta^2$. Differentiating twice the expressions for x, y, z in equations (A4.2) and substituting them into equation (5.27) and then finally into equation (5.25) gives the expression for κ_g:

$$\frac{1}{\kappa_g} = \tan\rho = \frac{(\sin^2 p + p'^2)^{3/2}}{\sin^2 p \cos p + 2p'^2 \cos p - p'' \sin p} \tag{5.28}$$

Equation (5.28) has been derived from a geometric point of view in (Meyer zur Capellen, 1971, 1983; Meyer zur Capellen & Willkommen, 1974).

The torsion, as defined before, is $\tau = -\mathbf{c} \cdot (d\mathbf{b}/ds)$. The unit vector $\mathbf{c}$, being in the direction of $d\mathbf{t}$, is, by equations (5.19) and (5.22),

$$\mathbf{c} = \frac{d\mathbf{t}}{\kappa \, ds} = \frac{1}{\kappa v^2}(\ddot{\mathbf{r}} - \dot{v}\mathbf{t}) \tag{5.29}$$

It follows from the definition of the unit vector $\mathbf{b} = \mathbf{t} \times \mathbf{c}$ that

$$\tau = -\mathbf{c} \cdot \frac{d\mathbf{b}}{ds} = -\frac{\mathbf{c}}{v} \cdot (\dot{\mathbf{t}} \times \mathbf{c} + \mathbf{t} \times \dot{\mathbf{c}})$$

$$= -\frac{\mathbf{c}}{v} \cdot (\mathbf{t} \times \dot{\mathbf{c}}) \tag{5.30}$$

Substituting equations (5.29) and (5.21) into equation (5.30) results in

$$\tau = \frac{\dot{\mathbf{r}} \cdot (\ddot{\mathbf{r}} \times \dddot{\mathbf{r}})}{\kappa^2 v^6} \tag{5.31}$$

The denominator in equation (5.31) is, according to equation (5.24), equal to the square of the magnitude of the vector $\dot{\mathbf{r}} \times \ddot{\mathbf{r}}$, or

$$\tau = \frac{\dot{\mathbf{r}} \cdot (\ddot{\mathbf{r}} \times \dddot{\mathbf{r}})}{(\dot{\mathbf{r}} \times \ddot{\mathbf{r}}) \cdot (\dot{\mathbf{r}} \times \ddot{\mathbf{r}})} \tag{5.32}$$

5.2   Polodes

As can be seen from Fig. 4.10, the unit vector $\mathbf{r}_P$ is the axis of the angular velocity $\boldsymbol{\omega}_{cf}$, or $\boldsymbol{\omega}_c$ if f is fixed. The point P changes its position relative both to c and to f. It generates a curve on the spherical surface of f which is called the *fixed polode*, denoted by π_f, and a curve on the surface of c which is called the *moving polode*, denoted by π_c. Now consider a shell

c performing a general spherical motion relative to a fixed shell f as shown in Fig. 5.2. The instantaneous pole axis of rotation at a certain instant is OP. Suppose, after an infinitesimal motion of the shell c, the new pole axis is OP'. Denote the point P' on π_f by P'_f, and P' on π_c by P'_c. The change of pole axis is such that after the infinitesimal motion of c, P'_c coincides with P'_f and becomes the new instantaneous pole of rotation of the shell c. We may take for granted that the polodes π_c and π_f are tangent to each other at P, because, as will be seen later in Section 6.8.1, $\sphericalangle P'_f PP'_c$ is equal to $d\gamma$, the infinitesimal angle of rotation of the shell c.

Similar to the moving trihedron in Fig. 5.1, let a moving trihedron $\mathbf{t}_P, \mathbf{n}_P, \mathbf{r}_P$, which we denote here by h, be associated with the point P. During the motion of the shell c relative to the shell f, this trihedron h moves along π_f as well as along π_c. Suppose the infinitesimal angle of rotation of h relative to f is $\overrightarrow{d\theta}_{hf}$, and that of h relative to c is $\overrightarrow{d\theta}_{hc}$. By analogy with equation (5.1) we may write

$$\overrightarrow{d\theta}_{hf} = (d\theta_{hf})_t \mathbf{t}_P + (d\theta_{hf})_n \mathbf{n}_P + (d\theta_{hf})_r \mathbf{r}_P$$
$$\overrightarrow{d\theta}_{hc} = (d\theta_{hc})_t \mathbf{t}_P + (d\theta_{hc})_n \mathbf{n}_P + (d\theta_{hc})_r \mathbf{r}_P$$

Now, by the definition of relative infinitesimal angles of rotation, we have

$$\begin{aligned}
\overrightarrow{d\theta}_{cf} &= \overrightarrow{d\theta}_{ch} - \overrightarrow{d\theta}_{fh} \\
&= \overrightarrow{d\theta}_{hf} - \overrightarrow{d\theta}_{hc} \\
&= [(d\theta_{hf})_t - (d\theta_{hc})_t]\mathbf{t}_P + [(d\theta_{hf})_n - (d\theta_{hc})_n]\mathbf{n}_P \\
&\quad + [(d\theta_{hf})_r - (d\theta_{hc})_r]\mathbf{r}_P
\end{aligned} \tag{5.33}$$

Fig. 5.2. Rolling of spherical polodes.

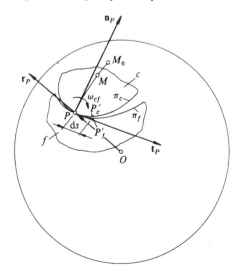

Noting that $\kappa_n \equiv 1$, and substituting equation (5.3) into equation (5.14) we have correspondingly

$$(d\mathbf{r}_P)_{hf} = (d\theta_{hf})_n \mathbf{t}_P \tag{5.34}$$

and

$$(d\mathbf{r}_P)_{hc} = (d\theta_{hc})_n \mathbf{t}_P \tag{5.35}$$

Since the vector $\overrightarrow{d\theta}_{cf}$ is in the direction of $\mathbf{r}_P$, therefore the coefficients of $\mathbf{t}_P$ and $\mathbf{n}_P$ in equation (5.33) must vanish identically, and $(d\theta_{hf})_n = (d\theta_{hc})_n$. Consequently, from equations (5.34) and (5.35),

$$(d\mathbf{r}_P)_{hc} = (d\mathbf{r}_P)_{hf} \tag{5.36}$$

However, $(d\mathbf{r}_P)_{hc}$ is equal to the infinitesimal curve length PP'_c on π_c, and $(d\mathbf{r}_P)_{hf}$ is equal to the infinitesimal curve length PP'_f on π_f. Equation (5.36) implies that during the spherical motion of the shell c relative to f, the moving polode π_c rolls without slip on the fixed polode π_f.

Equation (5.33) now becomes, taking equation (5.4) into consideration,

$$\overrightarrow{d\theta}_{cf} = [(d\theta_{hf})_r - (d\theta_{hc})_r] \mathbf{r}_P$$
$$= (\kappa_{gf} - \kappa_{gc}) \, ds \mathbf{r}_P \tag{5.33a}$$

where κ_{gf} and κ_{gc} represent respectively the geodetic curvatures of π_f and π_c at P, and ds is the infinitesimal curve length along the polodes. Referring to Fig. 5.2, note that the magnitude $d\theta_{cf}$ of the vector

$$\overrightarrow{d\theta}_{cf} = d\theta_{cf} \mathbf{r}_P$$

is negative, hence equation (5.33a) can be written as

$$\kappa_{gc} - \kappa_{gf} = -\frac{d\theta_{cf}}{ds} = -\frac{\dot\theta_{cf}}{\dot s} = -\frac{\omega_{cf}}{u} \tag{5.33b}$$

where ω_{cf} is the magnitude of the angular velocity of c relative to f, which is negative as shown in Fig. 5.2 according to our definition in Section 4.1.2, and u is the magnitude of the pole changing velocity. If M and M_0 represent respectively the centres of curvature of π_c and π_f at P, then by the definition of the geodetic curvature of a spherical curve, equation (5.17), we may further rewrite equation (5.33b) as

$$\frac{1}{\tan PM} - \frac{1}{\tan PM_0} = -\frac{\omega_{cf}}{u} \tag{5.33c}$$

Equation (5.33c) is the Euler–Savary equation for the special point pair M and M_0 (see Section 5.4).

Algebraic expressions for the fixed polode and moving polode of a spherical four-bar linkage will be discussed in Section 6.2.3.

5.3   Hartmann construction

Consider a spherical crank a rotating with a certain angular velocity about a fixed axis OA_0 as shown in Fig. 5.3(a). As expressed in equation (4.17), the velocity $\mathbf{v}_A$ of any point A on the crank is proportional to its distance from the axis OA_0, hence the end points of the velocity vectors of all points on the great circle A_0A lie in a plane passing through the axis OA_0. Fig. 5.3(b) shows a view in the direction A_0O. In this view the great circle A_0A appears as a straight line, and the velocities of all points on the great circle A_0A are parallel and appear as their true lengths. The end points of all these velocity vectors appear to lie on a straight line passing through A_0, just as in the case of plane kinematics. Therefore if $\mathbf{v}_A$ is known, the velocity $\mathbf{v}_E$ of any point E on the great circle A_0A can be determined by passing a plane through the end point of the vector $\mathbf{v}_A$ and through OA_0, the intercept of a line drawn from E parallel to $\mathbf{v}_A$ by this plane being the length of $\mathbf{v}_E$.

In Section 4.2.4 we derived the magnitude and direction of the changing velocity of the pole P of the coupler of a spherical four-bar linkage. There the use of the Bobillier theorem to accomplish the derivation was taken for granted. The pole changing velocity $\mathbf{u}$ of the pole P can be determined, as in the case of a plane four-bar linkage, purely by linear velocity relations without using the Bobillier theorem. In Fig. 5.4, the velocity $\mathbf{v}_{Pa}$ of a point

Fig. 5.3. (a) Crank a rotating about axis OA_0 with angular velocity ω_a. (b) View X.

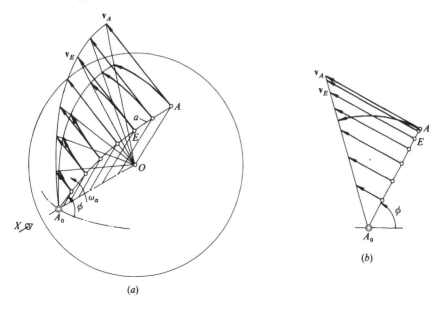

(a)

(b)

P_a on a, instantaneously coinciding with P, can be determined if the velocity v_A of A is known, as described above. Because u is in the tangent plane Γ_P to the sphere at P, the end point of u is on a line lying in the tangent plane, drawn from the end point of v_{Pa} and perpendicular to v_{Pa}, as we have already done in Fig. 4.10. Similarly let the point on the crank b but instantaneously coinciding with P be denoted by P_b. If the velocity of B as a point on the coupler shell is known, the velocity v_{Pb} can also be determined. The end point of u must also be on a line lying in the tangent plane Γ_P, drawn from the end point of v_{Pb} and perpendicular to v_{Pb}. The intersection point of these two perpendicular lines locates the end point of u, hence the magnitude and direction of u.

Fig. 5.4. Derivation of pole changing velocity of the coupler of a spherical four-bar.

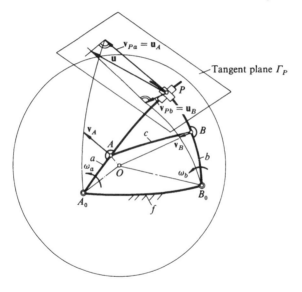

Fig. 5.5. Spherical velocity.

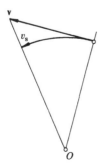

The vectors $\mathbf{u}$, $\mathbf{v}_{P_a}$ and $\mathbf{v}_{P_b}$ all lie in the tangent plane Γ_P. Conversely, if the pole P, the pole changing velocity $\mathbf{u}$ and the velocity $\mathbf{v}_A$ of a moving point A are known, the centre of curvature A_0 of the path of A can be determined by the following procedure: First resolve $\mathbf{u}$ in the tangent plane Γ_P into a component $\mathbf{v}_{P_a}$ parallel to $\mathbf{v}_A$, which we want to denote by $\mathbf{u}_A$, and another component perpendicular to it. Passing a plane through the end points of $\mathbf{u}_A$ and $\mathbf{v}_A$, and the sphere centre O, will cut the great circle PA in the point A_0. This is the spherical version of the Hartmann construction.

Now it seems to be more succinct to carry out the above procedure solely on the surface of the unit sphere. Imagine that all linear velocities are projected, by taking the sphere centre O as the centre of projection, onto the spherical surface. Use the subscript 's' to signify a *spherical velocity* (Veldkamp, 1967b). For instance, v_s represents the spherical projection of $\mathbf{v}$, as shown in Fig. 5.5. We have then the following relation between v and v_s:

$$v = \tan v_s \tag{5.37}$$

In Fig. 5.3(a) the plane passing through the end points of the velocity vectors and the sphere centre O cuts the unit sphere in a great circle. This great circle passes through the end points of the spherical projections of all these velocity vectors. Hence if, in Fig. 5.4, the velocities $\mathbf{u}$, $\mathbf{u}_A$, $\mathbf{v}_A$ are projected onto the spherical surface to yield the *spherical velocities* u_s, u_{As}, v_{As}, we obtain the configuration shown in Fig. 5.6. Let the angle between $\mathbf{u}$ and the plane PA in Fig. 5.4 be denoted by θ_A (Fig. 5.6). $\mathbf{u}_A$ is the component of $\mathbf{u}$ which is perpendicular to PA, or

$$u_A = u \sin \theta_A \tag{5.38}$$

Applying the relation (5.37) to both u_A and u in equation (5.38), we get

$$\tan u_{As} = \tan u_s \sin \theta_A \tag{5.39}$$

Comparison of equation (5.37) with equations (A1.6) shows that in Fig. 5.6,

Fig. 5.6. Hartmann construction.

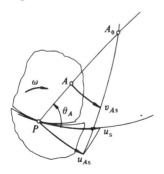

u_s and u_{As} are respectively the hypotenuse and a leg of a spherical right triangle. u_{As} may be considered as a *component* of u_s in the direction perpendicular to PA. The spherical version of the Hartmann construction may be stated as follows:

For a spherically moving shell, if the spherical pole changing velocity u_s and the spherical velocity v_{As} of a moving point A are known, the centre of curvature A_0 of the path of A can be found as the point on the great circle PA cut by a great circle joining the end points of u_{As} and v_{As}, where u_{As} is the spherical component of u_s in the direction perpendicular to PA.

5.4   The spherical counterpart of the Euler–Savary equation

In fact, the above mentioned Hartmann construction can easily be proved from a kinematic point of view (Dittrich, 1964; Müller, 1962). Consider a moving polode π_c rolling on a fixed polode π_f as shown in Fig. 5.7. Suppose after an infinitesimal time interval dt, the pole P changes to another pole P', and a point A on the moving body moves to a position A', the points P', A', A_0 being on a great circle. Extend the great circle A_0P' to a point Q such that $A_0Q = A_0P$. We then have, from the two spherical right triangles $\triangle A_0AA'$ and $\triangle A_0PQ$, by equation (A1.4),

$$\frac{\tan AA'}{\tan PQ} = \frac{\sin AA_0}{\sin PA_0}$$

In the limit, $\tan AA' \approx AA'$ and $\tan PQ \approx PQ = ds \sin \theta_A$, where $ds = PP'$. Therefore

$$\frac{AA'/dt}{ds \sin \theta_A / dt} = \frac{\sin AA_0}{\sin PA_0}$$

or

$$\frac{v_A}{u \sin \theta_A} = \frac{\sin AA_0}{\sin PA_0} \qquad (5.40)$$

According to equations (5.37) and (5.38), equation (5.40) can be transformed

Fig. 5.7.

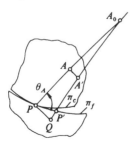

to

$$\frac{\tan v_{As}}{\tan u_{As}} = \frac{\sin AA_0}{\sin PA_0} \tag{5.41}$$

This proves the correctness of the spherical version of the Hartmann construction.

Consider a spherical polar coordinate system by taking the origin at P and the great circle of u_s as the positive spherical polar line, as shown in Fig. 5.6. Note that in Fig. 5.6 the magnitude ω is negative. Hence $v_A = -\omega \sin PA$. Equation (5.40) can be written as

$$-\frac{\omega \sin PA}{u \sin \theta_A} = \frac{\sin AA_0}{\sin PA_0}$$

or

$$\frac{\sin AA_0}{\sin PA \sin PA_0} = \left(-\frac{\omega}{u}\right)\frac{1}{\sin \theta_A}$$

Noting that $AA_0 = PA_0 - PA$, we get finally the spherical version of the Euler–Savary equation,

$$\frac{1}{\tan PA} - \frac{1}{\tan PA_0} = \frac{1}{\Theta}\frac{1}{\sin \theta_A} \tag{5.42}$$

where $\Theta = -u/\omega$ is originally a linear quantity which, in plane kinematics, is equal to the diameter of the inflection circle. However, on the unit sphere, since a great circle arc length may be represented by the angle subtended by it at the sphere centre O, the dimension of u may also be considered as an angular velocity, hence Θ may also be considered as dimensionless.

The Euler–Savary equation enables us, as in the case of plane kinematics, to compute the location of A_0, if A is given, and vice versa. The extension of the Euler–Savary equation to spherical kinematics was started in 1860 by P. Serret (Garnier, 1956).

Similar to the case of plane kinematics, if A is taken at the position of M, the centre of curvature of the moving polode at P, then A_0 takes the position of M_0, the centre of curvature of the fixed polode at P, and the angle θ_A is

Fig. 5.8. Rolling polodes.

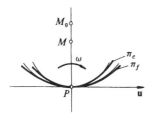

then equal to 90°, as shown in Fig. 5.8. Equation (5.42) becomes

$$\frac{1}{\tan PM} - \frac{1}{\tan PM_0} = \frac{1}{\Theta} \tag{5.43}$$

By the definition of the geodetic curvature of a spherical curve, equation (5.17), equation (5.43) implies that the quantity $1/\Theta$ is equal to the algebraic difference of the geodetic curvature of the moving polode and that of the fixed polode. The same equation has been alternatively derived as equation (5.33c) in Section 5.2. By substituting equation (5.43) into equation (5.42), the spherical version of the Euler–Savary equation may also be written in the form

$$\frac{1}{\tan PA} - \frac{1}{\tan PA_0} = \frac{1}{\sin \theta_A}\left(\frac{1}{\tan PM} - \frac{1}{\tan PM_0}\right) \tag{5.44}$$

In the following the great circle of u_s will be called the *poletangent great circle*, and the great circle of PMM_0 will be called the *polenormal great circle*.

5.5   The inflection curve and return curve

5.5.1   *The inflection curve*

The spherical radius of curvature of the path of a moving point A is (Fig. 5.9)

$$\rho_A = PA_0 - PA$$

Fig. 5.9. Spherical radius of curvature.

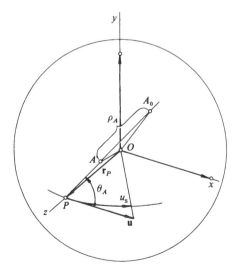

and we have

$$\cot \rho_A = \cot (PA_0 - PA)$$

$$= \frac{1 + \cot PA_0 \cot PA}{\cot PA - \cot PA_0} \tag{5.45}$$

Eliminating PA_0 between equations (5.42) and (5.45) gives

$$\cot \rho_A = -\cot PA + \frac{\Theta \sin \theta_A}{\sin^2 PA} \tag{5.46}$$

When $\rho_A = 90°$, hence $\cot \rho_A = 0$, the geodetic curvature of the path of the moving point A vanishes. In other words, the moving point A is passing through an inflection point of its path. Consequently the locus of such a moving point A can be obtained by equating the right-hand side of equation (5.46) to zero, namely,

$$k_w: \quad \cot PA = \Theta \sin \theta_A / \sin^2 PA \tag{5.47}$$

This equation can be transformed into a simple trigonometric form:

$$k_w: \quad \sin 2PA = 2\Theta \sin \theta_A \tag{5.48}$$

Equation (5.48) gives the location of the moving point A which is instantaneously passing through an inflection point, i.e. the inflection curve which we denote here by k_w. The locus of the inflection point A, or k_w, as given by equation (5.48), is expressed in its spherical polar coordinates (PA, θ_A), with the poletangent great circle as the spherical *polar axis*. It is evident that the inflection curve k_w is symmetrical with respect to the polenormal great circle, hence it is sufficient to consider the curve only in the range $-90° \leqslant \theta_A \leqslant +90°$.

Fig. 5.10. Inflection curves k_w's.

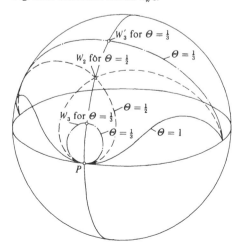

Equation (5.48) shows that values of PA exist provided that

$$|2\Theta \sin \theta_A| \leqslant 1$$

or

$$|\sin \theta_A| \leqslant \frac{1}{2\theta} \qquad (5.49)$$

Fig. 5.10 shows the inflection curve k_w for $\Theta = 1$, $1/2$ and $1/3$ (Dittrich, 1964; Pottmann, 1985). By analogy with plane kinematics, let the intersections of the inflection curve and the polenormal great circle be called the inflection poles W. It can be seen that for $\Theta > 1/2$, there are limiting values of θ_A. For instance, when $\Theta = 1$, the limiting values of θ_A are $\pm 30°$, and the inflection pole does not exist. For $\Theta = 1/2$, the value of θ_A is not limited, and the point of the curve at $\theta_A = 90°$ is the inflection pole. The inflection curve for $\Theta = 1/3$ exhibits according to equation (5.48) for $\sin 2PW = 2/3$ two inflection poles: $PW_3 = 20.905°$ and $PW'_3 = 69.095°$. These two inflection poles become, when $\Theta = 1/2$, a double point: $PW_2 = 45°$.

5.5.2   The return curve

If PA is eliminated between equations (5.42) and (5.45), we obtain

$$\cot \rho_A = \cot PA_0 + \frac{\Theta \sin \theta_A}{\sin^2 PA_0} \qquad (5.50)$$

The return curve, which is the locus of the centre point A_0 of the moving point A which is $90°$ apart from A_0, is given by equating the right-hand side of

Fig. 5.11. Return curves k_r's.

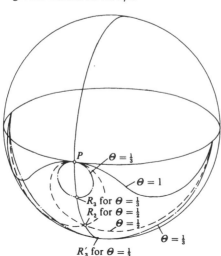

equation (5.50) to zero,

$$k_r: \quad \cot PA_0 = -\Theta \sin\theta_A/\sin^2 PA_0 \qquad (5.51)$$

Again transforming this equation into a simple trigonometric form gives

$$k_r: \quad \sin 2PA_0 = -2\Theta \sin\theta_A \qquad (5.51a)$$

The return curve k_r is therefore a mirror image of the inflection curve k_w with respect to the poletangent great circle, as shown in Fig. 5.11. Corresponding to the case of the inflection poles the return poles are denoted by R's.

Just as in plane kinematics, it should be noted that the inflection curve is a curve on the moving shell c, and that the return curve is a curve on the fixed shell f. Upon inversion the inflection curve and return curve exchange their rôles.

5.5.3 Equations of inflection curve and return curve in rectangular coordinates

Consider a right-handed coordinate system xyz as shown in Fig. 5.9, with its origin at the sphere centre O. The x-axis is in the direction of $\mathbf{u}$, the pole changing velocity, and the z-axis is OP. The coordinates of a moving point A with spherical polar coordinates (PA, θ_A) with respect to the positive direction of the poletangent great circle can be obtained by inspection:

$$\left.\begin{array}{l} x = \sin PA \cos\theta_A \\ y = \sin PA \sin\theta_A \\ z = \cos PA \end{array}\right\} \qquad (5.52)$$

Equations (5.52) are listed as equations (A9.2) in Appendix 4 for easy reference; they can also be obtained by applying the displacement matrix $\mathbb{D}_{12}$ in equation (A2.41), replacing ξ by 0, η by $-PA$ and ζ by $-(90° - \theta_A)$, to the unit vector OP. Eliminating PA and θ_A between equations (5.48) and (5.52) gives

$$k_w: \quad (x^2 + y^2)z - \Theta y = 0 \qquad (5.53)$$

where the variables x, y, z are subject to the condition (A3.1)

$$x^2 + y^2 + z^2 = 1$$

Equation (5.53) indicates that the inflection curve is a spherical cubic. As can also be seen from equation (5.47), for a given value of θ_A, this is a quadratic equation in the unknown $\cot PA$, and there are in general two real roots of this equation. This means that an arbitrary great circle passing through the pole $P(\bar{P})$ cuts the inflection curve in two more pairs of points represented by the above mentioned two roots of PA.

Similarly the equation of the return curve, equation (5.51), can be transformed into, with coordinates $A_0(x_0, y_0, z_0)$,

$$k_r: \quad (x_0^2 + y_0^2)z_0 + \Theta y_0 = 0 \qquad (5.54)$$

5.6   The equatorial curve and the central curve

With respect to a pair of corresponding points A, A_0, suppose it is required to find the locus of A when $PA_0 = 90°$. Let such a moving point A be denoted by A_q. The second term on the left-hand side of equation (5.42) vanishes, and we have the locus of the point A_q, which we denote here by k_q,

$$k_q: \quad \tan PA_q = \Theta \sin \theta_A \tag{5.55}$$

For $\theta_A = 90°$, the point A_q takes a position A_d, as shown in Fig. 5.12. Let the spherical length PA_d be denoted by d_q. Hence we have

$$\Theta = \tan PA_d = \tan d_q$$

and equation (5.55) can be written as

$$\tan PA_q = \tan d_q \sin \theta_A \tag{5.56}$$

It should be noted that the point A_d is in general different from the point W in the inflection curve. Comparison of equation (5.56) with equation (A1.6) shows that $\sphericalangle PA_qA_d = 90°$, and $\triangle PA_qA_d$ is a spherical right triangle. The locus of A_q is thus a spherical Thales ellipse (Dittrich, 1964, p. 12). This spherical ellipse is called the equatorial curve (Dittrich, 1964). With the relation of equation (5.55) we are now able to put the significant equations derived before into more meaningful forms. Thus, the Euler–Savary equation (5.42) becomes

$$\frac{1}{\tan PA} - \frac{1}{\tan PA_0} = \frac{1}{\tan PA_q} \tag{5.42a}$$

and the equations of the inflection curve (5.47) and (5.48) become respectively

$$\tan PA_q \cot^2 PA - \cot PA + \tan PA_q = 0 \tag{5.47a}$$

Fig. 5.12. Equatorial curve k_q and central curve k_z.

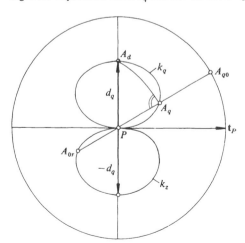

and

$$\sin 2PA = 2 \tan PA_q \qquad (5.48a)$$

In the limiting case when the radius of the sphere is increased indefinitely, we have $\sin 2PA \approx 2PA$, $\tan PA \approx PA$ and $\Theta \approx d_q$, and both equations (5.48) and (5.55) approach the well-known equation of the inflection circle in plane kinematics. This means that both the inflection curve and the equatorial curve approach the inflection circle in plane kinematics.

Similarly, for $PA = 90°$, the locus of A_0 can be obtained from equation (5.42) as, with the point A_0 denoted by A_{0r},

$$k_z: \quad \tan PA_{0r} = - \Theta \sin \theta_A$$

$$= - \tan PA_q \qquad (5.57)$$

The locus of the point A_{0r} is called the central curve (Dittrich, 1964), which we denote by k_z. Comparison of equation (5.57) with equation (5.55) shows that the central curve k_z is a mirror image of the equatorial curve k_q with respect to the poletangent great circle, as shown in Fig. 5.12. Upon kinematic inversion, the equatorial curve k_q and central curve k_z exchange their rôles. Also, in the limiting case when the radius of the sphere is increased indefinitely, both equations (5.51a) and (5.57) approach the equation of the return circle in plane kinematics.

5.7 Bobillier theorem

The well-known Bobillier theorem in plane kinematics is also valid in spherical kinematics. Its proof may be found in (Garnier, 1956; Dittrich, 1964; Veldkamp, 1967b; Hein 1959). However, we shall give here a simple yet understandable proof.

In Fig. 5.13(a) is shown a spherical four-bar linkage A_0ABB_0. The intersection points of the great circles A_0A and B_0B, and A_0B_0 and AB, are denoted, as usual, respectively by P and R. As mentioned before, P is the instantaneous velocity pole between c ($= AB$) and f ($= A_0B_0$). The great circle PR may be called a *collineation great circle*. The poletangent great circle is denoted by PU. The spherical version of the Bobillier theorem may be stated as follows:

The collineation great circle PR and the poletangent great circle PU are symmetrically disposed with respect to the spherical bisector of $\measuredangle APB$.

To prove this, it is convenient to consider the plane configuration of the gnomonic projection, i.e. the projection from the sphere centre O, of the points A_0, A, B, B_0, R and U onto a plane tangent to the unit sphere at P, Fig. 5.13(b). The corresponding projected points are earmarked by an '*', except the point P. All spherical angles with apexes at P are not altered by the gnomonic projection. Applying the sine law, equations (A1.7), to the plane triangles $\triangle PB^*R^*$ and $\triangle PB_0^*R^*$ gives

$$\frac{PR^*}{PB^*} = \frac{\sin(\delta + \lambda^*)}{\sin \lambda^*} = \sin \delta \cot \lambda^* + \cos \delta \qquad (5.58)$$

$$\frac{PR^*}{PB_0^*} = \frac{\sin(\delta + \lambda^* + \gamma^*)}{\sin(\lambda^* + \gamma^*)} = \sin \delta \cot(\lambda^* + \gamma^*) + \cos \delta \qquad (5.59)$$

where $\delta = \sphericalangle BPR = \sphericalangle B^*PR^*$, $\lambda^* = \sphericalangle B^*R^*P$ and $\gamma^* = \sphericalangle B_0^*R^*B^*$. Subtracting equation (5.59) from equation (5.58) gives

$$PR^*\left(\frac{1}{PB^*} - \frac{1}{PB_0^*}\right) = \sin \delta [\cot \lambda^* - \cot(\lambda^* + \gamma^*)] \qquad (5.60)$$

Noting that $PB^* = \tan PB$, $PB_0^* = \tan PB_0$ by equation (A4.8), and from the spherical Euler–Savary equation (5.42), we may rewrite equation (5.60) as

$$PR^*\left(\frac{1}{\tan PB} - \frac{1}{\tan PB_0}\right) = \sin \delta [\cot \lambda^* - \cot(\lambda^* + \delta^*)]$$

and

$$PR^* = \Theta \sin \theta_B \sin \delta [\cot \lambda^* - \cot(\lambda^* + \delta^*)] \qquad (5.61)$$

Similarly for the point-pair A, A_0, we can write by analogy with equation (5.61)

$$PR^* = \Theta \sin \theta_A \sin(\delta + \theta_B - \theta_A)[\cot \lambda^* - \cot(\lambda^* + \delta^*)] \qquad (5.62)$$

Comparison of equation (5.62) with equation (5.61) shows that

$$\theta_A = \delta \qquad (5.63)$$

This proves the theorem.

Fig. 5.13. Proof of Bobillier theorem.

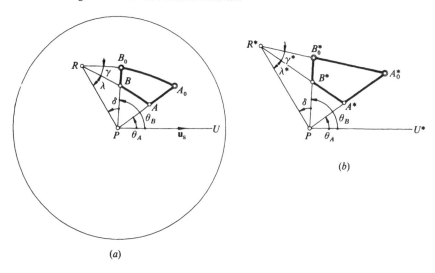

(a)

(b)

By means of the Bobillier theorem the orientation of the poletangent great circle and hence the kinematic curves of the coupler of a spherical four-bar linkage can easily be computed (see the example in Section 6.8.3).

It should be mentioned here that there are, in general, two different methods of projection to map a spherical configuration onto a plane for investigation purposes, namely, the gnomonic projection as mentioned before and the stereographic projection (Dobrovolskii, 1947a, pp. 7–8). In the stereographic projection, the centre of projection is at the surface of the sphere. Its advantages are that a circle is projected into another circle and that the magnitude of a spherical angle is maintained. Methods of synthesizing spherical linkages based on stereographic projection have been developed by a number of investigators (Sridhar & Torfason, 1970b; Bagci, 1973, 1984; Chen, 1968). However, for reasons such as we have just shown in the proof of the Bobillier theorem as well as those mentioned later in dealing with synthesis problems, we prefer to use gnomonic projection throughout this book.

5.8   Linear acceleration of certain specific moving points

5.8.1   Inflection curve as a locus of a point of vanishing normal acceleration
Consider a moving trihedron (t_A, n_A, r_A) associated with a moving point A as shown in Fig. 5.14. The orientation of the unit vectors t_A, n_A, r_A follows that defined in Section 5.1. The linear acceleration of a moving point, expressed in terms of components along these directions, has already been

Fig. 5.14. Moving trihedron (t_A, n_A, r_A).

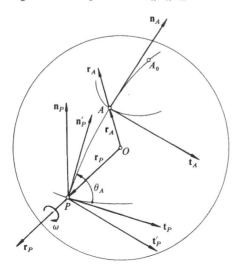

given in equation (5.23). Accordingly we may write for the linear acceleration of the point A,

$$\mathbf{a}_A = \dot{v}_A \mathbf{t}_A + \kappa_g v_A^2 \mathbf{n}_A - v_A^2 \mathbf{r}_A \tag{5.64}$$

For those moving points whose normal acceleration, i.e. the acceleration component in the direction $\mathbf{n}_A$, vanishes, the factor κ_g is equal to zero. Hence the inflection curve may also be defined as the locus of a moving point, whose normal acceleration in the tangent plane vanishes.

5.8.2   The tangential acceleration curve

We may ask what is the locus of the point whose tangential acceleration instantaneously vanishes. From equation (5.64) it can be seen that for such a moving point A, $\dot{v}_A = 0$. This means that the magnitude v_A of the velocity of A is instantaneously stationary. However, to find $\dot{v}_A$, we have to resort to equation (4.92). As can be seen from Fig. 5.14, the vector $\mathbf{t}_A$ is perpendicular to both $\boldsymbol{\omega}$ and $\mathbf{r}_A$. Therefore the second and third terms on the right-hand side of equation (4.92) contribute nothing to the tangential component of $\mathbf{a}_A$. This component is only included in the first term $\boldsymbol{\alpha} \times \mathbf{r}$ of equation (4.92), which we now write as $\boldsymbol{\alpha} \times \mathbf{r}_A$. The angular acceleration vector $\boldsymbol{\alpha}$ of the moving body has to be expressed in terms of the unit vectors of the frame $(\mathbf{t}_P, \mathbf{n}_P, \mathbf{r}_P)$ associated with the pole P. According to equations (4.71), (4.82) and (4.72) we have the two components of $\boldsymbol{\alpha}$:

$$\boldsymbol{\alpha} = \boldsymbol{\alpha}_t + \boldsymbol{\alpha}_r$$

$$= \omega u \mathbf{t}_P + 0\mathbf{n}_P + \dot{\omega}\mathbf{r}_P = \begin{bmatrix} \omega u \\ 0 \\ \dot{\omega} \end{bmatrix} \begin{matrix} (\mathbf{t}_P) \\ (\mathbf{n}_P) \\ (\mathbf{r}_P) \end{matrix} \tag{5.65}$$

This vector $\boldsymbol{\alpha}$ should now be expressed in terms of the axes of the frame $(\mathbf{t}_A, \mathbf{n}_A, \mathbf{r}_A)$ as shown in Fig. 5.14. We first rotate the frame $(\mathbf{t}_P, \mathbf{n}_P, \mathbf{r}_P)$ through an angle $-(90° - \theta_A)$ about $\mathbf{r}_P$ to reach the position $(\mathbf{t}'_P, \mathbf{n}'_P, \mathbf{r}_P)$, and then rotate it through an angle $-PA$ about $\mathbf{t}'_P$. These two rotations will bring the frame $(\mathbf{t}_P, \mathbf{n}_P, \mathbf{r}_P)$ to an orientation parallel to that of $(\mathbf{t}_A, \mathbf{n}_A, \mathbf{r}_A)$. The first and second rotation matrices correspond, respectively, to those in equations (A2.10) and (A2.6). Thus the same vector $\boldsymbol{\alpha}$, expressed in the system of axes $(\mathbf{t}_A, \mathbf{n}_A, \mathbf{r}_A)$, is:

$$\boldsymbol{\alpha} = \begin{bmatrix} 1 & 0 & 0 \\ 0 & \cos PA & -\sin PA \\ 0 & \sin PA & \cos PA \end{bmatrix} \begin{bmatrix} \sin\theta_A & -\cos\theta_A & 0 \\ \cos\theta_A & \sin\theta_A & 0 \\ 0 & 0 & 1 \end{bmatrix} \begin{bmatrix} \omega u \\ 0 \\ \dot{\omega} \end{bmatrix}$$

$$= \begin{bmatrix} \omega u \sin\theta_A \\ \omega u \cos\theta_A \cos PA - \dot{\omega}\sin PA \\ \omega u \cos\theta_A \sin PA + \dot{\omega}\cos PA \end{bmatrix} \begin{matrix} (\mathbf{t}_A) \\ (\mathbf{n}_A) \\ (\mathbf{r}_A) \end{matrix}$$

Consequently we have

$$\boldsymbol{\alpha} \times \mathbf{r}_A = (\omega u \cos \theta_A \cos PA - \dot{\omega} \sin PA) \mathbf{t}_A - \omega u \sin \theta_A \mathbf{n}_A \qquad (5.66)$$

The first term on the right-hand side of equation (5.66) is the tangential component of the linear acceleration $\mathbf{a}_A$. Hence the locus of the point whose tangential acceleration vanishes is given by

$$\omega u \cos \theta_A \cos PA - \dot{\omega} \sin PA = 0$$

or

$$k_t: \quad \tan PA = \left(\frac{\omega u}{\dot{\omega}}\right) \cos \theta_A$$

$$= \Psi \cos \theta_A \qquad (5.67)$$

where Ψ stands for $\omega u / \dot{\omega}$. For $\theta_A = 0$, the point A takes a position A_t, as shown in Fig. 5.15. Hence

$$\Psi = \tan PA_t$$

and equation (5.67) can be written as

$$\tan PA = \tan PA_t \cos \theta_A \qquad (5.68)$$

Comparing equation (5.68) with equations (A1.6) indicates that $\measuredangle PAA_t = 90°$, and that $\triangle PAA_t$ is a spherical right triangle. The locus of A is thus a spherical Thales ellipse (Dittrich, 1964, p. 12). This spherical Thales ellipse is called the tangential acceleration curve or constant speed curve (Meyer zur Capellen & Dittrich, 1966), and is denoted by k_t.

Eliminating PA and θ_A between equations (5.67) and (5.52) gives the equation

Fig. 5.15. Constant speed curve k_t.

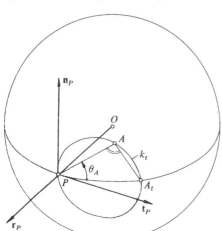

of the tangential acceleration curve in Cartesian coordinates:

$$k_t: \quad x^2 + y^2 - \Psi xz = 0 \tag{5.69}$$

where the variables x, y, z are again subject to the condition (A3.1). As a spherical quadric curve, k_t is cut by an arbitrary great circle passing through the pole-pair $P(\bar{P})$ in one more point-pair, given by solving equation (5.67) for PA, with θ_A as a parameter.

5.8.3   Acceleration of the velocity pole

Taking the pole P as a moving point A, we see from equation (5.64) that, because $v_P = 0$, the second and third terms vanish. The unit vector $\mathbf{t}_A$ becomes $\mathbf{n}_P$, but not $\mathbf{t}_P$ because $\mathbf{t}_P$ is tangent to the spherical polode while $\mathbf{n}_P$ is tangent to the path of the moving point P. Hence

$$\mathbf{a}_P = \dot{v}_P \mathbf{n}_P \tag{5.70}$$

The acceleration of the velocity pole P is therefore a tangential acceleration in the direction $\mathbf{n}_P$. It is the acceleration component due to the change of magnitude of the linear velocity of the point P. This can also be found by inspection from equation (4.92). Since $\boldsymbol{\omega} = \omega \mathbf{r}_P$, we now have

$$\mathbf{a}_P = \boldsymbol{\alpha} \times \mathbf{r}_P + \omega^2 \mathbf{r}_P - \omega^2 \mathbf{r}_P$$
$$= \boldsymbol{\alpha} \times \mathbf{r}_P \tag{5.71}$$

This is consistent with what was mentioned in the preceding section, that the tangential acceleration is only included in the term $\boldsymbol{\alpha} \times \mathbf{r}_P$. We shall show that this vector is in the direction $\mathbf{n}_P$. Substituting equation (5.65) into equation (5.71), we have

$$\mathbf{a}_P = (\omega u \mathbf{t}_P + \dot{\omega} \mathbf{r}_P) \times \mathbf{r}_P$$
$$= -\omega u \mathbf{n}_P \tag{5.72}$$

For a negative ω, as shown in Fig. 5.14, $\mathbf{a}_P$ is in the positive direction of $\mathbf{n}_P$. The pole as a moving point is a singular point on the constant speed curve k_t, because it possesses a finite tangential acceleration.

5.9   The acceleration axes

It is well known in plane kinematics that in a body performing a general plane motion there exists a point whose linear acceleration completely vanishes, and that this point is called the acceleration pole. The corresponding problem in spherical kinematics was long known to mathematicians (Garnier, 1956) and then interpreted alternatively by kinematicians (Bottema, 1965; Meyer zur Capellen & Dittrich, 1966). It can be shown that a point with completely vanishing acceleration does not exist in a spherically moving shell. For, first of all, we have seen from equations (5.71) and (5.72) in the preceding section that the velocity pole P is not such a point, unless the pole changing velocity $\mathbf{u}$ is zero; in other words unless $\boldsymbol{\alpha}$ and $\mathbf{r}_P$ are parallel. Secondly, for any other moving point A, v_A does not vanish. Consequently from equation (5.64)

$$\mathbf{a}_A = \dot{v}_A \mathbf{t}_A + \kappa_g v_A^2 \mathbf{n}_A - v_A^2 \mathbf{r}_A \qquad [(5.64)]$$

we can see that the third term always exists. However, there are moving points for which both the first the second terms in the right-hand side of equation (5.64) vanish. In other words, there exist points which have no acceleration component lying in the tangential plane. By analogy with plane kinematics these points are called the acceleration poles, and the lines joining them with the sphere centre are called, accordingly, acceleration axes.

Because the inflection curve k_w is the locus of the point A whose normal acceleration component in the direction $\mathbf{n}_A$ vanishes, and the constant speed curve k_t is the locus of the point A whose tangential acceleration component in the direction $\mathbf{t}_A$ vanishes, therefore the acceleration poles are the intersection points of k_w and k_t. As mentioned before in Sections 5.5.1 and 5.8.2, k_w is a spherical cubic and k_t is a spherical Thales ellipse. They should intersect in six points. In order to investigate the nature of these intersections, it is convenient to consider the gnomonic projections, i.e. plane projections from the sphere centre O, of the spherical curves onto a plane tangent to the sphere at P. According to equations (A4.10) and referring to Fig. A4.2, we can transform the equation of the inflection curve k_w, equation (5.47), into a cubic k_w^* in the tangent plane (Denavit, 1965; Garnier, 1956, p. 113):

$$k_w^*: \ (\xi^2 + \zeta^2)(\Theta\zeta - 1) + \Theta\zeta = 0 \qquad (5.73)$$

The constant speed curve k_t, equation (5.67), is then transformed according to equations (A4.9) and (A4.10) into

$$k_t^*: \ \left(\xi - \frac{\Psi}{2}\right)^2 + \zeta^2 = \frac{\Psi^2}{4} \qquad (5.74)$$

The curve k_w^* is a circular cubic. Consequently it intersects the circle k_t^* in the two imaginary circular points at infinity. Moreover, both k_w^* and k_t^* pass through the origin P. Of the six intersection points the two curves k_w^* and k_t^* should intersect in three more points. To find these three points, let us go back to the spherical polar equations of k_w and k_t. Eliminating PA between equations (5.47) and (5.67) results in the following cubic equation in the unknown $\tan \theta_A$:

$$\tan^3 \theta_A - \frac{\Psi}{\Theta} \tan^2 \theta_A + (1 + \Psi^2) \tan \theta_A - \frac{\Psi}{\Theta} = 0 \qquad (5.75)$$

In order to investigate the reality of the roots of equation (5.75), we reduce it by the substitution

$$\tan\theta_A = \chi + \frac{\Psi}{3\Theta}$$

into the following cubic equation in the unknown χ:

$$\chi^3 + m\chi + n = 0 \tag{5.76}$$

where

$$\left.\begin{aligned} m &= 1 - \frac{\Psi^2}{3\Theta^2} + \Psi^2 \\ n &= -\frac{2}{27}\frac{\Psi^3}{\Theta^3} - \frac{2}{3}\frac{\Psi}{\Theta} + \frac{\Psi^3}{3\Theta} \end{aligned}\right\} \tag{5.77}$$

The roots of equation (5.76) are real, if and only if the discriminant

$$\Delta \equiv 4m^3 + 27n^2 \leqslant 0 \tag{5.78}$$

Substituting equations (5.77) into equation (5.78), and using the notations

$$\left.\begin{aligned} \mu &= \Theta^2 = \left(\frac{u}{\omega}\right)^2 \\ \nu &= \frac{\Theta^2}{\Psi^2} = \frac{\dot\omega^2}{\omega^4} \end{aligned}\right\} \tag{5.79}$$

Fig. 5.16. Diagram for determining number of acceleration poles.

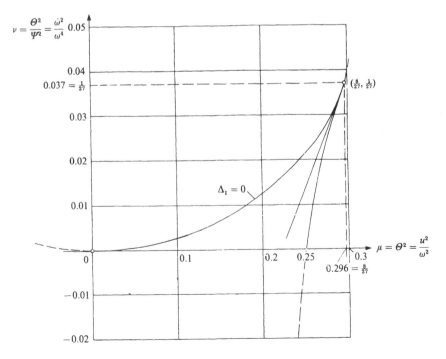

we obtain a discriminant of the form

$$\Delta_1 = v^3 \Delta$$
$$= 4v^3 + 4v^2(3\mu + 2) + 4v(3\mu^2 - 5\mu + 1) + \mu^2(4\mu - 1) \leqslant 0 \qquad (5.80)$$

Fig. 5.16 shows the curve $\Delta_1(\mu, v) = 0$, which has a cusp at the point $\mu = 8/27$, $v = 1/27$. The equation of the cuspidal tangent is $9\mu - 18v - 2 = 0$. For values of (μ, v) within the triangular shaped area bounded by the curve $\Delta_1 = 0$ and the μ-axis, the inequality $\Delta_1 < 0$ in (5.80) holds, and all three acceleration poles are real and discrete. For values of (μ, v) on the curve $\Delta_1 = 0$, there are one discrete and two coincident acceleration poles. For $\mu = 8/27$ and $v = 1/27$, three acceleration axes are coincident. For other values of (μ, v) there is only one real acceleration pole.

Example (Denavit, 1965): Fig. 5.17(a) shows a planetary bevel gear train, in which all three gears are of the same size. Gear f is fixed and gear a rotates with an angular velocity ω_{af} in the sense shown by the arrowhead. In addition to this, the gear a rotates with an angular acceleration $\dot{\omega}_{af}$ in an increasing sense of ω_{af}. Let it be required to find the acceleration poles of the planetary gear c.

Applying equation (4.3) to the present case, namely,

$$\boldsymbol{\omega}_{cf} = \boldsymbol{\omega}_{ca} + \boldsymbol{\omega}_{af}$$

we can construct an angular velocity diagram as shown in Fig. 5.17(b). It is evident that

$$\omega_{cf} = \omega_c = \frac{\sqrt{2}}{2} \omega_{af}$$

Fig. 5.17.

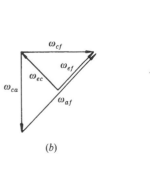

(b)

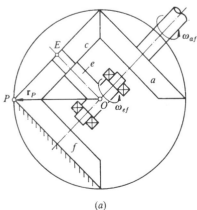

(a)

and consequently

$$\dot{\omega}_{cf} = \dot{\omega}_c = \frac{\sqrt{2}}{2}\dot{\omega}_{af}$$

Imagine a unit sphere passing through the pitch circles of the three bevel gears. In terms of the unit vector $\mathbf{r}_P$, the angular velocity of the gear c and its angular acceleration due to the change of magnitude of the angular velocity are:

$$\boldsymbol{\omega}_c = \omega_{cf}\mathbf{r}_P = \omega_c\mathbf{r}_P = -\frac{\sqrt{2}}{2}\omega_{af}\mathbf{r}_P$$

$$\boldsymbol{\alpha}_{cr} = \dot{\omega}_{cf}\mathbf{r}_P = \dot{\omega}_c\mathbf{r}_P = -\frac{\sqrt{2}}{2}\dot{\omega}_{af}\mathbf{r}_P$$

The values of ω_{af} and $\dot{\omega}_{af}$, according to our definition in Section 4.1.2, are both positive. Hence both ω_c and $\dot{\omega}_c$ are negative. Let the planetary arm be denoted by e. Again in the angular velocity diagram, Fig. 5.17(b), we have

$$\boldsymbol{\omega}_{ef} = \boldsymbol{\omega}_{ec} + \boldsymbol{\omega}_{cf}$$

and hence $\boldsymbol{\omega}_e = \boldsymbol{\omega}_{ef} = \boldsymbol{\omega}_{af}/2$. The pole changing velocity $\mathbf{u}$ is equal to the linear velocity of a point E which is a point on the arm e, flush with the plane of the pitch circle of the gear c. Therefore

$$\mathbf{u} = u\mathbf{t}_P = \mathbf{v}_E = \boldsymbol{\omega}_e \times \overrightarrow{OE} = \frac{\sqrt{2}}{4}\omega_{af}\mathbf{t}_P$$

The quantity Θ is now equal to $-u/\omega_c = 1/2$, the inflection curve k_w corresponding to which has already been shown in Fig. 5.10. The equation of k_w^*, the gnomonic projection of k_w, in plane polar coordinates, can easily be transformed from equation (5.47) by considering equation (A4.8) rather than transforming from equation (5.73):

$$k_w^*: \quad \sin\theta = \frac{PA^*}{1 + PA^{*2}}\frac{1}{\Theta} = \frac{2PA^*}{1 + PA^{*2}}$$

The equation in plane polar coordinates of the curve k_t^*, whose equation expressed in plane rectangular coordinates has already been given in equation (5.74), can also be obtained directly from equation (5.67) by considering equation (A4.8):

$$k_t^*: \quad \cos\theta = \frac{PA^*}{\Psi} = PA^*\left(\frac{\dot{\omega}_c}{\omega_c u}\right) = PA^*\left(-\frac{\dot{\omega}_c}{\omega_c^2}\right)\frac{1}{\Theta} = 2PA^*\left(-\frac{\dot{\omega}_c}{\omega_c^2}\right)$$

The spherical curve k_w for $\Theta = 1/2$ is reproduced in Fig. 5.18(a), together with the two spherical ellipses k_t's for $-\dot{\omega}_c/\omega_c^2 = 1/4$ and $1/8$. The corresponding plane curves k_w^* and k_t^*'s are shown in Fig. 5.18(b).

We see that for $\Theta = 1/2$ and $\Theta/\Psi = -\dot{\omega}_c/\omega_c^2 = 1/4$, we have $\Psi = 4\Theta = 2$,

$\mu = \Theta^2 = 1/4$, $\gamma = (-\dot{\omega}_c/\omega_c^2)^2 = 1/16$. This (μ, ν) point is outside the triangular area in Fig. 5.16. Hence there is only one intersection point of k_w and k_t, as shown in Figs. 5.18 (a) and (b). The corresponding cubic equation in $\tan\theta$, equation (5.75), becomes

$$\tan^3\theta - 4\tan^2\theta + 5\tan\theta - 4 = 0$$

There is only one real root, which is $\tan\theta = 2.6956$, or $\theta = 69.65°$. *PA* is computed by equation (5.67) to be $PA = 34.82°$. The same example has been shown in (Bisshopp, 1969), where the acceleration axes are found by using vector algebra.

Fig. 5.18.

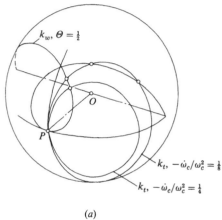

k_w, $\Theta = \frac{1}{2}$

O

P

k_t, $-\dot{\omega}_c/\omega_c^2 = \frac{1}{8}$

k_t, $-\dot{\omega}_c/\omega_c^2 = \frac{1}{4}$

(a)

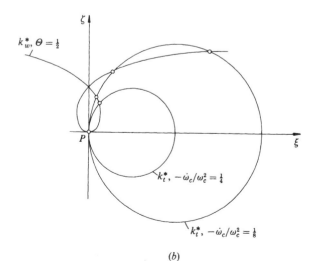

ζ

k_w^*, $\Theta = \frac{1}{2}$

P

ξ

k_t^*, $-\dot{\omega}_c/\omega_c^2 = \frac{1}{4}$

k_t^*, $-\dot{\omega}_c/\omega_c^2 = \frac{1}{8}$

(b)

For $\Theta = 1/2$ and $\Theta/\Psi = -\dot{\omega}_c/\omega_c^2 = 1/8$, we have $\Psi = 8\Theta = 4$, $\mu = \Theta^2 = 1/4$, $v = (-\dot{\omega}_c/\omega_c^2)^2 = 1/64$. This (μ, v) point is within the triangular area in Fig. 5.16. There are three acceleration poles. The cubic equation in $\tan\theta$ becomes

$$\tan^3\theta - 8\tan^2\theta + 17\tan\theta - 8 = 0$$

The three real roots are: $\tan\theta = 4.814, 0.657, 2.529$. The corresponding values of (PA, θ) are computed to be: $(39.14°, 78.26°)$, $(73.35°, 33.30°)$, $(55.78°, 68.43°)$. As a check of the results the three PA's should satisfy the condition that $\sum_{i=1}^{3} \cos^2 PA_i = 1$ (Bottema, 1965). In the present case, it is

$$\cos^2 39.14° + \cos^2 73.35° + \cos^2 55.78° = 1$$

6

Dimensional synthesis – body guidance problems

In the present and two subsequent chapters we are going to investigate the techniques of synthesizing a spherical mechanism, principally a spherical four-bar linkage, to meet certain requirements. Just as in plane kinematics, the dimensional synthesis problems in spherical kinematics can in general be subdivided into three fundamental kinds, namely, body guidance, path generation and function generation. Certainly there can be a number of synthesis problems which involve a combination of two or three kinds of these fundamental synthesis problems. In the following we shall begin with the body guidance problems. To some extent the techniques of solving these synthesis problems are similar to those used in the corresponding plane synthesis problems.

6.1   Guiding a body through two finitely separated positions

6.1.1   Geometrical considerations

When we mention a spherically moving body, it is understood that the body is considered only as a spherical shell, as we have mentioned in Section 2.1. However, as the word *body* is a familiar term, we shall keep using it throughout the following sections.

The position of a spherically moving body is completely determined by the locations of its two points on the surface of the unit sphere. Therefore, a body can be represented by a great circle arc which connects two points on the body. In Fig. 6.1 the two positions of a body c are given by the great circle arcs A_1B_1 and A_2B_2. Let it be required to guide the body c from A_1B_1 to A_2B_2. Join the great circle arc A_1A_2 and denote the perpendicular bisector of A_1A_2 by a_{12}. A point A_0 which can serve as a centre of rotation of a link A_0A to transfer the point A from A_1 to A_2 must be equally distant from both A_1 and A_2, hence A_0 must lie on a_{12}. Similarly the centre of rotation

B_0 of a link B_0B to transfer the point B from B_1 to B_2 must also lie on the perpendicular bisector b_{12} of the great circle arc B_1B_2. Once A_0 and B_0 have been chosen, the spherical four-bar linkage A_0ABB_0 is uniquely determined. As in plane kinematics, we shall call the points $A_1, B_1, \ldots$ the circle-points, and the points $A_0, B_0, \ldots$, the centre-points.

For given positions of c_1 and c_2, there are ∞^2 possibilities of choosing A_1, and ∞^2 possibilities of choosing B_1. Once A_1 and B_1 have been chosen, there are ∞^1 possibilities of choosing A_0 on a_{12}, and ∞^1 possibilities of choosing B_0 on b_{12}. Altogether there are ∞^6 solutions of possible spherical four-bar linkages, or ∞^6 different ways of guiding the body c from c_1 to c_2.

Suppose both A_0 and B_0 are chosen at P_{12}, the intersection point of a_{12} and b_{12}, the length A_0B_0 diminishes to null, and the spherical four-bar A_0ABB_0 becomes a spherical triangle. The body c is then guided from the position c_1 to c_2 through a single rotation about the axis OP_{12}. The point P_{12} is thus called the pole of rotation, or simply *pole*, of the body c (relative to the fixed spherical shell) between position 1 and position 2, i.e. between c_1 and c_2. The point P_{12} is called by some investigators a *virtual* pole to distinguish it from the instantaneous pole of rotation, e.g. (Dijksman, 1976). However, as no ambiguity will arise, we shall keep using the term *pole*, as defined here in a general sense, to indicate a centre of rotation, no matter whether the rotation is finite or instantaneous, thus establishing a definition consistent with those mentioned in Sections 2.1 and 4.1.1. The angle of rotation of the body c is

$$\gamma_{12} = \sphericalangle A_1P_{12}A_2 = \sphericalangle B_1P_{12}B_2$$

Consequently, with respect to a pair of arbitrarily chosen centres of rotation

Fig. 6.1. Pole between two finitely separated positions.

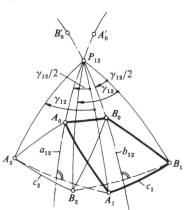

A_0, B_0, as shown in Fig. 6.1, we have

$$\gamma_{12}/2 = \sphericalangle A_1 P_{12} A_0 = \sphericalangle B_1 P_{12} B_0 \qquad (6.1)$$

Adding to both $\sphericalangle A_1 P_{12} A_0$ and $\sphericalangle B_1 P_{12} B_0$ the angle $\sphericalangle B_0 P_{12} A_1$, as shown in Fig. 6.1, we obtain

$$\sphericalangle B_0 P_{12} A_0 = \sphericalangle B_1 P_{12} A_1 \qquad (6.2)$$

Equations (6.1) and (6.2) indicate that the opposite sides of the synthesized four-bar linkage subtend equal angles at the pole P_{12}.

Suppose the centre point A_0 is chosen at A_0', as shown in Fig. 6.1. We then have

$$180° - \sphericalangle B_0 P_{12} A_0' = \sphericalangle B_1 P_{12} A_1$$

If the centre point B_0 is chosen at B_0', we then have

$$180° - \sphericalangle B_0' P_{12} A_0 = \sphericalangle B_1 P_{12} A_1$$

and

$$\sphericalangle B_0' P_{12} A_0' = \sphericalangle B_1 P_{12} A_1$$

We can therefore draw the following conclusion: *The great circle arc of the circle-point pair $A_1 B_1$ (or $A_2 B_2$) and the great circle arc of the centre-point pair $A_0 B_0$ subtend* (1) *equal angles at P_{12} if the sense of reading $A_1 \to B_1$ (or $A_2 \to B_2$) is the same as that of reading $A_0 \to B_0$ about P_{12}, or* (2) *supplementary angles if the sense of reading $A_1 \to B_1$ (or $A_2 \to B_2$) is opposite to that of reading $A_0 \to B_0$ about P_{12}.*

It is understood that the great circle arc between P_{12} and any centre-point or circle-point should always be less than 180°, because the other intersection point $\bar{P}_{12}$ of a_{12} and b_{12} is 180° apart from P_{12}.

When a_{12} and b_{12} coincide, the pole P_{12} is simply the intersection of $A_1 B_1$ and $A_2 B_2$, as shown in Fig. 6.2, no matter whether the spherical quadrilateral $A_1 B_1 B_2 A_2$ is *open* or *crossed*.

Fig. 6.2.

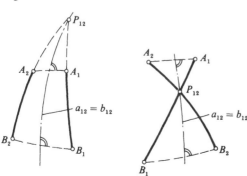

6.1.2   *Algebraic formulations*

It is more practicable to determine the location of a point on the surface of the unit sphere in an algebraic way. Again suppose, in Fig. 6.1, that the locations of two points A, B of a body c in two positions, namely, A_1, B_1 and A_2, B_2 with respect to a certain reference coordinate system xyz, are specified. In other words, let (x_{A1}, y_{A1}, z_{A1}), (x_{B1}, y_{B1}, z_{B1}) and (x_{A2}, y_{A2}, z_{A2}), (x_{B2}, y_{B2}, z_{B2}) be given. The perpendicular bisector a_{12} of $A_1 A_2$ is represented, according to equation (A3.3), with (x_0, y_0, z_0) as variables, by

$$a_{12}: \quad (x_{A2} - x_{A1})\frac{x_0}{z_0} + (y_{A2} - y_{A1})\frac{y_0}{z_0} = -(z_{A2} - z_{A1}) \tag{6.3}$$

together with equation (A3.1a) of the unit sphere

$$\left(\frac{x_0}{z_0}\right)^2 + \left(\frac{y_0}{z_0}\right)^2 + 1 = \frac{1}{z_0^2} \tag{[(A3.1a)]}$$

Similarly the perpendicular bisector b_{12} of $B_1 B_2$ is represented, also with (x_0, y_0, z_0) as variables, by

$$b_{12}: \quad (x_{B2} - x_{B1})\frac{x_0}{z_0} + (y_{B2} - y_{B1})\frac{y_0}{z_0} = -(z_{B2} - z_{B1}) \tag{6.4}$$

together with equation (A3.1a). Selection of the point A_0 on a_{12} can be carried out by assuming a suitable value of y_0/z_0 (or x_0/z_0) and then solving x_0/z_0 (or y_0/z_0) and z_0 from equations (6.3) and (A3.1a). The selection of B_0 on b_{12} can also be carried out in a similar way by means of equations (6.4) and (A3.1a). Finally the lengths of the four links can be found by using equation (A3.2).

Example: Given two positions of two points A, B on a body with respect to a fixed coordinate system xyz: $A_1(0.7, 0.4, 0.591608)$, $A_2(0.5, 0.6, 0.624500)$, $B_1(0.6, 0.196336, 0.775533)$, $B_2(0.3, 0.5, 0.812404)$. It is required to design a spherical four-bar to guide the body from position 1 to position 2.

Selection of A_0: assume $(x_0/z_0)_{A0} = 1.37$. Substitution of this value into equations (6.3) and (A3.1a) gives: $x_{A0} = 0.65836$, $y_{A0} = 0.57933$, $z_{A0} = 0.48056$. Next assume $(x_0/z_0)_{B0} = 1.10$. Substitution of this value into equations (6.4) and (A3.1a) gives: $x_{B0} = 0.62059$, $y_{B0} = 0.54460$, $z_{B0} = 0.56417$. The lengths of the four bars are found by means of equation (A3.2): $A_0 A = 12.342°$, $AB = 16.795°$, $B_0 B = 23.536°$, $A_0 B_0 = 5.623°$.

The displacement of a body from a position 1 to position 2 can be expressed by a displacement matrix $\mathbb{D}_{12}$, like those given in equations (A2.33), (A2.39) and (A2.41). Although it is possible to find $\mathbb{D}_{12}$ from the coordinates of A_1, A_2; B_1, B_2 by introducing two corresponding locations of a third point on the body, a more direct procedure is as follows.

On the assumption that the body is rotated about a single pole-axis OP_{12} through an angle γ_{12} from position 1 to position 2, solving the three equations (6.3), (6.4) and (A3.1a) simultaneously will give the coordinates of P_{12} (x_0, y_0, z_0). Now in order to build up the displacement matrix $\mathbb{D}_{12}$ in equation (A2.33) the angle of rotation γ_{12} is required. To find γ_{12}, the simplest way is to use the displacement matrix $\mathbb{D}_{12}$ itself by replacing l_x, l_y, l_z in equations (A2.34) by x_0, y_0, z_0 respectively, and then applying equation (A2.35) to the known coordinates of A_1 and A_2. In so doing, we have, after collecting terms, the following three linear equations in the three unknowns vers γ_{12}, $\cos \gamma_{12}$ and $\sin \gamma_{12}$:

$$
\left.
\begin{aligned}
(x_0^2 x_{A1} + x_0 y_0 y_{A1} + x_0 z_0 z_{A1}) \operatorname{vers} \gamma_{12} + x_{A1} \cos \gamma_{12} + (y_0 z_{A1} - y_{A1} z_0) \sin \gamma_{12} = x_{A2} \\
(x_0 y_0 x_{A1} + y_0^2 y_{A1} + y_0 z_0 z_{A1}) \operatorname{vers} \gamma_{12} + y_{A1} \cos \gamma_{12} + (z_0 x_{A1} - z_{A1} x_0) \sin \gamma_{12} = y_{A2} \\
(x_0 z_0 x_{A1} + y_0 z_0 y_{A1} + z_0^2 z_{A1}) \operatorname{vers} \gamma_{12} + z_{A1} \cos \gamma_{12} + (x_0 y_{A1} - x_{A1} y_0) \sin \gamma_{12} = z_{A2}
\end{aligned}
\right\}
$$
(6.5)

Solving this system of equations for $\cos \gamma_{12}$ and $\sin \gamma_{12}$, the value of γ_{12} can be obtained.

Example: Find the displacement matrix $\mathbb{D}_{12}$ in the previous example.

Substituting the given coordinates of $A_1, B_1; A_2, B_2$ into equations (6.3) and (6.4), and solving them together with equation (A3.1a), yields the coordinates of P_{12}: $x_{P12} = x_0 = 0.70915$, $y_{P12} = y_0 = 0.67645$, $z_{P12} = z_0 = 0.19881$. Substituting these data and the coordinates of A_1 and A_2 into equations (6.5) we obtain finally $\gamma_{12} = -35.5516°$. The displacement matrix $\mathbb{D}_{12}$ can then be built up according to equations (A2.34):

$$
\mathbb{D}_{12} = \begin{bmatrix} 0.90733 & 0.20501 & -0.36703 \\ -0.02617 & 0.89889 & 0.43739 \\ 0.41959 & -0.38726 & 0.82096 \end{bmatrix}
$$

(1) On the assumption that the body is rotated successively about the axes x, y, z of a fixed coordinate system, through respective angles α, β, γ, comparison of the elements of $\mathbb{D}_{12}$ with those in equation (A2.39) gives: $\alpha = 154.745°$, $\beta = -155.190°$, $\gamma = 178.347°$.

(2) On the assumption that the body is rotated in sequence about the axes z, x, z of a fixed coordinate system, through respective Eulerian angles ξ, η, ζ, comparison of the elements of $\mathbb{D}_{12}$ with those of $\mathbb{D}_{12}$ in equation (A2.41) gives: $\xi = -47.295°$, $\eta = -34.820°$, $\zeta = 40.000°$.

The concept of a displacement matrix based on successive rotations α, β, γ about three axes x, y, z embedded in the moving body has been applied to find the centre-point curve and circle-point curve for four given positions of the body in (Dowler, Duffy & Tesar, 1978), and even in the synthesis of geared five-bar function generators in (Riddle, Tesar & Duffy, 1975).

If, on the contrary, the displacement matrix $\mathbb{D}_{12}$ is given first, a comparison of the elements of the given $\mathbb{D}_{12}$ with those listed in equations (A2.34) will readily yield the location of the pole P_{12} and the angle of rotation γ_{12}. When equations (A2.34) are not available, the coordinates of the pole P_{12} can still be found easily. The pole-axis OP_{12} is just the well-known eigenvector of $\mathbb{D}_{12}$ for the eigenvalue $+1$. Now the components of the displacement of any point F on the body are

$$
\begin{bmatrix} \Delta x_F \\ \Delta y_F \\ \Delta z_F \end{bmatrix} = \mathbb{D}_{12} \begin{bmatrix} x_{F1} \\ y_{F1} \\ z_{F1} \end{bmatrix} - \begin{bmatrix} x_{F1} \\ y_{F1} \\ z_{F1} \end{bmatrix}
$$

$$
= \begin{bmatrix} d_{11}-1 & d_{12} & d_{13} \\ d_{21} & d_{22}-1 & d_{23} \\ d_{31} & d_{32} & d_{33}-1 \end{bmatrix} \begin{bmatrix} x_{F1} \\ y_{F1} \\ z_{F1} \end{bmatrix} \tag{6.6}
$$

If the point F is taken at the pole P_{12}, then $\Delta x_F, \Delta y_F, \Delta z_F$ are all zero, and we have the following homogeneous linear equations in the three unknowns $x_{P12}, y_{P12}, z_{P12}$:

$$
\left. \begin{aligned}
(d_{11}-1)x_{P12} + d_{12}y_{P12} + d_{13}z_{P12} &= 0 \\
d_{21}x_{P12} + (d_{22}-1)y_{P12} + d_{23}z_{P12} &= 0 \\
d_{31}x_{P12} + d_{32}y_{P12} + (d_{33}-1)z_{P12} &= 0
\end{aligned} \right\} \tag{6.7}
$$

Because the solutions of this system of equations definitely exist, the determinant of the coefficients of this system of equations is zero. It is therefore sufficient to solve any two of the equations. Taking for instance the first two equations, and using the quotients x_{P12}/z_{P12} and y_{P12}/z_{P12} as unknowns, we have

$$
(d_{11}-1)\frac{x_{P12}}{z_{P12}} + d_{12}\frac{y_{P12}}{z_{P12}} + d_{13} = 0 \tag{6.8}
$$

$$
d_{21}\frac{x_{P12}}{z_{P12}} + (d_{22}-1)\frac{y_{P12}}{z_{P12}} + d_{23} = 0 \tag{6.9}
$$

Solving these two linear equations together with equation (A3.1a): $(x_{P12}/z_{P12})^2 + (y_{P12}/z_{P12})^2 + 1 = 1/z_{P12}^2$, we can find the coordinates $x_{P12}, y_{P12}, z_{P12}$ of the pole P_{12}.

6.2   Guiding a body through two infinitesimally separated positions

6.2.1   *Geometrical considerations*

Consider the case in which the points A_2 and B_2 in Fig. 6.1 approach respectively A_1 and B_1 indefinitely. The spherical distances A_1A_2 and B_1B_2 become infinitesimally small, and will be denoted respectively by ds_A and ds_B, where s_A and s_B are the respective spherical distances along the paths of A and B. Dividing ds_A and ds_B by the corresponding infinitesimal time element dt gives the velocities

$$v_A = ds_A/dt, \quad v_B = ds_B/dt$$

This means that the directions of the velocities of the points A and B in their respective tangent planes may be prescribed. Fig. 6.3 shows such a case. The perpendicular bisectors a_{12} and b_{12} are perpendicular to the directions of v_A and v_B respectively. The intersection point of a_{12} and b_{12} is again the pole of rotation of the body c, which we denote by P instead of P_{12} because the positions c_1 and c_2 are infinitesimally separated. The pole P is thus an instantaneous pole of rotation or velocity pole, as has already been discussed in Section 2.1 and shown in Fig. 2.1.

Similar to the case of guiding a body through two finitely separated positions, the fixed centres A_0 and B_0 can arbitrarily be chosen on a_{12} and b_{12} respectively. There are again ∞^6 solutions of possible spherical four-bar linkages to fulfil the guiding requirements.

6.2.2   Algebraic formulations

From the algebraic point of view, if two positions of a moving body are infinitesimally separated, the angles of rotation α, β, γ about the respective axes x, y, z become infinitesimally small. Substituting in equation (A2.39) $S_\alpha \approx d\alpha$, $S_\beta \approx d\beta$, $S_\gamma \approx d\gamma$, $C_\alpha \approx C_\beta \approx C_\gamma \approx 1$ and neglecting higher orders such as $d\alpha\, d\beta$, the displacement matrix becomes

$$\mathbb{D} = \begin{bmatrix} 1 & -d\gamma & d\beta \\ d\gamma & 1 & -d\alpha \\ -d\beta & d\alpha & 1 \end{bmatrix}$$

Any position vector $\overrightarrow{OA} = \mathbf{r}_A = x_A\mathbf{i} + y_A\mathbf{j} + z_A\mathbf{k}$ of a point A on the body will

Fig. 6.3. Instantaneous pole.

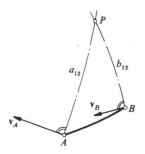

be displaced infinitesimally to a new vector $\mathbf{r}_A + d\mathbf{r}_A = \mathbb{D}\mathbf{r}_A$, or

$$d\mathbf{r}_A = \mathbb{D}\mathbf{r}_A - \mathbf{r}_A = \left\{ \begin{bmatrix} 1 & -d\gamma & d\beta \\ d\gamma & 1 & -d\alpha \\ -d\beta & d\alpha & 1 \end{bmatrix} \begin{bmatrix} x_A \\ y_A \\ z_A \end{bmatrix} \begin{matrix} \text{(i)} \\ \text{(j)} \\ \text{(k)} \end{matrix} - \begin{bmatrix} x_A \\ y_A \\ z_A \end{bmatrix} \begin{matrix} \text{(i)} \\ \text{(j)} \\ \text{(k)} \end{matrix} \right.$$

$$= \left\{ \begin{bmatrix} 0 & -d\gamma & d\beta \\ d\gamma & 0 & -d\alpha \\ -d\beta & d\alpha & 0 \end{bmatrix} \begin{bmatrix} x_A \\ y_A \\ z_A \end{bmatrix} \begin{matrix} \text{(i)} \\ \text{(j)} \\ \text{(k)} \end{matrix} \right.$$

The linear velocity of the point A is then

$$\mathbf{v}_A = d\mathbf{r}_A/dt = \left\{ \begin{bmatrix} 0 & -d\gamma/dt & d\beta/dt \\ d\gamma/dt & 0 & -d\alpha/dt \\ -d\beta/dt & d\alpha/dt & 0 \end{bmatrix} \begin{bmatrix} x_A \\ y_A \\ z_A \end{bmatrix} \begin{matrix} \text{(i)} \\ \text{(j)} \\ \text{(k)} \end{matrix} \right. \quad (6.10)$$

Note that $d\alpha/dt$, $d\beta/dt$, $d\gamma/dt$ are the respective angular velocity components of the moving body about the axes x, y, z which we have denoted respectively by ω_x, ω_y, ω_z in equation (4.27). Both matrices in equations (6.10) and (4.27) are identical, and are denoted by $\mathbb{V}_\omega$.

As mentioned in the preceding section and shown in Fig. 6.3, the instantaneous axis of rotation OP should be determinable if the velocities $\mathbf{v}_A$ and $\mathbf{v}_B$ of two points A and B are specified. For the linear velocity $\mathbf{v}_A$, equation (6.10), which is also identical with equation (4.26), becomes the following three linear equations in the three unknowns ω_x, ω_y, ω_z:

$$v_{Ax} = \qquad -\omega_z y_A + \omega_y z_A \qquad\qquad (6.11)$$

$$v_{Ay} = \quad \omega_z x_A \qquad -\omega_x z_A \qquad\qquad (6.12)$$

$$v_{Az} = -\omega_y x_A + \omega_x y_A \qquad\qquad (6.13)$$

However, the above three equations are not independent. Any one of the three equations can be derived as a linear combination of the other two equations. This is because the vector $\mathbf{v}_A$ must lie in the tangent plane to the unit sphere at A, or $\mathbf{v}_A \cdot \mathbf{r}_A = 0$. Therefore only two of the three components v_{Ax}, v_{Ay}, v_{Az} may be specified arbitrarily; the third component is determined by these two components. Hence the above three equations, counted as two independent equations, are not sufficient for solving the three unknowns ω_x, ω_y, ω_z. One additional equation is required. Similar to equations (6.11)–(6.13), application of the same velocity matrix $\mathbb{V}_\omega$ to the position vector $\mathbf{r}_B$ results in the components of $\mathbf{v}_B$:

$$v_{Bx} = \qquad -\omega_z y_B + \omega_y z_B \qquad\qquad (6.14)$$

$$v_{By} = \quad \omega_z x_B \qquad -\omega_x z_B \qquad\qquad (6.15)$$

$$v_{Bz} = -\omega_y x_B + \omega_x y_B \qquad\qquad (6.16)$$

The third condition to be added may be, for instance, a specification of the magnitude or the direction of $\mathbf{v}_B$, or even one single component of $\mathbf{v}_B$. As a specified direction of v_B it can be a given ratio of v_{By}/v_{Bx} or of v_{Bz}/v_{Rx}. The following example illustrates the procedure of computation.

Example: Given the coordinates of two points on a moving body: $A(0.7, 0, 0.714143)$, $B(0, 1, 0)$, and two components of the velocity $\mathbf{v}_A$: $v_{Ax} = 0.20$, $v_{Ay} = 0.15$, and the magnitude of $v_B = 1$. Design a spherical four-bar to generate these velocity requirements (Fig. 6.4).

Substituting the given data into equations (6.11), (6.12) and (6.14)–(6.16), and noting that the magnitude of $\mathbf{v}_B$ is given by $v_B^2 = v_{Bx}^2 + v_{By}^2 + v_{Bz}^2$, we get two sets of solutions: (1) $\omega_x = 0.584959$, $\omega_y = 0.280056$, $\omega_z = 0.811063$; (2) $\omega_x = -0.799202$, $\omega_y = 0.280056$, $\omega_z = -0.601064$. Using only the first set of solutions, we find $\omega = (\omega_x^2 + \omega_y^2 + \omega_z^2)^{1/2} = 1.038476$. The coordinates of the pole P are then $x_P = \omega_x/\omega = 0.563286$, $y_P = \omega_y/\omega = 0.269680$, $z_P = \omega_z/\omega = 0.781013$. Again apart from equation (A3.1), the great circle PA is represented, according to equation (A3.4), by

$$-0.192590x_0 - 0.144442y_0 + 0.188776z_0 = 0$$

The location of A_0 can be selected, for instance, by setting the length of A_0A on PA, say, equal to $25°$, with A_0 outside of PA. According to equation (A3.2), this condition for the coordinates of A_0 becomes

$$0.7x_0 + 0.714143z_0 = \cos 25° = 0.906308$$

Solving the last two equations together with equation (A3.1), the coordinates of A_0 are found to be: $A_0(0.776914, -0.372550, 0.507561)$. Similarly the great circle PB is represented by

$$-0.781013x_0 + 0.563268z_0 = 0$$

Fig. 6.4.

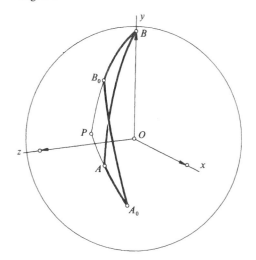

The location of B_0 on PB can also be selected in a similar way by setting, say, $B_0B = 45°$ with B_0 between P and B. Again according to equation (A3.2), this condition for the coordinates of B_0 becomes

$$y_0 = \cos 45° = 0.707107$$

The location of B_0 can then be found by solving the last two equations together with equation (A3.1). The result is: $B_0(0.413620, 0.707107, 0.573515)$. The lengths of the links are: $A_0B_0 = 69.812°$, $A_0A = 25°$, $AB = 90°$, $B_0B = 45°$.

6.2.3   Polodes of a spherical four-bar linkage

The foregoing example shows that the velocities of two points on a moving body determine the three components of the angular velocity of the moving body, hence its pole-axis. If, in general, the motion of the body follows a certain function, for instance the three angles of rotation α, β, γ of the body as defined in Appendix A2.5 are linked together by a certain relationship, say $\alpha = \alpha(\gamma)$ and $\beta = \beta(\gamma)$, then the loci of the pole, i.e. the fixed polode and the moving polode, can be formulated as functions of γ without difficulty (Dowler, Duffy & Tesar, 1976). Recently these polodes of a spherical four-bar have been investigated by (Sodhi & Shoup, 1982). In spite of the lengthy equations, the derivation of these equations is no more complicated than for the corresponding planar case (Müller, 1903). Referring to Fig. 4.3(*a*), since the directions of the velocities v_A and v_B are completely determined by the positions of the links A_0A and B_0B, the pole P of the coupler c is also completely determined. It is the intersection of the great circles A_0A and B_0B. For the sake of brevity let the coordinates of the pole P with respect to the fixed coordinate system xyz be denoted by (x, y, z). The coordinates of the four points A_0, A, B_0, B are, respectively, $A_0(1, 0, 0)$, $A(C_a, S_aC_\phi, S_aS_\phi)$, $B_0(C_f, S_f, 0)$, $B(C_fC_b - S_fS_bC_\psi, S_fC_b + C_fS_bC_\psi, S_bS_\psi)$. According to equation (A3.4), apart from the unit sphere condition, equation (A3.1), the great circle A_0AP is represented by

$$\begin{vmatrix} x & y & z \\ C_a & S_aC_\phi & S_aS_\phi \\ 1 & 0 & 0 \end{vmatrix} = 0$$

Expansion of the determinant gives

$$C_\phi = \frac{y}{z}S_\phi \tag{6.17}$$

Similarly the great circle B_0BP is represented by

$$\begin{vmatrix} x & y & z \\ C_fC_b - S_fS_bC_\psi & S_fC_b + C_fS_bC_\psi & S_bS_\psi \\ C_f & S_f & 0 \end{vmatrix} = 0$$

which gives

$$C_\psi = \frac{-xS_f + yC_f}{z} S_\psi \tag{6.18}$$

Now the relationship between ϕ and ψ is governed by equation (2.5a):

$$k_1 - k_2 + k_3C_\phi - k_4C_\psi + k_5C_\phi C_\psi + k_6S_\phi S_\psi = 0 \tag{[(2.5a)]}$$

Substituting equations (6.17) and (6.18) into the above equation, and rearranging terms, we obtain

$$LS_\phi - MS_\psi = -NS_\phi S_\psi - K \tag{6.19}$$

where

$$L = k_3 \frac{y}{z}, \quad M = k_4 \frac{-xS_f + yC_f}{z},$$

$$N = \frac{k_5 y(-xS_f + yC_f) + k_6 z^2}{z^2}, \quad K = k_1 - k_2$$

Now from equations (6.17) and (6.18),

$$S_\phi^2 = \frac{z^2}{y^2 + z^2} \tag{6.20}$$

and

$$S_\psi^2 = \frac{z^2}{(yC_f - xS_f)^2 + z^2} \tag{6.21}$$

Before substituting equations (6.20) and (6.21) into equation (6.19), the latter equation has to be rearranged and squared twice until only powers of S_ϕ^2 and S_ψ^2 appear in the equation. The result is

$$N^4 S_\phi^4 S_\psi^4 - 2L^2 N^2 S_\phi^4 S_\psi^2 - 2M^2 N^2 S_\phi^2 S_\psi^4 + L^4 S_\phi^4 + M^4 S_\psi^4$$
$$- (2L^2 M^2 + 2K^2 N^2 + 8LMKN) S_\phi^2 S_\psi^2$$
$$- 2L^2 K^2 S_\phi^2 - 2K^2 M^2 S_\psi^2 + K^4 = 0 \tag{6.22}$$

The equation of the fixed polode can therefore be obtained by substituting equations (6.20) and (6.21) into equation (6.22). It can be seen that this equation, after elimination of denominators, is a homogeneous equation in x, y, z of eighth degree. To obtain the equation of the moving polode, the coordinate system is taken as the $x_1 y_1 z_1$-system as shown in Fig. 4.3(a), and the equation is obtained by interchanging c and f in equation (6.22). For special spherical four-bar linkages, these equations are greatly simplified.

As an example of the polode equation, consider a right-angled double-slider as mentioned in Section 2.5.1(4) and shown in Fig. 2.48 (Dittrich, 1964, pp. 18–20). For the fixed polode we now have $a = b = f = 90°$, $k_1 = k_3 = k_4 = k_5 = 0$, $k_2 = \cos c$ and $k_6 = 1$, hence $L = M = 0$, $N = 1$ and $K = -\cos c$.

Equation (6.19) becomes simply

$$S_\phi S_\psi - C_c = 0 \tag{6.23}$$

Substituting equations (6.20) and (6.21) into equation (6.23), and noting that $C_f = 0$ and $S_f = 1$, we obtain the equation of the fixed polode,

$$\pi_f: \quad z^4 = C_c^2(x^2 + z^2)(y^2 + z^2) \tag{6.24}$$

Fig. 6.5 shows the fixed polode π_f, as seen in a direction normal to the xy-(A_0B_0)-plane. This is a spherical curve of fourth degree, symmetrical with respect to both the xz-plane and the yz-plane.

Fig. 6.5. Polodes of a right-angled double-slider.

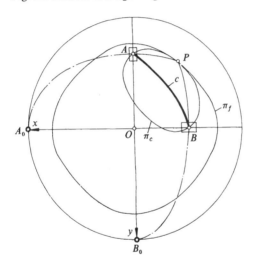

Fig. 6.6. Polodes of linkage with $a = b$ and $c = f$.

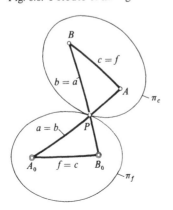

For the moving polode, the coordinate system $x_1 y_1 z_1$ is so chosen that the axis OX_1 coincides with OA, and the $x_1 y_1$-plane coincides with the AB-plane. In the present case, since the right-angled double-slider is the inversion of a Hooke's universal joint, its moving polode is just the fixed polode of the latter. Setting in equation (6.19) $a = b = c = 90°$ and $f = c$, the equation of the moving polode becomes simply $N = 0$, or

$$\pi_c: \quad y_1^2 C_c^2 + z_1^2 - x_1 y_1 S_c C_c = 0 \tag{6.25}$$

The moving polode π_c is therefore a spherical ellipse, as shown in Fig. 6.5, in which however the $x_1 y_1 z_1$-system is not shown. The spherical major axis of this ellipse is $AB = c$, and its spherical minor axis $2b_s$ is determined, comparing equation (6.25) with equation (A1.19), by $\cos^2 b_s = 2/(2 + C_c - C_c^2)$, but the ellipse does not pass through the z-axis of the π_f-curve. These rolling polodes correspond to the well-known Cardan circle-pair in plane kinematics.

Consider, as a further example, the polodes of the spherical four-bar linkage with $a = b$ and $c = f$. This linkage corresponds to the parallel-crank and antiparallel-crank linkages in plane kinematics. However, when the spherical linkage is in an *open* position, the two rotating links a and b do not rotate with the same angular velocity, and the pole of the coupler always lies within the spherical surface. For the fixed polode we now have $k_1 = C_a^2 C_c$, $k_2 = C_c$, $k_3 = k_4 = S_a C_a S_c$, $k_5 = S_a^2 C_c$ and $k_6 = S_a^2$. The equation of the fixed polode becomes the following quartic equation:

$$\pi_f: \quad [(C_a - C_c)^2 x^2 + (C_a^2 - C_c^2)y^2 - 2S_c(C_a - C_c)xy - S_a^2 z^2]$$
$$\cdot [(C_a + C_c)^2 x^2 + (C_a^2 - C_c^2)y^2 - S_a^2 z^2 + 2S_c(C_a + C_c)xy] = 0 \tag{6.26}$$

The first bracket in equation (6.26) represents the part of the fixed polode π_f for the *crossed* configuration of the linkage. For $a > c$, this is a spherical ellipse with A_0 and B_0 as its two foci, as shown in Fig. 6.6. In fact this equation could have been obtained directly from the condition that $PA_0 + PB_0 = A_0 A = a$. The corresponding part of the moving polode π_c is an identical ellipse, with A, B as its foci. For $a < c$, these two polodes become two spherical hyperbolas, which are not shown.

The second bracket in equation (6.26) represents a separate part of the fixed polode π_f for the *open* configuration of the linkage, also not shown in the figure.

6.3   Three finitely separated positions – geometrical considerations

The problem of guiding a body through three given finitely separated positions in plane kinematics from the geometrical point of view has been thoroughly studied (Beyer, 1953). The corresponding problem in spherical kinematics was investigated by Hein (1959) in quite a similar way. In the following we shall first look into this problem from this point of view.

6.3.1   The poletriangle and cardinal point

In Fig. 6.7(a) three positions of a spherically moving shell c are shown as c_1, c_2 and c_3. As has been mentioned in Section 6.1, there exists a pole P_{12} between the positions c_1 and c_2, and a pole P_{23} between c_2 and c_3. We take the great circle joining P_{12} and P_{23} to represent c in the position c_2. In the position c_1, the point P_{23} is at P_{23}^1. The dihedral angle between $P_{12}P_{23}^1$ and $P_{12}P_{23}$ is the angle of rotation γ_{12} of c from c_1 to c_2. Similarly in the position c_3 the position of P_{12} is denoted by P_{12}^3, and the dihedral angle between $P_{23}P_{12}$ and $P_{23}P_{12}^3$ is the angle of rotation γ_{23} of c from c_2 to c_3. Note that both γ_{12} and γ_{23} as shown in Fig. 6.7 are negative. Certainly

Fig. 6.7. Poletriangle.

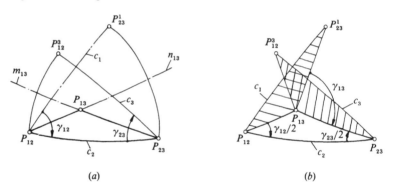

(a)   (b)

Fig. 6.8. Cardinal point of three homologous points.

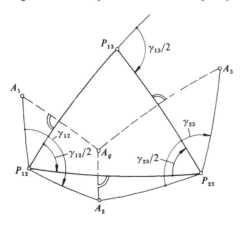

there must exist a pole P_{13} between c_1 and c_3. Taking P_{12} and P_{23}^1 as two points of c_1, and P_{12}^3 and P_{23} as two points of c_3, we can find, by analogy with Fig. 6.1, the pole P_{13} by drawing the respective perpendicular bisectors m_{13} and n_{13} of $P_{12}P_{12}^3$ and $P_{23}P_{23}^1$, and locating their intersection. The spherical triangle $\triangle P_{12}P_{23}P_{13}$ is the spherical poletriangle. It is evident that the apex angles at P_{12}, P_{23} and P_{13} are respectively equal to $\gamma_{12}/2$, $\gamma_{23}/2$ and $180° - \gamma_{13}/2$, Fig. 6.7(b), where γ_{13} is the angle of rotation of c from c_1 to c_3. Note that γ_{13} as shown here is also negative. However, because the sum of the three apex angles of a spherical triangle is in general larger than $180°$, we have therefore

$$\gamma_{13} \neq \gamma_{12} + \gamma_{23} \tag{6.27}$$

The inequality (6.27) reminds us that, unless the axes of rotation are the same, the angle of rotation γ_{13} cannot be obtained by simply adding γ_{23} to γ_{12}, as we have frequently done in plane kinematics.

If the three positions c_1, c_2 and c_3 of a body c are known, it is a simple matter to locate the homologous points, say A_2, A_3 of a point A on the body c if A_1 is given. However, if the spherical poletriangle $\triangle P_{12}P_{23}P_{13}$ is known, the homologous points A_2, A_3 can also be located from geometrical considerations. Fig. 6.8 shows a poletriangle $\triangle P_{12}P_{23}P_{13}$, with A_1 given. It is evident that the spherical distances $P_{12}A_1 = P_{12}A_2$ and $\sphericalangle A_1P_{12}A_2 = \gamma_{12}$. With the poletriangle given, we may simply find first the mirror image A_g of A_1 with respect to $P_{12}P_{13}$, and then the mirror image A_2 of A_g with respect to $P_{12}P_{23}$. In this construction, $A_1A_g \perp P_{12}P_{13}$ and $A_gA_2 \perp P_{12}P_{23}$. Similarly $P_{23}A_2 = P_{23}A_3$ and $\sphericalangle A_2P_{23}A_3 = \gamma_{23}$, and the construction of A_3 can simply be accomplished by locating the mirror image of A_g with respect to $P_{23}P_{13}$. As in plane kinematics, the point A_g is called the *cardinal point*.

6.3.2   The circle passing through three homologous points and the R_M and R^1 curves

Suppose a poletriangle $\triangle P_{12}P_{23}P_{13}$ is given, and the three homologous points A_1, A_2, A_3 of a point A are also known. A spherical circle passing through the three points A_1, A_2, A_3 is in general uniquely determined, as shown in Fig. 6.9. Let this circle be denoted by k_A, and its centre on the spherical surface be denoted by A_0. It is clear that $P_{12}A_0$ is the bisector of $\sphericalangle A_1P_{12}A_2$, hence

$$\sphericalangle A_1P_{12}A_0 = \gamma_{12}/2 \tag{6.28}$$

Similarly for a second set of homologous points B_1, B_2, B_3 with a corresponding centre-point B_0, we have

$$\sphericalangle B_1P_{12}B_0 = \gamma_{12}/2 \tag{6.29}$$

Again there are ∞^2 possibilities of choosing A_1 and ∞^2 possibilities of choosing B_1. Altogether there ∞^4 possible spherical four-bar linkages to guide the body c through three given positions c_1, c_2 and c_3.

In fact, both equations (6.28) and (6.29) have already been verified as equation (6.1). Consequently equation (6.2) is also valid. Now we can extend the conclusion of Section 6.1.1 to all three poles P_{12}, P_{23}, P_{13}, namely: $A_i B_i$ (or $A_j B_j$, $i, j = 1, 2, 3$) and $A_0 B_0$ subtend (1) equal angles at P_{ij} if the sense of reading $A_i \to B_i$ (or $A_j \to B_j$) is the same as the sense of reading $A_0 \to B_0$ about P_{ij}, or (2) supplementary angles if the sense of reading $A_i \to B_i$ (or $A_j \to B_j$) is opposite to the sense of reading $A_0 \to B_0$ about P_{ij}.

Referring to Fig. 6.9, let $\sphericalangle P_{13}P_{12}A_1$ be denoted by θ. As mentioned in Section 6.3.1,

$$\sphericalangle P_{13}P_{12}P_{23} = \gamma_{12}/2 \tag{6.30}$$

Comparing equation (6.30) with equation (6.28) shows that

$$\sphericalangle P_{23}P_{12}A_0 = \theta$$

On the other hand, by the definition of the cardinal point A_g, it is evident that $\sphericalangle A_g P_{12}P_{13}$ is also equal to θ. Consequently the two great circles joining each of the points A_g, A_0 to the pole P_{12} make equal angles, but in opposite senses, with the two adjacent sides of the poletriangle at the apex P_{12}. The same applies to the other two apexes P_{23} and P_{13} for the pair of points A_g, A_0, just as in plane kinematics.

Fig. 6.9. Circle passing through three homologous points.

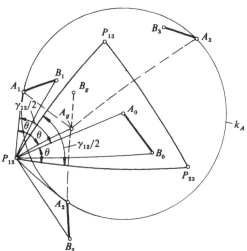

For the sake of clarity let the spherical distances $P_{12}P_{23}$, $P_{12}A_0$ and $P_{12}A_1$ ($= P_{12}A_2$) be denoted, respectively, by s, p_0 and p; and let $\measuredangle P_{12}P_{23}A_0$ be denoted by σ, Fig. 6.10. The location of the centre-point A_0 may be given by its spherical polar coordinates (p_0, θ) with respect to the *spherical origin* P_{12} and spherical polar line $P_{12}P_{23}$. From the foregoing we know that

$$\measuredangle A_2P_{12}A_0 = -\gamma_{12}/2 \tag{6.31}$$

and

$$\measuredangle A_0P_{23}A_2 = -\gamma_{23}/2 \tag{6.32}$$

Applying the cotangent law, equation (A1.11), to the spherical triangles $\triangle P_{12}A_0P_{23}$ and $\triangle P_{12}A_2P_{23}$, we get

$$\cos s \cos \theta = \sin s \cot p_0 - \sin \theta \cot \sigma \tag{6.33}$$

$$\cos s \cos (\measuredangle A_2P_{12}A_0 - \theta) = \sin s \cot p - \sin (\measuredangle A_2P_{12}A_0 - \theta)$$
$$\cdot \cot (\measuredangle A_0P_{23}A_2 - \sigma) \tag{6.34}$$

Eliminating $\cot \sigma$ between equations (6.33) and (6.34) and taking (6.31) and (6.32) into consideration yields

$$\frac{\sin s \cot p_0 - \cos s \cos \theta}{\sin \theta}$$

$$= \frac{-\cot(\gamma_{23}/2)[\cos s \cos (\gamma_{12}/2 + \theta) - \sin s \cot p] + \sin (\gamma_{12}/2 + \theta)}{\cot (\gamma_{23}/2)\{\sin (\gamma_{12}/2 + \theta) + \tan(\gamma_{23}/2)[\cos s \cos (\gamma_{12}/2 + \theta) - \sin s \cot p]\}} \tag{6.35}$$

Equation (6.35) relates, for a poletriangle $\triangle P_{12}P_{23}P_{13}$ defined by the three quantities s, γ_{12}, γ_{23}, the spherical length p_0 to the spherical length p, for a certain value of θ.

Equation (6.35) can be rearranged in the following form:

$$\frac{E}{\tan p} + \frac{F}{\tan p_0} - \frac{K}{\tan p \tan p_0} + G = 0 \tag{6.35a}$$

Fig. 6.10. Spherical polar coordinates of a centre-point and of a circle-point.

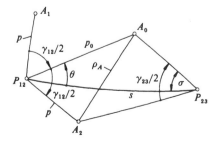

where K is a constant, while E, F, G are functions of θ:

$$K = -\sin s \sin \frac{\gamma_{23}}{2}$$

$$E = \cos \frac{\gamma_{23}}{2} \sin \theta - \cos s \sin \frac{\gamma_{23}}{2} \cos \theta$$

$$F = \left(\cos s \sin \frac{\gamma_{12}}{2} \sin \frac{\gamma_{23}}{2} - \cos \frac{\gamma_{12}}{2} \cos \frac{\gamma_{23}}{2} \right) \sin \theta$$

$$- \left(\cos s \cos \frac{\gamma_{12}}{2} \sin \frac{\gamma_{23}}{2} + \sin \frac{\gamma_{12}}{2} \cos \frac{\gamma_{23}}{2} \right) \cos \theta \qquad (6.36)$$

$$G = -\sin s \sin \frac{\gamma_{23}}{2} \cos \theta \cos \left(\frac{\gamma_{12}}{2} + \theta \right)$$

$$+ \frac{1}{\sin s} \left(\cos s \sin \frac{\gamma_{12}}{2} \cos \frac{\gamma_{23}}{2} + \cos \frac{\gamma_{12}}{2} \sin \frac{\gamma_{23}}{2} \right)$$

Equation (6.35a) can be solved for $\tan p$ or $\tan p_0$, i.e. $\tan p$ can be expressed in terms of p_0, and vice versa:

$$\tan p = \frac{K - E \tan p_0}{F + G \tan p_0} \qquad (6.37)$$

$$\tan p_0 = \frac{K - F \tan p}{E + G \tan p} \qquad (6.38)$$

Now applying the cosine law for sides, equation (A1.9), to $\triangle P_{12} A_2 A_0$, Fig. 6.10, we have, denoting $A_0 A_2$ by ρ_A,

$$\cos \rho_A = \cos p \cos p_0 + \sin p \sin p_0 \cos \frac{\gamma_{12}}{2} \qquad (6.39)$$

Equation (6.39) can be rearranged into the following form:

$$\cos^2 \rho_A (1 + \tan^2 p)(1 + \tan^2 p_0) - \left(1 + \cos \frac{\gamma_{12}}{2} \tan p \tan p_0 \right)^2 = 0 \qquad (6.40)$$

The equation of the locus of the point A_0, the centre-point for a specific radius ρ_A of the circle k_A, can be obtained by eliminating $\tan p$ between equations (6.37) and (6.40)

$$R_M: \quad (1 + \tan^2 p_0)[(G \tan p_0 + F)^2 + (E \tan p_0 - K)^2] \cos^2 \rho_A$$

$$= \left[(E \tan p_0 - K) \tan p_0 \cos \frac{\gamma_{12}}{2} - (G \tan p_0 + F) \right]^2 \qquad (6.41)$$

Equation (6.41) gives the locus of A_0, in its spherical polar coordinates (p_0, θ) for a specific ρ_A. This locus is, by analogy with plane kinematics (Alt, 1921), called the R_M-curve. By substituting the transformation equations (A4.1) into

Fig. 6.11. R_M-curve for a poletriangle of $s = 60°$, $\gamma_{12} = -2 \times 63°$, $\gamma_{23} = -2 \times 75°$ and for $\rho_A = 75°$.

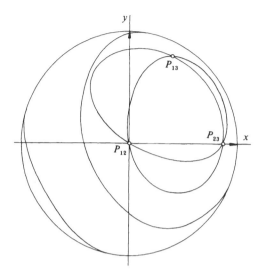

Fig. 6.12. R^1-curve for a poletriangle of $s = 60°$, $\gamma_{12} = -2 \times 63°$, $\gamma_{23} = -2 \times 75°$ and for $\rho_A = 75°$.

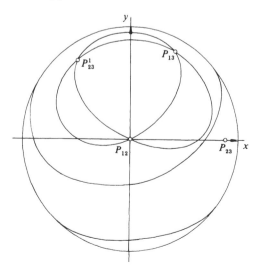

equation (6.41), it can be seen that the R_M-curve is in general a curve of sixth degree in (x_0, y_0, z_0), the coordinates of the point A_0 (see equation (6.85)). Fig. 6.11 shows the R_M-curve for a poletriangle of $s = 60°$, $\gamma_{12} = -2 \times 63°$ and $\gamma_{23} = -2 \times 75°$, for $\rho_A = 75°$. The curve has a double point at each of the three poles P_{12}, P_{23} and P_{13}.

In order to find the locus of A_1 for a specific ρ_A, the equation can be obtained in a similar manner by eliminating $\tan p_0$ between equations (6.38) and (6.40). This gives

$$R^1: \quad (1 + \tan^2 p)[(G \tan p + E)^2 + (F \tan p - K)^2] \cos^2 \rho_A$$

$$= \left[(F \tan p - K) \tan p \cos \frac{\gamma_{12}}{2} - (G \tan p + E) \right]^2 \quad (6.42)$$

The R^1-curve is also a curve of sixth degree, but in (x_{A1}, y_{A1}, z_{A1}), the co-ordinates of the point A_1 (see equation (6.87)). The locus of A_1 on the moving body in position 1 is congruent with the locus of A_2 on the body in position 2, or with the locus of A_3 on the body in position 3. Hence it is, by analogy with plane kinematics, called the R^1-curve (Alt, 1921). It should be noted that, although equation (6.42) is a relation between the length $p = P_{12}A_1$ and θ, the spherical polar coordinates of A_1 are not (p, θ), but $(p, \theta - \gamma_{12}/2)$ with respect to the *spherical origin* P_{12} and spherical polar line $P_{12}P_{23}$. In Fig. 6.12 the R^1-curve is shown for the same poletriangle as for Fig. 6.11 and for $\rho_A = 75°$. It can be seen that the R_M-curve and R^1-curve are symmetrically disposed with respect to the great circle $P_{12}P_{13}$. The R^1-curve has a double point at each of the three poles P_{12}, P_{13} and P_{23}^1, where P_{23}^1 is the mirror image of P_{23} with respect to the great circle $P_{12}P_{13}$.

For a specific value of ρ_A, corresponding points A_0 and A_1 can thus be located with respect to the poletriangle. A second pair of points B_0 and B_1 can also be located, either for the same ρ_A or for another specified spherical radius ρ_B, in a similar manner. The four-bar $A_0A_1B_1B_0$ thus constructed is the linkage which will guide the coupler body through three specified finitely separated positions.

6.3.3   Three homologous points on a great circle

When $\rho_A = 90°$, the three homologous points A_1, A_2, A_3 are on a great circle. The equation of the R_M-curve, equation (6.41), now becomes

$$R_{M90}: \quad E \cos \frac{\gamma_{12}}{2} \tan^2 p_0 - \left(K \cos \frac{\gamma_{12}}{2} + G \right) \tan p_0 - F = 0 \quad (6.43)$$

which, when transformed into the coordinate system x, y, z, is a spherical cubic. Let this cubic be denoted by R_{M90}. The corresponding equation of the R^1-curve, equation (6.42), then becomes

$$R^1_{90}: \quad F\cos\frac{\gamma_{12}}{2}\tan^2 p - \left(K\cos\frac{\gamma_{12}}{2} + G\right)\tan p - E = 0 \qquad (6.44)$$

This is also a spherical cubic, which we denote by R^1_{90}. Fig. 6.13 shows the R_{M90} and R^1_{90} curves for a poletriangle of $s = 60°$, $\gamma_{12} = -2 \times 63°$ and $\gamma_{23} = -2 \times 75°$.

It is interesting to note in this respect the discrepancies between plane kinematics and spherical kinematics. Imagine that the configuration of Fig. 6.10 is in a planar case. It is well-known that if A_1 goes to infinity, A_2 and A_3 also go to infinity, but in different directions. The radius ρ_A goes to infinity as well, and the locus of A_0 is the circumcircle of the poletriangle $\triangle P_{12}P_{23}P_{13}$. However, in spherical kinematics, setting $p = 90°$ and setting $\rho_A = 90°$ are two different things. The condition $p = 90°$ alone is not sufficient to ensure that $\rho_A = 90°$ too, because the point A_3 does not necessarily lie on the great circle determined by A_1 and A_2. This can also be seen algebraically. If we divide both sides of equation (6.42) by $\tan^4 p$ and set $p = 90°$, we get

$$(G^2 + F^2)\cos^2 \rho_A = F^2 \cos^2 (\gamma_{12}/2) \qquad (6.45)$$

It is evident from the above equation that $\cos \rho_A = 0$ only when F vanishes. Similarly the condition $p_0 = 90°$ alone is also not sufficient to ensure that $\rho_A = 90°$.

Fig. 6.13 R_M and R^1-curves for a poletriangle of $s = 60°$, $\gamma_{12} = -2 \times 63°$, $\gamma_{23} = -2 \times 75°$ and for $\rho_A = 90°$.

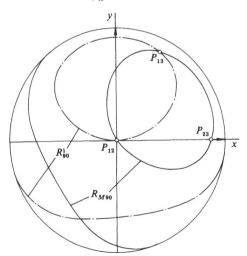

6.4   Three finitely separated positions – algebraic method

In practice the spherical poletriangle may not readily be available. Algebraic methods based on the concept of a displacement matrix have been developed (Suh & Radcliffe, 1967; Dowler *et al.*, 1976). The three positions c_1, c_2, c_3 of a moving body c to be guided are in general given by specifying the locations of the three positions of two points A and B on the unit sphere. As has been shown in the example in Section 6.1.2, the displacement matrix $\mathbb{D}_{12}$ can be found by displacing the coordinates of any two points on the body from position 1 to position 2, and the matrix $\mathbb{D}_{13}$ from the displacement from position 1 to position 3. As will be shown in the following, it is quite sufficient to solve the guidance problem without referring to the poletriangle provided that $\mathbb{D}_{12}$ and $\mathbb{D}_{13}$ are determined.

Conversely, the poletriangle can also easily be determined from the displacement matrices $\mathbb{D}_{12}$ and $\mathbb{D}_{23}$, where $\mathbb{D}_{23}$ is the displacement matrix for the displacement from position 2 to position 3, because the poles P_{12}, P_{23} and the corresponding angles of rotation γ_{12}, γ_{23} are determined, and the spherical distance $s = P_{12}P_{23}$ can be found from the coordinates of P_{12} and P_{23} by means of equation (A3.2).

On the other hand, it is sometimes desirable to form the displacement matrix $\mathbb{D}_{13}$ as a superposition of two successive displacements $\mathbb{D}_{12}$ and $\mathbb{D}_{23}$, provided that P_{12}, γ_{12} and P_{23}, γ_{23} are given, i.e.

$$\mathbb{D}_{13} = \mathbb{D}_{23}\mathbb{D}_{12} \qquad (6.46)$$

It should be noted that all displacement matrices are so formed that the body is always rotated about an axis fixed in space. No reference is made to any coordinate system embedded in the moving body throughout this book.

6.4.1   *Correspondence between centre-point and circle-point*

Suppose the three positions of a body c to be guided are given, and the displacement matrices $\mathbb{D}_{12}, \mathbb{D}_{13}$ are found. Application of $\mathbb{D}_{12}$ to the coordinates of any point A (not necessarily the point for specifying the position of the body c) in A_1 gives those of A in A_2, or

$$\begin{bmatrix} x_{A2} \\ y_{A2} \\ z_{A2} \end{bmatrix} = \mathbb{D}_{12} \begin{bmatrix} x_{A1} \\ y_{A1} \\ z_{A1} \end{bmatrix} \qquad (6.47)$$

and

$$\begin{bmatrix} x_{A3} \\ y_{A3} \\ z_{A3} \end{bmatrix} = \mathbb{D}_{13} \begin{bmatrix} x_{A1} \\ y_{A1} \\ z_{A1} \end{bmatrix} \qquad (6.48)$$

After having computed the coordinates of A_2 and A_3, applying equation (A3.3), the equation of the perpendicular bisector, to A_1A_2 and A_2A_3, or to

A_1A_2 and A_1A_3, results in the conditions to be satisfied by the location of the centre-point A_0 which corresponds to the circle-point A_1. The coordinates of A_0 will be denoted by $A_0(x_0, y_0, z_0)$:

$$(x_{A2} - x_{A1})x_0 + (y_{A2} - y_{A1})y_0 + (z_{A2} - z_{A1})z_0 = 0 \qquad (6.49)$$

$$(x_{A3} - x_{A1})x_0 + (y_{A3} - y_{A1})y_0 + (z_{A3} - z_{A1})z_0 = 0 \qquad (6.50)$$

The form of these equations is exactly the same as that of equation (6.3), hence the ratios x_0/z_0, y_0/z_0 can be solved without difficulty. Substitution of these solutions into the unit sphere equation (A3.1a) gives the coordinates of the corresponding centre-point $A_0(x_0, y_0, z_0)$. Two selected circle-points A_1 and B_1, together with the two corresponding centre-points A_0 and B_0 thus computed, can serve to form a spherical four-bar linkage $A_0A_1B_1B_0$ to guide the body c through three given positions.

When a centre-point A_0 is first selected, it is required to find the corresponding circle-point A_1. The procedure can be carried out by means of an inversion concept, as in the corresponding planar case. In Fig. 6.14, consider A_0 as a point belonging to the body c_2. Bringing the body c_2 back to c_1 will displace A_0 to a position A_{02}^1, whose coordinates will be denoted by $A_{02}^1(x_{02}^1, y_{02}^1, z_{02}^1)$. They can be computed from

$$\begin{bmatrix} x_{02}^1 \\ y_{02}^1 \\ z_{02}^1 \end{bmatrix} = \mathbb{D}_{21} \begin{bmatrix} x_0 \\ y_0 \\ z_0 \end{bmatrix}$$

where

$$\mathbb{D}_{21} = \mathbb{D}_{12}^{-1} = \mathbb{D}_{12}^{\mathrm{T}}$$

Next consider A_0 as a point belonging to the body c_3. Again bringing c_3 back to c_1 will displace A_0 to a position A_{03}^1, whose coordinates will be denoted by

Fig. 6.14. Determination of A_1 by inversion when A_0 is given.

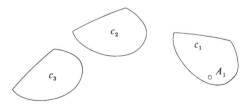

$A_{03}^1(x_{03}^1, y_{03}^1, z_{03}^1)$, and

$$\begin{bmatrix} x_{03}^1 \\ y_{03}^1 \\ z_{03}^1 \end{bmatrix} = \mathbb{D}_{31} \begin{bmatrix} x_0 \\ y_0 \\ x_0 \end{bmatrix}$$

where

$$\mathbb{D}_{31} = \mathbb{D}_{13}^{-1} = \mathbb{D}_{13}^{T}$$

Having found the coordinates of A_{02}^1 and A_{03}^1, the coordinates of A_1 can be found as the centre of the spherical circle passing through the three points A_0, A_{02}^1 and A_{03}^1. This is done by solving a system of two equations similar to equations (6.49) and (6.50), where the coordinates of A_1, A_2, A_3 are replaced respectively by those of A_0, A_{02}^1, A_{03}^1.

In fact the above mentioned inversion concept may be ignored. Since the elements of $\mathbb{D}_{12}$ and $\mathbb{D}_{13}$ are all known, substitution of equations (6.47) and (6.48) into equations (6.49) and (6.50) results in two linear equations in the unknowns x_{A1}, y_{A1}, z_{A1}, if the coordinates of $A_0(x_0, y_0, z_0)$ are given. These equations are exactly the same as the equations obtained from the inversion concept. It is interesting to note that, in this respect, the formulation of the relation between the coordinates of a centre-point and those of the corresponding circle-point is much simpler than in the corresponding planar case. However, a similar inversion concept will be of use in path generation problems (see Section 7.3.1).

In order to facilitate computation, for a given location of A_1, we shall rewrite equations (6.49) and (6.50) in terms of the elements of $\mathbb{D}_{12}$ and $\mathbb{D}_{13}$. Upon substitution of equations (6.47) and (6.48) into equations (6.49) and (6.50) we obtain

$$G_2 x_0 + S_2 y_0 + T_2 z_0 = 0 \tag{6.51}$$

$$G_3 x_0 + S_3 y_0 + T_3 z_0 = 0 \tag{6.52}$$

where

$$G_i = (d_{11i} - 1)x_{A1} + d_{12i}y_{A1} + d_{13i}z_{A1} \tag{6.53}$$

$$S_i = d_{21i}x_{A1} + (d_{22i} - 1)y_{A1} + d_{23i}z_{A1} \tag{6.54}$$

$$T_i = d_{31i}x_{A1} + d_{32i}y_{A1} + (d_{33i} - 1)z_{A1} \tag{6.55}$$

Here the symbols $d_{11i}, d_{12i}, \ldots$ are used to distinguish the elements of $\mathbb{D}_{12}$ from those of $\mathbb{D}_{13}$, i.e.

$$\mathbb{D}_{1i} = \begin{bmatrix} d_{11i} & d_{12i} & d_{13i} \\ d_{21i} & d_{22i} & d_{23i} \\ d_{31i} & d_{32i} & d_{33i} \end{bmatrix} \tag{6.56}$$

Simiarly for a given location of A_0, equations (6.51) and (6.52) can also be written as

$$L_2 x_{A1} + Q_2 y_{A1} + H_2 z_{A1} = 0 \tag{6.57}$$
$$L_3 x_{A1} + Q_3 y_{A1} + H_3 z_{A1} = 0 \tag{6.58}$$

where

$$L_i = (d_{11i} - 1)x_0 + d_{21i} y_0 + d_{31i} z_0 \tag{6.59}$$
$$Q_i = d_{12i} x_0 + (d_{22i} - 1)y_0 + d_{32i} z_0 \tag{6.60}$$
$$H_i = d_{13i} x_0 + d_{23i} y_0 + (d_{33i} - 1)z_0 \tag{6.61}$$

Expressions for G_i, S_i, T_i and L_i, Q_i, H_i in a selected coordinate system for a given poletriangle will be given in Section 6.4.3.

The solutions of equations (6.51) and (6.52), i.e. the coordinates of the centre-point A_0 for a given circle-point A_1, are

$$\frac{x_0}{z_0} = \frac{F_1}{F_3} \tag{6.62}$$

and

$$\frac{y_0}{z_0} = \frac{F_2}{F_3} \tag{6.63}$$

where

$$F_1 = S_2 T_3 - S_3 T_2, \quad F_2 = T_2 G_3 - T_3 G_2, \quad F_3 = G_2 S_3 - G_3 S_2 \tag{6.64}$$

The solutions of equations (6.57) and (6.58), i.e. the coordinates of the circle-point A_1 for a given centre-point A_0, are

$$\frac{x_{A1}}{z_{A1}} = \frac{W_1}{W_3} \tag{6.65}$$

and

$$\frac{y_{A1}}{z_{A1}} = \frac{W_2}{W_3} \tag{6.66}$$

where

$$W_1 = Q_2 H_3 - Q_3 H_2, \quad W_2 = H_2 L_3 - H_3 L_2, \quad W_3 = L_2 Q_3 - L_3 Q_2 \tag{6.67}$$

6.4.2 R_M and R^1-curves

The loci of A_0 and A_1 for a prescribed spherical radius $\rho_A(= A_0 A_1)$ are called, respectively, the R_M and R^1-curves, as mentioned in Section 6.3.2. The spherical radius ρ_A is determined by the locations of A_0 and A_1, according to equation (A3.2),

$$x_{A1} x_0 + y_{A1} y_0 + z_{A1} z_0 = \cos \rho_A \tag{6.68}$$

Equations (6.57), (6.58) and (6.68) constitute a system of nonhomogeneous linear equations in the unknowns x_{A1}, y_{A1}, z_{A1} if x_0, y_0, z_0 are considered as given. Solving these equations and substituting the expressions for x_{A1}, y_{A1}, z_{A1}

into the unit sphere equation (A3.1) $x_{A1}^2 + y_{A1}^2 + z_{A1}^2 = 1$, results in the following equation of the R_M-curve:

$$R_M: \quad (W_1 x_0 + W_2 y_0 + W_3 z_0)^2 - (W_1^2 + W_2^2 + W_3^2)\cos^2 \rho_A = 0 \quad (6.69)$$

Equation (6.69) is a spherical curve of sixth degree, an example of which has already been shown in Fig. 6.11.

Equations (6.51), (6.52) and (6.68) also constitute a system of nonhomogeneous linear equations, but in the unknowns x_0, y_0, z_0 if x_{A1}, y_{A1}, z_{A1} are considered as given. Solving these equations for x_0, y_0, z_0 and substituting their expressions into the unit sphere equation (A3.1) $x_0^2 + y_0^2 + z_0^2 = 1$ results in the following equation of the R^1-curve:

$$R^1: \quad (F_1 x_{A1} + F_2 y_{A1} + F_3 z_{A1})^2 - (F_1^2 + F_2^2 + F_3^2)\cos^2 \rho_A = 0 \quad (6.70)$$

Equation (6.70) is also a spherical curve of sixth degree, but in x_{A1}, y_{A1}, z_{A1}, an example of which has already been shown in Fig. 6.12.

6.4.3   Selection of coordinate system

It is to be noted that the initial position of the fixed coordinate system xyz, relative to which a body is to be guided, can be chosen at our discretion. Although all computing tasks can be left to a computer, a suitable choice of the position of the xyz-system will not only greatly simplify the elements of the displacement matrices $\mathbb{D}_{12}$ and $\mathbb{D}_{13}$, but will also result in a clear picture of the curve, such as that shown in Fig. 6.11 or that in Fig. 6.12. The position of the xyz-system is oriented in two steps:

(1) The z-axis is chosen to coincide with the pole-axis OP_{12}. This causes the displacement matrix $\mathbb{D}_{12}$ to become

$$\mathbb{D}_{12} = \begin{bmatrix} C_{\gamma 12} & -S_{\gamma 12} & 0 \\ S_{\gamma 12} & C_{\gamma 12} & 0 \\ 0 & 0 & 1 \end{bmatrix} \quad (6.71)$$

with the abbreviations $S_{\gamma 12} = \sin \gamma_{12}$ and $C_{\gamma 12} = \cos \gamma_{12}$.

(2) Secondly, the position of the x-axis is chosen such that the pole-axis OP_{23} (the axis OP_{23} is in the fixed shell) lies on the xz-plane, with P_{23} having a positive x-coordinate. The matrix $\mathbb{D}_{13}$ in equation (6.46) then becomes

$$\mathbb{D}_{13} = \mathbb{D}_{23}\mathbb{D}_{12} =$$

$$\begin{bmatrix} C_{\gamma 12}(S_s^2 V_{\gamma 23} + C_{\gamma 23}) - S_{\gamma 12}C_s S_{\gamma 23}, & -S_{\gamma 12}(S_s^2 V_{\gamma 23} + C_{\gamma 23}) - C_{\gamma 12}C_s S_{\gamma 23}, & S_s C_s V_{\gamma 23} \\ C_{\gamma 12}C_s S_{\gamma 23} + S_{\gamma 12}C_{\gamma 23}, & -S_{\gamma 12}C_s S_{\gamma 23} + C_{\gamma 12}C_{\gamma 23}, & -S_s S_{\gamma 23} \\ C_{\gamma 12}S_s C_s V_{\gamma 23} + S_{\gamma 12}S_s S_{\gamma 23}, & -S_{\gamma 12}S_s C_s V_{\gamma 23} + C_{\gamma 12}S_s S_{\gamma 23}, & C_s^2 V_{\gamma 23} + C_{\gamma 23} \end{bmatrix}$$

$$(6.72)$$

where $S_s = \sin s$, $C_s = \cos s$, $V_{\gamma 23} = \text{vers } \gamma_{23}$.

It is to be noted that, if the known positions of a moving body are specified by the locations of its two points, but with coordinates referring to a coordinate system other than the selected one, that coordinate system has first to be rotated to the selected position before applying the matrices of equations (6.71) and (6.72). In the following it will be assumed, unless otherwise specified, that the coordinate system xyz is selected as mentioned above, although some equations are applicable even if the step (2) is not carried out. With the coordinate system so selected, some of the expressions for L_i, Q_i, H_i and G_i, S_i, T_i are considerably simplified. These are listed below. For each term the first expression is in terms of the elements of the displacement matrices, and is applicable if only step (1) is carried out, and the second expression on the right is derived from equations (6.71) and (6.72), on the assumption that both steps (1) and (2) are carried out.

$$L_2 = (d_{112} - 1)x_0 + d_{212}y_0 = -V_{\gamma 12}x_0 + S_{\gamma 12}y_0 \qquad (6.73), (6.73a)$$

$$Q_2 = d_{122}x_0 + (d_{222} - 1)y_0 = -S_{\gamma 12}x_0 - V_{\gamma 12}y_0 \qquad (6.74), (6.74a)$$

$$H_2 = 0 \qquad (6.75)$$

$$L_3 = (d_{113} - 1)x_0 + d_{213}y_0 + d_{313}z_0$$
$$= [C_{\gamma 12}(S_s^2 V_{\gamma 23} + C_{\gamma 23}) - S_{\gamma 12}C_s S_{\gamma 23} - 1]x_0$$
$$+ (C_{\gamma 12}C_s S_{\gamma 23} + S_{\gamma 12}C_{\gamma 23})y_0$$
$$+ (C_{\gamma 12}S_s C_s V_{\gamma 23} + S_{\gamma 12}S_s S_{\gamma 23})z_0 \qquad (6.76), (6.76a)$$

$$Q_3 = d_{123}x_0 + (d_{223} - 1)y_0 + d_{323}z_0$$
$$= [-S_{\gamma 12}(S_s^2 V_{\gamma 23} + C_{\gamma 23}) - C_{\gamma 12}C_s S_{\gamma 23}]x_0$$
$$+ (-S_{\gamma 12}C_s S_{\gamma 23} + C_{\gamma 12}C_{\gamma 23} - 1)y_0$$
$$+ (-S_{\gamma 12}S_s C_s V_{\gamma 23} + C_{\gamma 12}S_s S_{\gamma 23})z_0 \qquad (6.77), (6.77a)$$

$$H_3 = d_{133}x_0 + d_{233}y_0 + (d_{333} - 1)z_0$$
$$= S_s C_s V_{\gamma 23}x_0 - S_s S_{\gamma 23}y_0 - S_s^2 V_{\gamma 23}z_0 \qquad (6.78), (6.78a)$$

$$G_2 = (d_{112} - 1)x_{A1} + d_{122}y_{A1} + d_{132}z_{A1}$$
$$= -V_{\gamma 12}x_{A1} - S_{\gamma 12}y_{A1} \qquad (6.79), (6.79a)$$

$$S_2 = d_{212}x_{A1} + (d_{222} - 1)y_{A1} + d_{232}z_{A1}$$
$$= S_{\gamma 12}x_{A1} - V_{\gamma 12}y_{A1} \qquad (6.80), (6.80a)$$

$$T_2 = 0 \qquad (6.81)$$

$$G_3 = (d_{113} - 1)x_{A1} + d_{123}y_{A1} + d_{133}z_{A1}$$
$$= [C_{\gamma 12}(S_s^2 V_{\gamma 23} + C_{\gamma 23}) - S_{\gamma 12}C_s S_{\gamma 23} - 1]x_{A1}$$
$$- [S_{\gamma 12}(S_s^2 V_{\gamma 23} + C_{\gamma 23}) + C_{\gamma 12}C_s S_{\gamma 23}]y_{A1}$$
$$+ S_s C_s V_{\gamma 23}z_{A1} \qquad (6.82), (6.82a)$$

$$S_3 = d_{213}x_{A1} + (d_{223} - 1)y_{A1} + d_{233}z_{A1}$$
$$= (C_{\gamma12}C_sS_{\gamma23} + S_{\gamma12}C_{\gamma23})x_{A1}$$
$$+ (-S_{\gamma12}C_sS_{\gamma23} + C_{\gamma12}C_{\gamma23} - 1)y_{A1}$$
$$- S_sS_{\gamma23}z_{A1} \qquad (6.83),(6.83a)$$

$$T_3 = d_{313}x_{A1} + d_{323}y_{A1} + (d_{333} - 1)z_{A1}$$
$$= (C_{\gamma12}S_sC_sV_{\gamma23} + S_{\gamma12}S_sS_{\gamma23})x_{A1}$$
$$+ (-S_{\gamma12}S_sC_sV_{\gamma23} + C_{\gamma12}S_sS_{\gamma23})y_{A1}$$
$$- S_s^2V_{\gamma23}z_{A1} \qquad (6.84),(6.84a)$$

The equation of the R_M-curve, equation (6.69), now becomes, if only step (1) is carried out,

$$R_M: \quad [-(x_0^2 + y_0^2)S_{\gamma12}H_3 + W_3z_0]^2$$
$$- [2(x_0^2 + y_0^2)V_{\gamma12}H_3^2 + W_3^2]\cos^2\rho_A = 0 \qquad (6.85)$$

where, if step (2) is also carried out,

$$W_3 = -C_s(C_sS_{\gamma12}V_{\gamma23} + S_{\gamma23}V_{\gamma12})x_0^2 - (C_sS_{\gamma23}V_{\gamma12} + S_{\gamma12}V_{\gamma23})y_0^2$$
$$- S_s^2V_{\gamma12}V_{\gamma23}x_0y_0 + S_s(S_{\gamma12}S_{\gamma23} - C_sV_{\gamma12}V_{\gamma23})y_0z_0$$
$$+ S_s(V_{\gamma12}S_{\gamma23} + S_{\gamma12}C_sV_{\gamma23})x_0z_0 \qquad (6.86)$$

and equation (6.70), the equation of the R^1-curve, becomes, if only step (1) is carried out,

$$R^1: \quad [(x_{A1}^2 + y_{A1}^2)S_{\gamma12}T_3 + F_3z_{A1}]^2$$
$$- [2(x_{A1}^2 + y_{A1}^2)V_{\gamma12}T_3^2 + F_3^2]\cos^2\rho_A = 0 \qquad (6.87)$$

where, if step (2) is also carried out,

$$F_3 = [V_{\gamma12}C_sS_{\gamma23} + S_{\gamma12}V_{\gamma23}(C_s^2C_{\gamma12} - V_{\gamma12})]x_{A1}^2$$
$$+ [S_{\gamma12}V_{\gamma23} + V_{\gamma12}(C_sS_{\gamma23} - S_{\gamma12}S_s^2V_{\gamma23})]y_{A1}^2$$
$$+ S_s^2(1 + 2C_{\gamma12})V_{\gamma12}V_{\gamma23}x_{A1}y_{A1}$$
$$+ S_s(S_{\gamma12}S_{\gamma23} + V_{\gamma12}C_sV_{\gamma23})y_{A1}z_{A1}$$
$$+ S_s(V_{\gamma12}S_{\gamma23} - S_{\gamma12}C_sV_{\gamma23})x_{A1}z_{A1} \qquad (6.88)$$

Example: With the coordinate system chosen as explained, the equation of the R_M-curve shown in Fig. 6.11 becomes, according to equation (6.85),

$$[0.809017(x_0^2 + y_0^2)H_3 + W_3z_0]^2$$
$$- [3.175571(x_0^2 + y_0^2)H_3^2 + W_3^2]\cos^2\rho_A = 0$$

where

$$H_3 = 0.808013x_0 + 0.433013y_0 - 1.399519z_0$$

and

$$W_3 = 0.774358x_0^2 + 1.906593y_0^2 - 2.222136x_0y_0$$
$$- 0.932636y_0z_0 - 1.341227x_0z_0$$

The equation of the R^1-curve shown in Fig. 6.12 becomes, according to equation (6.87),

$$[-0.809017(x_{A1}^2 + y_{A1}^2)T_3 + F_3 z_{A1}]^2$$
$$- [3.175571(x_{A1}^2 + y_{A1}^2)T_3^2 + F_3^2]\cos^2 \rho_A = 0$$

where

$$T_3 = -0.124623 x_{A1} + 0.908215 y_{A1} - 1.399519 z_{A1}$$

and

$$F_3 = -2.572104 x_{A1}^2 - 0.108847 y_{A1}^2 - 0.390142 x_{A1} y_{A1}$$
$$+ 1.633265 y_{A1} z_{A1} - 0.033835 x_{A1} z_{A1}$$

6.4.4 Three homologous points on a great circle

When the three homologous points A_1, A_2, A_3 lie on a great circle, the locus of the centre point A_0 is a special case of the R_M-curve. Simply setting $\cos \rho_A = 0$ in equation (6.69) gives

$$W_1 x_0 + W_2 y_0 + W_3 z_0 = 0 \tag{6.89}$$

which, when expressed in coordinates of the chosen coordinate system, becomes, according to equation (6.85),

$$(x_0^2 + y_0^2)S_{\gamma 12}H_3 - W_3 z_0 = 0 \tag{6.90}$$

Substituting equations (6.59), (6.60), (6.61) and (6.67) into equation (6.90) changes the latter into the form

$$R_{M90}: \quad n_1 y_0^3 + n_2 x_0 y_0^2 + n_3 x_0^2 y_0 + n_4 x_0^3 + n_7 y_0^2 z_0 + n_8 x_0 y_0 z_0$$
$$+ n_9 x_0^2 z_0 + n_5 y_0 z_0^2 + n_6 x_0 z_0^2 = 0 \tag{6.90a}$$

Expressions for $n_1, n_2, \ldots, n_9$ are given in Appendix 6. After transformation into spherical polar coordinates by means of equations (A4.2), equation (6.90a) becomes, with the spherical polar coordinates of A_0 denoted by $A_0(p_0, \theta_0)$,

$$R_{M90}: \quad N_2 \tan^2 p_0 + N_1 \tan p_0 + N_0 = 0 \tag{6.91}$$

where the expressions for N_2, N_1 and N_0 are also listed in Appendix 6. The general R_M-curve of sixth degree now reduces to a spherical cubic, which is denoted here by R_{M90}. An example has been shown in Fig. 6.13.

The equation of the corresponding locus of A_1 is then a special case of the R^1-curve. From equation (6.70) this is

$$F_1 x_{A1} + F_2 y_{A1} + F_3 z_{A1} = 0 \tag{6.92}$$

which in the selected coordinate system, according to equation (6.87), becomes

$$(x_{A1}^2 + y_{A1}^2)S_{\gamma 12}T_3 + F_3 z_{A1} = 0 \tag{6.93}$$

Substitution of equations (6.53), (6.54), (6.55) and (6.64) into equation (6.93) changes the latter into the form

$$R_{90}^1: \quad c_1 y_{A1}^3 + c_2 x_{A1} y_{A1}^2 + c_3 x_{A1}^2 y_{A1} + c_4 x_{A1}^3 + c_7 y_{A1}^2 z_{A1}$$
$$+ c_8 x_{A1} y_{A1} z_{A1} + c_9 x_{A1}^2 z_{A1} + c_5 y_{A1} z_{A1}^2 + c_6 x_{A1} z_{A1}^2 = 0 \qquad (6.93a)$$

Expressions for $c_1, c_2, \ldots, c_9$ are also given in Apendix 6. Expressed in spherical polar coordinates, equation (6.93a) becomes, with the spherical polar coordinates of A_1 denoted by $A_1(p_{A1}, \theta_{A1})$,

$$R_{90}^1: \quad C_2 \tan^2 p_{A1} + C_1 \tan p_{A1} + C_0 = 0 \qquad (6.94)$$

Expressions for the coefficients C_2, C_1 and C_0 are also given in Appendix 6. The general R^1-curve of sixth degree also reduces to a spherical cubic, which is denoted here by R_{90}^1. An example has also been shown in Fig. 6.13.

6.5   Three infinitesimally separated positions

When the three positions of a body are infinitesimally separated, the foregoing relations mentioned in preceding sections for three finitely separated positions take special forms, some of which have already been discussed in Chapter 5, on instantaneous kinematics of a moving body.

6.5.1   *Geometrical considerations*

For three infinitesimally separated positions 1, 2, 3 of a moving body, we may write $\gamma_{12} = d\gamma^\dagger$, $\gamma_{23} = d\gamma + d^2\gamma$ and $s = P_{12}P_{23} = ds$. Substituting these expressions into equations (6.36), and noting that $\sin ds \approx ds$, $\cos ds \approx 1$, $\sin d\gamma/2 \approx d\gamma/2$, $\cos d\gamma/2 \approx 1$, $\sin[(d\gamma + d^2\gamma)/2] \approx (d\gamma + d^2\gamma)/2$, $\cos[(d\gamma + d^2\gamma)/2] \approx 1$, we get, neglecting higher order terms,

$$\left. \begin{aligned}
K &= -\frac{ds\, d\gamma}{2} \approx 0 \\[2mm]
E &= \sin\theta - \frac{d\gamma + d^2\gamma}{2}\cos\theta \approx \sin\theta \\[2mm]
F &= \left[\frac{d\gamma(d\gamma + d^2\gamma)}{4} - 1\right]\sin\theta - \left(\frac{d\gamma + d^2\gamma}{2} + \frac{d\gamma}{2}\right)\cos\theta \approx -\sin\theta \\[2mm]
G &= -ds\frac{d\gamma + d^2\gamma}{2}\cos^2\theta + \frac{1}{ds}\left(\frac{d\gamma}{2} + \frac{d\gamma + d^2\gamma}{2}\right) \approx \frac{d\gamma}{ds}
\end{aligned} \right\}$$

$$(6.95)$$

Note that $G = d\gamma/ds = (d\gamma/dt)/(ds/dt) = \omega/u = -1/\Theta$, as defined in Section 5.4. Consequently equation (6.35a) becomes

$$\frac{\sin\theta}{\tan p} - \frac{\sin\theta}{\tan p_0} = \frac{1}{\Theta}$$

---

† Not to be confused with the infinitesimal increment of $\sphericalangle A_0 RA$ shown in Fig. 2.3 or 4.2(a). Note that $\sphericalangle A_0 RA$ there always carries a definite magnitude.

This equation is exactly equivalent to equation (5.42), the spherical version of the Euler–Savary equation that has been derived before.

The spherical radius ρ_A of the circle passing through the three homologous points A_1, A_2, A_3 now becomes the spherical radius of curvature of the path of a moving point A. The locus of $A_0(p_0, \theta)$, the centre of curvature of the path of the moving point A, for a prescribed value of ρ_A, will be called, as in plane kinematics (Alt, 1932a), the ρ_M-curve. Its equation can be obtained by substituting equations (6.95) into equation (6.41),

$$\rho_M: \quad (\Theta \sin \theta + \sin p_0 \cos p_0)^2$$
$$- (\Theta^2 \sin^2 \theta + 2\Theta \sin \theta \sin p_0 \cos p_0 + \sin^2 p_0) \cos^2 \rho_A = 0 \quad (6.96)$$

Equation (6.96) is identical with equation (5.50). The corresponding loci of A_1, A_2 and A_3, becoming a single locus of the moving point A, will then be called, also as in plane kinematics, the ρ-curve. Its equation is obtained by substituting equations (6.95) into equation (6.42),

$$\rho: \quad (\Theta \sin \theta - \sin p \cos p)^2$$
$$- (\Theta^2 \sin^2 \theta - 2\Theta \sin \theta \sin p \cos p + \sin^2 p) \cos^2 \rho_A = 0 \quad (6.97)$$

Equation (6.97) is identical with equation (5.46). It can be seen that both the ρ_M-curve and ρ-curve are symmetrical with respect to the polenormal great circle. Furthermore, the ρ-curve is a mirror image of the ρ_M-curve with respect to the poletangent great circle. Characteristics of the ρ-curve and the distribution of the $\sin \rho$ value can be found in (Meyer zur Capellen, 1983a, b, c). The equation of the inflection curve is obtained by setting $\cos \rho_A = 0$ in equation (6.97), or $\Theta \sin \theta - \sin p \cos p = 0$, which is identical with equation (5.48). Similarly the equation of the return curve is obtained by setting $\cos \rho_A = 0$ in equation (6.96), or $\Theta \sin \theta + \sin p_0 \cos p_0 = 0$, which is identical with equation (5.51a).

6.5.2 Algebraic formulations

Now in the case of three infinitesimally separated positions of a moving body, in which the three quantities γ_{12}, γ_{23} and s become infinitesimally small, we write $\gamma_{12} = d\gamma$, $\gamma_{23} = d\gamma + d^2\gamma$ and $s = ds$ as before, and use the approximations $\sin d\gamma \approx d\gamma$, $\sin(d\gamma + d^2\gamma) \approx d\gamma + d^2\gamma$, $\cos d\gamma \approx \cos(d\gamma + d^2\gamma) \approx 1 - d\gamma^2/2$, vers $d\gamma \approx d\gamma^2/2$[†], and $\sin ds \approx ds$, $\cos ds \approx 1$. The selected

---

[†] In arranging terms to obtain equations (6.85)–(6.88), the identity $\sin^2 \gamma_{12} + \cos^2 \gamma_{12} \equiv 1$ has been applied. Thus the approximations $\sin d\gamma \approx d\gamma$, $\cos d\gamma \approx 1$ would mean that the term $d\gamma^2$ is neglected. In order to comply with this identity to avoid erroneous results, it is justifiable in the present case to use the approximations $\cos d\gamma \approx 1 - d\gamma^2/2$ and vers $d\gamma \approx d\gamma^2/2$, while in cases where only two infinitesimally separated positions are involved, the approximations $\cos d\gamma \approx 1$ and vers $d\gamma \approx 0$ are still justified.

coordinate system becomes the so-called canonical system (Veldkamp, 1967a). The displacement matrices in the present case, according to equations (6.71) and (6.72), after neglecting higher orders, are

$$\mathbb{D}_{12} = \begin{bmatrix} 1 - d\gamma^2/2, & -d\gamma, & 0 \\ d\gamma, & 1 - d\gamma^2/2, & 0 \\ 0 & 0 & 1 \end{bmatrix} \qquad (6.98)$$

$$\mathbb{D}_{13} = \begin{bmatrix} 1 - 2d\gamma^2, & -2d\gamma - d^2\gamma, & 0 \\ 2d\gamma + d^2\gamma, & 1 - 2d\gamma^2, & -ds\,d\gamma \\ 3ds\,d\gamma^2/2, & ds(d\gamma + d^2\gamma), & 1 \end{bmatrix} \qquad (6.99)$$

The equation of the R_M-curve, equation (6.85), now reduces to

$$[ds\,y_0 - d\gamma(x_0^2 + y_0^2)z_0]^2 - \{ds^2 y_0^2 + d\gamma(x_0^2 + y_0^2)$$
$$\cdot [d\gamma(x_0^2 + y_0^2) - 2ds\,y_0 z_0]\}\cos^2 \rho_A = 0 \qquad (6.100)$$

Transforming the rectangular coordinates of the point $A_0(x_0, y_0, z_0)$ into its spherical polar coordinates $A_0(p_0, \theta)$ by means of equations (A4.2), equation (6.100) becomes equation (6.96). The equation of the return curve in rectangular Cartesian coordinates is obtained simply by equating the first bracket on the left-hand side of equation (6.100) to zero, or

$$(x_0^2 + y_0^2)z_0 + \Theta y_0 = 0$$

which is equation (5.54).

Similarly the corresponding R^1-curve reduces, upon substitution of these approximations into equation (6.87), to the so-called ρ-curve,

$$[ds y_A + d\gamma(x_A^2 + y_A^2)z_A]^2$$
$$- \{ds^2 y_A^2 + d\gamma(x_A^2 + y_A^2)[d\gamma(x_A^2 + y_A^2) + 2ds y_A z_A]\}\cos^2 \rho_A = 0 \qquad (6.101)$$

Again transforming the rectangular coordinates of $A(x_A, y_A, z_A)$ into its spherical polar coordinates $A(p, \theta)$ by means of equations (A4.2), equation (6.101) becomes equation (6.97). The equation of the inflection curve in rectangular coordinates is then obtained by equating the first bracket on the left-hand side of equation (6.101) to zero, which is equation (5.53).

6.6   Three multiply separated positions

In order to distinguish two infinitesimally separated positions from two finitely separated positions, Tesar (1967) suggested using the symbol P to denote a single position. Thus, $P–P$ represents two finitely separated positions, and PP represents two infinitesimally separated positions. In addition to this, the subscripts $1, 2, \ldots$ will be used to indicate definite single positions. For three positions, between the cases $P_1–P_2–P_3$ and $P_1 P_2 P_3$ there are two intermediate cases, namely $P_1 P_2 – P_3$ and $P_1 – P_2 P_3$. All these four cases are termed by Tesar multiply separated positions, in order to treat thèm in a unified way. In fact, general equations have been derived for three multiply separated positions (Dowler *et al.*, 1976). We shall deal here only with the two cases $P_1P_2-P_3$ and $P_1-P_2P_3$. Geometrically there is no difference between these two cases, as will be seen by exchanging P_1 with P_3. The algebraic formulations for these two cases, however, are not quite the same, because of the selection of the position of the coordinate system.

6.6.1   *The case $P_1P_2-P_3$*

In this case, the poles P_{23} and P_{13} coincide, and the angle of rotation γ_{12} becomes infinitesimally small, which we shall write $\gamma_{12} = d\gamma$. However, the angle of rotation γ_{23} and the spherical distance $s = P_{12}P_{23}$, as shown in Fig. 6.15(*a*), remain finite. With the approximations $\sin d\gamma \approx d\gamma$, $\cos d\gamma \approx 1$, the displacement matrix $\mathbb{D}_{12}$ in equation (6.71) becomes

$$\mathbb{D}_{12} = \begin{bmatrix} 1 & -d\gamma & 0 \\ d\gamma & 1 & 0 \\ 0 & 0 & 1 \end{bmatrix} \tag{6.102}$$

Note that the coefficients in equations (6.73)–(6.84) are all elements of the matrix $\mathbb{D}_{12} - \mathbb{I}$ or of $\mathbb{D}_{13} - \mathbb{I}$, where $\mathbb{I}$ is the unit matrix. In the present case we have

$$\mathbb{D}_{12} - \mathbb{I} = \begin{bmatrix} 0 & -d\gamma & 0 \\ d\gamma & 0 & 0 \\ 0 & 0 & 0 \end{bmatrix} \tag{6.103}$$

The equation of the R_M-curve, equation (6.85), becomes

$$R_M\colon \quad [-(x_0^2 + y_0^2)H_3 + W_3^*z_0]^2 - W_3^{*2}\cos^2\rho_A = 0 \tag{6.104}$$

where the expressions for H_3 remain unchanged as given by equation (6.78), and $W_3^* = W_3/d\gamma = Q_3y_0 + L_3x_0$ with Q_3 and L_3 given by equations (6.77)

Fig. 6.15. Situation of poles. (*a*) Case $P_1P_2-P_3$. (*b*) Case $P_1-P_2P_3$.

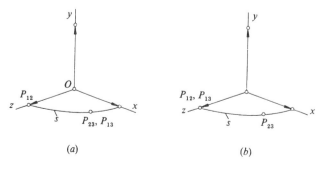

(*a*) (*b*)

and (6.76) if the elements of matrix $\mathbb{D}_{13}$ are known, or

$$W_3^* = W_3/d\gamma = -C_s^2 V_{\gamma 23} x_0^2 - V_{\gamma 23} y_0^2 + S_s S_{\gamma 23} y_0 z_0 + S_s C_s V_{\gamma 23} x_0 z_0$$
(6.105)

The equation of the locus of the centre-point A_0 for three homologous points A_1, A_2, A_3 on a great circle is

$$R_{M90}: \quad -(x_0^2 + y_0^2)H_3 + W_3^* z_0 = 0$$
(6.106)

or

$$-(x_0^2 + y_0^2)H_3 + (Q_3 y_0 + L_3 x_0)z_0 = 0$$
(6.106a)

The equation of the R^1-curve, equation (6.87), now becomes

$$R^1: \quad [(x_{A1}^2 + y_{A1}^2)T_3 + F_3^* z_{A1}]^2 - F_3^{*2} \cos^2 \rho_A = 0$$
(6.107)

where T_3 can be found from the elements of the matrix $\mathbb{D}_{13}$ from equation (6.84) or

$$T_3 = S_s C_s V_{\gamma 23} x_{A1} + S_s S_{\gamma 23} y_{A1} - S_s^2 V_{\gamma 23} z_{A1}$$

and $F_3^* = F_3/d\gamma = -S_3 y_{A1} - G_3 x_{A1}$ with S_3 and G_3 given by equations (6.83) and (6.82) if the elements of the matrix $\mathbb{D}_{13}$ are known, or

$$F_3^* = F_3/d\gamma = C_s^2 V_{\gamma 23} x_{A1}^2 + V_{\gamma 23} y_{A1}^2 + S_s S_{\gamma 23} y_{A1} z_{A1}$$
$$- S_s C_s V_{\gamma 23} x_{A1} z_{A1}$$
(6.108)

The equation of the locus of A_1 for three homologous points A_1, A_2, A_3 on a great circle is

$$R_{90}^1: \quad (x_{A1}^2 + y_{A1}^2)T_3 + F_3^* z_{A1} = 0$$
(6.109)

Fig. 6.16.

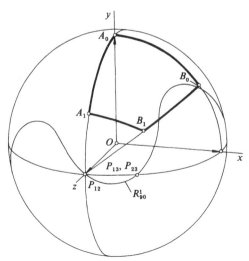

or
$$(x_{A1}^2 + y_{A1}^2)T_3 - (S_3 y_{A1} + G_3 x_{A1})z_{A1} = 0 \qquad (6.109a)$$

Note that the angular velocity is not involved in these equations. The equations (6.106) and (6.109) are symmetrical with respect to the xz-plane. The geometrical meaning of this case is that the location of the instantaneous pole P_{12} and a subsequent finite displacement $\mathbb{D}_{13}$ are prescribed.

Example: It is required to guide a body so that (1) it rotates instantaneously about the z-axis and then (2) it rotates about the axis OP_{23} through an angle of $\gamma_{23} = -75°$, where $s = P_{12}P_{23} = 28°$.

Choose, for instance, the coordinates of the fixed points A_0 and B_0 in the xy-plane, Fig. 6.16, such that A_0 is at $(0, 1, 0)$ and B_0 at $(0.8, 0.6, 0)$. Now according to equations (6.65), (6.66), (6.67) and (6.73a)–(6.76a),

$$\frac{x_{A1}}{z_{A1}} = \frac{-x_{A0}H_{3A0}}{W_{3A0}^*}, \quad \frac{y_{A1}}{z_{A1}} = \frac{-y_{A0}H_{3A0}}{W_{3A0}^*}$$

from which we obtain $x_{A1} = 0$, $y_{A1} = 0.521895$, $z_{A1} = 0.853010$, and

$$\frac{x_{B1}}{z_{B1}} = \frac{-x_{B0}H_{3B0}}{W_{3B0}^*}, \quad \frac{y_{B1}}{z_{B1}} = \frac{-y_{B0}H_{3B0}}{W_{3B0}^*}$$

from which we obtain $x_{B1} = 0.504831$, $y_{B1} = 0.378624$, $z_{B1} = 0.775751$. The synthesized linkage is shown in Fig. 6.16. The curve shown in this figure is R_{90}^1, i.e. the locus of a coupler point A_1 (not the A_1 shown in the figure), equation (6.109), which, together with its homologous points A_2, A_3, lies on a great circle.

6.6.2 *The case P_1–$P_2 P_3$*

In this case, the poles P_{12} and P_{13} coincide, and the angle γ_{23} becomes infinitesimally small, for which we write $\gamma_{23} = d\gamma$. Now the angle of rotation γ_{12} and the spherical distance $s = P_{12}P_{23}$, as shown in Fig. 6.15(b), remain finite. With the approximations $\sin d\gamma \approx d\gamma$ and $\cos \gamma \approx 1$, according to equation (6.72) the matrix $\mathbb{D}_{13}$ becomes

$$\mathbb{D}_{13} = \begin{bmatrix} C_{\gamma 12} - S_{\gamma 12}C_s\,d\gamma, & -S_{\gamma 12} - C_{\gamma 12}C_s\,d\gamma, & 0 \\ C_{\gamma 12}C_s\,d\gamma + S_{\gamma 12}, & -S_{\gamma 12}C_s\,d\gamma + C_{\gamma 12}, & -S_s\,d\gamma \\ S_{\gamma 12}S_s\,d\gamma, & C_{\gamma 12}S_s\,d\gamma & 1 \end{bmatrix} \qquad (6.110)$$

The equation of the R_M-curve, equation (6.85), becomes

$$R_M: \quad [(x_0^2 + y_0^2)S_{\gamma 12}S_s y_0 + W_3^{**}z_0]^2$$
$$- [2(x_0^2 + y_0^2)V_{\gamma 12}S_s^2 y_0^2 + W_3^{**2}]\cos^2 \rho_A = 0 \qquad (6.111)$$

where

$$W_3^{**} = W_3/d\gamma = -C_s V_{\gamma 12}x_0^2 - C_s V_{\gamma 12}y_0^2$$
$$+ S_s S_{\gamma 12}y_0 z_0 + S_s V_{\gamma 12}x_0 z_0 \qquad (6.112)$$

The equation of the locus of the centre-point A_0 for three homologous points A_1, A_2, A_3 on a great circle is

$$R_{M90}: \quad (x_0^2 + y_0^2)S_{\gamma12}S_s y_0 + W_3^{**}z_0 = 0 \tag{6.113}$$

The equation of the R^1-curve, equation (6.87), becomes

$$R^1: \quad [(x_{A1}^2 + y_{A1}^2)S_{\gamma12}T_3^{**} + F_3^{**}z_{A1}]^2$$
$$- [2(x_{A1}^2 + y_{A1}^2)V_{\gamma12}T_3^{**2} + F_3^{**2}]\cos^2\rho_A = 0 \tag{6.114}$$

where

$$T_3^{**} = T_3/d\gamma = S_s(S_{\gamma12}x_{A1} + C_{\gamma12}y_{A1})$$

and

$$F_3^{**} = F_3/d\gamma = V_{\gamma12}C_s(x_{A1}^2 + y_{A1}^2) + S_s(S_{\gamma12}y_{A1}z_{A1} + V_{\gamma12}x_{A1}z_{A1})$$
$$\tag{6.115}$$

The equation of the locus of A_1 for three homologous points A_1, A_2, A_3 on a great circle is

$$R_{90}^1: \quad (x_{A1}^2 + y_{A1}^2)S_{\gamma12}T_3^{**} + F_3^{**}z_{A1} = 0 \tag{6.116}$$

The geometrical meaning of this case is that the angle of rotation γ_{12} about the z-axis (pole-axis OP_{12}) and the location of the subsequent instantaneous pole-axis P_{23} are prescribed.

6.7   Four finitely separated positions

For four finitely separated positions, i.e. for the case $P_1-P_2-P_3-P_4$, there are altogether six poles, namely, $P_{12}, P_{13}, P_{14}, P_{23}, P_{24}$ and P_{34}. It is possible to establish a geometrical rule, similar to that in plane kinematics, for the locus of the centre-point, which we may call the spherical centre-point curve, that the *opposite sides* of a *spherical opposite-pole quadrilateral* subtend at a point on this locus either equal angles or supplementary angles (Beyer, 1953; Theorem 33). A similar rule may also be established for the spherical circle-point curve. However, as it is quite impracticable to carry out graphical construction on the spherical surface, we shall confine our investigations to algebraic methods.

6.7.1   *The spherical circle-point curve and spherical centre-point curve*

In the case of four finitely separated positions of a body to be guided, there is, in addition to the two displacement matrices $\mathbb{D}_{12}$ and $\mathbb{D}_{13}$ mentioned in Section 6.4.1, one more displacement matrix $\mathbb{D}_{14}$ for displacing the body from position 1 to position 4. We can simply set $i = 2, 3, 4$ in turn in equation (6.56), and form the expressions for G_4, S_4 and T_4 according to equations (6.53)–(6.55). Consequently we have an additional equation of the form (6.51) or

(6.52) for position 4. Writing these three equations together we have

$$G_2 x_0 + S_2 y_0 + T_2 z_0 = 0$$
$$G_3 x_0 + S_3 y_0 + T_3 z_0 = 0$$
$$G_4 x_0 + S_4 y_0 + T_4 z_0 = 0$$
(6.117)

If the location of A_1 is considered as known, the equations (6.117) are a system of three homogeneous linear equations in the three unknowns x_0, y_0, z_0, or a system of nonhomogeneous linear equations in the two unknowns x_0/z_0, y_0/z_0. For the existence of the solutions of this system of equations, it is well known that the matrix of the coefficients of this system must have a rank less than three. In other words, the determinant of the coefficients must vanish:

$$\begin{vmatrix} G_2 & S_2 & T_2 \\ G_3 & S_3 & T_3 \\ G_4 & S_4 & T_4 \end{vmatrix} = 0$$
(6.118)

Because each element of this determinant is linear in x_{A1}, y_{A1}, z_{A1}, equation (6.118) is a spherical cubic cone which, together with equation (A3.1) of the unit sphere, represents the spherical circle-point curve, or the locus of the point A_1, which we denote here by k_1. The point A_1 and its three homologous points A_2, A_3, A_4 lie on a spherical circle with centre A_0. This spherical cubic k_1 passes through the six poles $P_{12}, P_{13}, P_{14}, P_{23}^1, P_{24}^1, P_{34}^1$, where the last three poles are the respective positions of P_{23}, P_{24}, P_{34} in position 1 of the body. As mentioned before in Section 6.4.3, with the special coordinate system selected so that the z-axis coincides with OP_{12}, expansion of the determinant in equation (6.118) results in the following homogeneous cubic equation in x_{A1}, y_{A1}, z_{A1},

$$k_1: \quad d_1 y_{A1}^3 + d_2 x_{A1} y_{A1}^2 + d_3 x_{A1}^2 y_{A1} + d_4 x_{A1}^3 + d_7 y_{A1}^2 z_{A1}$$
$$+ d_8 x_{A1} y_{A1} z_{A1}$$
$$+ d_9 x_{A1}^2 z_{A1} + d_5 y_{A1} z_{A1}^2 + d_6 x_{A1} z_{A1}^2 = 0 \qquad (6.118a)$$

Expressions for the coefficients $d_1, d_2, \ldots, d_9$ are given in Appendix 6. From this equation it is evident that the curve passes through the point $P_{12}(0, 0, 1)$. For this reason, when equation (6.118a) is transformed into spherical polar coordinates by means of equations (A4.2), it becomes, with $A_1(x_{A1}, y_{A1}, z_{A1}) = A_1(p_{A1}, \theta_{A1})$,

$$k_1: \quad D_2 \tan^2 p_{A1} + D_1 \tan p_{A1} + D_0 = 0 \qquad (6.119)$$

where the coefficients D_2, D_1, D_0, being functions of θ_{A1}, are also listed in Appendix 6. This means that the cubic curve k_1 can be treated as a quadratic function.

Similarly for the centre-point curve, we have three equations of the form of equations (6.57) or (6.58):

$$\left.\begin{array}{l} L_2 x_{A1} + Q_2 y_{A1} + H_2 z_{A1} = 0 \\ L_3 x_{A1} + Q_3 y_{A1} + H_3 z_{A1} = 0 \\ L_4 x_{A1} + Q_4 y_{A1} + H_4 z_{A1} = 0 \end{array}\right\} \tag{6.120}$$

Again for the existence of the solutions (x_{A1}, y_{A1}, z_{A1}) of equations (6.120), the determinant of the coefficients must vanish:

$$\begin{vmatrix} L_2 & Q_2 & H_2 \\ L_3 & Q_3 & H_3 \\ L_4 & Q_4 & H_4 \end{vmatrix} = 0 \tag{6.121}$$

Equation (6.121) is a spherical cubic cone which, together with equation (A3.1) of the unit sphere, represents the spherical centre-point curve, or the location of the point A_0, which will be denoted by k_m. This spherical cubic k_m passes through the six poles $P_{12}, P_{13}, P_{14}, P_{23}, P_{24}$ and P_{34}. Expansion of the determinant in equation (6.121) results in the following homogeneous cubic equation in x_0, y_0, z_0,

$$\begin{aligned} k_m: \quad & m_1 y_0^3 + m_2 x_0 y_0^2 + m_3 x_0^2 y_0 + m_4 x_0^3 + m_7 y_0^2 z_0 + m_8 x_0 y_0 z_0 \\ & + m_9 x_0^2 z_0 + m_5 y_0 z_0^2 + m_6 x_0 z_0^2 = 0 \end{aligned} \tag{6.121a}$$

Expressions for the coefficients $m_1, m_2, \ldots, m_9$ are listed in Appendix 6. Upon transforming the coordinates of $A_0(x_0, y_0, z_0)$ into spherical polar coordinates $A_0(p_0, \theta_0)$, equation (6.121a) becomes

$$k_m: \quad M_2 \tan^2 p_0 + M_1 \tan p_0 + M_0 = 0 \tag{6.122}$$

where the expressions for the coefficients M_2, M_1, M_0 are also listed in Appendix 6. The spherical centre-point curve can also be treated as a quadratic function.

Because there are ∞^1 possible ways of choosing each of the two centre-points on the k_m-curve, there are altogether ∞^2 possible spherical four-bars to guide a body through four given positions.

Example: Four positions of two points A' and B' of a body to be guided are given as follows:

$$A_1'(-0.625893, -0.283406, 0.726594),$$
$$A_2'(-0.552116, -0.406230, 0.728110),$$
$$A_3'(-0.506139, -0.491591, 0.708634),$$
$$A_4'(-0.456310, -0.539105, 0.707918),$$
$$B_1'(0.573518, -0.727436, 0.376713),$$
$$B_2'(0.547526, -0.828264, 0.119141),$$
$$B_3'(0.421975, -0.894377, -0.148417),$$
$$B_4'(0.180350, -0.899505, -0.397950)$$

It is required to find the centre-point curve k_m and the circle-point curve k_1, and then design a spherical four-bar linkage to guide the body through the four given positions.

We find first the coordinates of the poles P_{12} and P_{23}, which are:

$$P_{12}(-0.825429, -0.492405, 0.276050)$$

and

$$P_{23}(-0.730166, -0.499623, 0.466084)$$

Select a new coordinate system according to Section 6.4.3 such that OP_{12} coincides with the z-axis and the xz-plane coincides with the plane $P_{12}OP_{23}$. The coordinates of the above eight points are transformed into those with respect to the new coordinate system:

$$A'_1(0.472251, \quad 0.207231, 0.856758),$$
$$A'_2(0.511042, \quad 0.069295, 0.856758),$$
$$A'_3(0.517030, -0.029407, 0.855462),$$
$$A'_4(0.538537, -0.092311, 0.837530),$$
$$B'_1(\quad 0.620481, -0.784141, -0.011215),$$
$$B'_2(\quad 0.380780, -0.924598, -0.011215),$$
$$B'_3(\quad 0.092739, -0.994378, \quad 0.051113),$$
$$B'_4(-0.225906, -0.956576, \quad 0.184199)$$

Based on these data, three displacement matrices are found by following the procedure described in Section 6.1.2:

$$\mathbb{D}_{12} = \begin{bmatrix} 0.96140 & 0.27514 & 0 \\ -0.27514 & 0.96140 & 0 \\ 0 & 0 & 1 \end{bmatrix}$$

$$\mathbb{D}_{13} = \begin{bmatrix} 0.83838 & 0.54500 & 0.0095266 \\ -0.54443 & 0.83640 & 0.063463 \\ 0.026619 & -0.058393 & 0.99794 \end{bmatrix}$$

$$\mathbb{D}_{14} = \begin{bmatrix} 0.62071 & 0.77785 & 0.098288 \\ -0.78007 & 0.60011 & 0.17708 \\ 0.078760 & -0.18659 & 0.97928 \end{bmatrix}$$

The equation of the centre-point curve k_m, apart from the unit sphere equation (A3.1), is

$$-0.82198y_0^3 + 1.49421x_0y_0^2 - 0.58927x_0^2y_0 + 1.59497x_0^3$$
$$-0.75666y_0^2z_0 + 1.18699x_0y_0z_0 - 0.69291x_0^2z_0$$
$$-0.24217y_0z_0^2 + 0.075254x_0z_0^2 = 0$$

with its corresponding equation in spherical polar coordinates

$$(-0.82198S_{\theta0}^3 + 1.49421S_{\theta0}^2C_{\theta0} - 0.58927S_{\theta0}C_{\theta0}^2 + 1.59497C_{\theta0}^3)$$
$$\cdot\tan^2 p_0 + (-0.75666S_{\theta0}^2 + 1.18699S_{\theta0}C_{\theta0} - 0.69291C_{\theta0})$$
$$\cdot\tan p_0 + (-0.24217S_{\theta0} + 0.075254C_{\theta0}) = 0$$

The equation of the circle-point curve k_1 is

$$-0.19771y_{A1}^3 + 0.20855x_{A1}y_{A1}^2 + 0.054077x_{A1}^2y_{A1} + 0.12918x_{A1}^3$$
$$+ 0.071892y_{A1}^2z_{A1} + 1.14984x_{A1}y_{A1}z_{A1} - 0.19138x_{A1}^2z_{A1}$$
$$- 0.26124y_{A1}z_{A1}^2 + 0.038096x_{A1}z_{A1}^2 = 0$$

with its corresponding equation in spherical polar coordinates

$$(-0.19771S_{\theta A1}^3 + 0.20855S_{\theta A1}^2C_{\theta A1} + 0.054077S_{\theta A1}C_{\theta A1}^2$$
$$+ 0.12918C_{\theta A1}^3)\tan^2 p_{A1} + (0.071892S_{\theta A1}^2 + 1.14984S_{\theta A1}C_{\theta A1}$$
$$- 0.19138C_{\theta A1}^2)\tan p_{A1} + (-0.26124S_{\theta A1} + 0.038096C_{\theta A1}) = 0$$

Both curves are shown in Fig. 6.17. Two centre-points on k_m are selected: $A_0(0.29649, -0.05001, 0.95372)$ and $B_0(0.22887, -0.44075, 0.86796)$. The corresponding circle-points on k_1 are: $A_1(0.83374, -0.02312, 0.55167)$ and $B_1(0.53189, -0.74769, 0.39757)$. The spherical four-bar linkage so synthesized is also shown in Fig. 6.17. It is a drag-link and serves to fulfil the requirement of guiding the body through the four given positions.

It is to be noted that the linkage thus synthesized should be free from branch and order problems, as in planar cases (Filemon, 1971; Modler, 1972; Waldron & Strong, 1978).

Fig. 6.17. Spherical circle-point curve k_1 and spherical centre-point curve k_m.

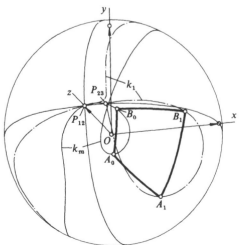

Obviously all spherical curves are closed. However, they can still be divided into *open* and *closed*. Those spherical curves whose front branches and diametrically opposite rear branches join together may be called *open*, because their gnomonic projections go to infinity and are open. Those whose front branches and diametrically opposite rear branches are separated may be called *closed*, because their gnomonic projections are closed. It can be seen that in the above example the centre-point curve is open and the circle-point curve consists of a closed portion and an open portion.

Because a homogeneous equation of a spherical curve can easily be transformed into an equation of its gnomonic projection by means of equations (A4.11), such a homogeneous equation can be considered as the equation of the gnomonic projection of the spherical curve expressed in homogeneous coordinates. It can be seen from equations (6.118a) and (6.121a) that, when the coefficients d_2 and d_4, d_1 and d_3, m_2 and m_4, m_1 and m_3 are in general not identical, the gnomonic projection of a spherical centre-point curve and that of a spherical circle-point curve are in general *not* circular cubics.

6.7.2   Four homologous points on a great circle

A point A_1 may lie together with its three homologous points A_2, A_3, A_4, on a great circle. There are, in general, two procedures to find such points. In the first procedure, a further condition to be satisfied by the A_0, A_1 point-pair in addition to the system of equations (6.117), or the system of equations (6.120), is

$$x_{A1}x_0 + y_{A1}y_0 + z_{A1}z_0 = 0 \qquad (6.123)$$

which is a special case of equation (6.68) for $\rho_A = 90°$. It is possible to derive a polynomial equation from any one of the two sets of equations in the unknown, say x_0/z_0, or x_{A1}/z_{A1}, of sixth degree (Dowler *et al.*, 1978). This means that there are in general six points (diametrically opposite points on the sphere surface are counted as one point only) which satisfy the above mentioned requirement. The second procedure makes use of the intersections of the spherical centre-point curve and the R_{M90}-curve, or of the spherical circle-point curve and the R_{90}^1-curve. The equation thus resulting includes extraneous roots. However, as the equations involved in both procedures are of similar complexity, and the concept of intersection points of two curves will be of use in later synthesis problems, we shall deal only with the second procedure.

The advantage of using the gnomonic projection of a spherical curve lies in the fact that two diametrically opposite points on the sphere project onto a single point on the tangent plane, thus causing these two points be considered as a single point if the intersections of the gnomonic projections of two spherical curves are considered. The same is true with the equation of a spherical curve expressed in spherical polar coordinates in terms of $\tan p$, because this is a single-valued function for two diametrically opposite points, as can be seen from equation (A4.8). Consider now the intersections of the spherical centre-point curve and the R_{M90}-curve. As mentioned in the preceding section, the gnomonic projection of the spherical centre-point curve is not a circular cubic, while the form of the equation of the R_{M90}-curve, equation (6.90), shows that its gnomonic projection is a circular cubic. These two spherical cubics should intersect in nine points, among which are the three poles P_{12}, P_{23} and P_{13}, the remaining six intersections being the centre-points which correspond to the circle-points in question. Because the pole P_{12} has been selected as the origin of the spherical polar coordinates, in the following formulations with spherical polar coordinates the root corresponding to the pole P_{12} is automatically excluded from the equation, leaving a polynomial equation in a certain unknown of only eighth degree. The equation of the centre-point curve, equation (6.122), is

$$k_m: \quad M_2 \tan^2 p_0 + M_1 \tan p_0 + M_0 = 0 \qquad [(6.122)]$$

and the equation of the R_{M90}-curve, equation (6.91), is

$$R_{M90}: \quad N_2 \tan^2 p_0 + N_1 \tan p_0 + N_0 = 0 \qquad [(6.91)]$$

Eliminating $\tan p_0$ from the last two equations results in

$$\begin{vmatrix} M_2 & M_0 \\ N_2 & N_0 \end{vmatrix}^2 + \begin{vmatrix} M_2 & M_1 \\ N_2 & N_1 \end{vmatrix} \begin{vmatrix} M_0 & M_1 \\ N_0 & N_1 \end{vmatrix} = 0 \qquad (6.124)$$

Equation (6.124) can be written, by dividing the elements of the determinants by the powers of $C_{\theta 0}$ ($= \cos \theta_0$), in the following form:

$$\begin{vmatrix} M_2/C_{\theta 0}^3 & M_0/C_{\theta 0} \\ N_2/C_{\theta 0}^3 & N_0/C_{\theta 0} \end{vmatrix}^2 + \begin{vmatrix} M_2/C_{\theta 0}^3 & M_1/C_{\theta 0}^2 \\ N_2/C_{\theta 0}^3 & N_1/C_{\theta 0}^2 \end{vmatrix} \begin{vmatrix} M_0/C_{\theta 0} & M_1/C_{\theta 0}^2 \\ N_0/C_{\theta 0} & N_1/C_{\theta 0}^2 \end{vmatrix} = 0$$

$$(6.125)$$

Expansion of the determinants in equation (6.125) results in the following polynomial equation of eighth degree in the unknown $\tau = \tan \theta_0$:

$$g_8 \tau^8 + g_7 \tau^7 + g_6 \tau^6 + g_5 \tau^5 + g_4 \tau^4 + g_3 \tau^3 + g_2 \tau^2 + g_1 \tau = 0 \qquad (6.126)$$

The roots of equation (6.126) are the $\tau = \tan \theta_0$ values of the eight intersections, apart from the pole P_{12}, of the two spherical cubics. Now deleting the two extraneous roots $\tau = \tan \theta_0 = 0$ and $\tau = \tan \theta_0 = \tan(-\gamma_{12}/2)$, which correspond respectively to the arguments of the poles P_{23} and P_{13}, equation (6.126) is reduced to the following sextic equation:

$$g_8 \tau^6 + g_{05} \tau^5 + g_{04} \tau^4 + g_{03} \tau^3 + g_{02} \tau^2 + g_{01} \tau + g_{00} = 0 \qquad (6.127)$$

The coefficients of equation (6.127) are given in Appendix 7.

Corresponding to each real root τ_0 of equation (6.127) there should be a unique value of $\tan p_0$ solved simultaneously from equations (6.122) and (6.91), namely, by the equation

$$\tan p_0 = - \begin{vmatrix} M_2 & M_0 \\ N_2 & N_0 \end{vmatrix} \bigg/ \begin{vmatrix} M_2 & M_1 \\ N_2 & N_1 \end{vmatrix} \tag{6.128}$$

The expanded form of equation (6.128) is given in Appendix 7.

Each pair of (p_0, θ_0) values thus obtained locates the centre-point of the spherical circle passing through the four homologous points. The six circle-points A_1's themselves can be obtained by applying equations (6.65) and (6.66).

Example: The four positions of a body are given by the following three displacement matrices:

$$\mathbb{D}_{12} = \begin{bmatrix} 0 & 1 & 0 \\ -1 & 0 & 0 \\ 0 & 0 & 1 \end{bmatrix}$$

$$\mathbb{D}_{13} = \begin{bmatrix} 0.5 & -0.5 & 0.707107 \\ 0.5 & -0.5 & -0.707107 \\ 0.707107 & 0.707107 & 0 \end{bmatrix}$$

$$\mathbb{D}_{14} = \begin{bmatrix} 0.433013 & 0.75 & -0.5 \\ 0.866025 & -0.5 & 0 \\ -0.25 & -0.433013 & -0.866025 \end{bmatrix}$$

It is required to find the circle-points in position 1, which lie, together with their homologous points, on a great circle.

Comparing the given $\mathbb{D}_{12}$ with equation (6.71), it is obvious that P_{12} is already in the position $(0, 0, 1)$. From the matrix

$$\mathbb{D}_{23} = \mathbb{D}_{13}\mathbb{D}_{12}^{-1} = \begin{bmatrix} -0.5 & -0.5 & 0.707107 \\ -0.5 & -0.5 & -0.707107 \\ 0.707107 & -0.707107 & 0 \end{bmatrix}$$

the coordinates of the pole P_{23} are found: $P_{23}(0.5, -0.5, 0.707107)$. Its spherical polar coordinates are: $(45°, -45°)$. Therefore rotating the coordinate system about the z-axis through an angle of $-45°$ will bring the xz-plane passing through the pole P_{23}. This rotation matrix is

$$\mathbb{M} = \begin{bmatrix} \cos 45° & -\sin 45° & 0 \\ \sin 45° & \cos 45° & 0 \\ 0 & 0 & 1 \end{bmatrix}$$

The three displacement matrices are then transformed by means of equation (A2.47), namely:

$$\mathbb{D}'_{12} = \begin{bmatrix} 0 & 1 & 0 \\ -1 & 0 & 0 \\ 0 & 0 & 1 \end{bmatrix}, \quad \mathbb{D}'_{13} = \begin{bmatrix} 0 & 0 & 1 \\ 1 & 0 & 0 \\ 0 & 1 & 0 \end{bmatrix}$$

$$\mathbb{D}'_{14} = \begin{bmatrix} -0.841506 & 0.408494 & -0.353553 \\ 0.524519 & 0.774519 & -0.353553 \\ 0.129410 & -0.482963 & -0.866025 \end{bmatrix}$$

The coefficients of the equation of the centre-point curve k_m are then computed, by equations (A6.7) and (A6.8):

$$k_m: \quad (-0.707107S_{\theta0}^3 - 1.103225S_{\theta0}^2C_{\theta0} + 2.548710S_{\theta0}C_{\theta0}^2$$
$$- 1.786566C_{\theta0}^3)\tan^2 p_0 + (-2.628826S_{\theta0}^2 - 0.587950S_{\theta0}C_{\theta0}$$
$$- 0.433013C_{\theta0}^2)\tan p_0 + (2.478398S_{\theta0} + 2.219579C_{\theta0}) = 0$$

and those of the equation of the R_{M90}-curve are, by equations (A6.1) and (A6.2):

$$R_{M90}: \quad (-S_{\theta0}^2C_{\theta0} - C_{\theta0}^3)\tan^2 p_0 + (-S_{\theta0}^2 + S_{\theta0}C_{\theta0})\tan p_0$$
$$+ (S_{\theta0} + C_{\theta0}) = 0$$

These k_m and R_{M90} curves intersect, apart from the poles P_{12}, P_{23}, P_{13}, in six points, denoted by $U_{01}, U_{02}, \ldots, U_{06}$, as shown in Fig. 6.18. Their spherical polar coordinates with respect to the rotated coordinate system are:

$$U'_{01}(39.800°, -8.904°), U'_{02}(-64.337°, -61.284°),$$
$$U'_{03}(-45.373°, -9.187°), U'_{04}(10.128°, -37.743°),$$
$$U'_{05}(-76.800°, 76.435°), U'_{06}(-36.490°, -76.508°)$$

The coordinates of the required circle-points in position 1 are computed by means of equations (6.65) and (6.66), and are denoted by $U_1, U_2, \ldots, U_6$ (not shown). These expressed in rectangular Cartesian coordinates with respect to the rotated coordinate system are:

$$U'_1(-0.6940, -0.5101, 0.5081), U'_2(0.5395, -0.1576, 0.8271),$$
$$U'_3(0.6593, 0.4756, 0.5823), U'_4(-0.9842, -0.1253, 0.1253),$$
$$U'_5(-0.1642, 0.2686, 0.9492), U'_6(0.7556, -0.4632, 0.4632)$$

Fig. 6.18. Example: intersections of k_m and R_{M90}-curves.

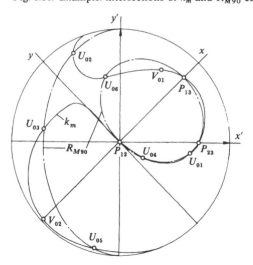

The coordinates of these points with respect to the original unrotated coordinate system are:

$$U_{01}(0.3771, -0.5172, 0.7683), U_{02}(0.2527, 0.8652, 0.4331),$$
$$U_{03}(-0.4164, 0.5771, 0.7025), U_{04}(0.0222, -0.1744, 0.9844),$$
$$U_{05}(-0.8307, -0.5078, 0.2283), U_{06}(0.3106, 0.5067, 0.8042)$$

and

$$U_1(-0.8514, 0.1300, 0.5081), U_2(0.2700, -0.4929, 0.8271),$$
$$U_3(0.8025, -0.1299, 0.5823), U_4(-0.7845, 0.6073, 0.1253),$$
$$U_5(0.0738, 0.3060, 0.9492), U_6(0.2068, -0.8618, 0.4632)$$

6.8 Four infinitesimally separated positions

The kinematics of a moving body for four infinitesimally separated positions, i.e. for the case $P_1 P_2 P_3 P_4$, has been studied by some investigators (Schoenflies, 1886; Dittrich, 1964; Tölke, 1975; Dowler *et al.*, 1978). The equation of the spherical circling-point curve and the equation of the spherical centering-point curve are analogous to those in plane kinematics. Dittrich has analysed important cases of break-ups of these curves. Also analogous to plane kinematics, the Ball points play an important rôle in instantaneous kinematics of spherical mechanisms.

6.8.1 The spherical circling-point curve

For four infinitesimally separated positions of a body, the spherical circle-point curve becomes a spherical circling-point curve. To derive the equation of this curve, again consider the case of three infinitesimally separated positions of a body. In Section 6.5.1 we defined the spherical radius of curvature ρ_A of the path of the moving point A as the limiting value of the spherical radius of the circle passing through three homologous points A_1, A_2, A_3 when these approach one another indefinitely. Similarly there is another spherical radius of curvature, which is the limiting value of the spherical radius of the circle passing through the points A_2, A_3, A_4 when they approach one another indefinitely. For an arbitrary point on the moving body these two spherical radii of curvature are in general different. There are, however, certain points on the moving body for which these two spherical radii are equal. In other words, there are certain points on the moving body the spherical radii of curvature of whose paths are instantaneously stationary. The locus of such points is the above mentioned circling-point curve. The equation of the circling-point curve can therefore be obtained by differentiating the expression for the radius of curvature ρ_A with respect to a certain independent variable and equating it to zero. Taking now, for this purpose, equation (5.46) and differentiating it with respect to the curvilinear length s along the fixed polode gives

$$-\frac{\rho'_A}{\sin^2 \rho_A} = \frac{1}{\sin^3 p} \left[\Theta' \sin \theta \sin p \cos^2 p + \Theta \theta' \cos \theta \sin p \cos^2 p \right.$$
$$- 2p' \sin \theta \cos p + p' \sin p + \Theta' \sin \theta \sin^3 p$$
$$\left. + \Theta \theta' \cos \theta \sin^3 p \right] \tag{6.129}$$

where (') denotes derivatives with respect to s, and PA and θ_A are now written respectively as p and θ. Noting that $\Theta = -u/\omega = -ds/d\gamma$ as defined in Section 5.4, with γ representing the angle of rotation of the moving body, we have $\Theta = -1/\gamma'$ and $\Theta' = \gamma''/\gamma'^2$. Setting $\rho'_A = 0$ in equation (6.129) results in

$$\gamma'' \sin \theta \tan p + p'(\gamma'^2 \tan p + 2\gamma' \sin \theta) - \gamma' \theta' \cos \theta \tan p = 0 \tag{6.130}$$

In equation (6.130) there are two quantities p' and θ' which have to be found. Let us find first the expression for p'. Fig. 6.19(a) shows the details of the polodes in Fig. 5.2. Here a moving body c is shown in its position c_1 relative to a fixed body f. In Fig. 6.19(b) the body is shown in position c_2, where the point A has been moved to A' and the pole P_{23} becomes the new pole of rotation. Extend A_0A' to a point Q such that $A_0Q = A_0P_{12}$. The configuration is identical with that shown in Fig. 5.7. In $\triangle P_{12}QP_{23}$ we have, according to equation (A1.1),

$$\sin QP_{23} = \sin ds \sin (90° - \theta) \tag{6.131}$$

In approaching the limit $QP_{23} = -dp$, which represents a shortening of the spherical length p, equation (6.131) becomes

$$- dp = ds \cos \theta$$

or

$$p' = \frac{dp}{ds} = - \cos \theta \tag{6.132}$$

Fig. 6.19.

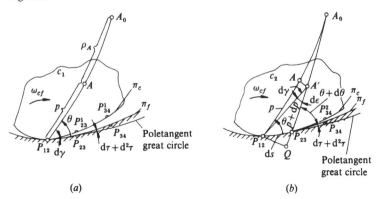

(a)   (b)

Next find the expression for θ'. Let us define the *contingence angle* as the angle between two adjacent elements along a polode at a certain pole. Thus the contingence angle of the fixed polode at P_{23} is the angle between $P_{12}P_{23}$ and $P_{23}P_{34}$. Following this definition the contingence angle of the fixed polode at P_{12} may be denoted by $d\tau$, and that at P_{23} by $d\tau + d^2\tau$. Applying the cosine law for angles, equation (A1.10), to $\triangle P_{12}P_{23}A'$ gives

$$-\cos(\theta + d\theta + d\tau + d^2\tau) = -\cos(\theta + d\gamma)\cos d\varepsilon$$
$$+ \sin(\theta + d\gamma)\sin d\varepsilon \cos p \qquad (6.133)$$

Note that the angle $d\gamma$ shown in Fig. 6.19 is negative. Applying the sine law, equation (A1.7), to the same triangle gives

$$\sin d\varepsilon = \sin ds \frac{\sin(\theta + d\gamma)}{\sin(p + dp)} \qquad (6.134)$$

Substituting equation (6.134) into equation (6.133) and neglecting terms of higher orders yields

$$d\theta = \frac{\sin\theta}{\tan p}ds + (d\gamma - d\tau)$$

or

$$\theta' = \frac{\sin\theta}{\tan p} + \gamma' - \tau' \qquad (6.135)$$

Substituting now the expressions for p' and θ' in equations (6.132) and (6.135) into equation (6.130) gives

$$\tan p[\gamma'(2\gamma' - \tau')\cos\theta - \gamma''\sin\theta] + 3\gamma'\sin\theta\cos\theta = 0 \qquad (6.136)$$

Let

$$\frac{3\gamma'}{\gamma''} = \tan m \qquad (6.137)$$

and

$$-\frac{3}{2\gamma' - \tau'} = \tan l \qquad (6.138)$$

Equation (6.136) can then be written in the following form:

$$k_u: \quad \frac{1}{\tan p} = \frac{1}{\tan m\cos\theta} + \frac{1}{\tan l\sin\theta} \qquad (6.139)$$

Equation (6.139) is the equation, in spherical polar coordinates, of the spherical circling-point curve, or of the spherical cubic of stationary curvature, which is the locus of a moving point whose path possesses a four-point contacting circle of curvature, and is denoted by k_u. Equation (6.139) can be transformed into right-handed Cartesian coordinates by means of equations (A4.1):

$$k_u: \quad (x^2 + y^2)(\tan m\cdot x + \tan l\cdot y) - \tan m\tan l\cdot xyz = 0 \qquad (6.140)$$

From equation (6.140) it can be seen that the spherical circling-point curve has a double point at P, and that it is tangent to both the poletangent great circle and the polenormal great circle at P. It can be shown that the geodetic curvatures in the directions of the poletangent and the polenormal are respectively $2/\tan m$ and $2/\tan l$. It is also evident that the gnomonic projection of k_u is a circular cubic.

From equation (5.20) it can be seen that the circling-point curve can also be interpreted as the locus of a moving point, the torsion of whose path vanishes. Hence equation (6.139) can also be derived by equating the numerator of the fraction in equation (5.32) to zero (Kamphuis, 1969).

In Fig. 6.20 a spherical circling-point curve k_u with $\tan l = 0.70$ and $\tan m = 0.95$ is shown.

6.8.2   The spherical centering-point curve

The locus of the corresponding centre of geodetic curvature of a point on the circling-point curve is called the spherical centering-point curve. Its equation can simply be derived from the equation of the spherical circling-point curve, equation (6.136). From the Euler–Savary equation (5.42), in which PA and PA_0 are now written respectively as p and p_0, and Θ is replaced by $-1/\gamma'$, we have

$$\tan p = \frac{\sin \theta \tan p_0}{\sin \theta - \gamma' \tan p_0} \tag{6.141}$$

Fig. 6.20. Spherical circling-point curve k_u for $\tan l = 0.70$, $\tan m = 0.95$ and spherical centering-point curve k_a for $\tan l_o = -1.88$, $\tan m = 0.95$.

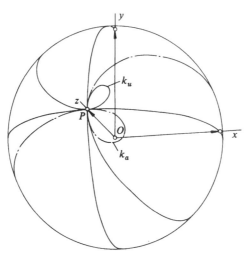

Substituting equation (6.141) into equation (6.136) and rearranging terms gives

$$\tan p_0 [-\gamma'(\gamma' + \tau')\cos\theta - \gamma'' \sin\theta] + 3\gamma' \sin\theta\cos\theta = 0 \qquad (6.142)$$

Let

$$\frac{3}{\gamma' + \tau'} = \tan l_0 \qquad (6.143)$$

Equation (6.142) can be written in the following form in spherical polar coordinates:

$$k_a: \quad \frac{1}{\tan p_0} = \frac{1}{\tan m \cos\theta} + \frac{1}{\tan l_0 \sin\theta} \qquad (6.144)$$

Equation (6.144) is the equation of the spherical centering-point curve, which is denoted here by k_a. This equation can also be transformed into right-handed Cartesian coordinates:

$$k_a: \quad (x_0^2 + y_0^2)(\tan m \cdot x_0 + \tan l_0 \cdot y_0) - \tan m \tan l_0 \cdot x_0 y_0 z_0 = 0 \qquad (6.145)$$

The spherical centering-point curve also has a double-point at the pole P and it is tangent to both the poletangent great circle and the polenormal great circle at P. The geodetic curvatures of k_a at P are $2/\tan m$ and $2/\tan l_0$. The gnomonic projection of the spherical centering-point curve k_a is also a circular cubic. In Fig. 6.20 the spherical centering-point curve k_a corresponding to k_u with $\tan l = 0.70$, $\tan m = 0.95$ is also shown, with $\tan l_0 = -1.88$.

A *radial* great circle drawn from the origin P will intersect k_u and k_a respectively in the corresponding circle-point and centre-point. As in the case of four finitely separated positions of a body, there exists a one-to-one correspondence between the set of circle-points and the set of centre-points, except in special cases.

From equations (6.138) and (6.143) we get the relation

$$\frac{1}{\tan l} - \frac{1}{\tan l_0} = -\gamma' = \frac{1}{\Theta} \qquad (6.146)$$

Note that $\tau' = d\tau/ds = 1/\tan PM_0$ is the geodetic curvature of the fixed polode. From the definitions of $\tan l$ and $\tan l_0$, equations (6.138) and (6.143), and the relations (5.43) and (6.146), the following relations for the geodetic curvatures of the fixed polode and of the moving polode can be obtained:

$$\frac{1}{\tan PM_0} = \frac{1}{\tan l} + \frac{2}{\tan l_0} \qquad (6.147)$$

$$\frac{1}{\tan PM} = \frac{2}{\tan l} + \frac{1}{\tan l_0} \qquad (6.148)$$

6.8.3   Determination of the circling-point curve and centering-point curve of the coupler of a given spherical four-bar linkage

A spherical circling-point curve k_u is determined by the two quantities $\tan l$ and $\tan m$, and a spherical centering-point curve k_a is determined by $\tan l_0$ and $\tan m$. For a given spherical four-bar linkage A_0ABB_0 (Fig. 6.21), these two curves of the coupler are uniquely determined, hence its $\tan l$, $\tan l_0$ and $\tan m$ values should be determinable. Consider A and B as two known points on the circling-point curve k_u. Substituting their coordinates into equation (6.139) results in two linear equations in the unknowns $1/\tan m$ and $1/\tan l$ which can easily be solved. Similarly the points A_0 and B_0 can be considered as two known points on the centering-point curve k_a, and by substituting their coordinates into equation (6.144) the two unknowns $1/\tan l_0$ and $1/\tan m$ can be found. In fact only the coordinates of either A_0 or B_0 are sufficient for finding $1/\tan l_0$, because $1/\tan m$ has already been found. It should be noted that before applying these equations the coordinate system has to be rotated to the canonical system position. The angular position of the poletangent great circle relative to the given four-bar can be determined by applying the Bobillier theorem, described in Section 5.7. This can best be illustrated by the following example.

Example: Given a spherical four-bar linkage A_0ABB_0 in a certain position. The spherical polar coordinates (p, θ) of the four joints are as follows: $A_0(75°, 45°)$, $A(30°, 45°)$; $B_0(45°, 100°)$, $B(35°, 100°)$. It is required to find the

Fig. 6.21.

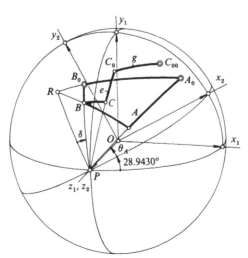

values of $1/\tan l$, $1/\tan l_0$ and $1/\tan m$ of the coupler AB, and the geodetic curvature of the fixed polode and that of the moving polode.

It is evident that the pole P of the coupler is already at the origin of the spherical polar coordinate system. The Cartesian coordinates of the four joints can be obtained by means of equations (A4.2):

$$A_0(0.683013, 0.683013, 0.258819), \ A(0.353553, 0.353553, 0.866025),$$
$$B_0(-0.122788, 0.696364, 0.707107),$$
$$B(-0.099601, 0.564863, 0.819152)$$

The equation of the great circle A_0B_0 and that of AB can be found by applying equation (A3.4). Solving these two equations simultaneously gives the location of the relative pole R (Fig. 6.21), which is given by $\theta_R = 116.0570°$. The angle $\measuredangle BPR$ is therefore $\delta = 116.0570° - 100° = 16.0570°$. This means that θ_A should also be equal to $16.0570°$ according to the Bobillier theorem. Simply rotating the coordinate system about the z_1-axis through an angle of $+ 28.9430°$ will bring it to the desired position $x_2y_2z_2$. The new spherical polar coordinates of the four joints are: $A_0(75°, 16.0570°)$, $A(30°, 16.0570°)$; $B_0(45°, 71.0570°)$, $B(35°, 71.0570°)$. Substituting these data respectively into equations (6.139) and (6.144) gives $1/\tan l = 0.38352$, $1/\tan l_0 = -0.021440$, $1/\tan m = 0.33199$. Then from equation (6.146) we have $\Theta = 2.4694$. The geodetic curvature of the fixed polode is, by equation (6.147), $1/\tan PM_0 = 0.34064$, and that of the moving polode is, by equation (6.148), $1/\tan PM = 0.74560$.

6.8.4 The Ball points

By analogy with plane kinematics, a Ball point is a circle-point whose path possesses a four-point contacting circle of curvature of radius 90°. In a generalized sense, the point that lies together with its other three homologous points on a great circle in the case of four finitely separated positions, as mentioned in Section 6.7.2, may also be called a *Ball point*, and the corresponding centre-points may be called *Ball centres*. Now in the present case of four infinitesimally separated positions, the Ball points can be found as the intersections of the circling-point curve k_u and the inflection curve k_w. We see from equation (5.73) that the gnomonic projection of k_w is a circular cubic, while from equation (6.140) it is evident that the gnomonic projection of k_u is also a circular cubic. These two curves should intersect in nine points, among which three are at the origin P and two at the imaginary circular points. There are therefore at most four real Ball points. Eliminating $\tan p$ between equations (6.139) and (5.47), where PA and θ_A are now written respectively as p and θ, and taking equation (6.146) into consideration, we obtain the equation for the determination of the orientations, or position angles θ_U's, of the Ball points:

$$\frac{\tan^4\theta_U}{M^2} + \frac{1}{M}\left(\frac{1}{L} + \frac{1}{L_0}\right)\tan^3\theta_U + \left(1 + \frac{1}{M^2} + \frac{1}{LL_0}\right)\tan^2\theta_U$$

$$+ \frac{1}{M}\left(\frac{1}{L} + \frac{1}{L_0}\right)\tan\theta_U + \frac{1}{LL_0} = 0 \qquad (6.149)$$

where $M^\dagger = \tan m$, $L = \tan l$ and $L_0 = \tan l_0$. For the sake of clarity, the four Ball points will be designated as U_1, U_2, U_3, U_4.

Example: Find the Ball points of the spherical four-bar linkage in the preceding example.

Substitute the values of $1/L$, $1/L_0$ and $1/M$ found before into equation (6.149) and solve for $\tan\theta_U$ and hence θ_U. Note that only values within the range $-90° \leqslant \theta_U \leqslant 90°$ are to be taken. Substitution of the θ_U values into equation (6.139) gives the corresponding values of p_U. The results are: $\theta_{U1} = 2.7228°$, $p_{U1} = 6.7844°$; $\theta_{U2} = -9.0064°$, $p_{U2} = -25.3183°$. The other two Ball points are imaginary. The coordinates of the two real Ball points with respect to the original coordinate system are: $U_1(6.7844°, 31.6658°)$; $U_2(-25.3183°, 19.9366°)$.

6.8.5   The velocity pole as a moving point

Considering the velocity pole P as a point on the moving body, we have seen in Section 5.8.3 that the path of P is tangent to the polenormal great circle. The situation of the radius of geodetic curvature of the path of P bears quite a close resemblance to that in plane kinematics (Müller, 1932, p. 52; Beyer, 1953; Dittrich, 1964). Fig. 6.22 shows the path of P as successive circle arcs of small circles when the moving body is rotated about the fixed poles P_{12}, P_{23}, P_{34} on the fixed polode π_f through respective infinitesimal angles $d\varepsilon$, $d\varepsilon + d^2\varepsilon$ and $d\varepsilon + 2d^2\varepsilon + d^3\varepsilon$. The contingence angles of π_f at P_{12}, P_{23} are, as defined in Section 6.8.1, $d\tau$ and $d\tau + d^2\tau$. During the first rotation the point P, considered as a moving point, remains unmoved at P'. The second rotation about P_{23} through an angle of $d\varepsilon + d^2\varepsilon$ moves P' to P'', which is denoted by P_{12}^3. The third rotation about P_{34} through an angle of $d\varepsilon + 2d^2\varepsilon + d^3\varepsilon$ moves P'' to P''', which is denoted by P_{12}^4.

Without loss of generality it may be assumed that $P_{12}P_{23} = P_{23}P_{34} = ds$. Hence $P_{23}P'' = ds$ as well. The small circle k_P which passes through P', P'', P''' with its spherical centre at P_0 will become, in approaching the limit, the osculating circle of the path of P. We now have

$$\measuredangle P''P_{23}P_{34} = 180° - [(d\varepsilon + d^2\varepsilon) + (d\tau + d^2\tau)]$$

---

† Not to be confused with the spherical centre of curvature of the moving polode.

The spherical triangle $\triangle P_{23}P_{34}P''$ is infinitesimally small, hence it may be treated as a plane triangle. It is also an isosceles triangle. Therefore

$$\angle\ P''P_{34}P_{23} = \frac{180° - \angle\ P''P_{23}P_{34}}{2} = \tfrac{1}{2}(d\varepsilon + d\tau + d^2\varepsilon + d^2\tau)$$

Moreover,

$$\angle\ P_{23}P_{34}P_0 = 180° - \angle\ P''P_{34}P_{23} - \tfrac{1}{2}(d\varepsilon + 2d^2\varepsilon + d^3\varepsilon)$$
$$\approx 180° - \tfrac{1}{2}(2d\varepsilon + 3d^2\varepsilon + d\tau + d^2\tau) \approx 180° - d\varepsilon_1$$

Therefore

$$\angle\ P_{34}P_{23}P_0 = \frac{d\varepsilon + d^2\varepsilon}{2} + d\tau + d^2\tau = d\varepsilon_2$$

Applying the cotangent law, equation (A1.11), to the spherical triangle $\triangle P_0P_{34}P_{23}$ results in

$$\cot P_0P_{34} = \frac{1}{\sin ds}(\sin d\varepsilon_1 \cot d\varepsilon_2 - \cos ds \cos d\varepsilon_1)$$
$$\approx \frac{1}{ds}\left(\frac{d\varepsilon_1 - d\varepsilon_2}{d\varepsilon_2}\right)$$

or

$$\tan P_0P_{34} \approx ds\,\frac{d\varepsilon + d^2\varepsilon + 2(d\tau + d^2\tau)}{d\varepsilon + 2d^2\varepsilon - d\tau - d^2\tau} \qquad (6.150)$$

As ds approaches zero, the limiting value of P_0P_{34} becomes the spherical radius of geodetic curvature of the path of P, which may be denoted by ρ_P. In Fig. 6.22 the angles of rotation $d\varepsilon$ and $d\varepsilon + d^2\varepsilon$ as shown are clockwise, while in our usual notations $d\gamma, d^2\gamma$, a clockwise angle of rotation is considered as negative,

Fig. 6.22.

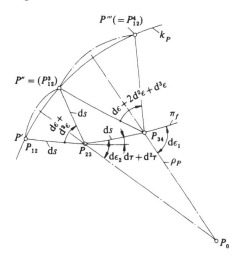

therefore $d\varepsilon = -d\gamma$ and $d^2\varepsilon = -d^2\gamma$. Equation (6.150) then becomes

$$\tan \rho_P = \lim_{ds \to 0} ds \frac{d\gamma - 2d\tau + d^2\gamma - 2d^2\tau}{d\gamma + d\tau + 2d^2\gamma + d^2\tau} \qquad (6.151)$$

Three cases will be considered.

(1) General case: $d\gamma \neq -d\tau$

In this case, the limiting value of ρ_P given by equation (6.151) is zero. Therefore it can be concluded that the moving point which coincides with the velocity pole describes in general a return point, or a cusp, of its path which is perpendicular to the poletangent great circle.

(2) Special case: $d\gamma = -d\tau$, *but* $2d^2\gamma \neq -d^2\tau$

In this case equation (6.151) becomes

$$\tan \rho_P = \lim_{ds \to 0} \frac{3d\gamma \, ds}{2d^2\gamma + d^2\tau} = \frac{3\gamma'}{2\gamma'' + \tau''} \qquad (6.152)$$

On this assumption the spherical radius of curvature of the path of P is not zero but of a finite value. According to equation (6.143) we now have $1/\tan l_0 = 0$ and according to equation (6.138) or (6.146) $\tan l = \Theta$. From equations (6.147) and (6.148) we have $\tan PM_0 = 2 \tan PM$. Therefore it can be concluded that, when the tangent function of the spherical radius of curvature of the fixed polode is twice that of the moving polode at the velocity pole, the moving point which coincides with the velocity pole describes a beak with a finite spherical radius of curvature. The centre of geodetic curvature of the path of P lies on the poletangent great circle and the two branches of the beak lie on the same side of the polenormal great circle.

For a general spherical four-bar linkage, this case occurs in one of the dead-centre positions as shown in Fig. 3.2(a) and (c). The joint B in these positions is the velocity pole P, and the poletangent great circle coincides with the link B_0B (see Fig. 6.24). Substituting the coordinates of B_0 into equation (6.144) gives

$$\frac{1}{\tan l_0} = \sin \theta_{B_0} \left(\frac{1}{\tan B_0B} - \frac{1}{\tan m \cos \theta_{B_0}} \right)$$

This equation shows that $1/\tan l_0 = 0$ because $\sin \theta_{B_0} = 0$. The point B describes a small circle, a special beak, with spherical centre at B_0 and spherical radius B_0B.

This case also occurs in the position where the collineation great circle PR is perpendicular to the *line* of centres A_0B_0. This is the position in which ω_{cb}/ω_{ca} reaches an extreme as mentioned in Section 4.2.2. It can be shown that in this position the condition $\tan PB_0/\tan PA_0 = \cos\theta_B/\cos\theta_A$ is satisfied, and hence by means of equation (6.144) $1/\tan l_0 = 0$.

(3) Special case: $d\gamma = -d\tau$ *and* $2d^2\gamma = -d^2\tau$
In this case the denominator of the fraction in equation (6.151) vanishes and the pole as a moving point describes a return point with a spherical radius of curvature of 90°.

Comparing with what has just been mentioned in (2), this case occurs in the dead centre position of a spherical slider–crank, Fig. 2.10(a), because in addition to the condition $1/\tan l_0 = 0$, the joint B as a moving point coinciding with the velocity pole describes a path with a spherical radius of curvature of $B_0 B = 90°$.

This case also occurs in an internal bevel gear pair when a pinion is rolling on the inside of an internal bevel gear, provided that the spherical radii PM_0 and PM of the gear and pinion are such that $\tan PM_0 = 2\tan PM$ (see Section 7.6.2(1)). This condition means that $1/\tan l_0 = 0$. However, the path of the velocity pole can never be a beak as that mentioned in (2) because it must be symmetrical with respect to the polenormal great circle. The only possibility is that the path of P has a spherical radius of curvature of 90°.

6.8.6 Break-ups of circling-point curve and of centering-point curve and the corresponding location of Ball points

In certain special cases the circling-point curve or the centering-point curve breaks up into a great circle and a spherical ellipse (Dittrich, 1964). Important cases are as follows.

(1) The case $\gamma'' = 0$, *simultaneous break-ups of circling-point curve and centering-point curve*

This is the case when the magnitude of the angular velocity of the moving body, or $|\gamma'|$, remains constant, or when γ' has an extreme value. We now have $1/\tan m = 0$, and equation (6.139) becomes

$$k_u: \quad \cos\theta(\tan p - \tan l \sin\theta) = 0 \tag{6.153}$$

This means that the circling-point curve k_u breaks up into the polenormal great circle and a spherical Thales ellipse (see Appendix A1.3) which is symmetrically disposed about the polenormal great circle, as shown in Fig. 6.23. Similarly the equation of the centering-point curve, equation (6.144), becomes

$$k_a: \quad \cos\theta(\tan p_0 - \tan l_0 \sin\theta) = 0 \tag{6.154}$$

The centering-point curve k_a also breaks up into the polenormal great circle and a spherical Thales ellipse, as shown in Fig. 6.23. The coefficients of the terms of highest degree of equation (6.149) vanish, which means that there is a double root of $\tan \theta_U$ at infinity, or at $\theta_{U3} = \theta_{U4} = 90°$. Comparing Fig. 5.10 with Fig. 6.23 shows that the inflection poles W's become the Ball points. The two remaining roots, from equation (6.149), are

$$\frac{\tan \theta_{U1}}{\tan \theta_{U2}} = \pm \sqrt{\left(-\frac{1}{1 + \tan l \tan l_0} \right)} \qquad (6.155)$$

Equation (6.155) indicates that these two Ball points are real only when $1 + \tan l \tan l_0 \leqslant 0$, or when $\tan l \tan l_0 \leqslant -1$. l and l_0 should be of opposite signs. The locations of these Ball points can be found by substituting the values of θ_U's into equation (5.48) and solving for PA. It is clear that these two Ball points are symmetrically disposed about the polenormal great circle.

The case $\gamma' = $ constant occurs when the moving body is a bevel gear rolling on another fixed bevel gear (see Section 7.6.2). The case that γ' has an extreme value occurs in a spherical four-bar linkage, as mentioned in Section 4.2.2, where γ' was denoted by ω_{cf}, when the collineation great circle is perpendicular to A_0A or B_0B. According to the Bobillier theorem this means that the poletangent great circle is perpendicular to A_0A or to B_0B. Assume, for instance, that in Fig. 5.13(a) the collineation great circle PR is perpendicular to A_0A, then B_0B must be on the polenormal great circle. In this position the inflection poles, which are now on the great circle B_0B, are Ball points of the coupler.

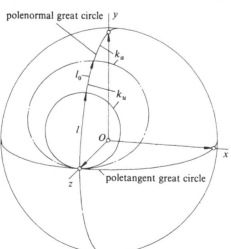

Fig. 6.23. Simultaneous break-ups of k_u and k_a.

(2) The case $\gamma' = -\tau'$

In this case $1/\tan l_0 = 0$. This was the case mentioned in Section 6.8.5(2). It was shown there that

and also
$$\left.\begin{array}{l} \tan PM_0 = 2\tan PM \\ \tan PM_0 = \tan l = \Theta \end{array}\right\} \tag{6.156}$$

The circling-point curve k_u does not break up, while the equation of the centering-point curve k_a, equation (6.144), becomes

$$k_a: \quad \sin\theta(\tan p_0 - \tan m\cos\theta) = 0 \tag{6.157}$$

This means that k_a breaks up into the poletangent great circle and a spherical Thales ellipse which is symmetrically disposed about the poletangent great circle, as shown in Fig. 6.24.

This is the case of a spherical four-bar linkage in one of its dead centre positions, as shown in Fig. 3.2(a) or (c). In Fig. 6.24 the centre-points A_0 and B_0 are on the broken up k_a curve, while A and B are on the corresponding k_u curve which is not broken up.

Equation (6.149) now becomes

$$\tan\theta_U\left[\frac{\tan^3\theta_U}{M^2} + \frac{\tan^2\theta_U}{ML} + \left(1 + \frac{1}{M^2}\right)\tan\theta_U + \frac{1}{ML}\right] = 0 \tag{6.158}$$

Obviously one of the roots of equation (6.158) is $\tan\theta_{U1} = 0$. This means that the point B is a Ball point, because B, as the velocity pole P, is the only moving point on the circling-point curve k_u having the orientation $\theta_B = 0$.

Fig. 6.24. Example: break-up of k_a.

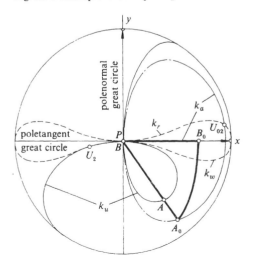

However, it has been shown in Section 6.8.5(2) that the joint B, as a moving point coinciding with the velocity pole, describes a beak which is now in fact a small circle with its spherical centre at B_0. (This small circle becomes a great circle when $B_0B = 90°$.) This paradox arises from the break up of the centering-point curve k_a. The portion of the circling-point curve k_u which corresponds to all centre-points on the poletangent great circle shrinks into a point P. In other words, the point P becomes a set of all moving points, the spherical centres of curvature of whose paths lie on the poletangent great circle. The one-to-one correspondence between the set of circle-points and the set of centre-points here loses its validity. There are infinite spherical radii of curvature of the infinite paths of all circle-points concentrating at P, among which the 90° spherical radius is also included and that circle-point is a Ball point. However, this Ball point is of no practical use.

Example: The link lengths of a spherical four-bar linkage are: $a = 20°$, $b = 45°$, $c = 40°$ and $f = 45°$. It is required to find the circling-point curve k_u, the centering-point curve k_a and the Ball points of the coupler in the outer dead centre position of the linkage.

The constants are found to be: $1/\tan l_0 = 1/L_0 = 0$, $1/\tan m = 1/M = 1/3$ and $1/\tan l = 1/L = 1/\Theta = -0.50166$. The k_u and k_a curves are shown in Fig. 6.24. The inflection curve k_w is also shown. Equation (6.158) now becomes

$$\tan \theta_U(\tan^3 \theta_U - 1.50497 \tan^2 \theta_U + 10 \tan \theta_U - 1.50497) = 0$$

One root is $\tan \theta_{U1} = 0$, which corresponds to the point B. The second root is $\tan \theta_{U2} = 0.1537$, or $\theta_{U2} = 8.738°$. The corresponding Ball point is at

Fig. 6.25. Example: break-up of k_u.

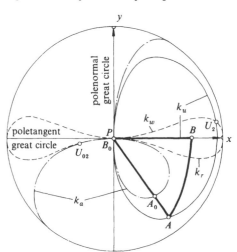

$p_{U2} = -18.637°$. The Ball centre is at $p_{UO2} = 71.363°$. The other two Ball points are imaginary.

(3) The case $2\gamma' = \tau'$
In this case $1/\tan l = 0$, and from equation (6.147) and (6.148) we have

and also $\left.\begin{array}{l} \tan PM = 2\tan PM_0 \\ \tan PM = \tan l_0 = -\Theta \end{array}\right\}$ (6.159)

The centering-point curve k_a does not break up, while the equation of the circling-point curve k_u, equation (6.139), becomes

$$k_u: \quad \sin\theta(\tan p - \tan m\cos\theta) = 0 \qquad (6.160)$$

This means that k_u breaks up into the poletangent great circle and a spherical Thales ellipse symmetrically disposed about the polètangent great circle, as shown in Fig. 6.25. Comparison of equations (6.159) with (6.156) and of equation (6.160) with (6.157) shows that the present case is just the kinematic inversion of case (2). The spherical four-bar is in one of the positions shown in Fig. 3.2(*b*) and (*d*). In Fig. 6.25 the centre-points A_0 and B_0 are shown on the k_a curve, which is not broken up, while A and B are on the broken up k_u curve. Equation (6.149) now becomes

$$\tan\theta_U\left[\frac{\tan^3\theta_U}{M^2} + \frac{\tan^2\theta_U}{ML_0} + \left(1 + \frac{1}{M^2}\right)\tan\theta_U + \frac{1}{ML_0}\right] = 0 \quad (6.161)$$

This equation is identical with equation (6.158) if L is replaced by L_0. One of its roots is again $\tan\theta_{U1} = 0$, which means that one of the Ball points is on the poletangent great circle, the corresponding Ball centre of which is at P, or B_0. Again, this Ball point is of no practical use.
Example: Take the inversion linkage of the spherical four-bar in the preceding example. The link lengths are now: $a = 20°$, $b = 45°$, $c = 45°$ and $f = 40°$. The position in question of this linkage is such that A_0A is in *line* with A_0B_0.

The linkage and the k_u and k_a curves of the coupler are shown in Fig. 6.25. We now have $1/\tan l_0 = 1/L_0 = -1/\Theta = -0.50166$, $1/\tan m = 1/M = 1/3$ and $1/\tan l = 1/L = 0$. It can be seen, by comparing Fig. 6.25 with Fig. 6.24, that upon inversion the two curves k_u and k_a exchange their rôles. The second root of equation (6.161) is the same as before: $\theta_{U2} = 8.738°$, with $p_{U2} = 71.363°$. The corresponding Ball point in the preceding example now becomes the Ball centre U_{02}.

(4) The case $\gamma'' = 0$ and $\gamma' = -\tau'$
This is a combination of cases (1) and (2), i.e. $1/\tan m = 0$ and $1/\tan l_0 = 0$, hence a combination of the break-ups of k_u and k_a in cases (1) and (2).

Figs. 6.26(*a*), (*b*) show this case. It has been shown in case (1) that the condition $\gamma'' = 0$ alone reduces both k_u and k_a to the polenormal great circle and a spherical ellipse. Now from equation (6.154) it can be seen that the additional condition $\gamma' = -\tau'$ (or $1/\tan l_0 = 0$) causes the equation of the spherical ellipse of k_a, namely, $\tan p_0 - \tan l_0 \sin\theta = 0$, to further break up into the poletangent great circle ($\sin\theta = 0$) and the meridian ($1/\tan p_0 = 0$). Moreover, because

Fig. 6.26. Simultaneous break-ups of k_u and k_a.

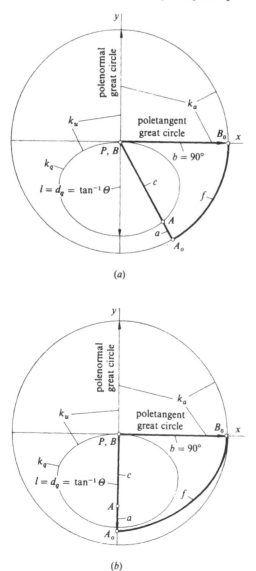

(*a*)

(*b*)

$\tan l = \Theta$, it can be seen from equation (6.153) that the equation of the spherical ellipse of k_u becomes the equatorial curve k_q, equation (5.55), and $l = d_q$, the spherical axis of the spherical ellipse k_q. According to Section 6.8.5(2) the point B, as a moving point coinciding with the velocity pole P, describes a beak, but now being a great circle with a spherical radius $B_0B = 90°$. Fig. 6.26(*a*) shows the case of a spherical four-bar with $a + c = 90°$, $b = 90°$ and $f \neq 90°$, in its dead centre position. This linkage can be considered as a special case of the one shown in Fig. 6.24, being in fact a special offset slider–crank as shown in Fig. 2.10(*a*). For the orientation of the Ball points, a double root of equation (6.158) is $\tan \theta_{U1} = \tan \theta_{U2} = 0$. This indicates that the joint B is now a true, and even a two-fold Ball point. The other two Ball points, remaining the same as in case (1), are those given by $\theta_{U3} = \theta_{U4} = 0$, and are the inflection poles W's if they exist.

Fig. 6.26(*b*) shows a further special spherical four-bar which also belongs to the present case, with $a + c \neq 90°$, $b = 90°$ and $f = 90°$, both A_0 and A being on the polenormal great circle. This is a central slider–crank as shown in Fig. 2.11. From the Euler–Savary equation (5.42), we get

$$\tan l = \Theta = \frac{\tan c \tan (a + c)}{\tan c - \tan (a + c)} \qquad (6.162)$$

For example, for a central slider–crank with $a = 20°$, $c = 40°$, we have $\Theta = -1.6276$, and the spherical axis of the spherical ellipse k_q is $d_q = l = \tan^{-1}(-1.6276) = -58.43°$.

This is also the case with a pair of internal bevel gears for which $\tan PM_0 = 2 \tan PM$, as mentioned in Section 6.8.5(3). The velocity pole P as a moving point describes a return point (see Section 7.6.2(1)).

(5) The case $\gamma'' = 0$ and $2\gamma' = \tau'$
This is a combination of cases (1) and (3), i.e. $1/\tan m = 0$ and $1/\tan l = 0$, or also $\tan PM = 2 \tan PM_0$, hence a combination of the break-ups of k_u and k_a in cases (1) and (3). Figs. 6.27(*a*), (*b*) show this case. The mechanism takes positions such that they are the kinematic inversions of the corresponding positions of the mechanism in case (4). The curves k_u and k_a exchange their rôles, and the Ball point and the Ball centre exchange their rôles too. Thus the linkage shown in Fig. 6.27(*a*) is the inversion of that shown in Fig. 6.26(*a*), with $a + f = 90°$, $b = 90°$ and $c \neq 90°$. This linkage is also a special offset slider–crank, as shown in Fig. 2.10(*a*). The spherical ellipse, which is identical in both Figs. 6.26(*a*) and 6.27(*a*), now becomes the central curve k_z, and because $\tan l_0 = -\Theta$, $l_0 = -d_q$ is the spherical axis of the spherical ellipse k_z.

The kinematic inversion of the linkage in Fig. 6.26(*b*) is shown in Fig. 6.27(*b*).

This is a central oscillating cylinder as shown in Fig. 2.15(b). Here the point B is a true two-fold Ball point. The other two Ball points are on the polenormal great circle and are the inflection poles. From the Euler–Savary equation (5.42) we now have

$$- \tan l_0 = \Theta = \frac{\tan(a+f)\tan f}{\tan(a+f) - \tan f} \qquad (6.163)$$

Fig. 6.27. Simultaneous break-ups of k_u and k_a.

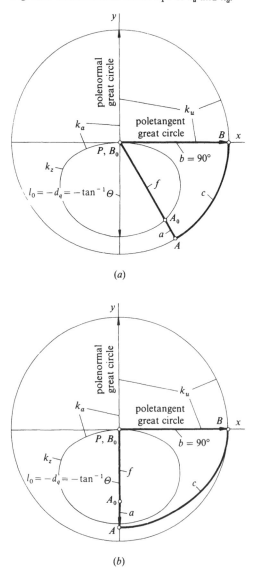

(a)

(b)

For example, for a central oscillating cylinder with $a = 20°$, $f = 40°$, we have $\Theta = 1.6276$, and the spherical axis of the spherical ellipse k_z is $l_0 = -d_q = -\tan^{-1} 1.6276 = -58.43°$.

This is also the case with a pair of internal bevel gears for which the condition $\tan PM = 2 \tan PM_0$ is fulfilled.

6.9 Five finitely separated positions

This is the case $P_1-P_2-P_3-P_4-P_5$. A moving point A_1 which lies, together with its four homologous points A_2, A_3, A_4, A_5, on a small circle, is called, by analogy with plane kinematics, a *Burmester point*[†]. To locate the Burmester points, the apparent way is to find the intersections of two circle-point curves. Let the circle-point curve for the four positions $P_1-P_2-P_3-P_4$ be denoted by $k_{1(1234)}$, and that for $P_1-P_2-P_3-P_5$ by $k_{1(1235)}$. As mentioned at the end of Section 6.7.1, the gnomonic projection of a spherical circle-point curve is in general not a circular cubic. The two cubics $k_{1(1234)}$ and $k_{1(1235)}$ intersect in nine points, among which three are known, namely, the poles P_{12}, P_{13} and P_{23}^1, where P_{23}^1 is the location of P_{23} on the moving body in position 1. These three points should be excluded, because they are relevant neither to position 4 nor to position 5 of the body, and hence are not Burmester points. There are at most six real Burmester points, as has been shown elsewhere (Dittrich, 1964; Roth, 1967). Let the centre-point curves corresponding to $k_{1(1234)}$ and $k_{1(1235)}$ be denoted respectively by $k_{m(1234)}$ and $k_{m(1235)}$, and let the centre-point of a Burmester point be called a *Burmester centre*. Then the six Burmester centres lie in the intersections of $k_{m(1234)}$ and $k_{m(1235)}$. These two spherical cubics also intersect in nine points, among which are the three known poles P_{12}, P_{13}, P_{23}. The present situation is quite similar to that of finding the intersections of k_m and R_{M90} as described in Section 6.7.2. For the reason that the root corresponding to orientation of the pole P_{23} ($\tan \theta_{P23} = 0$) can easily be deleted from the resulting polynomial equation of eighth degree, it is more convenient to use the two k_m's rather than the two k_1's. Let the equation of $k_{m(1234)}$ be, according to equation (6.122),

$$\left. \begin{array}{l} k_{m(1234)}: \quad M_2 \tan^2 p_0 + M_1 \tan p_0 + M_0 = 0 \\ \text{and that of } k_{m(1235)} \text{ be} \\ k_{m(1235)}: \quad E_2 \tan^2 p_0 + E_1 \tan p_0 + E_0 = 0 \end{array} \right\} \qquad (6.164)$$

The equation of $k_{m(1235)}$ in rectangular Cartesian coordinates can be written,

---

[†] In the literature of plane kinematics, the centre-point of the circle passing through five homologous points is often given the name *Burmester point* (Beyer, 1953; Freudenstein & Sandor, 1961; Hackmüller, 1938).

according to equation (6.121a), as

$$k_{m(1235)}: \quad e_1 y_0^3 + e_2 x_0 y_0^2 + e_3 x_0^2 y_0 + e_4 x_0^3 + e_7 y_0^2 z_0$$
$$+ e_8 x_0 y_0 z_0 + e_9 x_0^2 z_0 + e_5 y_0 z_0^2 + e_6 x_0 z_0^2 = 0 \qquad (6.165)$$

The expressions for the coefficients E_2, E_1, E_0 are exactly the same as those for M_2, M_1, M_0 in equations (A6.8), with the nine constant coefficients $e_1, e_2, \ldots, e_9$ computed in place of $m_1, m_2, \ldots, m_9$ by equations (A6.7), but for $i = 2, 3, 5$. To find the solutions of the simultaneous equations (6.164), the equations (6.124)–(6.128) apply, and the equations in Appendix 7 can be used as an algorithm, provided that N_2, N_1, N_0 are replaced by E_2, E_1, E_0, and $n_1, n_2, \ldots, n_9$ by $e_1, e_2, \ldots, e_9$ respectively.

The number of possible spherical four-bars to guide a body through five given positions is therefore 15, 6 or 1, depending on whether the number of real Burmester centres is 6, 4 or 2.

Example: Suppose in addition to the four positions of the body in the example in Section 6.7.2, a fifth position is given by the following displacement matrix:

$$\mathbb{D}_{15} = \begin{bmatrix} 0.433013 & 0.75 & -0.5 \\ 0.625 & -0.649519 & -0.433013 \\ -0.649519 & -0.125 & -0.75 \end{bmatrix}$$

It is required to find the Burmester points.

This displacement matrix, transformed by the rotation matrix $\mathbb{M}$, becomes

$$\mathbb{D}'_{15} = \begin{bmatrix} -0.795753 & 0.603766 & -0.047367 \\ 0.478766 & 0.579247 & -0.659740 \\ -0.370891 & -0.547668 & -0.75 \end{bmatrix}$$

Only two Burmester centres are real. Their spherical polar coordinates with respect to the rotated coordinate system are: $V'_{01}(47.699°, 60.521°)$ and $V'_{02}(-80.989°, 44.426°)$. These are denoted by V_{01} and V_{02} in Fig. 6.18. The corresponding Burmester points in position 1, according to equations (6.65) and (6.66), expressed in rectangular Cartesian coordinates with respect to the rotated coordinate system, are (not shown): $V'_1(0.2646, -0.9527, 0.1497)$, $V'_2(0.0071, 0.7128, 0.7013)$. The coordinates of these points with respect to the original, unrotated coordinate system are: $V_{01}(0.7126, 0.1979, 0.6730)$, $V_{02}(-0.9876, 0.0099, 0.1566)$; $V_1(-0.4866, -0.8607, 0.1497)$, $V_2(0.5091, 0.4990, 0.7013)$.

6.10   Five infinitesimally separated positions

This is the case $P_1 P_2 P_3 P_4 P_5$, which may be considered as the limiting case of $P_1 - P_2 - P_3 - P_4 - P_5$. A moving point A whose path possesses a five-point contacting spherical circle of curvature is the limiting case of the

Burmester point mentioned in Section 6.9. In fact, the term *Burmester point* was first used by Müller for the present case (Müller, 1892).

6.10.1   The Burmester points

To locate the Burmester points, they should satisfy not only the condition $d\rho_A/ds = 0$, but also the condition $d^2\rho_A/ds^2 = 0$. In other words, the Burmester points are the intersections of the circling-point curve k_u and the curve $d^2\rho_A/ds^2 = \rho_A'' = 0$. Upon differentiation of equation (6.129) it will be seen that, because $\rho_A' = 0$, the condition $\rho_A'' = 0$ is simply represented by the differentiation of equation (6.130), or even equation (6.139), the equation of the circling-point curve k_u, with respect to s (Dittrich, 1964). For the sake of brevity we write again M, L, L_0 in place of $\tan m$, $\tan l$, $\tan l_0$ respectively. Equation (6.139) now becomes

$$k_u: \quad \frac{1}{\tan p} = \frac{1}{M\cos\theta} + \frac{1}{L\sin\theta} \tag{6.166}$$

Differentiating equation (6.166) with respect to s gives the equation $\rho_A'' = 0$, which we denote by k_v, in the following form:

$$k_v: \quad \frac{p'}{\sin^2 p} + \frac{\theta'\sin\theta}{M\cos^2\theta} - \frac{M'}{M^2\cos\theta} - \frac{\theta'\cos\theta}{L\sin^2\theta} - \frac{L'}{L^2\sin\theta} = 0 \tag{6.167}$$

Substituting again equations (6.132) and (6.135) into equation (6.167), and taking equation (6.166) into consideration and noting that $\gamma' - \tau' = -2/L - 1/L_0$, we obtain

$$k_v: \quad -\frac{C_\theta}{\sin^2 p} - \frac{M'}{M^2 C_\theta} - \frac{L'}{L^2 S_\theta} + \left\{ \left(\frac{1}{MS_\theta} - \frac{1}{LC_\theta} \right) + \frac{1}{\tan p} \left(\frac{S_\theta}{C_\theta} - \frac{C_\theta}{S_\theta} \right) \right\}$$

$$\cdot \left(\frac{S_\theta}{\tan p} - \frac{2}{L} - \frac{1}{L_0} \right) = 0 \tag{6.168}$$

with $S_\theta = \sin\theta$, and $C_\theta = \cos\theta$. From the definitions of M, L and L_0, we obtain

$$M = \tan m = \frac{3\gamma'}{\gamma''}, \qquad M' = \frac{3(\gamma''^2 - \gamma'\gamma''')}{\gamma''^2}$$

$$L = \tan l = -\frac{3}{2\gamma' - \tau'}, \qquad L' = \frac{3(2\gamma'' - \tau'')}{(2\gamma' - \tau')^2} \tag{6.169}$$

Eliminating p between equations (6.166) and (6.168) and substituting the above expressions for M, L, M', L' yields the following polynomial equation of sixth degree in the unknown $\tan\theta_V$, where θ_V represents the orientation of a Burmester point:

$$a_6 \tan^6\theta_V + a_5 \tan^5\theta_V + a_4 \tan^4\theta_V + a_3 \tan^3\theta_V + a_2 \tan^2\theta_V$$

$$+ a_1 \tan\theta_V + a_0 = 0 \tag{6.170}$$

where

$$
\left.
\begin{aligned}
a_6 &= \gamma''^2 \\
a_5 &= \gamma'\gamma''(\gamma' - 2\tau') \\
a_4 &= 3(\gamma'\gamma''' - \gamma''^2) \\
a_3 &= \gamma'^2\gamma'' - 5\gamma'\gamma''\tau' + 3\gamma'^2\tau'' \\
a_2 &= 3\gamma'\gamma'' - 9\gamma'^2 - 4\gamma''^2 - \gamma'^2(\gamma' + \tau')(2\gamma' - \tau') \\
a_1 &= 3\gamma'(\gamma'\tau'' - \gamma''\tau') \\
a_0 &= -\gamma'^2(2\gamma' - \tau')(\gamma' + \tau')
\end{aligned}
\right\}
\tag{6.171}
$$

There are at most six real Burmester points, as has been shown in (Dobrovolskii, 1945). In the following these Burmester points will be denoted by $V_1, V_2, \ldots, V_6$. Several special cases will be considered.

(1) The case $\gamma'' = 0$
This was the case mentioned in Section 6.8.6(1), in which the circling-point curve k_u breaks up into the polenormal great circle and a spherical ellipse $\tan p - \tan l \sin \theta = 0$. Consequently the six Burmester points also lie on the polenormal great circle and this spherical ellipse. The coefficients a_6 and a_5 in equation (6.170) vanish, therefore two of its roots become $1/\tan \theta_{V1} = 0$ and $1/\tan \theta_{V2} = 0$. This means that two Burmester points lie on the polenormal great circle, and the remaining four Burmester points lie on the spherical ellipse.

(2) The case $\gamma' = -\tau'$
This was the case mentioned in Section 6.8.6(2), and also in Section 6.8.5(2). The coefficient a_0 in equation (6.170) vanishes, therefore one of its roots is $\tan \theta_{V6} = 0$. Because the circling-point curve k_u does not break up, the only moving point corresponding to $\theta_V = 0$ is the velocity pole P. Consequently P is a Burmester point which describes a five-point contacting circle of curvature.

(3) The case $\gamma'' = 0$ and $2\gamma' = \tau'$
This was the case mentioned in Section 6.8.6(5). Fig. 6.28 is essentially the same as Fig. 6.27(b), but with the inflection curve k_w added. As mentioned before, in this case the circling-point curve k_u breaks up into the poletangent great circle, the polenormal great circle and the meridian, and the centering-point curve k_a breaks up into the polenormal great circle and the spherical ellipse k_z symmetrical with respect to the polenormal great circle. Now the coefficients a_6, a_5 and a_0 in equation (6.170) vanish. This means that one of its roots is $\tan \theta_{V6} = 0$ and two roots are $1/\tan \theta_{V1} = 0$, $1/\tan \theta_{V2} = 0$. One

Burmester point is on the poletangent great circle, which is the joint B, and corresponds to $\theta_{V6} = 0$. Two Burmester points are on the polenormal great circle, one being the joint A, which corresponds to $\theta_{V1} = 90°$, and another one has yet to be located. Now because the polenormal great circle is a part of k_u as well as a part of k_a, it is not possible to locate this Burmester point on the polenormal great circle by its orientation $\theta_{V2} = 90°$ alone. However, this Burmester point can be located by means of equation (6.168) of the k_v curve. Note that in the present case $1/M = 0$, $1/L = 0$, but $M'/M^2 = -\gamma'''/3\gamma'$, $L'/L^2 = -\tau''/3$ and $L_0 = -\Theta$. Equation (6.168) now takes for $\theta = 90°$ the form

$$\frac{\gamma'''\Theta}{3}\tan^2 p_V - \frac{1}{\Theta}\tan p_V - 1 = 0 \tag{6.172}$$

Since one of the roots of the quadratic equation (6.172) corresponds to the joint A, for which $\tan p_{V1} = -\tan(a + f)$, hence the other root is

$$\tan p_{V2} = \frac{\Theta \tan(a + f)}{\Theta - \tan(a + f)} \tag{6.173}$$

Substituting the value of Θ in the present case, equation (6.163), into equation (6.173) gives finally

$$\tan p_{V2} = \frac{\tan(a + f)\tan f}{2\tan f - \tan(a + f)} \tag{6.174}$$

In order that the Burmester point V_2 be a Ball point, which in the present case is at each of the two inflection poles, as mentioned in Section 6.8.6(5),

Fig. 6.28. Situation of Burmester points in the case of Fig. 6.27(*b*).

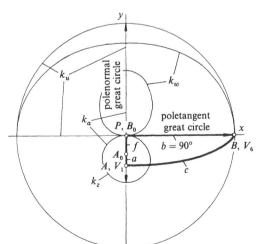

$\tan p_{V2}$ should satisfy the equation of the inflection curve k_w, equation (5.47). Substituting equation (6.174) and equation (6.163) into equation (5.47) and setting $\theta_A = 90°$ results in the following conditions to be satisfied by the relation of $\tan a$ to $\tan f$ for this requirement:

$$(1 + \tan^2 f)[2(1 + 3\tan^2 f)\tan^2 a - 3\tan f \tan a + \tan^2 f] = 0$$
(6.175)

Deleting the first bracket in equation (6.175), and considering $\tan a$ as an unknown in the quadratic equation represented by the second bracket, we see that the quadratic equation has real roots if

$$\tan f \leqslant \frac{1}{\sqrt{24}}, \quad \text{or } f \leqslant 11.537°$$

The roots are

$$\tan a = \frac{3 \pm \sqrt{(1 - 24\tan^2 f)}}{4(1 + 3\tan^2 f)}\tan f \tag{6.176}$$

A Ball point which is at the same time a Burmester point is said to have an excess 1, because it possesses a five-point contacting great circle. Similarly a Ball point with a six-point contacting great circle is said to have an excess 2, etc. Thus, a spherical oscillating cylinder whose dimensions satisfy the requirement of equation (6.176) will have a Ball point with excess 1 at the point computed from equation (6.174). Furthermore, because the linkage is in a symmetrical position with respect to the polenormal great circle, the number of contacting points of the path of this Ball point with its tangent great circle should be even, hence this Ball point has an excess 2.

A plane oscillating cylinder may be considered as the limiting case of a spherical oscillating cylinder if the sphere radius is considered to be increased indefinitely. Let the linear dimensions of a, f and p_{V2} be denoted by a_p, f_p and p_p respectively, and the length of the sphere radius by r. Then we have $\tan a = a_p/r$, $\tan f = f_p/r$ and $\tan p_{V2} = p_p/r$. When the radius r is increased indefinitely, equation (6.176) becomes

$$a_p = \frac{3 \pm 1}{4}f_p, \quad \text{i.e. } a_p = f_p \text{ or } \frac{f_p}{2}$$

The corresponding location of the Burmester point V_2 is, by equation (6.174), at infinity if $a = f$, or

$$p_p = 6a_p, \quad \text{if } a_p = \frac{f_p}{2}$$

The same problem has been investigated separately by Veldkamp, using derivatives of a displacement matrix (Veldkamp, 1969), and by Kamphuis, using derivatives of angular velocity components (Kamphuis, 1969).

6.10.2 Location of Burmester points of the coupler of a spherical four-bar linkage

For a given spherical four-bar linkage, its M, L and L_0 values can readily be computed, as shown in Section 6.8.3. The equation of k_v, equation (6.168), can be written as

$$k_v: \quad \frac{M'}{M^2 C_\theta} + \frac{L'}{L^2 S_\theta} = \left(\frac{S_\theta}{M C_\theta^2} - \frac{C_\theta}{L S_\theta^2} \right) \left(\frac{S_\theta}{\tan p} - \frac{2}{L} - \frac{1}{L_0} \right) - \frac{C_\theta}{\sin^2 p}$$

(6.177)

Since the joints A and B are known Burmester points, substituting their coordinates into equation (6.177) will result in two linear equations in the two unknowns M' and L', hence these can easily be determined. If all coefficients of equation (6.170) are divided through by γ''^2, the same equation becomes one with leading coefficient 1 and is

$$\tan^6 \theta_V + b_5 \tan^5 \theta_V + b_4 \tan^4 \theta_V + b_3 \tan^3 \theta_V$$
$$+ b_2 \tan^2 \theta_V + b_1 \tan \theta_V + b_0 = 0$$

(6.178)

where the coefficients $b_5, b_4, \ldots, b_0$ are now expressed in terms of M, L, L_0, M' and L':

$$\left.\begin{aligned}
b_5 &= -M\left(\frac{1}{L} + \frac{1}{L_0}\right) \\
b_4 &= -M' \\
b_3 &= -M\left(\frac{4}{L} + \frac{1}{L_0} + \frac{ML'}{L^2}\right) \\
b_2 &= M^2\left(\frac{1}{LL_0} - 1\right) - M' - 1 \\
b_1 &= -\frac{M}{L}\left(3 + \frac{ML'}{L}\right) \\
b_0 &= \frac{M^2}{LL_0}
\end{aligned}\right\}$$

(6.179)

Again, since the corresponding orientations $\tan \theta_A$ and $\tan \theta_B$ of the joints A and B are known roots of equation (6.178), the latter can be reduced to a quartic equation:

$$\tan^4 \theta_V + c_3 \tan^3 \theta_V + c_2 \tan^2 \theta_V + c_1 \tan \theta_V + c_0 = 0$$

(6.180)

Table 6.1 *Break-ups of circling-point curve k_u and centering-point curve k_a*

Case	$\dfrac{1}{M}$	$\dfrac{1}{L}$	$\dfrac{1}{L_0}$	k_u	k_a	Position of mechanism
$\gamma'' = 0$	0	—	—	Polenormal g.c. and spherical ellipse $\tan p - \tan l \sin \theta = 0$	Polenormal g.c. and spherical ellipse $\tan p_0 - \tan l_0 \sin \theta = 0$	Inflection poles W's are Ball points. (a) For a 4-bar, γ' has an extreme value which occurs when collineation g.c. is perpendicular to A_0A or B_0B. (b) γ' is stationary, which is always the case with a bevel gearing. Fig. 6.23
$\gamma' = -\tau'$	—	$1/\Theta$	0	Does not break up	Poletangent g.c. and spherical ellipse $\tan p_0 - \tan m \cos \theta = 0$	Polode curvatures: $\tan PM_0 = 2\tan PM$. For a 4-bar in a dead-centre position, B as pole P describes a beak, and B is also a Ball point, but of no use. Fig. 6.24
$2\gamma' = \tau'$	—	0	$-1/\Theta$	Poletangent g.c. and spherical ellipse $\tan p - \tan m \cos \theta = 0$	Does not break up	Polode curvatures: $\tan PM = 2\tan PM_0$. For a 4-bar in a position when A_0A is in *line* with A_0B_0, B as pole P is a Ball centre, but of no use. Fig. 6.25

$\gamma''=0$ and $\gamma'=-\tau'$	0	$1/\Theta$	0	Polenormal g.c. and equatorial curve k_q	Polynormal g.c., poletangent g.c. and meridian	Polode curvatures: $\tan PM_0 = 2\tan PM$. Inflection poles W's are Ball points. B as pole P describes a return point on a great circle. (a) A central slider-crank in a dead-centre position. (b) An internal bevel gear pair with $\tan PM_0 = 2\tan PM$. 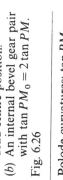 Fig. 6.26
$\gamma''=0$ and $2\gamma'=\tau'$	0	0	$1/\Theta$	Polenormal g.c., poletangent g.c. and meridian	Polenormal g.c. and central curve k_z	Polode curvatures: $\tan PM = 2\tan PM_0$. Inflection poles W's are Ball points. (a) A central oscillating cylinder in a position when A_0A is in *line* with A_0B_0. (b) An internal bevel gear pair with $\tan PM = 2\tan PM_0$. Fig. 6.27

where

$$
\left.
\begin{aligned}
c_3 &= (t_A + t_B) + b_5 \\
c_2 &= (t_A^2 + t_A t_B + t_B^2) + b_5(t_A + t_B) + b_4 \\
c_1 &= (t_A^3 + t_A^2 t_B + t_A t_B^2 + t_B^3) + b_5(t_A^2 + t_A t_B + t_B^2) \\
&\quad + b_4(t_A + t_B) + b_3 \\
c_0 &= (t_A^4 + t_A^3 t_B + t_A^2 t_B^2 + t_A t_B^3 + t_B^4) + b_5(t_A^3 + t_A^2 t_B + t_A t_B^2 + t_B^3) \\
&\quad + b_4(t_A^2 + t_A t_B + t_B^2) + b_3(t_A + t_B) + b_2
\end{aligned}
\right\} \quad (6.181)
$$

with $t_A = \tan \theta_A$ and $t_B = \tan \theta_B$. Equation (6.180) may have four, two or no real roots. Substituting the value of θ_V corresponding to each real root into equation (6.166) will give the coordinates of the Burmester point.

Example: Find the Burmester points of the coupler of the spherical four-bar linkage given in the example in Section 6.8.3.

The coefficients of the resulting equation (6.180) are: $c_3 = 2.11079$, $c_2 = 1.05355$, $c_1 = 4.93770$, $c_0 = -0.088974$. The coordinates (p_V, θ_V) of two Burmester points are: $V_3(42.5130°, 1.0282°)$, $V_4(43.1163°, -68.1184°)$. These expressed with respect to the original coordinate system are: $V_3(42.5130°, 29.9712°)$ and $V_4(43.1163°, -39.1754°)$. The other two Burmester points are imaginary.

In order to provide a general view of the special cases, particularly those of the break-ups of the circling-point curve k_u and the centering-point curve k_a, these are summarized in Table 6.1, according to (Dittrich, 1964).

6.11   Four and five multiply separated positions

For four separated positions, between the two extreme cases $P_1-P_2-P_3-P_4$ and $P_1P_2P_3P_4$, there are three combinations of the four positions, namely, $P_1P_2-P_3-P_4$, $P_1P_2-P_3P_4$ and $P_1P_2P_3-P_4$. Similarly for five separated positions, between the two extreme cases $P_1-P_2-P_3-P_4-P_5$ and $P_1P_2P_3P_4P_5$, there are five intermediate cases, namely, $P_1P_2-P_3-P_4-P_5$, $P_1P_2-P_3P_4-P_5$, $P_1P_2P_3-P_4-P_5$, $P_1P_2P_3-P_4P_5$ and $P_1P_2P_3P_4-P_5$. All five cases of four separated positions and all seven cases of five separated positions are treated by Dowler *et al.* as multiply separated positions, and have been treated in a unified way by means of derivatives of the elements of the displacement matrices (Dowler *et al.*, 1978). We shall deal only with the intermediate cases.

6.11.1   *Intermediate cases of four multiply separated positions*

These are the three cases mentioned above. Other combinations such as $P_1-P_2-P_3P_4$, $P_1-P_2P_3-P_4$ and $P_1-P_2P_3P_4$ may be included in these three cases and are not to be particularly considered. In fact, all concepts and procedures developed for the determination of the circle-point curve, the centre-point curve and the Ball points, for the case $P_1-P_2-P_3-P_4$, can be generalized for the intermediate cases, provided that the displacement matrices $\mathbb{D}_{12}$, $\mathbb{D}_{13}$, $\mathbb{D}_{14}$ in each case can be determined. In the following we shall assume that, as mentioned in Section 6.4.3, the coordinate system xyz is selected so that the pole P_{12} is always located at $(0, 0, 1)$, while the pole P_{23} may or may not be brought to lie on the xz-plane, depending on whether the displacement matrices can be simplified.

(1) The case $P_1P_2-P_3-P_4$
The displacement matrix $\mathbb{D}_{12}$ takes the form of equation (6.102), while $\mathbb{D}_{13}$ and $\mathbb{D}_{14}$ remain in the usual form of a displacement matrix for two finitely separated positions. It can be seen that, due to the simple form of $\mathbb{D}_{12}$, all coefficients $d_1, \ldots, d_9$ of the k_1-curve, equations (A6.5), and all coefficients $m_1, \ldots, m_9$ of the k_m-curve, equations (A6.7), contain the common factor $d\gamma$. Therefore these equations are still applicable provided that the elements of $\mathbb{D}_{12}$ are replaced by those of

$$\mathbb{D}_{12}^* = \begin{bmatrix} 1 & -1 & 0 \\ 1 & 1 & 0 \\ 0 & 0 & 1 \end{bmatrix} \tag{6.182}$$

The array $\mathbb{D}_{12}^*$ is not a matrix, hence possesses no geometrical meaning.

The equations of the R_{M90}- and R_{90}^1-curves have already been derived, and were given as equations (6.106a) and (6.109a). From the intersections of two corresponding curves, the Ball centres or Ball points can be located. The situation of the three poles P_{12}, P_{23}, P_{13} is as shown in Fig. 6.15(a), in which P_{23} and P_{13} coincide. As mentioned before, the pole P_{23} may not be brought into the xz-plane, but, its orientation should be determined.

(2) The case $P_1P_2-P_3P_4$
This may be considered as a combination of the two cases $P_1P_2-P_3$ and $P_1-P_3P_4$, as mentioned in Sections 6.6.1 and 6.6.2. The situation of the poles is shown in Fig. 6.29, which is comparable with Figs. 6.15(a), (b). The case $P_1P_2-P_3$ implies that P_{23} and P_{13} coincide, and γ_{12} becomes infinitesimally small, while the angle of rotation γ_{23} and the spherical distance $P_{12}P_{23}$ remain finite. The case $P_1-P_3P_4$ implies that P_{13} and P_{14} coincide, and the angle of rotation γ_{34} becomes infinitesimally small, while the angle of rotation γ_{13} and the spherical distance $P_{13}P_{34}$ remain finite. Because the positions P_1 and P_2 coincide, therefore γ_{13} is identical with γ_{23}.

Now $\mathbb{D}_{12}$ again takes the form of equation (6.102), hence the array $\mathbb{D}_{12}^*$, equation (6.182), can again be used in place of $\mathbb{D}_{12}$. The displacement matrix $\mathbb{D}_{13}$ remains in the usual form for two finitely separated positions. The only displacement matrix to which particular attention need be paid is $\mathbb{D}_{14}$. This is written as

$$\mathbb{D}_{14} = \mathbb{D}_{34}\mathbb{D}_{13} \qquad (6.183)$$

which implies that the displacement from position P_1 to position P_4 is considered as a finite displacement $\mathbb{D}_{13}$ followed by an infinitesimal displacement $\mathbb{D}_{34}$. The latter can be determined by means of equation (A2.34) by replacing l_x, l_y, l_z by the respective coordinates of P_{34} and by setting $\delta = d\gamma_{34}$. Without loss of generality it can be assumed that $d\gamma_{34} \approx d\gamma_{12} = d\gamma$. Denoting the coordinates of P_{34} by (x_P, y_P, z_P), we then have

$$\mathbb{D}_{34} = \begin{bmatrix} 1 & -z_P d\gamma & y_P d\gamma \\ z_P d\gamma & 1 & -x_P d\gamma \\ -y_P d\gamma & x_P d\gamma & 1 \end{bmatrix}$$

hence

$$\mathbb{D}_{14} = \begin{bmatrix} d_{113}+(-d_{213}z_P+d_{313}y_P)d\gamma, & d_{123}+(-d_{223}z_P+d_{323}y_P)d\gamma, & d_{133}+(-d_{233}z_P+d_{333}y_P)d\gamma \\ d_{213}+(d_{113}z_P-d_{313}x_P)d\gamma, & d_{223}+(d_{123}z_P-d_{323}x_P)d\gamma, & d_{233}+(d_{133}z_P-d_{333}x_P)d\gamma \\ d_{313}+(-d_{113}y_P+d_{213}x_P)d\gamma, & d_{323}+(-d_{123}y_P+d_{223}x_P)d\gamma, & d_{333}+(-d_{133}y_P+d_{233}x_P)d\gamma \end{bmatrix}$$

$$(6.184)$$

A comparison of equation (6.184) with equations (A6.7) and (A6.5) shows that in each determinant of the coefficients $m_1,\ldots,m_9$ and $d_1,\ldots,d_9$, if the second row is subtracted from the third row, all coefficients will contain a further common factor $d\gamma$, and for the evaluation of these coefficients it is equivalent to use the following array in place of the original displacement matrix $\mathbb{D}_{14}$:

$$\mathbb{D}_{14}^* = \begin{bmatrix} -d_{213}z_P+d_{313}y_P+1, & d_{223}z_P+d_{323}y_P, & -d_{233}z_P+d_{333}y_P \\ d_{113}z_P-d_{313}x_P, & d_{123}z_P-d_{323}x_P+1, & d_{133}z_P-d_{333}x_P \\ -d_{113}y_P+d_{213}x_P, & -d_{123}y_P+d_{223}x_P, & -d_{133}y_P+d_{233}x_P+1 \end{bmatrix}$$

$$(6.185)$$

The array $\mathbb{D}_{14}^*$ is not a matrix, hence possesses no geometrical meaning.

Fig. 6.29. Situation of poles in the case $P_1P_2-P_3P_4$.

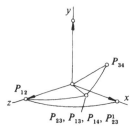

The equations of the R_{M90}- and R_{90}^1-curves are the same as those in case (1), being given respectively by equations (6.106a) and (6.109a).

Example: It is required to guide a body so that it is (1) rotated instantaneously about the z-axis, then (2) rotated about the axis $OP_{23}(1/\sqrt{3}, 1/\sqrt{3}, 1/\sqrt{3})$ through an angle of $\gamma_{23} = 120°$, and then (3) rotated instantaneously about the axis $OP_{34}(1, 0, 0)$.

The array $\mathbb{D}_{12}^*$ is as given in equation (6.182). The displacement matrix $\mathbb{D}_{13}$ is built up, according to equation (A2.34), as

$$\mathbb{D}_{13} = \begin{bmatrix} 0 & 0 & 1 \\ 1 & 0 & 0 \\ 0 & 1 & 0 \end{bmatrix}$$

The array $\mathbb{D}_{14}^*$ is then found, according to equation (6.185), as

$$\mathbb{D}_{14}^* = \begin{bmatrix} 1 & 0 & 0 \\ 0 & 0 & 0 \\ 1 & 0 & 1 \end{bmatrix}$$

In the present case it is not necessary at this stage to rotate the coordinate system to bring the xz-plane to pass through the pole P_{23}, whose spherical coordinates are simply $P_{23}(\cos^{-1} 1/\sqrt{3}, 45°)$. Using $\mathbb{D}_{12}^*$, $\mathbb{D}_{13}$ and $\mathbb{D}_{14}$, we find, by means of equations (A6.5) and (A6.7), the equations of the k_1 and k_m-curves:

$$k_1: \quad (\cos\theta_{A1} - \sin\theta_{A1})[\tan p_{A1} - (\sin\theta_{A1} + \cos\theta_{A1})] = 0$$

$$k_m: \quad (\cos\theta_0 \tan p_0 - 1)(\sin^2\theta_0 \tan p_0 - \cos\theta_0) = 0$$

Also by means of equations (6.109a) and (6.106a) we find the equations of the R_{90}^1 and R_{M90}-curves:

$$R_{90}^1: \quad \sin\theta_{A1} \tan^2 p_{A1} - \sin\theta_{A1} \cos\theta_{A1} \tan p_{A1} - \cos\theta_{A1} = 0$$

$$R_{M90}: \quad \cos\theta_0 \tan^2 p_0 - \sin\theta_0 \cos\theta_0 \tan p_0 - \sin\theta_0 = 0$$

These four curves k_1, k_m, R_{90}^1 and R_{M90} are shown in Fig. 6.30. The orientations of the intersection points of the k_m and R_{M90} curves, apart from the origin P_{12}, are given by equation (6.126), the coefficients of which can be evaluated by means of equation (A7.4). In the present case, the values of $m_1, \ldots, m_9$ are, respectively, $0, 1, 0; 0, 0, 1; -1, 0, -1$, and the values of $n_1, \ldots, n_9$, are, respectively, $0, 1, 0; 1, -1, 0; 0, -1, 0$. The resulting equation in the unknown $\tau = \tan\theta_0$, corresponding to equation (6.126), is

$$0\tau^8 - \tau^7 + 2\tau^6 - 2\tau^5 + 3\tau^4 - 3\tau^3 + 2\tau^2 - 2\tau + 1 = 0$$

Deleting the two known roots $\tau = 1$, $\tau = 1$, which correspond to the two poles P_{23} and P_{13}, leaves the following equation of sixth degree for the orientations of the Ball centres:

$$0\tau^6 - \tau^5 - \tau^3 + \tau^2 + 1 = 0$$

Only two Ball centres are real, and their coordinates are: $U_{01}(\cos^{-1} 1/\sqrt{3}, 45°)$ and $U_{02}(90°, 90°)$, the former being again the pole P_{23} $(= P_{13} = P^1_{23})$.

To find the Ball points, application of equations (6.65) and (6.66) would result in indeterminate forms. However, because the positions P_1 and P_2 are infinitesimally separated, therefore the three points, i.e. the Ball centre, the pole P_{12} and the corresponding Ball point, are on the same great circle. The two corresponding Ball points are found to be: $U_1(\cos^{-1} 1/\sqrt{3} - 90°, 45°)$ and $U_2(0, 90°)$, the latter being in fact the pole P_{12}. It can be seen that if the Ball points were determined first, by finding the intersections of the k_1 and R^1_{90}-curves, the procedure would be quite similar to that mentioned above, because both of these two curves pass through the poles P_{12}, P_{13} and P^1_{23}, and P^1_{23} and P_{23} coincide.

(3) The case $P_1P_2P_3-P_4$

As mentioned in Section 6.5.2, the displacement matrices $\mathbb{D}_{12}$ and $\mathbb{D}_{13}$ should take respectively the forms of equations (6.98) and (6.99). However, in evaluating the coefficients of the circle-point curve k_1 and of the centre-point curve k_m by means of equations (A6.5) and (A6.7), unlike in cases (1) and (2) there are no available substitutive arrays which can be used in place of the displacement matrices $\mathbb{D}_{12}, \mathbb{D}_{13}, \mathbb{D}_{14}$. It should be noted that, because $\mathbb{D}_{13}$, equation (6.99), being derived from equation (6.72), was so formed that the xyz-system

Fig. 6.30. Example: k_1, k_m, R^1_{90} and R_{M90}-curves in the case $P_1P_2-P_3P_4$.

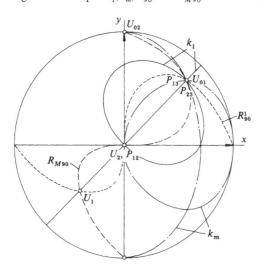

Table 6.2 *Three intermediate cases of four multiply separated positions*

	Array to be used in place of			
				xyz-system
Case	$\mathbb{D}_{12}$	$\mathbb{D}_{13}$	$\mathbb{D}_{14}$	selected with
$P_1P_2\text{--}P_3\text{--}P_4$	$\mathbb{D}^*_{12}$, eqn. (6.182)	$\mathbb{D}_{13}$	$\mathbb{D}_{14}$	P_{12} at $(0,0,1)$
$P_1P_2\text{--}P_3P_4$	$\mathbb{D}^*_{12}$, eqn. (6.182)	$\mathbb{D}_{13}$	$\mathbb{D}^*_{14}$, eqn. (6.185)	P_{12} at $(0,0,1)$
$P_1P_2P_3\text{--}P_4$	coefficients of $k_1, d_1, \ldots, d_9$, eqn. (A.6.9)		coefficients of $k_m, m_1, \ldots, m_9$, eqn. (A6.10)	P_{12} at $(0,0,1)$ and poletangnet g.c. in *xz*-plane

was in the selected position according to both steps (1) and (2) in Section 6.4.3, the matrix $\mathbb{D}_{14}$ should also be formed with respect to the canonical coordinate system. In other words, the instantaneous pole P_{12} should be at $(0,0,1)$, and the poletangent great circle should be in the *xz*-plane.

It can be shown that, in evaluating the expressions for the coefficients $d_1, \ldots, d_9$ and $m_1, \ldots, m_9$ by means of equations (A6.5) and (A6.7), after neglecting higher orders, there exists a common factor $d\gamma^3$. Thus, denoting as before $-ds/d\gamma$ by Θ, and with $d^*_1 = d_1/d\gamma^3$, $m^*_1 = m_1/d\gamma^3$, etc., the coefficients of the circle-point curve k_1 and those of the centre-point curve k_m are listed in equations (A6.9) and (A6.10) in Appendix 6.

The Ball points are given by the intersections of the k_1-curve and the inflection curve k_w, and the Ball centres by those of the k_m-curve and the return curve k_r, the equations of k_w and k_r being already given as equations (5.47) and (5.51).

For easy reference, information on the three intermediate cases is listed together in Table 6.2.

6.11.2 *Intermediate cases of five multiply separated positions*

These are the five cases mentioned above. For these cases, we are interested only in the locations of the Burmester points and the Burmester centres. As has been shown in Section 6.9, the Burmester points can be determined as the intersections of two circle-point curves, and the Burmester centres as those of two centre-point curves. In other words, these are the intersections of two spherical cubics generated from two corresponding four-position cases. Just as in Section 6.9, each one of the five intermediate cases can be resolved into two four-position cases as follows.

$$P_1P_2-P_3-P_4-P_5 \rightarrow (P_1P_2-P_3-P_4) + (P_1-P_3-P_4-P_5) \text{ or}$$
$$(P_1P_2-P_3-P_4) + (P_1P_2-P_3-P_5)$$
$$P_1P_2-P_3P_4-P_5 \rightarrow (P_1P_2-P_3P_4) + (P_1P_2-P_3-P_5)$$
$$P_1P_2P_3-P_4-P_5 \rightarrow (P_1P_2P_3-P_4) + (P_1P_2-P_4-P_5)$$
$$P_1P_2P_3-P_4P_5 \rightarrow (P_1P_2P_3-P_4) + (P_1P_2-P_4P_5)$$
$$P_1P_2P_3P_4-P_5 \rightarrow (P_1P_2P_3P_4) + (P_1P_2P_3-P_5)$$

Equations of circle-point curves (or circling-point curve) and centre-point curves (or centering-point curve) have all been derived. The Burmester points or Burmester centres in each intermediate case can therefore be located, by following the procedures mentioned in previous sections.

7

Dimensional synthesis – path generation problems

As in plane kinematics, the basic path generating mechanism in spherical kinematics is a spherical four-bar linkage, the path of a coupler point of which should possibly approximate a given spherical curve on the unit sphere. We shall start by investigating the algebraic expressions of the coupler curve of a given spherical four-bar linkage. In later sections paths generated by points on rolling cones will be considered.

7.1 Coupler curve

Algebraic expressions for the coupler curve of a spherical four-bar linkage have been derived by Dobrovolskii (1944) and Wörle (1962), but in different forms. Comparatively recent derivation of the coupler curve equations, expressed in terms of various coordinate systems, was given by Dittrich & Zakel (1975). We shall look into some of the different ways of presenting the coupler curve.

7.1.1 Coupler curve in spherical rectangular coordinates

Consider a spherical four-bar linkage A_0ABB_0 as shown in Fig. 7.1. The coupler is the spherical triangle $\triangle ABE$ with a coupler point E. Let the spherical distances AE, BE be denoted respectively by m, n, and $\measuredangle AEB$ by β. The spherical triangle $\triangle ABE$ is uniquely determined by the three constants m, n and β. From E draw ED perpendicular to A_0B_0. Further denote $\measuredangle DEA$ by β_a, and $\measuredangle BED$ by β_b. Suppose the great circle A_0B_0 is on the equator. The spherical rectangular coordinates of the coupler point E with respect to an origin at A_0 are: $u = A_0D$, $v = DE$. Applying equation (A1.12) to $\triangle A_0AD$, in which $\measuredangle A_0DA$ is denoted by τ, we obtain

$$\sin u \cos a = \sin AD \cos \tau + \sin a \cos u \cos \phi \tag{7.1}$$

Application of the sine law, equation (A1.7), to $\triangle ADE$ gives, noting that

$\measuredangle A_0DE = 90°,$

$$\sin AD \cos \tau = \sin m \sin \beta_a \tag{7.2}$$

Substituting equation (7.2) into equation (7.1) results in

$$\sin u \cos a = \sin m \sin \beta_a + \sin a \cos u \cos\phi \tag{7.3}$$

Next applying the cosine law for sides, equation (A1.9), to both $\triangle A_0AD$ and $\triangle EAD$ gives

$$\cos AD = \cos a \cos u + \sin a \sin u \cos \phi$$
$$= \cos m \cos v + \sin m \sin v \cos \beta_a \tag{7.4}$$

Eliminating $\cos \phi$ between equations (7.3) and (7.4) yields finally

$$S_m S_u S_{\beta a} + S_m C_u S_v C_{\beta a} = C_a - C_m C_u C_v \tag{7.5}$$

where, as usual, the symbols $S_m = \sin m$, $C_u = \cos u$, etc. are used for brevity. Similarly for the right-hand portion of the linkage we have

$$S_n S_{f-u} S_{\beta b} + S_n C_{f-u} S_v C_{\beta b} = C_b - C_n C_{f-u} C_v \tag{7.6}$$

Substituting $\beta_b = \beta - \beta_a$ into equation (7.6) will result in an equation containing $S_{\beta a}$ and $C_{\beta a}$, like equation (7.5). Solving this equation with equation (7.5) for $S_{\beta a}$ and $C_{\beta a}$, and substituting their expressions into the identity $S_{\beta a}^2 + C_{\beta a}^2 = 1$ results finally in the following equation of the coupler curve:

$$U^2 + V^2 = W^2 \tag{7.7}$$

where

$$
\begin{aligned}
U &= S_m S_u (C_b - C_n C_{f-u} C_v) \\
&\quad + S_n (C_a - C_m C_u C_v)(C_\beta S_{f-u} - S_\beta C_{f-u} S_v) \\
V &= S_m C_u S_v (C_b - C_n C_{f-u} C_v) \\
&\quad - S_n (C_a - C_m C_u C_v)(S_\beta S_{f-u} + C_\beta C_{f-u} S_v) \\
W &= S_m S_n (S_f C_\beta S_v - C_f S_\beta + S_\beta C_{f-u} C_u C_v^2)
\end{aligned}
\tag{7.8}
$$

Fig. 7.1. For derivation of coupler curve equation in spherical rectangular coordinates.

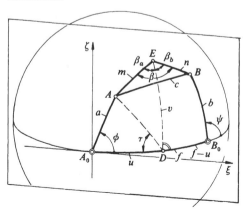

7.1.2 Gnomonic projection of the coupler curve

Imagine that the coupler curve is projected, from the sphere centre O, onto a plane tangent to the unit sphere at A_0, as shown in Fig. 7.1. Let the gnomonic projection of the coupler point E be denoted by E^* (not shown in Fig. 7.1). The spherical rectangular coordinates (u, v) of E can be transformed into the plane rectangular coordinates (ξ, ζ) of E^* by means of equations (A4.13) and (A4.14). Substituting these transformation equations into equation (7.7) results in a coupler curve equation of the form

$$U_1^2 = 4(1 + \xi^2 + \zeta^2)V_1^2 \tag{7.9}$$

where

$$\left.\begin{aligned}
U_1 &= S_m^2(\xi^2 + \zeta^2)[C_b^2(1 + \xi^2 + \zeta^2) + C_n^2(C_f + S_f\xi)^2] \\
&\quad + S_n^2[C_a^2(1 + \xi^2 + \zeta^2) + C_m^2][(S_f - C_f\xi)^2 + \zeta^2] \\
&\quad + 2S_f S_m S_n S_\beta \zeta(1 + \xi^2 + \zeta^2)[C_m C_b + C_n C_a(C_f + S_f\xi)] \\
&\quad + 2S_m S_n C_\beta [C_a C_b(1 + \xi^2 + \zeta^2) \\
&\quad + C_m C_n(C_f + S_f\xi)][S_f\xi - C_f(\xi^2 + \zeta^2)] \\
&\quad - S_m^2 S_n^2 S_\beta^2[S_f\xi - C_f(\xi^2 + \zeta^2)]^2 \\
&\quad - S_f^2 S_m^2 S_n^2 C_\beta^2 \zeta^2(1 + \xi^2 + \zeta^2) \\
V_1 &= C_b S_m^2 C_n(\xi^2 + \zeta^2)(C_f + S_f\xi) + C_a C_m S_n^2[\zeta^2 + (S_f - C_f\xi)^2] \\
&\quad + S_f S_m S_n S_\beta \zeta[C_a C_b(1 + \xi^2 + \zeta^2) + C_m C_n(C_f + S_f\xi)] \\
&\quad + S_m S_n C_\beta[S_f\xi - C_f(\xi^2 + \zeta^2)][C_m C_b + C_n C_a(C_f + S_f\xi)] \\
&\quad + S_f S_m^2 S_n^2 S_\beta C_\beta \zeta[S_f\xi - C_f(\xi^2 + \zeta^2)]
\end{aligned}\right\} \tag{7.10}$$

It can be shown that the coupler curve is a bicircular curve of eighth degree.

7.1.3 Coupler curve in spherical polar coordinates

(1) Coupler curve computed point-by-point

Referring to Fig. 7.2, the spherical polar coordinates of the coupler point E,

Fig. 7.2. For derivation of coupler curve equation in spherical polar coordinates.

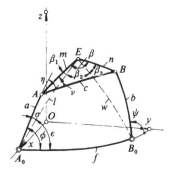

in a certain position of the spherical four-bar linkage A_0ABB_0, with respect to the origin A_0 and spherical polar great circle A_0B_0, are denoted by (l, ε). In order to find these coordinates, we compute first the angle η by means of equation (2.19), in which the correct value of η is to be selected according to the procedure mentioned in Section 3.5. The spherical distance l can then

Fig. 7.3. (a), (b) Coupler curves of a spherical four-bar linkage with $a = 36°$, $b = 50°$, $c = 60°$, $f = 70°$, $m = 35°$, $n = 35°$, $v = 34.458°$.

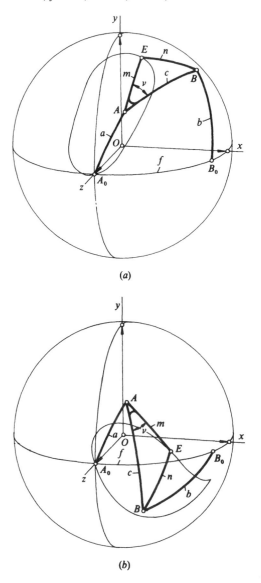

(a)

(b)

be computed by applying the cosine law for sides, equation (A1.9), to $\triangle A_0 AE$:

$$\cos l = \cos a \cos m - \sin a \sin m \cos (\eta - v) \tag{7.11}$$

where v is $\sphericalangle BAE$, being a constant. The angle $\sigma = \sphericalangle EA_0 A$ can then easily be found by applying equations (A1.7) to the same triangle:

$$\sin \sigma = \sin m \frac{\sin (\eta - v)}{\sin l} \tag{7.12}$$

Hence we get

$$\varepsilon = \phi - \sigma \tag{7.13}$$

The coupler curve can then be computed point-by-point for each assumed value of ϕ. Figs. 7.3(a), (b) show the coupler curves of the spherical four-bar linkage generated in two conjugate positions of the linkage.

(2) Coupler curve in implicit expression

Alternatively the coupler curve represented in spherical polar coordinates can be expressed in an implicit equation as follows. Again referring to Fig. 7.2, let the great circle arc $B_0 E$ be denoted by w, and the three angles $\sphericalangle A_0 EA$, $\sphericalangle B_0 EA_0$, $\sphericalangle BEB_0$ by β_1, β_2, β_3 respectively. The derivation of the coupler curve equation starts from the identity

$$\begin{aligned}
\cos (\beta - \beta_2) &= \cos (\beta_1 + \beta_3) \\
&= \cos \beta_1 \cos \beta_3 - \sin \beta_1 \sin \beta_3
\end{aligned} \tag{7.14}$$

Applying the cosine law for sides, equation (A1.9), to $\triangle A_0 EA$ gives

$$\cos \beta_1 = \frac{\cos a - \cos m \cos l}{\sin m \sin l}$$

and consequently

$$\sin^2 \beta_1 = \frac{\sin^2 a \sin^2 l - (\cos m - \cos a \cos l)^2}{\sin^2 m \sin^2 l}$$

Similar expressions can be obtained for $\cos \beta_3$ and $\sin^2 \beta_3$. Substituting these expressions into equation (7.14) and applying equations (A1.7) and (A1.9) to $\triangle A_0 B_0 E$ results in a coupler curve equation of the form

$$U_2 V_2 = W_2^2 \tag{7.15}$$

where

$$\left. \begin{aligned}
U_2 &= \sin^2 a \sin^2 l - (\cos m - \cos a \cos l)^2 \\
V_2 &= \sin^2 b \sin^2 n - (\cos b \cos n - \cos f \cos l - \sin f \sin l \cos \varepsilon)^2 \\
W_2 &= (\cos a - \cos m \cos l) \\
&\quad \cdot [\cos b - \cos n(\cos f \cos l + \sin f \sin l \cos \varepsilon)] \\
&\quad - \sin m \sin n \sin l [\cos \beta(\cos f \cos l - \sin f \cos l \cos \varepsilon) \\
&\quad + \sin \beta \sin f \sin \varepsilon]
\end{aligned} \right\} \tag{7.16}$$

It can be shown that the equation of the gnomonic projection of the coupler curve, transformed from equation (7.15) by means of equations (A4.9) and (A4.10), where (p, θ) are replaced by (l, ε), is identical with equation (7.9).

7.1.4   Coupler curve by transformation matrix

In Section 4.1.3 it was shown how the coordinates (x_{E1}, y_{E1}, z_{E1}) of a coupler point E, with respect to a coordinate system $x_1 y_1 z_1$ embedded in the coupler body, can be transformed into the coordinates (x_E, y_E, z_E) of the same point, but with respect to a fixed coordinate system xyz. The procedure was illustrated in a table form in the example at the end of Section 4.1.3. In this procedure the quantities η, e, g, γ (Fig. 4.3(a)) have to be determined for each assumed value of ϕ, in order to compute the elements of the transformation matrix $\mathbb{M}_{10}$ by equations (4.24). The three computed coordinates (x_E, y_E, z_E) give the path of E, or the coupler curve in the fixed coordinate system.

The transformation matrix $\mathbb{M}_{10}$ may also be found without computing the values of η, e, g, γ when the output angle ψ is determined. Referring to Figs. 4.2(a) and 4.3(a), we have the three components of the vector $\overrightarrow{OA} = \mathbf{i}_1 = \mathbf{r}_A$ with respect to the fixed xyz-system,

$$\mathbf{i}_1 = \mathbf{r}_A = C_a \mathbf{i} + S_a C_\phi \mathbf{j} + S_a S_\phi \mathbf{k} \tag{7.17}$$

and the three components of the vector $\overrightarrow{OB} = \mathbf{r}_B$,

$$\mathbf{r}_B = (C_b C_f - S_b S_f C_\psi)\mathbf{i} + (C_b S_f + S_b C_f C_\psi)\mathbf{j} + S_b S_\psi \mathbf{k}$$

The unit vector $\mathbf{k}_1$ is then

$$\mathbf{k}_1 = \frac{\mathbf{r}_A \times \mathbf{r}_B}{S_c} = \frac{1}{S_c} \begin{vmatrix} \mathbf{i} & \mathbf{j} & \mathbf{k} \\ C_a & S_a C_\phi & S_a S_\phi \\ C_b C_f - S_b S_f C_\psi & C_b S_f + S_b C_f C_\psi & S_b S_\psi \end{vmatrix}$$

$$= k_{1x}\mathbf{i} + k_{1y}\mathbf{j} + k_{1z}\mathbf{k} \tag{7.18}$$

The unit vector $\mathbf{j}_1$ is found from

$$\mathbf{j}_1 = \mathbf{k}_1 \times \mathbf{i}_1 = \begin{vmatrix} \mathbf{i} & \mathbf{j} & \mathbf{k} \\ k_{1x} & k_{1y} & k_{1z} \\ C_a & S_a C_\phi & S_a S_\phi \end{vmatrix} = j_{1x}\mathbf{i} + j_{1y}\mathbf{j} + j_{1z}\mathbf{k} \tag{7.19}$$

From equations (7.17)–(7.19) we see that the elements of the transformation matrix $\mathbb{M}_{10}$ in equation (4.23) are:

$$m_{11} = C_a$$

$$m_{12} = j_{1x} = S_a S_\phi k_{1y} - S_a C_\phi k_{1z}$$

$$= \frac{S_a S_\phi}{S_c}[-C_a S_b S_\psi + S_a S_\phi (C_b C_f - S_b S_f C_\psi)]$$

$$- \frac{S_a S_\phi}{S_c}[C_a(C_b S_f + S_b C_f C_\psi) - S_a C_\phi(C_b C_f - S_b S_f C_\psi)]$$

$$m_{13} = k_{1x} = \frac{1}{S_c}[S_aS_bC_\phi S_\psi - S_aS_\phi(C_bS_f + S_bC_fC_\psi)]$$

$$m_{21} = S_aC_\phi$$

$$m_{22} = j_{1y} = C_ak_{1z} - S_aS_\phi k_{1x}$$

$$= \frac{C_a}{S_c}[C_a(C_bS_f + S_bC_fC_\psi) - S_aC_\phi(C_bC_f - S_bS_fC_\psi)]$$

$$- \frac{S_aS_\phi}{S_c}[S_aS_bC_\phi S_\psi - S_aS_\phi(C_bS_f + S_bC_fC_\psi)]$$

$$m_{23} = k_{1y} = \frac{1}{S_c}[-C_aS_bS_\psi + S_aS_\phi(C_bC_f - S_bS_fC_\psi)]$$

$$m_{31} = S_aS_\phi$$

$$m_{32} = j_{1z} = S_aC_\phi k_{1x} - C_ak_{1y}$$

$$= \frac{S_aC_\phi}{S_c}[S_aS_bC_\phi S_\psi - S_aS_\phi(C_bS_f + S_bC_fC_\psi)]$$

$$- \frac{C_a}{S_c}[-C_aS_bS_\psi + S_aS_\phi(C_bC_f - S_bS_fC_\psi)]$$

$$m_{33} = k_{1z} = \frac{1}{S_c}[C_a(C_bS_f + S_bC_fC_\psi) - S_aC_\phi(C_bC_f - S_bS_fC_\psi)]$$

The complexity of computing these elements is about the same as that described in Section 4.1.3.

7.2 Double points of a coupler curve

When a coupler curve possesses a double point, then, in the position where the generating coupler point E is just at the double point, it must be at the same time the pole of rotation between two finitely separated positions A_1B_1 and A_2B_2 of the coupler, as shown in Fig. 7.4. The great circles A_0E and B_0E are, respectively, the bisectors of $\sphericalangle A_1EA_2$ and $\sphericalangle B_1EB_2$. Because

Fig. 7.4. Double point of a coupler curve.

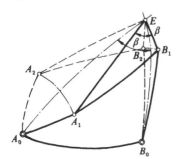

$\sphericalangle A_1EA_2 = \sphericalangle B_1EB_2$, therefore

$$\sphericalangle B_0EA_0 = \sphericalangle B_1EA_1 = \beta \tag{7.20}$$

The double point lies therefore on a curve which is the locus of a point at which the great circle arc A_0B_0 subtends a constant angle β. The equation of this curve, expressed in spherical polar coordinates (l, ε) with A_0 as the origin and A_0B_0 as the spherical polar great circle, is, by equation (A1.11),

$$\frac{\sin l}{\tan f} - \cos l \cos \varepsilon = \frac{\sin \varepsilon}{\tan \beta} \tag{7.21}$$

It can be shown that equation (7.21) is exactly equivalent to putting $W = 0$ in equation (7.8), its gnomonic projection being

$$S_\beta^2[S_f\xi - C_f(\xi^2 + \zeta^2)]^2 - C_\beta^2 S_f^2\zeta^2(1 + \xi^2 + \zeta^2) = 0 \tag{7.22}$$

This curve is therefore a spherical quartic, passing through A_0 and B_0. In plane kinematics this curve degenerates into a circle (Beyer, 1953, Fig. 206). From the two conditions for a double point E that A_0B_0 should subtend a constant angle β at E, and that both A_0A_1 and B_0B_1 should subtend equal angles at E, it can be shown that the maximum number of real double points in a spherical coupler curve is four (Primrose & Freudenstein, 1969).

For a given spherical four-bar linkage, for instance that in Fig. 7.4 in the position $A_0A_1B_1B_0$, the locus of the coupler point which is generating a double point is the locus of a point at which A_0B_0 and A_1B_1 subtend an equal angle (β being variable). This reminds us of the centre-point curve in plane kinematics, as well as that mentioned in Section 6.7, that the opposite sides of an opposite quadrilateral subtend at a point on the curve equal or supplementary angles. The locus of the coupler point which, in a certain position of the linkage, generates a double point is therefore of the nature of a spherical centre-point curve (Kraus, 1954). In other words, it is a spherical cubic.

For a given spherical four-bar linkage, the location of the coupler point E which, on the whole, generates a coupler curve with a double point, can be determined as the intersection of two bisectors A_0E and B_0E of any two corresponding angles $\sphericalangle A_1A_0A_2$ and $\sphericalangle B_1B_0B_2$. This intersection gives the coordinates (l, ε) of E in the fixed coordinate system, but these can be transformed into coordinates with respect to the coupler body.

If the coupler point coincides with the velocity pole of the coupler, then the double point becomes a cusp, and the coupler point is describing a return point of its path, as mentioned in Section 6.8.5. This situation is quite similar to that in plane kinematics.

7.3   Generating a path through given path points

Path generating problems in plane kinematics and in spatial kinematics have been extensively studied. It seems that investigations specifically dealing with path generating problems in spherical kinematics are relatively few (Johnson, 1965; Suh & Radcliffe, 1967; Sridhar & Torfason, 1970a, b; Verma & Bussel, 1970; Soni & Hamid, 1972). Theoretically it is possible to substitute the coordinates of the given path points into any one of the coupler curve equations mentioned above, and then solve them for the dimensions of the linkage. These equations are in general highly non-linear. As in plane kinematics, if only the locations of the path points are prescribed, the maximum number of path points which may be prescribed for a spherical four-bar linkage is nine. This is because, according to the principle of balancing valances in a synthesis procedure (Kraus, 1952), the number of available coordinates of the four joints A_0, A_1, B_1, B_0 and the coupler point E_1 is ten, while the prescribed location of the first path point E_1 requires two coordinates, and the location of each of the successive path points E_2, E_3, ...E_9 requires one coordinate. However, practical path generating problems usually include coordinations of coupler point movements with crank rotations. We shall consider two major cases (Chiang, 1986a).

7.3.1   Coordinations of three point-positions with two crank rotations

Consider first only the two-link chain A_0AE of a spherical four-bar linkage such as the one shown in Fig. 7.2. When the crank a rotates from its first position A_0A_1 through an angle ϕ_{1i} to a position A_0A_i, the coupler point E moves from E_1 to a position E_i. Suppose the location of A_0 and those of the three points E_1, E_2, E_3 and the two angles ϕ_{12}, ϕ_{13} are prescribed. It is

Fig. 7.5. Coordinations of three point-positions with two crank rotations.

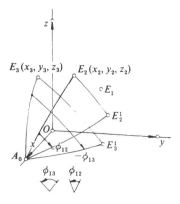

required to synthesize a four-bar to generate a coupler curve passing through E_1, E_2, E_3 and at the same time to coordinate the movements $E_1 \to E_2$ and $E_1 \to E_3$ with the respective crank rotations ϕ_{12} and ϕ_{13}.

To solve this problem, the first step is to find the location of the joint A say, in its first position A_1. This can be done by means of the well-known inversion concept used in plane kinematics, similar to that mentioned in Section 6.4.1. Referring to Fig. 7.5, because the point-positions E_1, E_2, E_3 are specified on the fixed shell f, and the angles of rotation ϕ_{12}, ϕ_{13} are those of the crank a, the relative motion is that between a and f. Join the great circle arcs $A_0 E_2$ and $A_0 E_3$, and displace them through angles $-\phi_{12}$ and $-\phi_{13}$ about the axis $O A_0$ to $A_0 E_2^1$ and $A_0 E_3^1$ respectively. The relative motion remains unchanged, as if the body a were fixed and the point E on the body f were displaced from E_1 through E_2^1 to E_3^1. The point on the crank a, equally distant from E_1, E_2^1 and E_3^1, is the point A_1, which is the spherical centre of the spherical circle passing through these three points.

Algebraically it is most convenient to orient one of the coordinate axes, say the x-axis, in line with the axis $O A_0$, as shown in Fig. 7.5, because this will make the displacement matrices very simple. Let the coordinates of E_1, E_2^1, E_3^1, etc. be denoted by (x_1, y_1, z_1), (x_2^1, y_2^1, z_2^1), (x_3^1, y_3^1, z_3^1), etc. respectively. The coordinates of E_2^1 can be obtained by applying equation(A2.22)to the coordinates of E_2, where $\alpha = -\phi_{12}$:

$$\begin{bmatrix} x_2^1 \\ y_2^1 \\ z_2^1 \end{bmatrix} = \begin{bmatrix} 1 & 0 & 0 \\ 0 & \cos\phi_{12} & \sin\phi_{12} \\ 0 & -\sin\phi_{12} & \cos\phi_{12} \end{bmatrix} \begin{bmatrix} x_2 \\ y_2 \\ z_2 \end{bmatrix}$$

$$= \begin{bmatrix} x_2 \\ y_2\cos\phi_{12} + z_2\sin\phi_{12} \\ -y_2\sin\phi_{12} + z_2\cos\phi_{12} \end{bmatrix} \tag{7.23}$$

Similarly the coordinates of E_3^1 can be computed from those of E_3 and $-\phi_{13}$ as

$$\begin{bmatrix} x_3^1 \\ y_3^1 \\ z_3^1 \end{bmatrix} = \begin{bmatrix} x_3 \\ y_3\cos\phi_{13} + z_3\sin\phi_{13} \\ -y_3\sin\phi_{13} + z_3\cos\phi_{13} \end{bmatrix} \tag{7.24}$$

Having computed the coordinates of E_2^1 and E_3^1, the coordinates of A_1 can be found from

$$(x_2^1 - x_1)x_{A1} + (y_2^1 - y_1)y_{A1} + (z_2^1 - z_1)z_{A1} = 0 \tag{7.25}$$

$$(x_3^1 - x_1)x_{A1} + (y_3^1 - y_1)y_{A1} + (z_3^1 - z_1)z_{A1} = 0 \tag{7.26}$$

Again equations (7.25) and (7.26) are of the form of equation (6.3). Hence they can be solved for the ratios x_{A1}/z_{A1} and y_{A1}/z_{A1}, and by the application of equation (A3.1a) the coordinates of $A_1(x_{A1}, y_{A1}, z_{A1})$ can be determined. The coordinates of the two homologous points A_2, A_3 ol A_1 can then be determined by displacing A_1 about the x-axis through angles $+\phi_{12}$ and $+\phi_{13}$.

With the three known positions A_1E_1, A_2E_2, A_3E_3 of the coupler body, there is no difficulty in choosing a suitable circle-point B_1 and centre-point B_0 by means of the procedure mentioned in Section 6.4.

7.3.2   Coordinations of four point-positions with three crank rotations

Suppose it is required to generate a path passing through four given point positions E_1, E_2, E_3, E_4 and at the same time to coordinate the movements $E_1 \rightarrow E_2, E_1 \rightarrow E_3, E_1 \rightarrow E_4$ with the respective given crank rotations $\phi_{12}, \phi_{13}, \phi_{14}$. In this case the fixed crank centre A_0 cannot be prescribed arbitrarily. The location of A_0 is subject to the condition that the three points E_2^1, E_3^1, E_4^1 thus produced should lie together with E_1 on a spherical circle, the spherical centre of which is A_1. Let the locus of A_0 be denoted by k_{A0}, whose characteristics we are going to find out.

For a certain crank centre A_0 with coordinates (x_0, y_0, z_0) which, in general, does not lie on any one of the coordinate axes x, y, z, as shown in Fig. 7.6, the point E_i, where $i = 2, 3, 4$, is displayed by rotating A_0E_i about OA_0 through an angle $-\phi_{1i}$ to $E_i^1(x_i^1 \, y_i^1 \, z_i^1)$. These coordinates are obtained by applying equations (A2.34) to the present case:

$$\begin{bmatrix} x_i^1 \\ y_i^1 \\ z_i^1 \end{bmatrix} = \begin{bmatrix} (V_{\phi i}x_0^2 + C_{\phi i})x_i + (V_{\phi i}x_0y_0 + S_{\phi i}z_0)y_i + (V_{\phi i}z_0x_0 - S_{\phi i}y_0)z_i \\ (V_{\phi i}x_0y_0 - S_{\phi i}z_0)x_i + (V_{\phi i}y_0^2 + C_{\phi i})y_i + (V_{\phi i}y_0z_0 + S_{\phi i}x_0)z_i \\ (V_{\phi i}z_0x_0 + S_{\phi i}y_0)x_i + (V_{\phi i}y_0z_0 - S_{\phi i}x_0)y_i + (V_{\phi i}z_0^2 + C_{\phi i})z_i \end{bmatrix}$$

$$i = 2, 3, 4 \qquad (7.27)$$

where ϕ_i stands for ϕ_{1i}, and $V_{\phi i}$ stands for $1 - \cos \phi_{1i}$.

By analogy with equation (6.3), the above mentioned condition is

$$(x_i^1 - x_1)x_{A1} + (y_i^1 - y_1)y_{A1} + (z_i^1 - z_1)z_{A1} = 0, \quad i = 2, 3, 4 \qquad (7.28)$$

Fig. 7.6. Coordinations of four point-positions with three crank rotations.

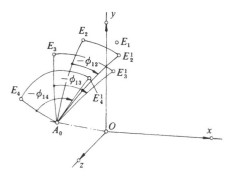

Equations (7.28) represent a system of three homogeneous linear equations in the unknowns x_{A1}, y_{A1}, z_{A1}. For the existence of the solution, the determinant of the coefficients must vanish, or

$$\begin{vmatrix} x_2^1 - x_1 & y_2^1 - y_1 & z_2^1 - z_1 \\ x_3^1 - x_1 & y_3^1 - y_1 & z_3^1 - z_1 \\ x_4^1 - x_1 & y_4^1 - y_1 & z_4^1 - z_1 \end{vmatrix} = 0 \tag{7.29}$$

Again for brevity, equation (7.29) is written in a single row form as follows:

$$k_{A0}: \quad \begin{vmatrix} x_i^1 - x_1 & y_i^1 - y_1 & z_i^1 - z_1 \end{vmatrix} = 0, \quad i = 2, 3, 4 \tag{7.29a}$$

According to equation (7.27), the variables x_0, y_0, z_0 are included in x_i^1, y_i^1, z_i^1. Equation (7.29a) is therefore the equation of k_{A0}. Substituting equations (7.27) into equation (7.29a) and expanding the determinant will result in a non-homogeneous equation of sixth degree in the three variables x_0, y_0, z_0. It can be shown that, because of the identical vanishing of the coefficients of the fifth and sixth-degree terms, and the reduction of the fourth-degree terms to second-degree terms by virtue of equation (A3.1), this equation becomes an equation of third degree in x_0, y_0, z_0. However, upon transformation into spherical polar coordinates (p_0, θ_0) of the point A_0 by means of equations (A4.2), the final equation of k_{A0} after eliminating the radical term by squaring it once, becomes

$$k_{A0}: \quad q_{06}t^6 + q_{05}t^5 + q_{04}t^4 + q_{03}t^3 + q_{02}t^2 + q_{01}t + q_{00} = 0 \tag{7.30}$$

where $t = \tan p_0$ and the coefficients $q_{06}, q_{05}, \ldots, q_{00}$ are functions of θ_0, whose expressions are given in Appendix 8. For each assumed value of θ_0, there are six values, real or imaginary, of $t = \tan p_0$, or six points on the curve k_{A0}. The k_{A0}-curve is therefore a spherical sextic.

If the spherical polar coordinate system is chosen so that the origin lies on

Fig. 7.7. Selected coordinate system $x'y'z'$.

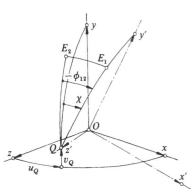

the curve k_{A0}, then the constant term q_{00} in equation (7.30) will vanish identically. Consider a point Q on the perpendicular bisector of the great circle E_1E_2, as shown in Fig. 7.7, such that $\not\prec E_2QE_1 = -\phi_{12}$, and that when the great circle QE_2 is displaced through an angle $-\phi_{12}$ about the axis OQ, it will coincide with QE_1. The point Q is a point on the locus k_{A0}, because if A_0 were taken at Q, then Q would become the pole P_{12} of the coupler and the point E_2^1 would coincide with E_1, which, together with the two corresponding points E_2^1 and E_3^1, would certainly lie on a spherical circle. This is just the well-known principle of point-position reduction in plane kinematics, which has also been applied in spherical kinematics (Soni & Huang, 1971). Points similar to Q can also be located on the perpendicular bisectors of E_1E_3 and E_1E_4, with respective subtended angles $-\phi_{13}$ and $-\phi_{14}$. These points should also lie on k_{A0}. Suppose we want to rotate the coordinate system until the z-axis is oriented in the direction OQ and the yz-plane passes through E_1, as shown in the $x'y'z'$ position in Fig. 7.7. Let the spherical rectangular coordinates of Q with respect to the original xyz-system be (u_Q, v_Q) as defined in Fig. 7.7, and the angle between QE_1 and the meridian passing through Q be denoted by χ, which is negative as shown. The coordinates (x, y, z) of a point with respect to the original xyz-system are then transformed into coordinates (x', y', z') with respect to the rotated $x'y'z'$-system by the following equation:

$$\begin{bmatrix} x' \\ y' \\ z' \end{bmatrix} = \mathbb{M}_Q \begin{bmatrix} x \\ y \\ z \end{bmatrix} \tag{7.31}$$

where

$$\mathbb{M}_Q = \begin{bmatrix} C_u C_\chi - S_u S_v S_\chi & C_v S_\chi & -S_u C_\chi - C_u S_v S_\chi \\ -C_u S_\chi - S_u S_v C_\chi & C_v C_\chi & S_u S_\chi - C_u S_v C_\chi \\ S_u C_v & S_v & C_u C_v \end{bmatrix} \tag{7.32}$$

where $S_u = \sin u_Q$, $S_v = \sin v_Q$, etc. The derivation of the transformation matrix $\mathbb{M}_Q$ is given in Appendix 8.

A suitable point on the k_{A0}-curve can then be chosen as A_0. Substituting the coordinates of A_0, preferably transformed into (x_0, y_0, z_0) by means of equations (A4.1), into any two of equations (7.28), we can solve these equations for x_{A1}/z_{A1} and y_{A1}/z_{A1} as before. The coordinates (x_{A1}, y_{A1}, z_{A1}) are determined by the application of equation (A3.1a). The point A_2, A_3 and A_4 can then be determined without difficulty.

With the four positions A_1E_1, A_2E_2, A_3E_3 and A_4E_4 of the coupler thus determined, the point B_0 can be chosen on the corresponding spherical centre-point curve k_m, which can be determined by following the procedure mentioned in Section 6.7.1. Care should be taken that the elements of the determinant in equation (6.121) are to be computed directly from equations

(6.59)–(6.61), not from the equations in Section 6.4.3, because the coordinate system in the present case is not oriented as the system selected there. In fact, equations (A6.7) can still be used in computing the coefficients $m_1, \ldots, m_9$ of equation (6.121a), but an additional term $m_{10} z_0^3$ must be added to the k_m-equation, with $m_{10} = |d_{31i}, d_{32i}, d_{33i} - 1|$. The circle-point B_1 corresponding to B_0 can then be determined accordingly.

Alternatively the circle-point B_1 can first be chosen on the spherical circle-point curve k_1, and the centre-point B_0 determined accordingly. There are again ∞^2 possible solutions, corresponding to the ∞^1 ways of choosing A_0 on k_{A0}, and ∞^1 ways of choosing B_0 on k_m or of choosing B_1 on k_1.

Again the synthesized linkage should be free from branch and order problems, similar to that mentioned in Section 6.7.1.

Example: Given the locations of four path points of a coupler point E, with respect to an xyz-system:

$$E_1(0.295584, 0.895806, 0.331906),$$
$$E_2(0.177549, 0.927015, 0.330332),$$
$$E_3(6.11074 \times 10^{-2}, 0.925088, 0.374805),$$
$$E_4(-4.26727 \times 10^{-2}, 0.881602, 0.470060).$$

It is required to generate a coupler curve passing through these four points and at the same time to coordinate the movements $E_1 \to E_2$, $E_1 \to E_3$, $E_1 \to E_4$ with the respective crank rotations $\phi_2\ (=\phi_{12}) = 20°$, $\phi_3\ (=\phi_{13}) = 40°$, $\phi_4\ (=\phi_{14}) = 60°$.

The point Q, as shown in Fig. 7.7, is first located according to Appendix 8: $Q(0.188795, 0.746236, 0.638348)$. The transformation matrix in equation (7.32) is then built up:

$$\mathbb{M}_Q = \begin{bmatrix} 0.922006 & -0.358452 & 0.146345 \\ 0.338025 & 0.560932 & -0.755708 \\ 0.188795 & 0.746236 & 0.638348 \end{bmatrix}$$

The above four positions of E are transformed into those referred to the new coordinate system $x'y'z'$:

$$E_1'(0, 0.351577, 0.936159),$$
$$E_2'(-0.120247, 0.330374, 0.936159),$$
$$E_3'(-0.220407, 0.256324, 0.941126),$$
$$E_4'(-0.286565, 0.124866, 0.949889)$$

Based on these new coordinates and the given values of ϕ_2, ϕ_3, ϕ_4, the 20 coefficients $k_{31}, k_{32}, \ldots, k_0$ in equation (A8.4) are computed:

0.809728	2.201127	-1.287208	2.385640	-0.661197
-2.425968	0.727341	1.264633	2.234742	-0.519179
9.37306×10^{-3}	1.789340	0.646058	0.606304	-0.841482
-0.937265	-0.327192	-0.399016	1.265194	-0.624045

The corresponding k_{A0}-curve together with the four path points is shown in Fig. 7.8.

Choose a point on the k_{A0}-curve as A_0', say $A_0'(0.131015, -0.743020,$

Fig. 7.8. Example: k_{A0}-curve.

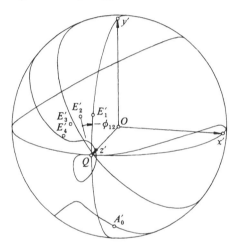

Fig. 7.9. Example: synthesized path generator.

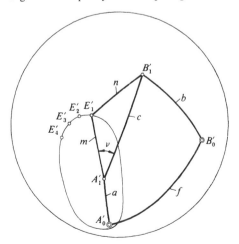

0.656320). The corresponding point A'_1 is found according to the procedure mentioned in Section 7.3.1: $A'_1(0.140837, -0.219402, 0.965416)$. The homologous points of A'_1 are found by applying equation (A2.34) to the present case, namely, by rotating $A'_0A'_1$ about the axis OA'_0 through respective angles 20°, 40°, 60°:

$$A'_2(-0.057305, -0.254340, 0.965416)$$
$$A'_3(-0.235655, -0.331649, 0.913497)$$
$$A'_4(-0.372701, -0.442004, 0.815921)$$

With the four known positions $A'_1E'_1$, $A'_2E'_2$, $A'_3E'_3$, $A'_4E'_4$ of the coupler, a centre-point B'_0 on the spherical centre-point curve is chosen, say $B'_0(0.916438, 0.060706, 0.395546)$, and the corresponding circle-point B'_1 is found: B'_1 (0.401002, 0.680874, 0.612869). Having found the locations of the points A'_0, A'_1, B'_0, B'_1, E'_1, the dimensions of the spherical four-bar linkage are:

$$a = A'_0A'_1 = 35.4033°, \ b = B'_0B'_1 = 49.3646°, \ c = A'_1B'_1 = 60.0817°,$$
$$f = A'_0B'_0 = 70.4539°, \ m = A'_1E'_1 = 34.2443°, \ n = B'_1E'_1 = 35.5978°,$$
$$v = 34.7342°.$$

The synthesized four-bar path generator together with the coupler curve is shown in Fig. 7.9. The coupler curve passes through the four given path points as required.

7.4   Higher path curvature

Theory of higher path curvature in plane kinematics was first generalized by (Freudenstein, 1965a) to match an arbitrary plane curve by the path of a moving point, using the so-called *characteristic numbers*. These characteristic numbers can also be expressed in terms of *instantaneous invariants*. By instantaneous invariants is meant the geometrical quantities which must be common to all moving bodies if they are to have the same instantaneous motion up to a certain order (Bottema, 1961; Bottema & Roth, 1979; Ting & Soni, 1983). This concept was then extended to spherical kinematics by (Yang & Roth, 1973) using spherical instantaneous invariants derived by (Kamphuis, 1969) originally for matching spherical circles. Recently these instantaneous invariants are related to the differential properties of the so-called image curve of the motion by a mapping method (Ravani & Roth, 1984; McCarthy & Ravani, 1986.)

7.4.1   Characteristic numbers of a spherical curve

It was shown in Section 5.1 that the geodetic curvature of a spherical curve is $\kappa_g = 1/\tan \rho$, and the curvature of this spherical curve is $\kappa = 1/\sin \rho$, where ρ is the spherical radius of curvature, as shown in Fig. 5.1(b). The relation between κ_g and κ is $\kappa^2 = \kappa_n^2 + \kappa_g^2 = 1 + \kappa_g^2$, because $\kappa_n \equiv 1$ for a spherical curve on the unit sphere. Either κ_g, κ or ρ can be used to specify the curvature of a spherical curve. If two spherical curves, tangent to each other at a certain point, have the same value of ρ, i.e. the same osculating spherical circle, they are said to be in a three-point contact, or to match to the third order. If these two curves have, besides the same ρ, also the same ratio of the rate of change of ρ to ρ, they are said to be in a four-point contact, or to match to the fourth order. Furthermore, if they have, besides the same ρ and the same ratio of the rate of change of ρ to ρ, also the same ratio of the second rate of change of ρ to ρ, they are said to be in a five-point contact, or to match to the fifth order, and so on. Now in place of ρ we use $1/\kappa = \sin \rho$. The jth characteristic number λ_j is defined as the ratio of the jth rate of change of $\sin \rho$ with respect to the infinitesimal curvilinear distance ds along the curve, to $\sin \rho$, or

$$\lambda_j = \frac{1}{\sin \rho} \left[\frac{d^j \sin \rho}{ds^j} \right]_{s=0} \tag{7.33}$$

By the definition of $\kappa_g = 1/\tan \rho$ and $\tau = -\,d\rho/ds$, equation (5.20), we have

$$\lambda_1 = -\kappa_g \tau \tag{7.34}$$

$$\lambda_2 = -\tau^2 - \kappa_g \tau' \tag{7.35}$$

$$\lambda_3 = \kappa_g \tau^3 - 3\tau\tau' - \kappa_g \tau'' \tag{7.36}$$

where (') denotes derivatives with respect to the curve parameter s along the path (not along a polode).

Two spherical curves having the same ρ, $\lambda_1, \lambda_2, \ldots, \lambda_j$ at a certain point are said to be in a $(j+3)$-point contact, or to match to the $(j+3)$ order. This designation also applies even when the two curves are not in real contact and in different positions, provided the respective point on each curve is clearly indicated.

The principle of higher path curvature may be stated as follows: for a given spherical curve, there always exist generating points on a moving body whose paths will match the given curve, at a given point, to a certain order, whatsoever the motion of the body may be.

7.4.2 Characteristic numbers in terms of instantaneous invariants

Kamphuis has shown that the instantaneous invariants of a spherically moving body can be represented by the components of the angular velocity and the time derivatives of these components (Kamphuis, 1969). It has been shown in equation (4.26) that, if the angular velocity vector of the moving body is $\boldsymbol{\omega} = \omega_x \mathbf{i} + \omega_y \mathbf{j} + \omega_z \mathbf{k}$, the velocity vector of a moving point, with coordinates (x, y, z) with respect to a fixed coordinate system, is

$$\dot{\mathbf{r}} = \dot{x}\mathbf{i} + \dot{y}\mathbf{j} + \dot{z}\mathbf{k} \tag{[(4.26)]}$$

where

$$\left.\begin{array}{l} \dot{x} = \omega_y z - \omega_z y \\ \dot{y} = \omega_z x - \omega_x z \\ \dot{z} = \omega_x y - \omega_y x \end{array}\right\} \tag{7.37}$$

Successive differentiations of **r** with respect to time give

$$\dddot{\mathbf{r}} = \dddot{x}\mathbf{i} + \dddot{y}\mathbf{j} + \dddot{z}\mathbf{k}$$
$$\ddddot{\mathbf{r}} = \ddddot{x}\,\mathbf{i} + \ddddot{y}\,\mathbf{j} + \ddddot{z}\,\mathbf{k} \qquad\qquad (7.38)$$

----

where $\dddot{x}$, $\dddot{y}$, $\dddot{z}$; $\ddddot{x}$, $\ddddot{y}$, $\ddddot{z}$, etc. can be derived by successively differentiating $\dot{x}$, $\dot{y}$, $\dot{z}$ in equations (7.37). In Section 5.1 we have already found the expressions for κ_g and τ in terms of **r**, $\dot{\mathbf{r}}$, $\ddot{\mathbf{r}}$ and $\dddot{\mathbf{r}}$, namely,

$$\kappa_g = \frac{\mathbf{r}\cdot(\dot{\mathbf{r}}\times\ddot{\mathbf{r}})}{(\dot{\mathbf{r}}\cdot\dot{\mathbf{r}})^{3/2}} \qquad\qquad [(5.26)]$$

and

$$\tau = \frac{\dot{\mathbf{r}}\cdot(\ddot{\mathbf{r}}\times\dddot{\mathbf{r}})}{(\dot{\mathbf{r}}\times\ddot{\mathbf{r}})\cdot(\dot{\mathbf{r}}\times\ddot{\mathbf{r}})} \qquad\qquad [(5.32)]$$

Hence, by substituting the expressions in equations (7.38) into equations (5.26) and (5.32) we can find the expressions for κ_g and τ in terms of ω_x, ω_y, ω_z and their time derivatives, and x, y, z. Now the fixed coordinate system can be chosen in a position such that at time $t = 0$, $\omega_x = 0$, $\omega_y = 0$, $\omega_z = \omega$, and $\dot{\omega}_x < 0$ and $\dot{\omega}_y = 0$ (Fig. 7.10). Note that this selected coordinate system is consistent with the canonical system described in Section 6.4.3. There we had $\omega_z = -\omega$ and the pole changing velocity **u** was in the $+x$ direction. Here we have $\omega_z = +\omega$ and $\dot{\omega}_x$ is in the $-x$ direction. Furthermore, since we are only concerned about the geometrical properties of the motion, we may set $\omega = +1$ without change of magnitude. In other words, at $t = 0$, $\dot{\omega}_z = 0$ too. Consequently, at $t = 0$,

$$\kappa_g = \frac{F_3}{(x^2 + y^2)^{3/2}} \qquad\qquad (7.39)$$

$$\tau = \frac{H_3}{G_4} \qquad\qquad (7.40)$$

where

$$F_3 = z(x^2 + y^2) + \dot{\omega}_x y$$
$$H_3 = (x^2 + y^2)[(2\dot{\omega}_x - \ddot{\omega}_y)x + \ddot{\omega}_x y] + 3\dot{\omega}_x^2 xyz$$
$$G_4 = \dot{\omega}_x^2 y^2(x^2 + y^2) + (x^2 + y^2 + \dot{\omega}_x yz)^2$$

The subscript indicates the degree of the corresponding polynomial. It should be noted that all the quantities $\dot{\omega}_x$, $\ddot{\omega}_y$, etc. are evaluated at $t = 0$.

To find τ', differentiating equation (5.32) with respect to time and evaluating the instantaneous invariants at $t = 0$ gives

$$\dot{\tau} = \frac{1}{G_4^2}(G_4 L_3 + H_3 B_4)$$

and

$$\tau' = \frac{\dot{\tau}}{ds/dt} = \frac{\dot{\tau}}{(\dot{\mathbf{r}}\cdot\dot{\mathbf{r}})^{1/2}} = \frac{\dot{\tau}}{(x^2+y^2)^{1/2}} = \frac{(G_4L_3+H_3B_4)}{G_4^2(x^2+y^2)^{1/2}} \qquad (7.41)$$

where

$$
\begin{aligned}
L_3 &= (x^2 + y^2 + \dot{\omega}_x yz)[\ddot{\omega}_x y + 3\ddot{\omega}_x x - \ddot{\omega}_y x - 3\dot{\omega}_x(y + \dot{\omega}_x z) + 3\ddot{\omega}_y y] \\
&\quad + \dot{\omega}_x y\{(1 - 4\ddot{\omega}_z)(x^2 + y^2) - 3\dot{\omega}_x^2 y^2 \\
&\quad + z[(\ddot{\omega}_x + \ddot{\omega}_y)x + (\dot{\omega}_x + \ddot{\omega}_y - \ddot{\omega}_x)y]\} \\
B_4 &= 2\{\dot{\omega}_x(x^2 + y^2)y[(\ddot{\omega}_y - 2\dot{\omega}_x)x - \ddot{\omega}_x y] \\
&\quad + z(x^2 + y^2 + \dot{\omega}_x yz)[(\ddot{\omega}_x + \ddot{\omega}_y)x - \ddot{\omega}_x y]\}
\end{aligned}
$$

Substituting equations (7.39)–(7.41) into equations (7.34) and (7.35), we get

$$\lambda_1^2: \quad \lambda_1^2 G_4^2(x^2+y^2)^3 = F_3^2 H_3^2 \qquad (7.42)$$

$$\lambda_2: \quad \lambda_2 G_4^2(x^2+y^2)^2 = -H_3^2(x^2+y^2)^2 - F_3(G_4L_3+H_3B_4) \qquad (7.43)$$

It can be shown that, for a prescribed λ_1, equation (7.42) is a spherical curve of 14th degree on the unit sphere, with the velocity pole, the point $(0,0,1)$, as a sextuple point on the curve, and the poletangent great circle as a four-fold tangent and the polenormal great circle as a two-fold tangent at the pole. This curve will be called the λ_1^2-curve. For a specified value of λ_1^2, all points of the moving body on the λ_1^2-curve will generate curves with the same characteristic number $|\lambda_1|$.

It can also be shown that, for a prescribed λ_2, equation (7.43) is a spherical curve of 12th degree on the unit sphere, with the velocity pole as a quadruple point on the curve, and the poletangent great circle as a four-fold tangent at this point. This curve will be called the λ_2-curve.

7.4.3 Matching a given spherical curve
(1) Matching to the third order
To match the ρ value, say ρ_1, of a given spherical curve at a certain point, we set equation (7.39) to this prescribed ρ_1, or

$$\rho: \quad F_3 \tan\rho_1 = (x^2+y^2)^{3/2} \qquad (7.44)$$

Equation (7.44) is exactly the same as equation (6.97), the ρ-curve, and we see that $\dot{\omega}_x = -\Theta$. This means that all points on the ρ-curve generate paths matching the given spherical curve, to the third order. The ρ-curve is a spherical sextic which passes twice through the velocity pole and with the poletangent great circle as a two-fold tangent.

(2) Matching to the fourth order
To match the ρ and λ_1 values of a given spherical curve at a given point, the generating points on the moving body whose paths satisfy these require-

ments are the intersections of the ρ-curve and the λ_1^2-curve. Both curves intersect in 84 points, among which 20 are at the velocity pole. Furthermore, the gnomonic projection of the ρ-curve is a bicircular sextic and that of the λ_1^2-curve is a curve of 14th degree which passes seven times through each of the two circular points. There remain therefore 36 real or imaginary intersections.

However, for $\lambda_1 = 0$, i.e. when the rate $d\rho/ds$ vanishes, the λ_1^2-curve degenerates into $F_3 = 0$ and $H_3 = 0$. The locus $F_3 = 0$ corresponds to $\kappa_g = 0$, its equation being exactly the same as equation (5.53), i.e. the inflection curve. For all generating points on this curve the value of ρ is uniquely determined, $\rho = 90°$. The locus $H_3 = 0$ corresponds to $\tau = 0$, its equation being exactly the same as equation (6.140), i.e. the spherical circling-point curve, as has been mentioned in Section 6.8.1. The intersections of the ρ-curve for a prescribed ρ-value, say ρ_1, and $H_3 = 0$ give the locations of the generating points whose paths will match a given spherical curve with stationary spherical radius of curvature ρ_1 at a certain point, to the fourth order.

(3) Matching to the fifth order
To match the ρ, λ_1 and λ_2 values of a given spherical curve at a given point, the generating points on the moving body whose paths satisfy these require- ments should be at the intersections of all three curves, i.e. the ρ-, λ_1^2- and λ_2-curves. Since the value of λ_2 is arbitrarily chosen, there is no guarantee that the 36 intersections of the ρ- and λ_1^2-curves should also lie on the λ_2-curve. It is therefore, in general, not possible to match a given spherical curve to the fifth order.

(4) Special case of fifth order matching
However, if we leave the value ρ open, we see that for $\lambda_2 = 0$, i.e. for vanishing $d^2\rho/ds^2$, and $H_3 = 0$ (hence $\lambda_1 = 0$), the λ_2-curve degenerates into three curves $F_3 = 0$, $L_3 = 0$ and $G_4 = 0$. The curve $G_4 = 0$ contains no real points. Since $L_3 = \dot{H}_3$, the intersections of $H_3 = 0$ and $L_3 = 0$ are the six, real or imaginary, Burmester points. But the corresponding values of ρ's are determined by the locations of these Burmester points by means of equation (6.97) or (5.46), and cannot be prescribed.

On the other hand, the intersections of $H_3 = 0$ and $F_3 = 0$ are the six, real or imaginary, Ball points. In this case $\rho = 90°$ is already fixed by the condition $F_3 = 0$ and cannot be arbitrarily assumed.

Example: Consider a circular cone of half-angle α rolling externally with an angular velocity of constant magnitude ω on a fixed circular cone of half-angle β, as shown in Fig. 7.18. At time $t = 0$, the two cones contact along OP, and at time t, they contact along OP_t. The circle of the base of the fixed cone is the fixed polode. At time t the angular velocity vector $\boldsymbol{\omega}$ of the rolling cone points in the direction of OP_t. Let $\sphericalangle PM_0P_t = \psi$, and $K = \sin\alpha/\sin(\alpha+\beta)$, then $\psi = K\omega t$, $\dot\psi = K\omega$ and $\ddot\psi = 0$. Therefore

$$\begin{bmatrix} \omega_x \\ \omega_y \\ \omega_z \end{bmatrix} = \begin{bmatrix} -S_\beta S_\psi \omega \\ S_\beta C_\beta (C_\psi - 1)\omega \\ (S_\beta^2 C_\psi + C_\beta^2)\omega \end{bmatrix}, \quad \begin{bmatrix} \dot\omega_x \\ \dot\omega_y \\ \dot\omega_z \end{bmatrix} = \begin{bmatrix} -KS_\beta C_\psi \omega^2 \\ -KS_\beta C_\beta S_\psi \omega^2 \\ -KS_\beta^2 S_\psi \omega^2 \end{bmatrix},$$

$$\begin{bmatrix} \ddot\omega_x \\ \ddot\omega_y \\ \ddot\omega_z \end{bmatrix} = \begin{bmatrix} K^2 S_\beta S_\psi \omega^3 \\ -K^2 S_\beta C_\beta C_\psi \omega^3 \\ -K^2 S_\beta^2 C_\psi \omega^3 \end{bmatrix}$$

In order to simplify the computation, the magnitude of $\boldsymbol{\omega}$ may be taken as $\omega \equiv 1$. The equation of the gnomonic projection of the ρ-curve on a plane tangent to the unit sphere at P, expressed in plane polar coordinates (p^*, θ) (see Appendix A4.3), can be derived from equation (7.44):

$$(\dot\omega_x^2 S_\psi^2 - \kappa_g^2)p^{*4} + 2\dot\omega_x S_\psi p^{*3} + (1 + 2\dot\omega_x S_\psi^2)p^{*2} + 2\dot\omega_x S_\psi p^* + \dot\omega_x^2 S_\psi^2 = 0$$

Similarly the equation of the gnomonic projection of the λ_1^2-curve can be

Fig. 7.10. Example: (a) gnomonic projection of ρ-curve for $\alpha = \beta = 30°$. (b) enlarged section of (a).

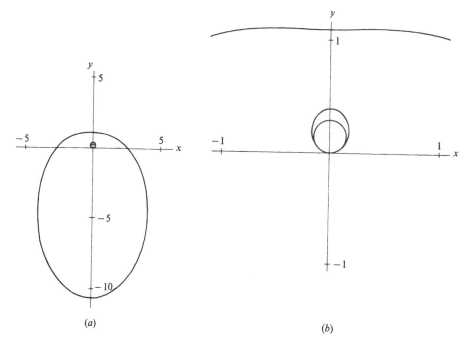

Fig. 7.11. Example: (a) gnomonic projection of λ_1^2-curve for $\alpha = \beta = 30°$ and $|\lambda_1| = 0.1$. (b) enlarged section of (a).

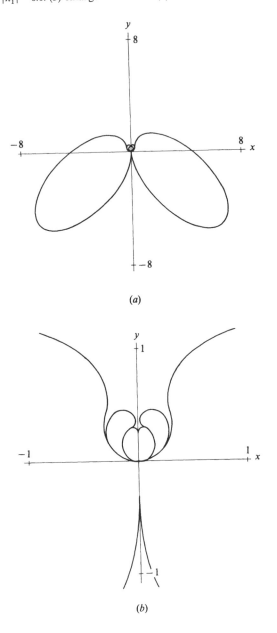

(a)

(b)

derived from equation (7.42):

$$\lambda_1^2[(p^* + \dot{\omega}_x S_\psi)^2 + \dot{\omega}_x^2 S_\psi^2 p^{*2}]^2 p^{*4}$$
$$- [(2\dot{\omega}_x - \ddot{\omega}_y)C_\psi p^* + \dot{\omega}_x S_\psi p^* + 3\dot{\omega}_x^2 S_\psi C_\psi]^2$$
$$\cdot [(\dot{\omega}_x S_\psi p^* + 1)p^* + \dot{\omega}_x S_\psi]^2 (p^{*2} + 1) = 0$$

For $\alpha = \beta = 30°$, $K = 0.57735$, and at $\phi = 0°$, $\dot{\omega}_x = -0.28868$, $\ddot{\omega}_x = 0$, $\ddot{\omega}_y = -0.14434$. On the assumption $\kappa_g = 0.38552$, the gnomonic projection of the ρ-curve is shown in Figs. 7.10(a),(b). Also on the assumption $|\lambda_1| = 0.1$, the gnomonic projection of the λ_1^2-curve is shown in Figs. 7.11(a),(b). These two curves intersect, apart from the origin point, in 12 real points:

$$\xi = \pm 1.9732 \times 10^{-3}, \quad \zeta = 1.3497 \times 10^{-5}$$
$$\xi = \pm 1.9760 \times 10^{-3}, \quad \zeta = 1.3516 \times 10^{-5}$$
$$\xi = \pm 3.6230 \times 10^{-3}, \quad \zeta = 0.2810$$
$$\xi = \pm 0.02741, \quad \zeta = 0.3899$$
$$\xi = \pm 0.7, \quad \zeta = 1.0$$
$$\xi = \pm 4.0353, \quad \zeta = -5.0923$$

It can be shown that only the points $\xi = \pm 0.7$, $\zeta = 1.0$ are on the gnomonic projection of a λ_2-curve for $\lambda_2 = 0.1$.

7.5 Coupler dwell mechanisms

As in plane kinematics, spherical coupler dwell mechanisms can also be deduced from the nature of coupler curves (Dittrich & Zakel, 1975; Dittrich, 1964). Thus, for instance, in the spherical four-bar linkage shown in Fig. 6.21, if a coupler point C is given, then in a certain position of the linkage the spherical centre of curvature C_0 of the path of C can be located by means of the Euler–Savary equation. Join the points C and C_0 by a link e, and the point C_0 to a fixed point C_{00} by another link g. As the coupler point C moves passing through the position shown in the figure, the link g remains temporarily at rest. Because the path of C and its osculating circle with spherical centre at C_0 are in a three-point contact, this dwell may be called a three-point dwell. If the point C is chosen at a Burmester point, a mechanism with a five-point dwell can be obtained.

Example: Suppose the spherical polar coordinates of the coupler point C in the example of Section 6.8.3 (Fig. 6.21) with respect to Px_1 are given: $C(40°, 80°)$. It is required to find the location of C_0.

The spherical polar coordinates of C with respect to Px_2 are then: $(40°, 80° - 28.9430°)$. With the known value of $\Theta = 2.4694$, the *length* PC_0 can be found by means of the Euler–Savary equation (5.42): $PC_0 = 56.1350°$.

The coordinates of both points C and C_0 with respect to the original $x_1y_1z_1$-system are: $C(0.111619, 0.633022, 0.766044)$, $C_0(0.144189, 0.817738, 0.557238)$.

Coupler dwell mechanisms can also be deduced in a *sliding-pair* version. If the *sliding slot* of the link to be steered is made in conformity, to a certain order, with the coupler curve, a dwell motion of the link to be steered can be obtained. Thus, for instance, if a great circle slot of the steered link is put in a position tangent to the path of a coupler point which is instantaneously an inflection point, a three-point dwell of the steered link is obtained. Another simple implementation of this kind, on the basis of instantaneous properties of the coupler curve, is to set a great circle slot of the steered link tangent to the path of a coupler point which is instantaneously a Ball point of the coupler, to obtain a four-point dwell. We shall consider two cases.

(1) The central slider–crank as a steering mechanism
As mentioned in Section 6.8.6(4) and shown in Fig. 6.26(b), when a central slider–crank is in its outer dead centre position, the two inflection poles of the coupler becomes the two Ball points U_3 and U_4. These two inflection poles, according to equation (5.48), are determined by, for $\theta_U = 90°$,

$$PU_3 = \tfrac{1}{2}\sin^{-1}2\Theta \text{ and } PU_4 = -90° - \tfrac{1}{2}\sin^{-1}2\Theta \tag{7.45}$$

These inflection poles exist if

$$|2\Theta| \leqslant 1 \tag{7.46}$$

Since the value of Θ, in this position, is determined by the dimensions a and c according to equation (6.162), therefore the inflection poles exist if

$$\left| \frac{2\tan c \tan (a+c)}{\tan c - \tan (a+c)} \right| \leqslant 1$$

Fig. 7.12. Curve $\tan a = (1 - \cos 2c)/(1 - \sin 2c)$.

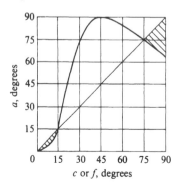

a, degrees

c or f, degrees

or

$$\tan a \geqslant \frac{1 - \cos 2c}{1 - \sin 2c} \tag{7.47}$$

The curve in Fig. 7.12 represents $\tan a = (1 - \cos 2c)/(1 - \sin 2c)$. Hence, the inflection poles exist only for values of the (c, a) pair above the curve. On the other hand, in order to ensure the rotatability of the crank, we must have $a < c$. Therefore, only values of the (c, a) pair in the shaded areas in Fig. 7.12 are usable. Fig. 7.13 shows such a dwell mechanism. The dimensions of the steering slider–crank are: $a = 12.5°$, $c = 14°$. The value of $\Theta = -0.4987$. Hence the length BC is taken as $BC = |PU_3| = |\frac{1}{2}\sin^{-1}2\Theta| = 42.9581°$. Link g is the one to be steered, its fixed centre being C_{00}. A similar coupler curve may also be obtained if the length BC is taken as $BC = |PU_4| = |90° + \frac{1}{2}\sin^{-1}2\Theta| = 47.0419°$.

Similarly in the inner dead centre position of the central slider–crank, the two inflection poles of the coupler also become two Ball points U_3 and U_4. Equations (7.45) and (7.46) are still valid. However, in this case the value of Θ is determined by

$$\Theta = \frac{\tan c \tan (c - a)}{- \tan (c - a) + \tan c}$$

Therefore the inflection poles exist if

$$\left| \frac{2 \tan c \tan (c - a)}{- \tan (c - a) + \tan c} \right| \leqslant 1$$

Fig. 7.13. Coupler dwell mechanism steered by a central slider–crank in its outer dead centre position.

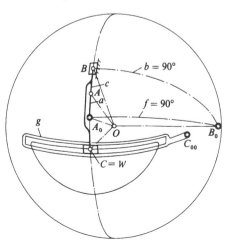

or

$$\tan a \geqslant \frac{1 - \cos 2c}{1 + \sin 2c} \tag{7.48}$$

The curve in Fig. 7.14 represents $\tan a = (1 - \cos 2c)/(1 + \sin 2c)$. Hence, the inflection poles exist only for values of the (c, a) pair above the curve. Again, because of the condition $a < c$, only values of the (c, a) pair within the shaded area are usable. Fig. 7.15 shows a steering slider–crank in its inner dead centre position with dimensions $a = 20°$, $c = 35°$. The value of $\Theta = +0.4340$. Hence the length BC is taken as $BC = |PU_3| = 30.1188°$. A similar coupler curve may be obtained if the length BC is taken as $BC = |PU_4| = |90° - \frac{1}{2}\sin^{-1}2\Theta|$ $= 59.8812°$.

Fig. 7.14. Curve $\tan a = (1 - \cos 2c)/(1 + \sin 2c)$.

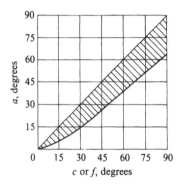

Fig. 7.15. Coupler dwell mechanism steered by a central slider–crank in its inner dead centre position.

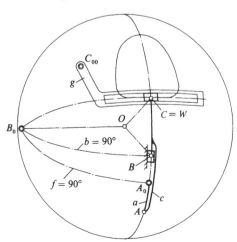

Note that in Fig. 6.26(*b*), if any point on the polenormal great circle, which is now a part of the circling-point curve k_u, is taken as a steering coupler point, then because its path possesses a four-point contacting spherical circle of curvature, a dwell mechanism of a version similar to that shown in Fig. 6.21 can be constructed, with a four-point dwell.

(2) The central oscillating cylinder as a steering mechanism
As mentioned in Section 6.8.6(5) and shown in Fig. 6.27(*b*), a central

Fig. 7.16. Coupler dwell mechanism steered by a central oscillating cylinder in the stretched position of crank and frame.

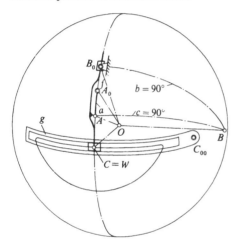

Fig. 7.17. Coupler dwell mechanism steered by a central oscillating cylinder in the folded position of crank and frame.

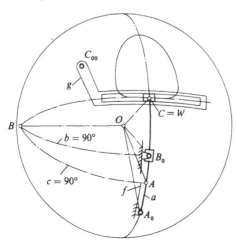

oscillating cylinder in the stretched position of the crank and frame has the two Ball points U_3 and U_4 at its inflection poles. Again equations (7.45) and (7.46) are valid. However, the value of Θ in the present case is given by equation (6.163), therefore the inflection poles exist if

$$\left| \frac{2\tan f \tan(a+f)}{\tan f - \tan(a+f)} \right| \leqslant 1$$

or

$$\tan a \geqslant \frac{1-\cos 2f}{1-\sin 2f} \tag{7.49}$$

Comparison of equation (7.49) with equation (7.47) shows that both equations are identical provided c is replaced by f. Hence Fig. 7.12 may be used for determining the usable range of values of the (f,a) pair if the abscissa is considered as the variable f. Fig. 7.16 shows a dwell mechanism steered by an oscillating cylinder with $a = 12.5°$, $f = 14°$, $\Theta = -0.4987$, and B_0C (instantaneously) $= 42.9581°$.

Similarly in the folded position of the crank and frame of the central oscillating cylinder, the two inflection poles of the coupler also become the two Ball points U_3 and U_4. Equations (7.45) and (7.46) are still valid. In this case the value of Θ is given by

$$\Theta = \frac{\tan f \tan(f-a)}{\tan(f-a) - \tan f}$$

Therefore the inflection poles exist if

$$\tan a \geqslant \frac{1-\cos 2f}{1+\sin 2f} \tag{7.50}$$

Hence the diagram in Fig. 7.14 may be used for determining the usable range of values of the (f,a) pair if the abscissa is considered as the variable f. Fig. 7.17 shows a steering central oscillating cylinder in the folded position of the crank and frame with $a = 20°$, $f = 35°$, $\Theta = -0.4340$ and B_0C (instantaneously) $= 59.8812°$.

7.6   Rolling circular cones

Two circular cones rolling on each other constitute a spherical mechanism consisting of three members. Beside the two circular cones, the third member is the link, or arm, which keeps the axes of the two circular cones a constant angle apart. We shall consider only the case of a circular cone rolling on another fixed circular cone, as shown in Fig. 7.18. The path generated by a moving point on the rolling cone is a spherical trochoid. If the moving point is on the circumference of the base of the rolling cone, the generated path is a spherical epicycloid, or a spherical hypocycloid, depending on whether the rolling is an external or an internal one. Characteristics of the spherical epicycloid can be investigated from either a mathematical or a kinematic point of view (Primrose & Freudenstein, 1969; Dittrich, 1964).

7.6.1 Equations of the spherical epicycloid

Consider a circular cone c of half-angle α rolling externally on a fixed circular cone with half-angle β, as shown in Fig. 7.18, in which a canonical coordinate system xyz as described in Section 6.4.3 is used. Let $\sphericalangle PMP_t^1 = \phi$ and $\sphericalangle PM_0P_t = \psi$, where the circular arc lengths $PP_t^1 = PP_t$. When the rolling cone moves to the position shown by the chain line, a point on it with initial coordinates (x_1, y_1, z_1) is displaced to a position with coordinates (x, y, z). These coordinates (x, y, z) can be found by twice applying the displacement matrix (A2.33) to (x_1, y_1, z_1), namely, first by rotating the body c about the axis $OM(0, S_\alpha, C_\alpha)$ through an angle $+\phi$, and then by rotating it about the axis $OM_0(0, -S_\beta, C_\beta)$ through an angle $+\psi$. Hence

$$\begin{bmatrix} x \\ y \\ z \end{bmatrix} = \begin{bmatrix} C_\psi & -C_\beta S_\psi & -S_\beta C_\psi \\ C_\beta S_\psi & S_\beta^2 + C_\beta^2 C_\psi & -S_\beta C_\beta V_\psi \\ S_\beta S_\psi & -S_\beta C_\beta V_\psi & C_\beta^2 + S_\beta^2 C_\psi \end{bmatrix} \begin{bmatrix} C_\phi & -C_\alpha S_\phi & S_\alpha S_\phi \\ C_\alpha S_\phi & S_\alpha^2 + C_\alpha^2 C_\phi & S_\alpha C_\alpha V_\phi \\ -S_\alpha S_\phi & S_\alpha C_\alpha V_\phi & C_\alpha^2 + S_\alpha^2 C_\phi \end{bmatrix} \begin{bmatrix} x_1 \\ y_1 \\ z_1 \end{bmatrix}$$

$$(7.51)$$

Without loss of generality, the initial position of the moving point may be assumed to be at the pole P, or $(x_1, y_1, z_1) = (0, 0, 1)$. Therefore the coordinates of the generating point are:

$$\left. \begin{aligned} x &= S_\alpha C_\psi S_\phi - S_\alpha C_\alpha C_\beta S_\psi V_\phi - S_\beta S_\psi (C_\alpha^2 + S_\alpha^2 C_\phi) \\ y &= S_\alpha C_\beta S_\psi S_\phi + S_\alpha C_\alpha (S_\beta^2 + C_\beta^2 C_\psi) V_\phi - S_\beta C_\beta V_\psi (C_\alpha^2 + S_\alpha^2 C_\phi) \\ z &= S_\alpha S_\beta S_\psi S_\phi - S_\alpha C_\alpha S_\beta C_\beta S_\psi V_\phi V_\phi + (C_\alpha^2 + S_\alpha^2 C_\phi)(C_\beta^2 + S_\beta^2 C_\psi) \end{aligned} \right\} \quad (7.52)$$

Fig. 7.18. Rolling circular cones.

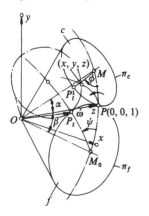

The angles ϕ, ψ are coupled by the relation

$$\frac{\psi}{\phi} = \frac{\sin \alpha}{\sin \beta} \tag{7.53}$$

The ratio $|\psi/\phi|$ is the angular velocity ratio of the circular cones relative to the arm $M_0 M$. If the ratio is rational, it can be expressed as a rational fraction

$$\frac{\sin \alpha}{\sin \beta} = \frac{n}{m} \tag{7.54}$$

where n and m are two relatively prime integers. Although the case being dealt with is for external rolling, internal rolling, i.e. equations for a spherical hypocycloid, can be considered as a special case by setting $\beta > 90°$. Let[†]

$$t = e^{i\phi/m} = e^{i\psi/n} \tag{7.55}$$

Then

$$S_\phi = -\tfrac{i}{2}(t^m - t^{-m}), \; C_\phi = \tfrac{1}{2}(t^m + t^{-m}) \left.\begin{array}{c}\\ \\\end{array}\right\} \tag{7.56}$$
$$S_\psi = -\tfrac{i}{2}(t^n - t^{-n}), \; C_\psi = \tfrac{1}{2}(t^n + t^{-n})$$

Substituting equations (7.56) into equations (7.52) results in

$$\begin{aligned}
x = {}& i\left[-\frac{S_\alpha}{4}(t^n + t^{-n})(t^m - t^{-m}) + \frac{S_\alpha C_\alpha C_\beta}{2}(t^n - t^{-n}) \right.\\
& \left. \cdot\left(1 - \frac{t^m + t^{-m}}{2}\right) + \frac{S_\beta}{2}(t^n - t^{-n})\left(C_\alpha^2 + S_\alpha^2 \frac{t^m + t^{-m}}{2}\right) \right] \\[2mm]
y = {}& -\frac{S_\alpha C_\beta}{4}(t^n - t^{-n})(t^m - t^{-m}) \\
& + S_\alpha C_\alpha\left(S_\beta^2 + C_\beta^2 \frac{t^n + t^{-n}}{2}\right)\left(1 - \frac{t^m + t^{-m}}{2}\right) \\
& - S_\beta C_\beta\left(1 - \frac{t^n + t^{-n}}{2}\right)\left(C_\alpha^2 + S_\alpha^2 \frac{t^m + t^{-m}}{2}\right) \\[2mm]
z = {}& -\frac{S_\alpha S_\beta}{4}(t^n - t^{-n})(t^m - t^{-m}) \\
& - S_\alpha C_\alpha S_\beta C_\beta\left(1 - \frac{t^n + t^{-n}}{2}\right)\left(1 - \frac{t^m + t^{-m}}{2}\right) \\
& + \left(C_\beta^2 + S_\beta^2 \frac{t^n + t^{-n}}{2}\right)\left(C_\alpha^2 + S_\alpha^2 \frac{t^m + t^{-m}}{2}\right)
\end{aligned} \right\} \tag{7.57}$$

Equations (7.57) can be considered as parametric equations of the spherical epicycloid, x, y, z being expressed as rational functions of the parameter t,

---

† Not to be confused with the symbol $t = $ time.

and such a spherical epicycloid is a rational curve. As explained in Appendix A4.5, if the gnomonic projection of the spherical epicycloid is $F(\xi, \zeta) = 0$, where $\xi = x/z, \zeta = y/z$, equations (7.57) can be considered as the parametric equations of the plane curve expressed in homogeneous coordinates (x, y, z). An arbitrary straight line $\lambda\xi + \mu\zeta + \nu = 0$, where λ, μ, ν are arbitrary constants, on the plane of projection intersects $F(\xi, \zeta) = 0$ in points determined by substituting equations (7.57) into the equation $\lambda x + \mu y + \nu z = 0$. It can be seen that the number of intersection points is $2(m + n)$. Hence the degree (or order) of the spherical cycloid is $2(m + n)$.

Since m and n are relatively prime, their LCM is mn. Take the pole P as a moving point on the rolling cone c. The rolling cone has to make m complete revolutions to bring the point P to the initial starting position. Thus, for instance, for a pair of bevel gears with a 60-tooth pinion rolling on a 70-tooth fixed gear, $m = 7$ and $n = 6$. The LCM is 42 and the rolling gear has to complete seven revolutions to come to the initial starting position.

As mentioned in Section 6.8.5, the pole P as a moving point describes in general a cusp. Therefore the spherical epicycloid possesses in general m cusps. Further characteristics of spherical epi- and hypocycloids can be read in (Primrose & Freudenstein, 1969).

7.6.2 Kinematic state of a rolling circular cone

As mentioned in Section 6.8.6(1), the kinematic state of a rolling circular cone corresponds to the case $\gamma'' = 0$, in which both the circling-point curve k_u and the centering-point curve k_a break up into the polenormal great circle and a spherical ellipse. The inflection poles, if they exist, are the Ball points. Various cases will be considered, as investigated in (Dittrich, 1964).

(1) Internal rolling

Referring to Fig. 5.8, in which the polodes π_c and π_f are now spherical circles, we find from equation (5.43)

$$\Theta = \frac{\tan PM_0 \tan PM}{\tan PM_0 - \tan PM} \tag{7.58}$$

As mentioned in Section 5.5.1, the inflection poles exist only if $|\Theta| \leqslant 1/2$. They are determined by

$$PW = \frac{1}{2}\sin^{-1}\frac{2\tan PM_0 \tan PM}{\tan PM_0 - \tan PM}, \text{ and } PW' = 90° - PW \tag{7.59}$$

Fig. 7.19 shows, in first angle projection, a circular cone of spherical radius $PM = 12.5°$ rolling internally on a fixed circular cone of spherical radius $PM_0 = 59.9694°$, the gear ratio being $n/m = \sin PM/\sin PM_0 = 1/4$. The inflection poles are at $PW = 15.2841°$ and $PW' = 74.7159°$. The path generated by the point P is a spherical hypocycloid. If the generating point lies inside (or outside) the base of the rolling cone, the generated path becomes a spherical curtate (or prolate) trochoid. In particular, the path of the inflection pole W of the rolling cone in Fig. 7.19 is also shown. It looks like a spherical square with rounded corners. Imagining that the sides of the spherical square are great circles, two opposite sides intersect in a point (not shown) 90° distant from the point M_0. If this point is chosen as the fixed centre of a slot to be steered, somewhat like that shown in Fig. 7.13 or Fig. 7.15, a dwell mechanism with two dwells can be devised with the rolling cone as a steering member. In general, for other gear ratio $n/m = 1/m$, the path of the inflection pole of the rolling cone will look like a regular polygon with m sides.

Fig. 7.19. Internally rolling circular cones, $PM = 12.5°$, $PM_0 = 59.9694°$, $n/m = \sin PM/\sin PM_0 = 1/4$, $PW = 15.2841°$.

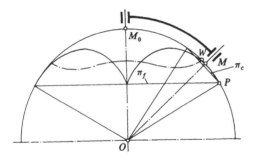

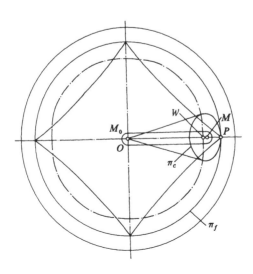

If, in addition, the spherical radii of the circular cones are such that

$$\tan PM_0 = 2 \tan PM \tag{6.156a}$$

the case becomes that mentioned in Section 6.8.6(4). The velocity pole P describes a return point with a spherical radius of curvature of 90°. Substituting the gear ratio $n/m = \sin PM/\sin PM_0$ into equation (6.156a) results in

$$\sin^2 PM = \frac{1}{3}\left(\frac{4n^2}{m^2} - 1\right) \tag{7.60}$$

Equation (7.60) indicates that, if it is required to find the spherical radii PM_0 and PM to satisfy equation (6.156a), real values of PM exist only if $1/2 \leqslant n/m \leqslant 1$, or $1 \leqslant m/n \leqslant 2$; hence m/n cannot be an integer. Fig. 7.20 shows such a pair of circular cones with $n/m = 3/4$. The spherical radii are found:

Fig. 7.20. Internally rolling circular cones, $PM = 40.2030°$, $PM_0 = 59.3911°$, $n/m = \sin PM/\sin PM_0 = 3/4$, $\tan PM/\tan PM_0 = 1/2$.

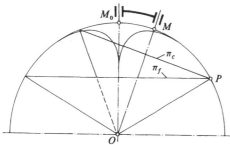

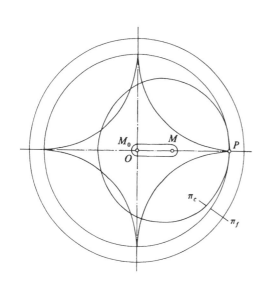

$PM = 40.2030°$, $PM_0 = 59.3911°$. The hypocycloid looks like a regular poly-gon, although $m/n = 4/3$ is not an integer. This is because now $m - n = 4 - 3 = 1$, and when the rolling cone completes one revolution, it has rolled over 3/4 of the fixed polode, leaving 1/4 uncovered, thus four revolutions complete the whole polygon.

Let us think of the spherical counterpart of the Cardan circle-pair in plane kinematics. Such a pair of spherical radii PM_0 and PM must satisfy the conditions (a) $\sin PM_0 = 2\sin PM$, to ensure that the circumference of the larger fixed spherical circle equals twice that of the smaller rolling circle, (b) $\tan PM_0 = 2\tan PM$, to enable the generating point to become a Ball point at least at the return point of its path, and (c) $PM_0 = 2PM$, to ensure that the generating point indeed passes through the spherical centre M_0 of the

Fig. 7.21. Externally rolling circular cones, $PM = \alpha = 12.5°$, $PM_0 = -\beta = -59.9694°$, $n/m = \sin \alpha/\sin \beta = 1/4$.

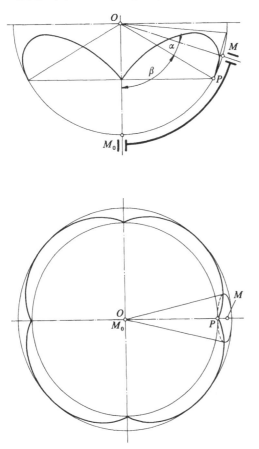

larger spherical circle. As it is not possible to have a pair of PM_0 and PM values to satisfy all three conditions simultaneously, unless the radius of the sphere is increased indefinitely, we can conclude that there is no spherical counterpart of the Cardan circle-pair in plane kinematics. As mentioned in Section 6.2.3, the rolling polodes in spherical kinematics which correspond to the planar Cardan circle-pair are a spherical quartic curve and a spherical ellipse, but not circles.

(2) External rolling
Equation (7.58) is still valid for external rolling, provided that PM_0 is considered as negative. In other words, setting $PM_0 = -\beta$, we obtain

$$\Theta = \frac{\tan \alpha \tan \beta}{\tan \alpha + \tan \beta} \tag{7.61}$$

where α, β, as shown in Fig. 7.18, are the half-angles of the cones. Accordingly the inflection poles are determined by

$$PW = \tfrac{1}{2}\sin^{-1}\frac{2\tan \alpha \tan \beta}{\tan \alpha + \tan \beta}, \quad \text{and } PW' = 90° - PW \tag{7.62}$$

Fig. 7.21 shows a pair of externally rolling cones with $\alpha = 12.5°$, $\beta = 59.9694°$. The gear ratio is $n/m = \sin \alpha / \sin \beta = 1/4$. The inflection poles are at $PW = 11.5713°$ and $PW' = 78.4287°$ (not shown).

In the case $\alpha + \beta = 90°$, the axes of the two circular cones are perpendicular to each other, and $\tan \alpha = 1/\tan \beta$, hence $PW = \alpha$ and $PW' = \beta$. The centre M

Fig. 7.22. Externally rolling circular cones, $\alpha = \beta = 45°$.

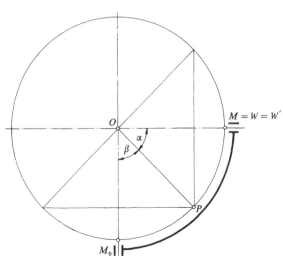

of the spherical base of the rolling cone becomes the inflection pole W, and the other inflection pole W' is at $PW' = \beta$. It is obvious that the path generated by M is a great circle. Fig. 7.22 shows such a pair of rolling cones with $\alpha = \beta = 45°$. In this case both inflection poles W and W' coincide with M.

In the case $\alpha < 90°$ and $\beta = 90°$, the fixed cone becomes a circular plate. The path generated by a point on the circle of the base of the rolling cone becomes simply a *spherical cycloid*. In the case $\alpha = 90°$ and $\beta < 90°$, the rolling cone becomes a flat plate, and the path generated by a point on the edge of the plate becomes a *spherical involute*.

Dittrich devised a spherical double-rocker, somewhat like the Chebychev straight-line mechanism in plane kinematics, to pinpoint a predetermined Ball point on the coupler of a spherical four-bar linkage to be synthesized (Dittrich, 1964). Starting from a pair of externally rolling circular cones, as shown in Fig. 7.23, we see that the inflection pole W is uniquely determined by equation (7.62) if the half-angles α and β are given. The values of $1/\tan l$ and $1/\tan l_0$, after being solved from equations (6.147) and (6.148), are also determined by α and β, if we note that $PM = \alpha$ and $PM_0 = -\beta$:

$$\frac{1}{\tan l} = \frac{1}{3}\left(\frac{2}{\tan \alpha} + \frac{1}{\tan \beta}\right)$$

$$\frac{1}{\tan l_0} = -\frac{1}{3}\left(\frac{1}{\tan \alpha} + \frac{2}{\tan \beta}\right)$$

(7.63)

Fig. 7.23. Spherical 4-bar derived from externally rolling cones, $PM = \alpha$, $PM_0 = -\beta$.

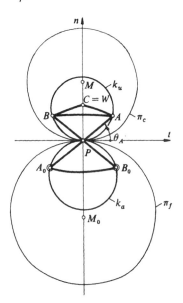

The elliptical parts of the circling-point curve k_u and of the centering-point curve k_a, represented by the brackets in equations (6.153) and (6.154) respectively, are thus also determined. If two points A, B are chosen on the ellipse of k_u, and the two centre-points A_0, B_0 are located correspondingly on k_a, a spherical four-bar linkage A_0ABB_0 can be constructed whose coupler point $C = W$ will become a Ball point, i.e. exhibit a path with a four-point contacting great circle. For simplicity, A and B may be chosen so that they are symmetrically disposed with respect to the polenormal great circle, although this is not necessary.

Conversely, if the points $C = W$ and A are predetermined, the half-angles α and β, as well as the whole configuration, are uniquely determined. Thus, with given values of PW, PA and θ_A, and noting that $\Theta = \frac{1}{2}\sin 2PW$, we can find the location of A_0 by means of the Euler–Savary equation (5.42):

$$\tan PA_0 = -\frac{\tan PA \sin 2PW \sin \theta_A}{2\tan PA - \sin 2PW \sin \theta_A} \tag{7.64}$$

Note that PA_0 is computed without knowing α and β. The link lengths can be found by first converting the spherical polar coordinates of C, A, A_0 into rectangular Cartesian coordinates by means of equations (A4.1), and then applying equation (A3.2).

8

Dimensional synthesis – function generation problems

Like plane function generators, the purpose of a spherical function generator is to approximate a given function $y = y(x)$[†] by a function $\psi = \psi(\phi)$ generated by a spherical linkage, where ϕ, ψ are respectively the position angles of the input and output links. There exists a certain proportional factor between ϕ and x, as well as a proportional factor between ψ and y, namely

$$M_\phi = \frac{\triangle \phi}{\triangle x} \qquad (8.1)$$

$$M_\psi = \frac{\triangle \psi}{\triangle y} \qquad (8.2)$$

where M_ϕ, M_ψ are called scale factors. It seems that the approximation may simply be achieved by matching a plot of the desired ψ–ϕ curve with those

Fig. 8.1. Crank rotation pairs.

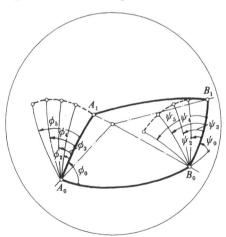

[†] Not to be confused with the Cartesian coordinates of a point.

of spherical four-bars of known dimensions by visual inspection (Sodhi & Shoup, 1983; Sodhi, Wilhelm & Shoup, 1985). However, the approximation is, in general, accomplished by coordinating a number of given pairs of angular rotations of input and output links: $\phi_2, \psi_2; \phi_3, \psi_3$; etc., as shown in Fig. 8.1. As mentioned in Section 2.2.1, the functional relationship $\psi = \psi(\phi)$ between ψ and ϕ depends on all four independent parameters a, b, c and f, not just on their ratios. In other words, one of the four link *lengths*, say f, has to be assumed. The function generators synthesized for different f's are different, because similarity does not exist in spherical geometry.

The problem can be solved by means of a displacement matrix, using again an inversion concept (Suh & Radcliffe, 1967; Suh, 1970; Sarkisharn, 1982), or by means of the transmission function, equation (2.5) (Denavit & Hartenberg, 1960; Hartenberg & Denavit, 1964; Zimmerman, 1967; Lakshminarayana, 1972; Luck, 1975; Angeles, 1986). However, for the reason that matching prescribed velocity ratios will be treated later on as coordinating infinitesimal rotations of input and output links, we shall use the method based on the concept of relative poles (Chiang, 1976), especially because this method lends itself to concise and systematic procedures. Another advantage of using the relative pole equations instead of loop equations is that the coupler length c is not involved in the equations as an unknown.

The structural error of the synthesized linkage is the difference between the theoretically correct value of the output angle and the actually generated output angle, referred to a certain precision point, or

$$\varepsilon = M_\psi \triangle y - \triangle \psi \tag{8.3}$$

Optimization of the structural error as a mathematical programming problem for spherical four-bar and even for Watt's type spherical six-bar function generators (see Section 9.6.1), irrespective of the number of precision-points, can be read from (Bagci & Parekh, 1971; Rao & Ambeker, 1974).

8.1   Coordination of finitely separated relative positions
Again we use the symbol P, as defined in Section 6.6, to denote a single relative position between the two links a and b. $P_1 - P_2 - P_3 - P_4$ and $P_1 - P_2 - P_3 - P_4 - P_5$ denote respectively four and five finitely separated relative positions. The functional relationship for the case $P_1 - P_2 - P_3 - P_4$ is shown diagrammatically in Fig. 8.2. As in plane kinematics, the maximum number of angle-pairs that can be coordinated is four, for the case $P_1 - P_2 - P_3 - P_4 - P_5$.

8.1.1   Coordination of a single angle-pair
To coordinate a single angle-pair ϕ_i, ψ_i of the rotating links a and

b, the relative pole R_i is located as shown in Fig. 8.3. From A_0 and B_0 draw great circles inclined respectively at $-\phi_i/2$ and $-\psi_i/2$ to the great circle A_0B_0. The intersection point R_i of these two great circles is the relative pole between a and b, for the link rotations ϕ_i and ψ_i. The *lengths* $A_0R_i = r_{ai}$ and $B_0R_i = r_{bi}$ are determined by applying the cotangent law, equation (A1.11), to $\triangle R_iA_0B_0$:

$$\cot r_{ai} = -\frac{\sin\frac{\phi_i}{2}\cot\frac{\psi_i}{2} - \cos f \cos\frac{\phi_i}{2}}{\sin f} \tag{8.4}$$

$$\cot r_{bi} = -\frac{-\sin\frac{\psi_i}{2}\cot\frac{\phi_i}{2} + \cos f\cos\frac{\psi_i}{2}}{\sin f} \tag{8.5}$$

Fig. 8.2. The case $P_1-P_2-P_3-P_4$.

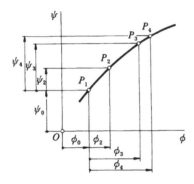

Fig. 8.3. Location of spherical relative pole R_i.

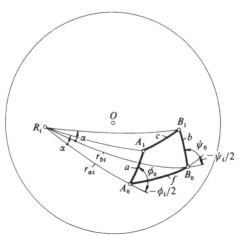

The $(-)$ signs in equations (8.4) and (8.5) indicate that the *moduli* r_{ai} and r_{bi}, as shown in Fig. 8.3, in relation to the respective *arguments* $-\phi_i/2$ and $-\psi_i/2$, are negative.

By analogy with Fig. 6.1, where opposite links subtend equal angles at the pole P_{12}, the locations of the two crank pin centres A_1 and B_1 for coordinating the angle pairs ϕ_i, ψ_i are subject to the condition that the great circles A_0A_1 and B_0B_1 should subtend equal angles α at R_i. To formulate this condition, applying equation (A1.11) to $\triangle R_iA_0A_1$ and $\triangle R_iB_0B_1$ gives

$$\cot \alpha = \frac{-\sin r_{ai}\cot a + \cos r_{ai}\cos\left(\phi_0 + \dfrac{\phi_i}{2}\right)}{\sin\left(\phi_0 + \dfrac{\phi_i}{2}\right)} \tag{8.6}$$

$$\cot \alpha = \frac{-\sin r_{bi}\cot b + \cos r_{bi}\cos\left(\psi_0 + \dfrac{\psi_i}{2}\right)}{\sin\left(\psi_0 + \dfrac{\psi_i}{2}\right)} \tag{8.7}$$

Equations (8.6) and (8.7) can readily be combined to yield the relation

$$\sin\left(\psi_0 + \frac{\psi_i}{2}\right)\sin r_{ai}\cot a - \sin\left(\phi_0 + \frac{\phi_i}{2}\right)\sin r_{bi}\cot b$$

$$= \sin\left(\psi_0 + \frac{\psi_i}{2}\right)\cos\left(\phi_0 + \frac{\phi_i}{2}\right)\cos r_{ai}$$

$$- \sin\left(\phi_0 + \frac{\phi_i}{2}\right)\cos\left(\psi_0 + \frac{\psi_i}{2}\right)\cos r_{bi} \tag{8.8}$$

Equation (8.8) contains four unknowns ϕ_0, a, ψ_0 and b. It is non-linear in the two unknowns ϕ_0 and ψ_0, but linear in the two unknowns $\cot a$ and $\cot b$. It can be seen from equation (8.8) that, if both r_{ai} and r_{bi} are replaced respectively by $180° - r_{ai}$ and $180° - r_{bi}$, this equation remains unchanged. This means that the R_i shown in Fig. 8.3 may be replaced by its antipode $\bar{R}_i$, without altering the results. However, care should be taken that both r_{ai} and r_{bi} are referred to the same R_i or its antipode.

8.1.2 Four precision-points $(P_1-P_2-P_3-P_4)$

In this case, the three angle-pairs $\phi_2, \psi_2; \phi_3, \psi_3; \phi_4, \psi_4$ and the length f of the fixed link are given, while the initial position angles ϕ_0 and ψ_0 of a and b have yet to be determined. We now have a set of three relative poles R_2, R_3 and R_4. Setting $i = 2, 3, 4$ in turn in equation (8.8) yields a system of three linear equations in the two unknowns $\cot a$ and $\cot b$. For the existence of the solutions for these two unknowns, the determinant of the coefficients of this system of equations must vanish:

$$
\begin{vmatrix}
\sin\!\left(\psi_0 + \dfrac{\psi_2}{2}\right)\sin r_{a2}, & -\sin\!\left(\phi_0 + \dfrac{\phi_2}{2}\right)\sin r_{b2}, & \sin\!\left(\psi_0 + \dfrac{\psi_2}{2}\right)\cos\!\left(\phi_0 + \dfrac{\phi_2}{2}\right)\cos r_{a2} \\
 & & -\sin\!\left(\phi_0 + \dfrac{\phi_2}{2}\right)\cos\!\left(\psi_0 + \dfrac{\psi_2}{2}\right)\cos r_{b2} \\
\sin\!\left(\psi_0 + \dfrac{\psi_3}{2}\right)\sin r_{a3}, & -\sin\!\left(\phi_0 + \dfrac{\phi_3}{2}\right)\sin r_{b3}, & \sin\!\left(\psi_0 + \dfrac{\psi_3}{2}\right)\cos\!\left(\phi_0 + \dfrac{\phi_3}{2}\right)\cos r_{a3} \\
 & & -\sin\!\left(\phi_0 + \dfrac{\phi_3}{2}\right)\cos\!\left(\psi_0 + \dfrac{\psi_3}{2}\right)\cos r_{b3} \\
\sin\!\left(\psi_0 + \dfrac{\psi_4}{2}\right)\sin r_{a4}, & -\sin\!\left(\phi_0 + \dfrac{\phi_4}{2}\right)\sin r_{b4}, & \sin\!\left(\psi_0 + \dfrac{\psi_4}{2}\right)\cos\!\left(\phi_0 + \dfrac{\phi_4}{2}\right)\cos r_{a4} \\
 & & -\sin\!\left(\phi_0 + \dfrac{\phi_4}{2}\right)\cos\!\left(\psi_0 + \dfrac{\psi_4}{2}\right)\cos r_{b4}
\end{vmatrix} = 0
$$

$$(8.9)$$

Equation (8.9) contains only two unknowns $\tan\phi_0$ and $\tan\psi_0$. By arbitrarily assuming a value of ϕ_0, it can be expanded and reduced to a quadratic equation in the unknown $q = \tan\psi_0$:

$$a_2 q^2 + a_1 q + a_0 = 0 \tag{8.10}$$

The coefficients a_2, a_1, a_0, each being a quadratic function of $t = \tan\phi_0$, may be evaluated by means of equations (A9.2) and (A9.3) in Appendix 9. Conversely equation (8.9) can also be reduced to a quadratic equation in the unknown $t = \tan\phi_0$, if ψ_0 is arbitrarily assumed. In other words, there are two ψ_0's corresponding to a single ϕ_0, and two ϕ_0's corresponding to a single ψ_0. There are therefore ∞^1 possible solutions, depending on the free choice of ϕ_0.

Having found the two ψ_0's for a given ϕ_0, the *lengths* a and b of the two rotating links may be found from the original system of three equations, the computing equations deduced from which are listed as equations (A9.4)–(A9.7). The point A_1, Fig. 8.3, lies on the spherical relative centre-point curve of the motion of the body b relative to a, and the point B_1 lies on the spherical relative circle-point curve of this relative motion. With the points A_1 and B_1 thus located, the length c of the coupler is uniquely determined by equation (A9.8), which in fact is identical with equation (2.5).

Again, as a usual procedure in synthesizing a function generator, it is to be noted that the synthesized linkage should be free from branch and order problems, similar to that mentioned in Section 6.7.1. The range of rotation of each rotating link should never include a dead centre position.

8.1.3 Five precision-points $(P_1 - P_2 - P_3 - P_4 - P_5)$

In this case four angle-pairs ϕ_2, ψ_2; ϕ_3, ψ_3; ϕ_4, ψ_4; ϕ_5, ψ_5 are to be coordinated. This synthesis problem is treated as a combination of two four-precision-point cases, e.g. $(P_1 - P_2 - P_3 - P_4)$ and $(P_1 - P_2 - P_3 - P_5)$. Similar to equation (8.10) a second quadratic equation in the unknown $q = \tan \psi_0$ involving a second set of three relative poles R_2, R_3, R_5 may be written:

$$b_2 q^2 + b_1 q + b_0 = 0 \tag{8.11}$$

The two simultaneous equations (8.10) and (8.11) are to be solved for t and q. Eliminating q from both equations yields

$$\begin{vmatrix} a_2 & a_0 \\ b_2 & b_0 \end{vmatrix}^2 + \begin{vmatrix} a_2 & a_1 \\ b_2 & b_1 \end{vmatrix}\begin{vmatrix} a_0 & a_1 \\ b_0 & b_1 \end{vmatrix} = 0 \tag{8.12}$$

Expansion of equation (8.12) results in the following equation of eighth degree in the unknown $t = \tan \phi_0$:

$$f_8 t^8 + f_7 t^7 + f_6 t^6 + f_5 t^5 + f_4 t^4 + f_3 t^3 + f_2 t^2 + f_1 t + f_0 = 0 \tag{8.13}$$

Since in each four-precision-point case there is a relative centre-point curve on which A_1 should lie, the roots of equation (8.13) correspond to the intersection points of the two spherical relative centre-point curves (not including A_0), among which the three known intersections are R_2, R_3 and R_{23}, where R_{23} is the relative pole between the second and third relative positions of the two links a and b with respect to a. The spherical argument of the great circle $A_0 R_{23}$ with respect to $A_0 B_0$ is $-(\phi_2 + \phi_3)/2$. Therefore we have three known roots, namely, $\tan(-\phi_2/2)$, $\tan(-\phi_3/2)$ and $\tan[-(\phi_2 + \phi_3)/2]$. The eighth degree equation can then be reduced to the following quintic equation:

$$f_8 t^5 + f_{40} t^4 + f_{30} t^3 + f_{20} t^2 + f_{10} t + f_{00} = 0 \tag{8.14}$$

The expressions for the coefficients in equation (8.14) are given in Appendix A9.2. The number of real roots of this quintic equation is one, three or five; in other words, at least one of the roots is real. A maximum of five different spherical four-bar function generators for coordinating the same four angle-pairs is possible.

There is a single value q_0 corresponding to each real root t_0 of the quintic equation. This is determined by

$$q_0 = - \begin{vmatrix} a_2 & a_0 \\ b_2 & b_0 \end{vmatrix} \Big/ \begin{vmatrix} a_2 & a_1 \\ b_2 & b_1 \end{vmatrix} \tag{8.15}$$

the expanded form of which is equation (A9.11).

The values of a, b and c can then be found by following the same procedure as in the four-precision-point case.

Example: It is required to generate the function $y = \log_{10} x$ in the interval

$1 \leqslant x \leqslant 10$ and $0 \leqslant y \leqslant 1$. The ranges of $\triangle \phi$ and $\triangle \psi$ are assumed to be $-90°$ and $90°$ respectively. The scale factors are therefore

$$M_\phi = -10° \text{ per unit of } x$$
$$M_\psi = 90° \text{ per unit of } y$$

Choosing five precision-points at $x = 1, 3, 5.5, 7.75$ and 10 gives the following ϕ_i's and ψ_i's to be coordinated:

x	$\triangle x_i$	ϕ_i	ψ_i
1.00			
3.00	2.00	$-20.00°$	$+42.9409°$
5.50	4.50	$-45.00°$	$+66.6326°$
7.75	6.75	$-67.50°$	$+80.0372°$
10.00	9.00	$-90.00°$	$+90.0000°$

Suppose $f = 90°$ is given. The quintic equation (8.14) now becomes

$$t^5 + 1.21355 \, t^4 + 2.44461 \, t^3 + 2.42633 \, t^2 + 1.47224 \, t + 1.18747 = 0$$

Only one root of this equation is real, and is negative. Therefore only one linkage is possible, the dimensions of which are:

$$\phi_0 = -44.340°, \ \psi_0 = 71.675°, \ a = 63.042°, \ b = 52.596°, \ c = 101.290°$$

This linkage is shown in Fig. 8.4 in its first position. It is to be noted that, in order to obtain the numerical results accurate to five to six significant figures, the input data should be accurate to six to seven significant figures.

Fig. 8.4. Example: synthesized function generator.

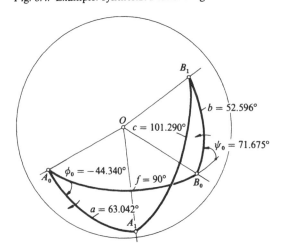

8.1.4   Six precision-points $(P_1-P_2-P_3-P_4-P_5-P_6)$

The synthesis problems for five and six precision-points have been treated in (Rao, Sandor, Kohli & Soni, 1973), but non-linear equations were involved. We shall extend the procedure mentioned in the preceding section to the six-precision-point case. As shown before, for a given length of the fixed link f, the solutions for five precision-points are uniquely determined. It is therefore in general not possible to coordinate a further angle-pair ϕ_6, ψ_6, unless f is left open. We may therefore take f as a parameter, and let it vary within a likely range. For each assumed value of f, we can find at least one spherical four-bar to coordinate the four angle-pairs ϕ_2, ψ_2; ϕ_3, ψ_3; ϕ_4, ψ_4; ϕ_5, ψ_5. By analysing the synthesized linkage (or linkages) by means of equation (2.8), we can find the value of ψ corresponding to the input angle $\phi = \phi_0 + \phi_6$. Let this ψ-value be denoted by $\psi(\phi_0 + \phi_6)$. We see that the change of ψ corresponding to ϕ_6 is $\psi(\phi_0 + \phi_6) - \psi_0$. Denote the difference between this change of ψ and the required change ψ_6 by

$$\delta\psi_6 = [\psi(\phi_0 + \phi_6) - \psi_0] - \psi_6 \tag{8.16}$$

We can adjust the assumed value of f until $\delta\psi_6$ becomes sufficiently small. The last value of f is the required one, and the last synthesized linkage is the required function generator for six precision-points. All the computation task may be left to a computer, and the program will not be lengthy.

8.2   Infinitesimally separated relative positions – order type synthesis

Suppose, in Fig. 8.2, the points P_2, P_3 and P_4 approach P_1 indefinitely. The requirement of coordinating the three angle-pairs ϕ_2, ψ_2; ϕ_3, ψ_3; ϕ_4, ψ_4 becomes a requirement of matching prescribed values of $\psi' = d\psi/d\phi$, $\psi'' = d^2\psi/d\phi^2$ and $\psi''' = d^3\psi/d\phi^3$ in position P_1. This case is denoted by $P_1 P_2 P_3 P_4$. This kind of synthesis procedure is called an order type synthesis.

Because $\dot{\phi} = \omega_a$ and $\dot{\psi} = \omega_b$, therefore

$$\omega_b = \psi'\omega_a \tag{8.17}$$

and for a constant ω_a,

$$\alpha_b = \psi''\omega_a^2 \tag{8.18}$$

$$\dot{\alpha}_b = \psi'''\omega_a^3 \tag{8.19}$$

Hence, a prescribed ψ' means a predetermined velocity ratio, and a prescribed ψ'' and ψ''' means, respectively, a predetermined ratio of angular acceleration of the output link to ω_a^2 and a predetermined ratio of the angular jerk of the output link to ω_a^3, etc.

For a given function $y = y(x)$, if the scale factors M_ϕ, M_ψ have been chosen in rad/unit of x and rad/unit of y respectively, the differential coefficients to be matched at a certain value $x = x_m$ are evaluated from the following equations:

$$\left.\begin{aligned}
\psi' &= \frac{d\psi}{d\phi} = \frac{M_\psi}{M_\phi}\frac{dy}{dx} = \frac{M_\psi}{M_\phi}y'(x) \\[2mm]
\psi'' &= \frac{d^2\psi}{d\phi^2} = \frac{M_\psi}{M_\phi^2}\frac{d^2y}{dx^2} = \frac{M_\psi}{M_\phi^2}y''(x) \\[2mm]
\psi''' &= \frac{d^3\psi}{d\phi^3} = \frac{M_\psi}{M_\phi^3}\frac{d^3y}{dx^3} = \frac{M_\psi}{M_\phi^3}y'''(x) \\[2mm]
\psi^{IV} &= \frac{d^4\psi}{d\phi^4} = \frac{M_\psi}{M_\phi^4}\frac{d^4y}{dx^4} = \frac{M_\psi}{M_\phi^4}y^{IV}(x)
\end{aligned}\right\} \tag{8.20}$$

If we could synthesize a four-bar function generator which exhibits, in a certain position $x = x_m$, all differential coefficients ψ', ψ'',..., the linkage would then exactly reproduce the given function. This fact can easily be seen from the Taylor's expansion of the function $y = y(x)$ at $x = x_m$:

$$y(x_m + \Delta x) = y(x_m) + \frac{\Delta x}{1!}y'(x_m) + \frac{\Delta x^2}{2!}y''(x_m) + ...$$

However, as in plane kinematics, the highest order of differential coefficients that can be matched, in general, is the fifth order, or the case $P_1P_2P_3P_4P_5$, if f is prescribed. A given function can therefore only be approximated by a function generator up to the fifth order. In the following we shall consider the cases up to $P_1P_2P_3P_4$ (Chen & Chiang, 1983).

8.2.1   Second, third and fourth order syntheses (P_1P_2, $P_1P_2P_3$ and $P_1P_2P_3P_4$)

(1) The case P_1P_2

As mentioned before, in the case of two infinitesimally separated relative positions P_1P_2, both ϕ_2 and ψ_2 approach infinitesimal, and the ratio ψ_2/ϕ_2 becomes the velocity ratio ψ' which is to be matched. The relative pole R_2 in Fig. 8.3 lies on the great circle A_0B_0, as shown in Fig. 8.9. From equations (8.4) and (8.5) it follows that

$$\left.\begin{aligned}
\sin r_{a2} &= -\frac{\psi'S_f}{K_0}, &\quad \cos r_{a2} &= \frac{1 - \psi'C_f}{K_0} \\[2mm]
\sin r_{b2} &= -\frac{S_f}{K_0}, &\quad \cos r_{b2} &= \frac{-\psi' + C_f}{K_0}
\end{aligned}\right\} \tag{8.21}$$

where $K_0 = \sqrt{(1 - 2\psi'\cos f + \psi'^2)}$, $S_f = \sin f$ and $C_f = \cos f$. Equation (8.8) now becomes, for $i = 2$,

$$-\psi'S_{\psi0}S_f\cot a + S_{\phi0}S_f\cot b = S_{\phi0}C_{\psi0}K_1 - C_{\phi0}S_{\psi0}K_2 \tag{8.22}$$

where again $S_{\phi 0} = \sin \phi_0$ and $C_{\psi 0} = \cos \psi_0$, etc., and $K_1 = \psi' - C_f$, $K_2 = \psi' C_f - 1$. Equation (8.22) is identical with equation (2.12). This equation enables us to design a spherical four-bar linkage to exhibit a prescribed ψ', by assuming any four of the five parameters f, a, b, ϕ_0 and ψ_0. If f is given, there are ∞^3 solutions.

(2) The case $P_1 P_2 P_3$

Differentiating equation (8.22) with respect to ϕ gives the following equation. It should be noted that, in the differentiation process, the variables ϕ_0 and ψ_0 should first be replaced respectively by ϕ and ψ, and then changed back to ϕ_0 and ψ_0 after differentiation:

$$-(\psi'' S_{\psi 0} + \psi'^2 C_{\psi 0}) S_f \cot a + C_{\phi 0} S_f \cot b = S_{\phi 0} S_{\psi 0} K_3$$
$$+ C_{\phi 0} C_{\psi 0} K_4 + S_{\phi 0} C_{\psi 0} K_5 + C_{\phi 0} S_{\psi 0} K_6 \tag{8.23}$$

where

$$\left.\begin{array}{l} K_3 = -1 + 2\psi' C_f - \psi'^2 \\ K_4 = -C_f + 2\psi' - \psi'^2 C_f \\ K_5 = \psi'' \\ K_6 = \psi'' C_f \end{array}\right\} \tag{8.24}$$

Equations (8.22) and (8.23) constitute two simultaneous equations in the two unknowns $\cot a$ and $\cot b$. If f is given, the parameters ϕ_0 and ψ_0 may be arbitrarily assumed, and the two equations can be solved for $\cot a$ and $\cot b$. There are ∞^2 solutions.

(3) The case $P_1 P_2 P_3 P_4$

Differentiating equation (8.23) again with respect to ϕ gives the following equation:

$$-(\psi''' S_{\psi 0} + 3\psi'' \psi' C_{\psi 0} - \psi'^3 S_{\psi 0}) S_f \cot a - S_{\phi 0} S_f \cot b = S_{\phi 0} S_{\psi 0} K_7$$
$$+ C_{\phi 0} C_{\psi 0} K_8 + S_{\phi 0} C_{\psi 0} K_9 + C_{\phi 0} S_{\psi 0} K_{10} \tag{8.25}$$

where

$$\begin{array}{l} K_7 = 3\psi'' C_f - 3\psi'' \psi' \\ K_8 = 3\psi'' - 3\psi'' \psi' C_f \\ K_9 = C_f - 3\psi' + 3\psi'^2 C_f - \psi'^3 + \psi''' \\ K_{10} = -1 + 3\psi' C_f - 3\psi'^2 + \psi'^3 C_f - \psi''' C_f \end{array}$$

Equations (8.22), (8.23) and (8.25) constitute a system of three linear equations in the two unknowns $\cot a$ and $\cot b$. For the existence of the solutions, the determinant of the coefficients of these three equations must vanish, or

$$\begin{vmatrix} -\psi'S_{\psi 0} & S_{\phi 0}, & S_{\phi 0}C_{\psi 0}K_1 - C_{\phi 0}S_{\psi 0}K_2 \\ -\psi''S_{\psi 0} - \psi'^2C_{\psi 0} & C_{\phi 0}, & S_{\phi 0}S_{\psi 0}K_3 + C_{\phi 0}C_{\psi 0}K_4 + S_{\phi 0}C_{\psi 0}K_5 + C_{\phi 0}S_{\psi 0}K_6 \\ -\psi'''S_{\psi 0} - 3\psi''\psi'C_{\psi 0} + \psi'^3S_{\psi 0}, & -S_{\phi 0}, & S_{\phi 0}S_{\psi 0}K_7 + S_{\phi 0}C_{\psi 0}K_8 + S_{\phi 0}C_{\psi 0}K_9 + C_{\phi 0}S_{\psi 0}K_{10} \end{vmatrix} = 0$$

$$(8.26)$$

Equation (8.26) contains two unknowns $\tan\phi_0$ and $\tan\psi_0$. By arbitrarily assuming a value of ϕ_0, it can be expanded and reduced to a quadratic equation in the unknown $q = \tan\psi_0$:

$$a_2 q^2 + a_1 q + a_0 = 0 \qquad (8.27)$$

where the coefficients a_2, a_1, a_0, being functions of $t = \tan\phi_0$, are now

$$a_2 = (-t\psi'' + \psi')(tK_7 - K_2 + K_{10})$$
$$- (\psi''' - \psi'^3 + \psi')(-t^2K_3 - tK_6 - K_2)$$

$$a_1 = (-t\psi'' + \psi')(tK_1 + tK_9 + K_8) - t\psi'^2(tK_7 - K_2 + K_{10})$$
$$+ (\psi''' - \psi'^3 + \psi')(t^2K_5 - tK_1 + tK_4)$$
$$- 3\psi''\psi'(-t^2K_3 - tK_6 - K_2)$$

$$a_0 = -t\psi'^2(tK_1 + tK_9 + K_8) + 3\psi''\psi'(t^2K_5 - tK_1 + tK_4)$$

Again there are two ψ_0's corresponding to a single ϕ_0, and two ϕ_0's corresponding to a single ψ_0. If f is given, taking ϕ_0 as the parameter, there are therefore ∞^1 solutions. Having found the two ψ_0's for a given ϕ_0, the *lengths a, b* of the two rotating links are given by

$$a = \tan^{-1}\frac{\delta}{\delta_a \cos\phi_0}$$

$$b = \tan^{-1}\frac{-\delta}{\delta_b \cos\psi_0}$$

where

$$\delta = \begin{vmatrix} \psi'q, & t \\ \psi''q + \psi'^2, & 1 \end{vmatrix} S_f$$

$$\delta_a = \begin{vmatrix} tK_1 - qK_2, & t \\ tqK_3 + tK_5 + qK_6 + K_4, & 1 \end{vmatrix}$$

$$\delta_b = \begin{vmatrix} \psi'q, & tK_1 - qK_2 \\ \psi''q + \psi'^2, & tqK_3 + tK_5 + qK_6 + K_4 \end{vmatrix}$$

The length of the coupler c is determined by equation (A9.8). The point A lies on the spherical relative centering-point curve of the motion of the body b relative to a, and the point B lies on the spherical relative circling-point curve of this relative motion.

Example: Fig. 8.5 shows a given spherical four-bar linkage with $f = 90°$, $a = 50°$, $b = 120°$, $c = 90°$. The linkage is analysed in the position $\phi_0 = 60°$ to give

$$\psi_0 = 57.9459°, \ \psi' = -0.7890, \ \psi'' = 0.8915, \ \psi''' = -1.0819$$

It is required to synthesize another spherical four-bar function generator to exhibit the above three differential coefficients ψ', ψ'', ψ''' with a given fixed link length $f = 90°$ and input angle $\phi_0 = 60°$.

By feeding the given data into a computer program following the mentioned procedure, two solutions are found. The first solution is the original linkage,

Fig. 8.5. Example: given linkage.

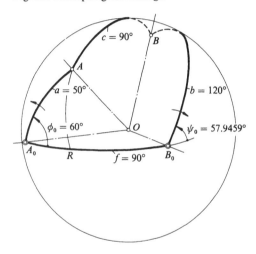

Fig. 8.6. Example: second solution.

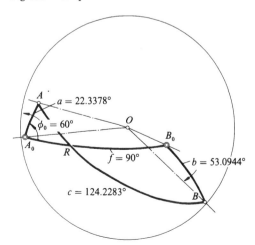

and the second solution gives the following dimensions of the linkage:

$a = 22.3378°$, $b = 53.0944°$, $c = 124.2283°$

This linkage is shown in Fig. 8.6.

If, in particular, $\psi'' = 0$, then the $\psi-\phi$ diagram exhibits a three-point contacting tangent at the point in question, and the velocity ratio $i = \psi'$ is stationary, or becomes an extreme. The synthesis procedure remains the same. If $\psi'' = \psi''' = 0$, the $\psi-\phi$ diagram exhibits a four-point contacting tangent at the point in question, and the linkage is called a proportional mechanism (Suh, 1970; Meyer zur Capellen, 1971; Meyer zur Capellen & Willkommen, 1974). If, in addition, $\psi'''' = 0$ too in this position, then the $\psi-\phi$ diagram exhibits a five-point contacting tangent (see Fig. 2.26). The above synthesis equations are then considerably simplified. No additional example will be given.

A synthesis method for a limited variation in ψ', i.e. for prescribed ψ'_{max} and range of ϕ within which this ψ'_{max} lies and the velocity ratio at both ends of which reduces to $\lambda\psi'_{max}$ (where $\lambda < 1$), as well as for the corresponding given locations of ϕ, has also been investigated, but the resulting equations are highly non-linear (Osman, Dukkipati & Osman, 1983).

8.2.2   Locus of P in a fourth order synthesis

Referring to Fig. 4.11, let the great circle arc RP be denoted by l, and let $A_0P = a + p = p_0$. The location of P is defined by its spherical polar coordinates $(l, \gamma + \lambda)$ with respect to an origin point at R and a spherical polar great circle RA_0. We shall see what is the locus of P in a fourth order synthesis. In $\triangle A_0B_0P$ we have, by equation (A1.11),

$$q = \tan \psi_0 = \frac{\sin \phi_0 \sin p_0}{\cos f \cos \phi_0 \sin p_0 - \sin f \cos p_0} \tag{8.28}$$

Substituting equation (8.28) into equation (8.27) gives

$$a_2 S_{\phi 0}^2 S_{p0}^2 + a_1 S_{\phi 0} S_{p0}(C_f S_{p0} C_{\phi 0} - S_f C_{p0})$$
$$+ a_0 (C_f C_{\phi 0} S_{p0} - S_f C_{p0})^2 = 0 \tag{8.29}$$

with $S_{p0} = \sin p_0$, $C_{p0} = \cos p_0$, etc. In $\triangle A_0PR$,

$$S_{p0} = \frac{S_l \sin(\gamma + \lambda)}{S_{\phi 0}} \tag{8.30}$$

Substituting equation (8.30) into equation (8.29) results in

$$k_p: \quad \tan l = d_c \cos(\gamma + \lambda) \tag{8.31}$$

where

$$d_c = 3(\psi''^2 - \psi'^2 K_3)S_f/[3\psi''^2(C_f - \psi') - \psi'(1 - \psi'^2)K_3 - \psi'''K_3]$$

$$(8.32)$$

The expression of K_3 is as defined in equation (8.24). Equation (8.31) indicates that the locus of P is a spherical Thales ellipse (see Appendix A1.3) which is symmetrically disposed about the great circle $A_0 B_0$. This spherical Thales ellipse corresponds to the Carter–Hall circle in plane kinematics. We denote

Fig. 8.7. k_p-curve of the linkage in Fig. 8.6.

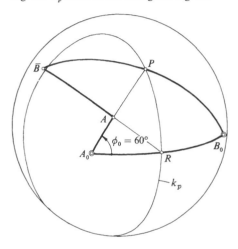

Fig. 8.8. Carter–Hall circle.

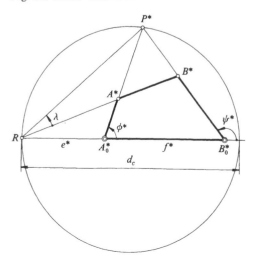

it here by k_p. Fig. 8.7 shows the k_p-curve in the last example, the spherical four-bar being a supplementary linkage of that shown in Fig. 8.6.

Consider now the gnomonic projection of the curve k_p onto a plane tangent to the unit sphere at R, somewhat like that shown in Fig. 8.9. Let the gnomonic projections of A_0, A, B, B_0 and P be denoted respectively by A_0^*, A^*, B^*, B_0^* and P^*. Further let the plane rectangular coordinates on the tangent plane be (ξ, ζ). Applying the transformation equations (A4.9) and (A4.10), where (p, θ) are replaced respectively by (l, ε), to equation (8.3), we get the gnomonic projection of k_p:

$$k_p^*: \quad \xi^2 - d_c\xi + \zeta^2 = 0 \tag{8.33}$$

It is evident that k_p^* is a circle with diameter d_c and with its centre lying on $A_0^*B_0^*$. Since the circle k_p^* passes through R and P^*, it is exactly the Carter–Hall circle pertaining to the quadrilateral $A_0^*A^*B^*B_0^*$, provided this quadrilateral is considered as an instantaneous plane four-bar linkage, as shown in Fig. 8.8.

8.2.3   Kinematic relations between a spherical four-bar linkage and its gnomonic projection

Fig. 8.9 shows a spherical four-bar linkage A_0ABB_0 and its gnomonic projection $A_0^*A^*B^*B_0^*$. In the following the projected quantities

Fig. 8.9. Gnomonic projection of A_0ABB_0 at R.

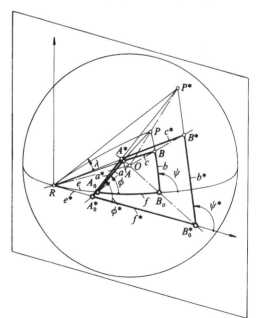

are signified with an (*). Angles at R are not altered by the projection, e.g. $\lambda^* = \lambda = \sphericalangle ARP = \sphericalangle A^*RP^*$. Certainly the lengths a^*, c^*, b^*, f^* are continuously varying as the original spherical linkage moves. However, if $A_0^* A^* B^* B_0^*$ is considered as a plane linkage separated from the original spherical linkage $A_0 ABB_0$, i.e. an instantaneous linkage with constant link lengths a^*, c^*, b^*, f^*, we may study its instantaneous kinematic properties, because these properties depend only on its instantaneous geometrical configuration. Thus, for instance, the angular velocity ratio of the linkage is RA_0^*/RB_0^*, which we denote by $\psi^{*\prime}$. It should be noted that the symbol $\psi^{*\prime}$ is to be considered as a geometrical quantity of the separated plane four-bar, rather than a kinematic quantity $d\psi^*/d\phi^*$, where both ϕ^* and ψ^* are functions of ϕ. In other words, $\psi^{*\prime}$, $\psi^{*\prime\prime}$, $\psi^{*\prime\prime\prime}$ are defined for the separated plane linkage $A_0^* A^* B^* B_0^*$ per equations (8.17)–(8.19).

$$\begin{aligned} \omega_{b^*} &= \psi^{*\prime} \omega_{a^*} \\ \alpha_{b^*} &= \psi^{*\prime\prime} \omega_{a^*}^2 \\ \dot{\alpha}_{b^*} &= \psi^{*\prime\prime\prime} \omega_{a^*}^3 \end{aligned} \tag{8.34}$$

There are quite remarkable relations between ψ', ψ'', ψ''' and $\psi^{*\prime}$, $\psi^{*\prime\prime}$, $\psi^{*\prime\prime\prime}$ (Chiang & Chen, 1983).

(1) Relation between ψ' and $\psi^{*\prime}$
Referring to Fig. 8.9, for the spherical four-bar, we have already obtained in equation (4.16) that

$$\psi' = \frac{\sin e}{\sin (e+f)} \tag{[(4.16)]}$$

For the instantaneous plane linkage, it is well known that

$$\psi^{*\prime} = \frac{e^*}{e^* + f^*} \tag{8.35}$$

Because

$$\left. \begin{aligned} e^* &= \tan e \\ e^* + f^* &= \tan (e+f) \end{aligned} \right\} \tag{8.36}$$

equation (8.35) can be written as

$$\psi^{*\prime} = \frac{\tan e}{\tan (e+f)} \tag{8.37}$$

Comparison of equation (8.37) with equation (4.16) shows that

$$\psi' = \frac{\cos e}{\cos (e+f)} \psi^{*\prime} \tag{8.38}$$

(2) Relation between ψ'' and $\psi^{*''}$

For the spherical four-bar, we have already found in equation (4.39) that

$$\psi'' = \frac{\sin e \sin f}{\sin^2 (e + f)} \cot \lambda \qquad\qquad ([(4.39)]$$

For the separated plane four-bar, it is also well known that (Freudenstein, 1956; Chiang, 1970)

$$\psi^{*''} = \frac{e^* f^*}{(e^* + f^*)^2} \cot \lambda \qquad\qquad (8.39)$$

Substituting equations (8.36) into equation (8.39) gives

$$\psi^{*''} = \frac{\tan e [\tan (e + f) - \tan e]}{\tan^2 (e + f)} \cot \lambda \qquad\qquad (8.40)$$

Comparison of equation (8.40) with equation (4.39) shows that

$$\psi'' = \frac{\cos^2 e}{\cos (e + f)} \psi^{*''} \qquad\qquad (8.41)$$

(3) Relation between ψ''' and $\psi^{*'''}$

From equations (8.38) and (8.41) it seems to be quite promising that there might be a relation between ψ''' and $\psi^{*'''}$, somewhat of the form

$$\psi''' = \frac{\cos^3 e}{\cos (e + f)} \psi^{*'''} \qquad\qquad (8.42)$$

We shall show that the relation (8.42) indeed exists. For, if it is required to synthesize a plane four-bar function generator to match prescribed $\psi^{*'}$, $\psi^{*''}$, $\psi^{*'''}$ with a given f^*, the procedure is to draw a Carter–Hall circle with a diameter d_c according to the equation (Chiang, 1971)

$$d_c^* = \frac{3f^* [\psi^{*'2} (1 - \psi^{*'})^2 + \psi^{*''2}]}{(1 - \psi^{*'}) [\psi^{*'}(1 + \psi^{*'})(1 - \psi^{*'})^2 + 3\psi^{*''2} + (1 - \psi^{*'}) \psi^{*'''}]} \qquad\qquad (8.43)$$

However, as mentioned in Section 8.2.2, the gnomonic projection of the k_p-curve for prescribed ψ', ψ'', ψ''' and f is the Carter–Hall circle pertaining to the projected plane four-bar $A_0^* A^* B^* B_0^*$ of the synthesized spherical four-bar $A_0 A B B_0$. Therefore d_c^* and d_c must be identical. Equating the expressions in equations (8.43) and (8.32), and taking equations (8.36), (8.38), (8.41) into consideration, we come eventually to equation (8.42).

(4) Applications of the kinematic relations

The relations in equations (8.38), (8.41) and (8.42) may be utilized in carrying out a fourth order synthesis of a spherical four-bar function generator. The given ψ', ψ'', ψ''' and f are first converted to give the values of $\psi^{*\prime}$, $\psi^{*\prime\prime}$, $\psi^{*\prime\prime\prime}$ and f^*. Based on these data, a plane four-bar function generator can be synthesized on the tangent plane by using known techniques. This synthesized plane linkage can then be projected back onto the spherical surface to yield the required solution.

Example: In a fourth order synthesis of a spherical four-bar function generator the prescribed derivatives are:

$$\psi' = -1.740, \quad \psi'' = 2.917, \quad \psi''' = 2.811$$

Fig. 8.10. Example: fourth order synthesis of a plane four-bar on the tangent plane.

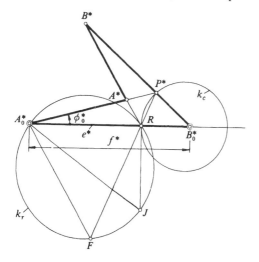

Fig. 8.11. Example: synthesized spherical four-bar function generator as projected back from the plane linkage in Fig. 8.10.

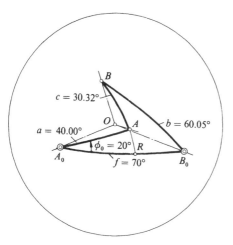

with $f = 70°$ and $\phi_0 = 20°$. The value of e is first found by equation (4.9): $e = -45.709°$, and then by equations (8.38), (8.41) and (8.42) we get

$$\psi^{*\prime} = -2.271, \quad \psi^{*\prime\prime} = 5.452, \quad \psi^{*\prime\prime\prime} = 7.524$$

Next, we compute by equations (8.36): $e^* = -1.025$, $f^* = 1.476$. Following the procedure suggested in (Chiang & Chung, 1980), the points A_0^*, B_0^* and R are first located as shown in Fig. 8.10. The diameter of the Carter–Hall circle is computed by equation (8.43): $d_c^* = +0.795$. Since d_c^* is positive, the Carter–Hall circle k_c lies on the right-hand side of R. The vertical line RJ is computed by $RJ = \psi^{*\prime\prime} f^* / (1 - \psi^{*\prime})^2 = 0.752$. The circle k_r is drawn with $A_0^* J$ as a diameter. The angle ϕ_0^* is determined from ϕ_0 by equation (A4.17): $\phi_0^* = 14.260°$. With these data, the points P^* and F in Fig. 8.10 are located, and the plane four-bar $A_0^* A^* B^* B_0^*$ is synthesized for matching the prescribed $\psi^{*\prime}$, $\psi^{*\prime\prime}$, $\psi^{*\prime\prime\prime}$. The following quantities are then determined:

$$RA^* = 0.262, \quad RB^* = 1.000,$$
$$\measuredangle A_0^* RA^* = 60.047°, \quad \measuredangle B_0^* RB^* = 119.953°$$

This synthesized plane four-bar is then projected back onto the spherical surface, as shown in Fig. 8.11. The results are:

$$RA = \tan^{-1} RA^* = 14.68°, \quad RB = \tan^{-1} RB^* = 45.00°$$
$$\measuredangle A_0 RA = \measuredangle A_0^* RA^* = 60.047°, \quad \measuredangle B_0 RB = \measuredangle B_0^* RB^* = 119.953°$$
$$a = 40.00°, \quad b = 60.05°, \quad c = RB - RA = 30.32°$$

8.2.4   Matching two prescribed velocity ratios–the case $P_1 P_2 - P_3 P_4$

Similar to body guidance problems, in the synthesis of four-bar function generators for four relative positions there are three intermediate cases between the two extreme cases $P_1 - P_2 - P_3 - P_4$ and $P_1 P_2 P_3 P_4$, and for five relative positions there are five intermediate cases between the two extreme cases $P_1 - P_2 - P_3 - P_4 - P_5$ and $P_1 P_2 P_3 P_4 P_5$. Out of all these intermediate cases, we shall only consider the case $P_1 P_2 - P_3 P_4$, because the syntheses of various

Fig. 8.12. The case $P_1 P_2 - P_3 P_4$.

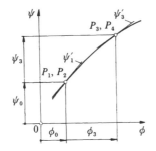

kinds of spherical four-bar linkages may be considered as its special cases (Chiang, 1983).

Suppose, in Fig. 8.2, the points P_2 and P_4 approach respectively the points P_1 and P_3 indefinitely. The corresponding $\psi - \phi$ diagram is shown in Fig. 8.12. In this case, the requirements are: (1) matching a prescribed velocity ratio ψ' at P_1, (2) coordinating the angle-pair ϕ_3, ψ_3, and (3) matching again another prescribed velocity ratio ψ' at P_3. These two prescribed velocity ratios will be denoted respectively by ψ'_1 and ψ'_3.

Now for $P_1 P_2$, equation (8.22) is written as

$$-\psi'_1 S_{\psi 0} S_f \cot a + S_{\phi 0} S_f \cot b$$
$$= S_{\phi 0} C_{\psi 0} (\psi'_1 - C_f) - C_{\phi 0} S_{\psi 0} (\psi'_1 C_f - 1) \tag{8.44}$$

For P_1–P_3, simply setting $i = 3$ in equation (8.8) gives

$$\sin\left(\psi_0 + \frac{\psi_3}{2}\right) \sin r_{a3} \cot a - \sin\left(\phi_0 + \frac{\phi_3}{2}\right) \sin r_{b3} \cot b$$
$$= \sin\left(\psi_0 + \frac{\psi_3}{2}\right) \cos\left(\phi_0 + \frac{\phi_3}{2}\right) \cos r_{a3}$$
$$- \sin\left(\phi_0 + \frac{\phi_3}{2}\right) \cos\left(\psi_0 + \frac{\psi_3}{2}\right) \cos r_{b3} \tag{8.45}$$

For $P_3 P_4$, the following equation can be written by analogy with equation (8.44):

$$-\psi'_3 \sin(\psi_0 + \psi_3) S_f \cot a + \sin(\phi_0 + \phi_3) S_f \cot b$$
$$= \sin(\phi_0 + \phi_3) \cos(\psi_0 + \psi_3)(\psi'_3 - C_f)$$
$$- \cos(\phi_0 + \phi_3) \sin(\psi_0 + \psi_3)(\psi'_3 C_f - 1) \tag{8.46}$$

The characteristic equation corresponding to the system of equations (8.44), (8.45), (8.46) in the unknowns $\cot a$ and $\cot b$ becomes

$$\begin{vmatrix} -\psi'_1 S_{\psi 0} S_f, & S_{\phi 0} S_f, & S_{\phi 0} C_{\psi 0} K_{11} - C_{\phi 0} S_{\psi 0} K_{21} \\ \sin\left(\psi_0 + \dfrac{\psi_3}{2}\right) \sin r_{a3}, & -\sin\left(\phi_0 + \dfrac{\phi_3}{2}\right) \sin r_{b3}, & \begin{array}{l} \sin\left(\psi_0 + \dfrac{\psi_3}{2}\right) \cos\left(\phi_0 + \dfrac{\phi_3}{2}\right) \cos r_{a3} \\ - \sin\left(\phi_0 + \dfrac{\phi_3}{2}\right) \cos\left(\psi_0 + \dfrac{\psi_3}{2}\right) \cos r_{b3} \end{array} \\ -\psi'_3 \sin(\psi_0 + \psi_3) S_f, & \sin(\phi_0 + \phi_3) S_f, & \begin{array}{l} \sin(\phi_0 + \phi_3) \cos(\psi_0 + \psi_3) K_{13} \\ - \cos(\phi_0 + \phi_3) \sin(\psi_0 + \psi_3) K_{23} \end{array} \end{vmatrix} = 0 \tag{8.47}$$

where $K_{11} = \psi'_1 - C_f$, $K_{21} = \psi'_1 C_f - 1$, $K_{13} = \psi'_3 - C_f$, $K_{23} = \psi'_3 C_f - 1$. As in all four-precision-point cases, equation (8.47) is expanded and reduced to a quadratic equation in the unknown $q = \tan \psi_0$:

$$a_2 q^2 + a_1 q + a_0 = 0 \qquad (8.48)$$

where the coefficients a_2, a_1, a_0 are again quadratic functions of $t = \tan \phi_0$, the expressions for which are given in Appendix 10.

Again there are two ψ_0's corresponding to a single ϕ_0, and two ϕ_0's corresponding to a single ψ_0. If ϕ_0 is taken as the parameter, there are ∞^1 solutions. Having found the two ψ_0's for a given ϕ_0, the *lengths* a and b of the two rotating links can be found from equations (A10.4) and (A10.5). The *length* of the coupler c is again determined by using equation (A9.8).

Example: Let us take the linkage shown in Fig. 8.4 as a given linkage to show the synthesis procedure. The bar lengths are: $f = 90°$, $a = 63.042°$, $b = 52.596°$, $c = 101.290°$. This linkage is analysed to give the following data:

In position 1, $\phi_0 = -44.3400°$, $\psi_0 = 71.6750°$, $\psi'_1 = -4.6124$

In position 3, $\phi = -89.3400°$, $\psi = 138.3076°$, $\psi'_3 = -0.7118$

The synthesis problem is therefore to find a spherical four-bar function generator to coordinate the crank rotation pair $\phi_3 = -89.3400° - (-44.3400°) = -45.0000°$, $\psi_3 = 138.3076° - 71.6750° = 66.6326°$, and to match two prescribed velocity ratios $\psi'_1 = 4.6124$ and $\psi'_3 = -0.7118$ with a given fixed link length $f = 90°$ and $\phi_0 = -44.3400°$.

By following the procedure in Appendix 10, the quadratic equation (8.48) is found to be

$$-0.2453 q^2 + 1.1272 q - 1.1664 = 0$$

This equation has two real roots. The first root leads to the original four-bar

Fig. 8.13. Example: second solution.

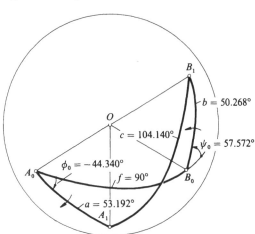

of Fig. 8.4. The second root gives $\psi_0 = \tan^{-1} q = 57.572°$, and the corresponding dimensions of the linkage are:

$$a = 53.192°, \quad b = 50.268°, \quad c = 104.140°$$

This second four-bar is shown in Fig. 8.13, and fulfils the same requirements as the original one.

8.3   Transmission angle problems

8.3.1   The transmission angle

Fig. 8.14(a) shows a spherical four-bar linkage A_0ABB_0. It is well known that in plane kinematics, if A_0ABB_0 were a plane four-bar linkage, the angle $\mu = \sphericalangle ABB_0$, diagonally opposite to the input angle ϕ, is called, after Alt, the transmission angle (Alt, 1932b). We shall see whether it is justified to take this angle μ, in the spherical case, as a transmission angle.

A spherical four-bar linkage can be considered as a special case of spatial four-link mechanisms. Its static force and torque analysis can best be solved by using dual vector algebra or screw coordinates (Yang, 1965; Yuan & Freudenstein, 1971; Yuan, Freudenstein & Woo, 1971; Bagci, 1971). However, for the determination of the transmission characteristics of the linkage only, it is not necessary to analyse the forces and torques acting at each joint of the whole mechanism. All we have to do is to find the nature, not the magnitude, of the force system acting at the joint B by the floating link, or coupler, c, and see how this force system can affect the rotation of the output link b. This force system can be conceived by simple conceptions of statics.

Fig. 8.14. (a) RCCC-type spherical four-bar. (b) Moment vectors.

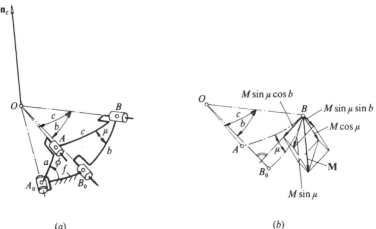

      (a)   (b)

As far as statics is concerned, a spherical four-bar linkage can be considered either as a special spatial RCCC-linkage or as a special spatial RSSR-linkage, where R denotes a revolute, C a cylindrical and S a spheric joint. These two cases will be considered separately.

(1) The RCCC-type spherical four-bar
For a general RCCC-linkage, the output link may perform a screw motion, i.e. a rotation about and a sliding along the joint axis of the last cylindrical pair. In other words, when an input torque is applied to the input link, the output may be a torque combined with an axial force. When the axes of the four joints intersect in a single point O, the RCCC-linkage becomes a spherical four-bar linkage, as shown in Fig. 8.14(a), with a special property that the output axial force vanishes identically. The reaction force system (or the so-called transmission wrench) applied by b on c at B and that applied by a on c at A must be equal and opposite. If the reaction force system at B contains any single force, it must be perpendicular to the axis OB. Similarly any single force of the opposite reaction force system at A must also be perpendicular to the axis OA. But this is not possible, unless both A and B are located at O. Hence this single force must vanish identically. This means that the reaction force system contains only a pure moment. This moment vector should have no component in the direction OB or in the direction OA. Consequently this moment vector must be in the direction of $\mathbf{n}_c$, the unit vector normal to the plane of c (or OAB). If the reaction on c by b is $\mathbf{M}$ in the $+\mathbf{n}_c$ sense, the reaction on c by a is $-\mathbf{M}$ in the $-\mathbf{n}_c$ sense, and vice versa. This is consistent with the results obtained in static analysis of a spherical four-bar linkage (Sieber, 1959; Yang, 1965; Bagci, 1971). Resolve the moment vector $\mathbf{M} = M\mathbf{n}_c$ into three mutually perpendicular components, as shown in Fig. 8.14(b), where M is negative. The vector $\mathbf{M}$ is first decomposed into a component $M\cos\mu$ normal to the plane $B_0 B$ and a component $M\sin\mu$ in this plane, and the latter is further decomposed into a component $M\sin\mu\sin b$ along the direction OB_0 and a component $M\sin\mu\cos b$ normal to OB_0. Imagine that a virtual angular rotation $\delta\psi$ is imparted to the link b. The only virtual work done is due to the component $M\sin\mu\sin b$, and is

$$M\,\delta\psi(\sin\mu\sin b)$$

The factor $\frac{1}{2}\sin\mu\sin b$ is called, after Ball, the *virtual coefficient* between $\mathbf{n}_c$, which is now a free vector, and a unit vector along OB_0 (Ball, 1900), or, we may write

$$VC_M = \tfrac{1}{2}\sin\mu\sin b$$

On the assumption that the coupler c is allowed any orientation relative to b, the value of VC_M becomes a maximum when $\mu = 90°$, or

$$VC_{M\max} = \tfrac{1}{2}\sin b$$

Sutherland and Roth (1973) defined the transmission index (TI) as the ratio $VC/VC_{\max}$, or, in the present case

$$TI = \frac{VC_M}{VC_{M\max}} = \sin \mu \qquad (8.49)$$

This justifies using μ as the transmission angle.

(2) The RSSR-type spherical four-bar

For a general RSSR-linkage, the axes of the two R-pairs do not intersect. When these two axes do intersect, the RSSR-linkage becomes a spherical four-bar, as shown in Fig. 8.15(a). The force system transmitted through the coupler c is simply a single force $\mathbf{F}$ along the direction AB, because no reaction moment can exist at the spheric joints A and B. Resolve the force F into three mutually perpendicular components, as shown in Fig. 8.15(b). The vector $\mathbf{F}$ is first decomposed, in the plane AB, into a component $F\sin(c/2)$ along the direction OB and a component $F\cos(c/2)$ normal to OB, and the latter is further decomposed into a component $F\cos(c/2)\sin\mu$ normal to the plane $B_0 B$ and a component $F\cos(c/2)\cos\mu$ in this plane. Again imagine that a virtual angular rotation $\delta\psi$ is imparted to the link b. The only virtual work done is due to the component $F\cos(c/2)\sin\mu$, and is

$$F\,\delta\psi\cos\frac{c}{2}\sin b\sin\mu$$

In this case the virtual coefficient between a unit vector along BA and a unit vector along OB_0 is

$$VC_F = \tfrac{1}{2}\cos\frac{c}{2}\sin b\sin\mu$$

Fig. 8.15. (a) RSSR-type spherical four-bar. (b) Force vectors.

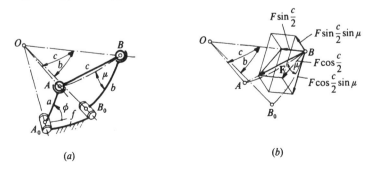

(a)   (b)

Hence the maximum value of VC_F is

$$VC_{F\max} = \tfrac{1}{2}\cos\frac{c}{2}\sin b$$

The transmission index now becomes

$$TI = \frac{VC_F}{VC_{F\max}} = \sin\mu \tag{8.50}$$

Again in this case it is justifiable to take μ as the transmission angle.

If the practical form of the RSSR-type spherical four-bar is one with differing lengths of OA and OB, i.e. with the two points A and B not on a common spherical surface, the transmission angle μ is simply the dihedral angle between the two planes OAB and OB_0B.

8.3.2 Optimization of transmission angle and of structural error in a three-precision-point synthesis

In a three-precision-point case, i.e. P_1–P_2–P_3 or P_1–P_2P_3, if the crank a is allowed to rotate across the great circle A_0B_0 it may be possible to synthesize the function generator so that, throughout the range of rotation of the crank a, the deviation of the transmission angle μ from $90°$ is kept to a minimum. The spherical version of this problem has been dealt with in (Soni & Dukkipati, 1975), following a similar procedure developed in (Shoup & Pelan, 1971) for the planar version of the problem. We shall follow the general trends of these investigations, but using instead the relative pole equations derived before, so that unnecessary non-linear equations can be circumvented.

Applying equation (A1.9) to $\triangle A_0AB_0$ and $\triangle BAB_0$ in Fig. 2.3 results in

$$S_bS_cC_\mu = C_aC_f - C_bC_c + S_aS_fC_\phi \tag{8.51}$$

where C_μ stands for $\cos\mu$. Equation (8.51) indicates that C_μ is a linear function of C_ϕ, and that μ remains unchanged if ϕ is replaced by $-\phi$. This fact can also easily be conceived from the geometrical configuration of the linkage as shown in Fig. 2.3. For if ϕ is replaced by $-\phi$, the length AB_0 ($= h$), hence $\measuredangle ABB_0 = \mu$, remains unchanged. This means that if the range of ϕ is disposed symmetrically with respect to the great circle $\phi = 0°$ or $\phi = 180°$, the μ–ϕ curve will look like that shown in Fig. 8.16. μ will become an extreme at the middle of the range of ϕ. This can be achieved if the range of ϕ is so allocated that

$$\phi_{\min} = 0° - \beta \tag{8.52}$$

or

$$\phi_{\min} = 180° - \beta \tag{8.53}$$

where

$$2\beta = \phi_{max} - \phi_{min} \tag{8.54}$$

is the total range of ϕ. Since the position of the initial angle ϕ_0 of the input link relative to the range of ϕ is predetermined, the position of ϕ_0 is also determined. The transmission angle μ, throughout the whole range of ϕ, can be optimized in a Chybeshev sense. In other words, the deviation of μ from 90° can be minimized if its maximum absolute values at the middle and at both ends of the range are equal and opposite, as shown by $+\delta$ and $-\delta$ in Fig. 8.16. Applying these requirements to equation (8.51) yields the conditions:

$$2(C_a C_f - C_b C_c) + S_a S_f (1 + \cos\beta) = 0, \quad \text{if } \phi_{min} = 0° - \beta \tag{8.55}$$

or

$$2(C_a C_f - C_b C_c) - S_a S_f (1 + \cos\beta) = 0, \quad \text{if } \phi_{min} = 180° - \beta \tag{8.56}$$

It is to be noted that the condition (8.52) and hence (8.55) will practically seldom be used, because it is very unlikely to exclude a dead centre position in the operating range unless the range 2β is kept quite small.

(1) Case $P_1 - P_2 - P_3$
In this case, two angle-pairs ϕ_2, ψ_2; ϕ_3, ψ_3 and f are given. As shown in Fig. 8.17, the relative poles R_2, R_3 are already fixed. There are ∞^2 possible solutions. This double-infinity may be represented, for instance, by the free

Fig. 8.16. Optimization of transmission angle.

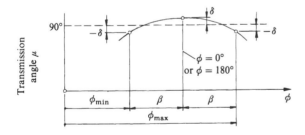

Fig. 8.17. Coordination of two angle-pairs.

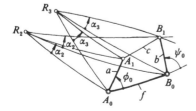

choice of the coordinates of the location of $A_1(a, \phi_0)$. Once the location of A_1 has been chosen, the angles α_2, α_3, which A_0A_1 and B_0B_1 should subtend at R_2, R_3 respectively (compare with Fig. 8.3), and hence the location of B_1, are all fixed. The linkage is also determined. Since ϕ_0 is already determined as mentioned above, there remains only the crank length a as a freely chosen parameter. In other words, A_1 can only be chosen along the great circle inclined at an angle ϕ_0 with A_0B_0. There are only ∞^1 possible solutions.

The synthesis equations are already available. Simply setting $i = 2, 3$ in equation (8.8) and dividing through by $\cos \psi_0$ gives

$$[C_{\psi 2/2}(S_{ra2}\cot a - C_{ra2}C_{\phi 02/2}) - S_{\phi 02/2}C_{rb2}S_{\psi 2/2}]q - S_{\phi 02/2}S_{rb2}X'$$
$$= - S_{\phi 02/2}C_{\psi 2/2}C_{rb2} - S_{\psi 2/2}(S_{ra2}\cot a - C_{ra2}C_{\phi 02/2}) \qquad (8.57)$$

$$[C_{\psi 3/2}(S_{ra3}\cot a - C_{ra3}C_{\phi 03/2}) - S_{\phi 03/2}C_{rb3}S_{\psi 3/2}]q - S_{\phi 03/2}S_{rb3}X'$$
$$= - S_{\phi 03/2}C_{\psi 3/2}C_{rb3} - S_{\psi 3/2}(S_{ra3}\cot a - C_{ra3}C_{\phi 03/2}) \qquad (8.58)$$

where $S_{\psi i/2}, C_{\psi i/2}; S_{\phi 0i/2}, C_{\phi 0i/2}; S_{rai}, C_{rai}; S_{rbi}$ and C_{rbi} stand for $\sin(\psi_i/2), \cos(\psi_i/2);$ $\sin(\phi_0 + \phi_i/2), \cos(\phi_0 + \phi_i/2); \sin r_{ai}, \cos r_{ai}; \sin r_{bi}$ and $\cos r_{bi}$ respectively, and

Fig. 8.18.

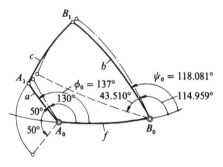

Fig. 8.19.

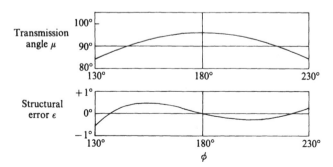

$q = \tan \psi_0, X' = \cot b/\cos \psi_0$ are the two unknowns. Equations (8.57) and (8.58) are two linear equations in q and X', and can easily be solved if the parameter a is assumed. Vary the parameter a and substitute the resulting ψ_0, b and the coupler length c determined by means of equation (A9.8) into equation (8.55) or (8.56) to see if they do satisfy this equation for the given β. The set which fits the correct β is the right solution.

Example: It is required to design a spherical four-bar linkage to generate the function $y = -0.87359 \times 10^{-3}x^2 + 0.53039x$, for $0 \leqslant x \leqslant 100$ and $0 \leqslant y \leqslant 44.3031$, so that the input link rotates through a range of $2\beta = 100°$ and the output link rotates through a range of approximately $45°$. It is also desired that the transmission angle is optimized throughout the range. Assume $f = 50°$.

The scale factors are simply: $M_\phi = \triangle \phi / \triangle x = 1$ and $M_\psi = \triangle \psi / \triangle y = 1$. Suppose the range of the input angle is disposed according to equation (8.53). For $\beta = 50°$ we now have $\phi_{\min} = 180° - 50° = 130°$. The following three precision-points are chosen:

$$x = \quad 7 \qquad 50 \qquad 92$$
$$y = \quad 3.6699 \quad 24.3355 \quad 41.4018$$

from which the angle-pairs to be coordinated are: $\phi_2 = 43°$, $\psi_2 = 20.6656°$; $\phi_3 = 85°$, $\psi_3 = 37.7319°$. Also $\phi_0 = 130° + 7° \doteq 137°$. Feeding these data into equations (8.57) and (8.58) and taking a as the varying parameter, we have for $a = 26.9540°$ the data for the linkage: $\psi_0 = 118.081°$, $b = 67.873°$, $c = 40.228°$, which satisfy equation (8.56) for $\beta = 50°$. Fig. 8.18 shows the synthesized linkage with the corresponding ranges of ϕ and ψ. Note that this linkage is a non-Grashof double-rocker of the type shown in Fig. 2.51. Fig. 8.19 shows the variation of μ, and that of the structural error ε of the synthesized linkage throughout the range. It is to be noted that not all functions can be so generated.

(2) Case $P_1-P_2P_3$

If both the transmission angle and structural error are to be optimized, the three precision-points have to be chosen as $P_1-P_2P_3$, in order to apply the precision-point respacing technique developed by McLarnan (McLarnan, 1968). In other words, one angle-pair ϕ_2, ψ_2 has to be coordinated and one velocity ratio $\psi_2' = d\psi/d\phi$ at P_2 has to be matched. Both synthesis equations are available. For the case P_1-P_2, the synthesis equation is again the one obtained by setting $i = 2$ in equation (8.8), which becomes equation (8.57) after dividing through by $\cos \psi_0$:

$$[C_{\psi 2/2}(S_{ra2} \cot a - C_{ra2}C_{\phi 02/2}) - S_{\phi 02/2}C_{rb2}S_{\psi 2/2}] q - S_{\phi 02/2}S_{rb2}X'$$
$$= -S_{\phi 02/2}C_{\psi 2/2}C_{rb2} - S_{\psi 2/2}(S_{ra2} \cot a - C_{ra2}C_{\phi 02/2}) \qquad [(8.57)]$$

For the case P_2P_3, the synthesis equation is just equation (8.46), where ϕ_3, ψ_3 and ψ'_3 should be replaced by ϕ_2, ψ_2 and ψ'_2 respectively. This equation, after dividing through by $\cos \psi_0$, becomes

$$[- \psi'_2 C_{\psi 2} S_f \cot a + S_{\phi 02} (\psi'_2 - C_f) S_{\psi 2} + C_{\phi 02} (\psi'_2 C_f - 1) C_{\psi 2}] q$$
$$+ S_{\phi 02} S_f X' = \psi'_2 S_{\psi 2} S_f \cot a + S_{\phi 02} (\psi'_2 - C_f) C_{\psi 2}$$
$$- C_{\phi 02} (\psi'_2 C_f - 1) S_{\psi 2} \tag{8.59}$$

where $S_{\psi 2}, C_{\psi 2}; S_{\phi 02}$ and $C_{\phi 02}$ stand respectively for $\sin \psi_2, \cos \psi_2; \sin (\phi_0 + \phi_2)$ and $\cos (\phi_0 + \phi_2)$. Equations (8.57) and (8.59) are two linear equations in the unknowns $q = \tan \psi_0$ and $X' = \cot b/\cos \psi_0$, and can easily be solved by taking a as the parameter. Again vary a and substitute the resulting ψ_0 and b and the coupler length c determined by means of equation (A9.8) into equation (8.55) or (8.56) to see if they do satisfy this equation for the given β. The set which fits the correct β is the solution for optimum transmission angle.

The next step is to analyse the structural error of the linkage just synthesized, as shown in Fig. 8.20. The next new spacing is given by the formula (McLarnan, 1968)

$$\triangle'_1 = \triangle_1 \frac{1}{\varepsilon_1^{1/m}} \frac{2\beta}{\dfrac{\triangle_1}{\varepsilon_1^{1/m}} + \dfrac{\triangle_2}{\varepsilon_2^{1/m}}} = \frac{2 \triangle_1 \beta \varepsilon_2^{1/m}}{\triangle_1 \varepsilon_2^{1/m} + \triangle_2 \varepsilon_1^{1/m}} \tag{8.60}$$

The exact value of the exponent $1/m$ is immaterial, because successive respacings will eventually converge to a steady $\triangle_1$, for which $\varepsilon_1 = \varepsilon_2$. In the present case, $\triangle_1 = \phi_2$ and $\triangle_2 = 2\beta - \phi_2$, the only new spacing to be determined is a renewed ϕ_2. Certainly a new linkage has to be synthesized for this new ϕ_2 and for optimum transmission angle. The whole process is repeated several times until $\varepsilon_1 \approx \varepsilon_2$. The final function generator thus synthesized is the solution for optimum transmission angle and optimum structural error, after shifting the output scale by $\varepsilon_1/2$. The following example, which is the spherical version of an example in (Shoup & Pelan, 1971), will serve to illustrate the procedure.

Example: It is required to generate the function $y = x^2$ for $0 \leqslant x \leqslant 1$ and $0 \leqslant y \leqslant 1$ so that the input link rotates through a range of $90°$ and the output

Fig. 8.20. Optimization of transmission angle and structural error.

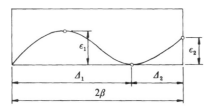

link rotates approximately through a range of 30°. Assume that $f = 50°$, and the range of ϕ is set according to equation (8.53), i.e. $\phi_{min} = 180° - 45° = 135°$ and $\phi_{max} = 225°$. The scale factors are:

$$M_\phi = \frac{90°}{1} = 90°/\text{unit of } x, \quad M_\psi = \frac{30°}{1} = 30°/\text{unit of } y$$

As a first trial, choose $\phi_2 = 71°$, and the following data are computed:

$$\phi_2 = 71°, \quad \psi_2 = (71/90)^2 \cdot 30 = 18.6704°,$$
$$\psi'_2 = 2(71/90)(30/90) = 0.525926$$

For $\phi_0 = 135°$, the value of $a = 18.9866°$ yields through equations (8.57), (8.59) and (A9.8) the following dimensions of the linkage: $b = 30.1551°$, $c = 62.8106°$, which satisfy equation (8.56) for $\beta = 45°$. After some respacing the final conditions are found:

$$\phi_2 = 70.6055°, \quad \psi_2 = 18.4635°, \quad \psi'_2 = 0.52300$$

and the solution is: $a = 18.974°$, $b = 30.204°$, $c = 62.779°$, $f = 50°$, $\phi_0 = 135°$ and $\psi_0 = 244.529°$. This linkage is a non-Grashof double-rocker of the type shown in Fig. 2.50. Fig. 8.21 shows this linkage in its starting position. Fig. 8.22 shows the variations of its transmission angle and structural error over the range of $\triangle \phi = 2\beta = 90°$. The maximum error is $|\varepsilon| = 0.466°$. Shifting the

Fig. 8.21.

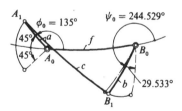

Fig. 8.22.

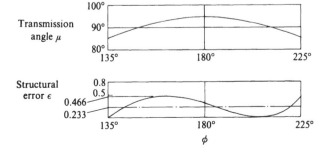

scale of the output angle by $|\varepsilon|/2$, the maximum structural error will be reduced to $|\varepsilon|/2 = 0.233°$.

Strictly speaking, the synthesized function generator is an erroneous one, because a dead centre position is included in its operating range. This dead centre position is at $\phi = 139.025°$. For $135° \leqslant \phi \leqslant 139.025°$, the rocker b swings clockwise or opposite to the desired direction as ϕ increases, until the limiting position is reached. Even after having passed the dead centre position, the rocker b indicates a negative value of the function until $\phi \approx 144°$. This function generator should therefore only be used within the range $144° \leqslant \phi \leqslant 225°$. This mistake in the function generator cannot be conceived from the structural error curve as shown in Fig. 8.22, because for $x \ll 1$, the value of x^2 is so small that it is overwhelmed by the structural error.

8.4   Design of crank–rockers

Referring to Fig. 2.6, a crank–rocker is characterized, apart from a prescribed link length, by the rocking angle $\triangle \psi$ of the rocker, and the corresponding crank angle difference $\triangle \phi = \phi_i - \phi_a$. Synthesis equations based on the geometrical configurations in the two dead centre positions can be derived by means of spherical trigonometrical relations (Bagci, 1973; Chen, 1975; Luck & Modler, 1974; Freudenstein & Primrose, 1972; Huang & Soni, 1969; Huang, Pamidi & Soni, 1970; Funabashi & Freudenstein, 1979; Streit & Soni, 1979). However, we may look at this problem from the point of view of synthesizing a four-bar function generator to match two prescribed velocity ratios, in a somewhat systematic way, especially because synthesis equations are readily available (Chiang, 1986b).

8.4.1   Synthesis equations

Fig. 8.23 shows the $\psi-\phi$ diagram of a crank–rocker, in which $\psi_1' = \psi_3' = 0$, as a special case of the general $\psi-\phi$ diagram for the $P_1P_2-P_3P_4$ case as shown in Fig. 8.12. The angle ψ_3 is the rocking angle $\triangle \psi$ in Fig. 2.6,

Fig. 8.23. $\psi-\phi$ diagram of a crank–rocker.

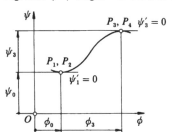

and the angle ϕ_3 is equal to $\phi_i - \phi_a$. As mentioned in Section 8.1.2, with the angles ϕ_3, ψ_3 and length of the fixed link f prescribed, the locus of A_a in Fig. 2.6, now denoted by A_1, is a spherical relative centre-point curve of the motion of b relative to a. We shall find this locus. Setting $\psi'_1 = \psi'_3 = 0$ in equations (8.44)–(8.46), and dividing each equation by a factor $C_{\phi 0} C_{\psi 0}$, we obtain the following three equations in the four variables $t = \tan \phi_0$, $X = \cot a / C_{\phi 0}$, $q = \tan \psi_0$, $X' = \cot b / C_{\psi 0}$:

$$\left.\begin{array}{l} S_f t X' - q + C_f t = 0 \\[4pt] S_{ra}(C_{\psi/2}\, q + S_{\psi/2}) X - S_{rb}(C_{\phi/2} t + S_{\phi/2}) X' \\[4pt] \quad + (C_{\psi/2}\, q + S_{\psi/2})(S_{\phi/2} t - C_{\phi/2}) C_{ra} \\[4pt] \quad - (C_{\phi/2} t + S_{\phi/2})(S_{\psi/2}\, q - C_{\psi/2}) C_{rb} = 0 \\[4pt] S_f(C_\phi t + S_\phi) X' + (C_\psi q + S_\psi)(S_\phi t - C_\phi) \\[4pt] \quad - C_f(C_\phi t + S_\phi)(S_\psi q - C_\psi) = 0 \end{array}\right\} \qquad (8.61)$$

where S_{ra}, C_{ra}, S_{rb}, C_{rb}, $S_{\phi/2}$, $C_{\phi/2}$, $S_{\psi/2}$, $C_{\psi/2}$, S_ϕ, C_ϕ, S_ψ and C_ψ stand for $\sin r_{a3}$, $\cos r_{a3}$, $\sin r_{b3}$, $\cos r_{b3}$, $\sin(\phi_3/2)$, $\cos(\phi_3/2)$, $\sin(\psi_3/2)$, $\cos(\psi_3/2)$, $\sin \phi_3$, $\cos \phi_3$, $\sin \psi_3$ and $\cos \psi_3$ respectively. If in the system of three equations (8.61) q and X' are considered as two unknowns, the characteristic equation obtained by setting the determinant of the coefficients equal to zero contains only t and X, and after lengthy arithmetic manipulations, becomes

$$k_{A1}: \quad (C_{\phi/2} t + S_{\phi/2})[(S_{\phi/2} C_{\psi/2} - C_f C_{\phi/2} S_{\psi/2})(1 + t^2)$$
$$\quad - S_f S_{\psi/2}(S_{\phi/2} t - C_{\phi/2}) X] = 0 \qquad (8.62)$$

Equation (8.62) represents the locus of A_1, which, being a spherical cubic, now breaks up into a great circle and a spherical quadric curve. The linear equation represented by the first factor is just the great circle $A_0 R_3$. Substituting the definitions of t and X into the second factor in equation (8.62), we obtain the following equation of the spherical quadric curve for the locus of $A_1(a, \phi_0)$ in spherical polar coordinates:

$$\tan a = \frac{S_f S_{\psi/2}}{C_f C_{\phi/2} S_{\psi/2} - S_{\phi/2} C_{\psi/2}} \cos(\phi_3/2 + \phi_0) \qquad (8.63)$$

A comparison of equation (8.63) with equation (A1.21) shows that this spherical quadric curve is a spherical Thales ellipse, with $A_0 R_3$ as its spherical major axis, as shown in Fig. 8.24.

Similarly, if in the system of three equations (8.61) t and X are considered as two unknowns, the characteristic equation thus obtained contains only q and X', and becomes

$$k_{B1}: \quad (C_{\psi/2}\, q + S_{\psi/2})\{(S_f S_\phi X' + C_\phi q + C_f S_\phi)[- S_f S_\phi X'$$
$$\quad + C_\phi(C_\psi q + S_\psi) + C_f S_\phi(S_\psi q - C_\psi)] - C_\psi q^2 - S_\psi q\} = 0 \quad (8.64)$$

Equation (8.64) represents the locus of B_1, which, being the spherical relative circle-point curve, is also a spherical cubic and breaks up into a great circle and a spherical quadric curve. The linear equation represented by the first factor in equation (8.64) is just the great circle B_0R_3. Substituting the definitions of q and X' into the second factor in equation (8.64) results in the following polar equation of the spherical quadric curve for the locus of $B_1(b, \psi_0)$:

$$\{S_\phi^2[\cos^2(\psi_3/2 + \psi_0) - C_{\psi/2}^2] - C_f^2S_\phi^2\cos^2(\psi_3/2 + \psi_0) - S_{\psi/2}^2]$$
$$+ C_fS_\phi C_\phi S_\psi\}\tan^2 b + 2S_f S_\phi(C_\phi S_{\psi/2} - C_f S_\phi C_{\psi/2})$$
$$\cdot\cos(\psi_3/2 + \psi_0)\tan b - S_f^2 S_\phi^2 = 0 \tag{8.65}$$

It is evident that this spherical quadric curve is symmetrical with respect to the great circle B_0R_3. In fact it is also a Thales ellipse with its major axis lying on B_0R_3. If the origin point of the spherical polar coordinates is transferred to the point A_0, this ellipse, being the locus of $B_1(a + c, \phi_0)$, is then represented by the simple equation

$$\tan(a + c) = S_f\frac{S_\psi\cos(\phi_3 + \phi_0) + C_f(1 - C_\psi)\sin(\phi_3 + \phi_0)}{C_fC_\phi S_\psi - S_\phi C_\psi - S_f^2(1 - C_\psi)\cos\phi_0\sin(\phi_3 + \phi_0)} \tag{8.66}$$

Note that when B_1 is located between R_3 and A_0 in Fig. 8.24, c is negative. Having found $a + c$ from equation (8.66), the length b of the rocker is determined by

$$\cos b = \cos f \cos(a + c) + \sin f \sin(a + c)\cos\phi_0 \tag{8.67}$$

Equations (8.63), (8.66) and (8.67) are the three synthesis equations for

Fig. 8.24. Loci k_{A1} and k_{B1} of crank–rockers for ϕ_3 in the lower range.

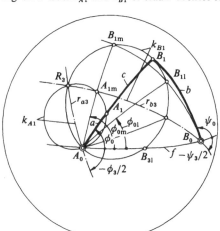

designing a spherical crank–rocker. The only parameter is the initial position angle ϕ_0 of the crank.

For central crank–rockers, $\phi_3 = 180°$, eliminating ψ_3 between equations (8.63) and (8.66), and then eliminating ϕ_0 between the resulting equation and equation (8.67) leads finally to equation (2.31), a relationship independent of ψ_3 and ϕ_0.

8.4.2 Ranges of ψ_3, ϕ_3 and ϕ_0

Because the rocker should never swing twice across the great circle A_0B_0, it is reasonable to set

$$0 \leqslant \psi_3 \leqslant 180°$$

Our major concern is therefore the ranges of ϕ_3 and the corresponding ranges of ϕ_0. Let us find first the lower limit of ϕ_3. In Fig. 8.24, a great circle is drawn from A_0 perpendicular to B_0R_3 and meets the latter in A_{1m} and the Thales ellipse k_{B1} in B_{1m}. A_{1m} is also on the Thales ellipse k_{A1} and $A_0A_{1m} = A_{1m}B_{1m}$. Once the fixed link length $f = A_0B_0$ and the rocking angle ψ_3 are chosen, the points A_{1m} and B_{1m} are uniquely determined. Join B_{1m} and B_0 by a great circle, intersecting the ellipse k_{B1} in another point B_{1l}. Denote $\sphericalangle B_0A_0A_{1m}$ by ϕ_{0m} and the second intersection of k_{B1} and A_0B_0 by B_{3l}. We see that the range of B_1 is $B_{1l}B_{1m}$. For if B_1 were chosen beyond B_{1m}, the coupler length c would be smaller than the crank length a and the synthesized linkage would become a double-rocker. On the other hand, if B_1 were chosen at B_{1l}, $\sphericalangle B_{1l}B_0B_{3l} = \psi_3$ would just be the rocking angle of the rocker B_0B_{1l}. The point B_1 should therefore not be chosen lower than B_{1l}; otherwise the rocker would swing across A_0B_0.

Applying equation (A1.5) to $\triangle A_0A_{1m}B_0$, we get

$$\phi_{0m} = \tan^{-1} \frac{1}{\cos f \tan \dfrac{\psi_3}{2}} \tag{8.68}$$

as the upper limit of ϕ_0 for the configuration shown in Fig. 8.24. It can easily be shown that $\sphericalangle B_0A_0B_{1l}$, as the lower limit of ϕ_0, is

$$\phi_{0l} = 180° - \phi_3 \tag{8.69}$$

However, as ϕ_0 should never be negative, when $\phi_3 > 180°$, the lower limit of ϕ_0 is $0°$.

Suppose the angle ϕ_3 is decreased. The smaller the angle ϕ_3, the farther is the point R_3 away from A_{1m}, and the ellipse k_{B1} shifts leftwards along B_0A_{1m}. Consequently the available range $B_{1l}B_{1m}$ for the location of B_1 is reduced. The lower limit of ϕ_3 is reached when B_{1l} reaches B_{1m}, or when B_{3l} reaches

A_0. To find this limiting value of ϕ_3, simply setting $q = \tan\psi_0 = 0$ in the second factor of equation (8.64) to obtain

$$(S_f S_\phi X' + C_f S_\phi)(- S_f S_\phi X' + C_\phi S_\psi - C_f S_\phi C_\psi) = 0 \tag{8.70}$$

and letting X' be a double root of this equation gives

$$\phi_{3\text{min}} = \tan^{-1}\frac{S_\psi}{C_f(C_\psi - 1)} = 180° - \phi_{0\text{m}} \tag{8.71}$$

Suppose, in Fig. 8.24, the angle ϕ_3 is increased until $\phi_3 = 2(180° - \phi_{0\text{m}})$, i.e. until R_3 reaches $A_{1\text{m}}$. The ellipse k_{B1} breaks up into two great circles, one being $A_0 B_{1\text{m}}$ and the other being also normal to $B_0 A_{1\text{m}}$ but 90° apart from $A_0 B_{1\text{m}}$. In other words, the spherical cubic k_{B1} breaks up into three mutually perpendicular great circles. Combining equations (8.68), (8.69) and (8.71), we may summarize: for values of ϕ_3 within the range (referred to as the lower range in later examples)

$$\tfrac{1}{2}(180° - \phi_{0\text{m}}) \leqslant \frac{\phi_3}{2} \leqslant 180° - \phi_{0\text{m}} \tag{8.72}$$

the range of ϕ_0 is

$$180° - \phi_3 \,(\text{or } 0°, \text{ if } \phi_3 > 180°) \leqslant \phi_0 \leqslant \phi_{0\text{m}} \tag{8.73}$$

We now find the upper limit of ϕ_3. Further increase of ϕ_3 from $2(180° - \phi_{0\text{m}})$ causes the point R_3 to be shifted to the right side of $A_{1\text{m}}$, as shown in Fig. 8.25. The ellipse of k_{B1}, which must pass through the three points A_0, R_3 and $B_{1\text{m}}$, becomes a spherical hyperbola, or a reversed spherical ellipse (see Appendix A1.3). The synthesis equations (8.63), (8.66) and (8.67) are still valid. In Fig. 8.25

Fig. 8.25. Loci k_{A1} and k_{B1} of crank–rockers for ϕ_3 in the upper range.

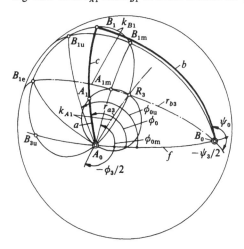

Table 8.1 *Ranges of ϕ_3 and ϕ_0*

ϕ_{0m}	$\tan^{-1} \dfrac{1}{\cos f \tan \dfrac{\psi_3}{2}}$		
	lower range	upper range	
Range of $\phi_3/2$	$\dfrac{180° - \phi_{0m}}{2}$ to	$180° - \phi_{0m}$ to $180° - \dfrac{\phi_{0m}}{2}$	
Range of ϕ_0	$\left.\begin{array}{l}180° - \phi_3 \\ \text{(or } 0°, \text{ if } \phi_3 > 180°)\end{array}\right\}$ to	ϕ_{0m} to $\left\{\begin{array}{l}360° - \phi_3 \\ \text{(or } 180°, \text{ if } \phi_3 < 180°)\end{array}\right.$	

the second intersection point of k_{B1} and B_0B_{1m} is denoted by B_{1u}, and that of k_{B1} and A_0B_0 by B_{3u}. For similar reasons like those for Fig. 8.24, the range of B_1 is now $B_{1m}B_{1u}$, on the left of B_{1m}. Again it can easily be shown that $\measuredangle\, B_0A_0B_{1u}$, as the upper limit of ϕ_0, is

$$\phi_{0u} = 360° - \phi_3 \qquad (8.74)$$

Now increasing ϕ_3 will shift the point R_3 away from A_{1m}. The larger the angle ϕ_3, the smaller the range $B_{1m}B_{1u}$. The upper limit of ϕ_3 is reached when B_{1u} reaches B_{1m}, or when B_{3u} reaches A_0. This limiting value of ϕ_3 is again determined by the condition that X' becomes a double root of equation (8.70), or

$$\phi_{3\max} = \tan^{-1}\frac{S_\psi}{C_f(C_\psi - 1)} + 180° = 360° - \phi_{0m} \qquad (8.75)$$

Combining equations (8.68), (8.74) and (8.75), we may summarize: for values of ϕ_3 within the range (referred to as the upper range in later examples)

$$180° - \phi_{0m} \leqslant \frac{\phi_3}{2} \leqslant \tfrac{1}{2}(360° - \phi_{0m}) \qquad (8.76)$$

the range of ϕ_0 is

$$\phi_{0m} \leqslant \phi_0 \leqslant 360° - \phi_3 \quad \text{(or } 180°, \text{ if } \phi_3 < 180°) \qquad (8.77)$$

The total range of ϕ_3 given by (8.72) and (8.76) is equivalent to that given in (Freudenstein & Primrose, 1972). For easy reference the ranges of ϕ_3 and ϕ_0 are listed in Table 8.1.

8.4.3 *Optimization of transmission angle*

As verified in Section 8.3.1, the angle $\mu = \measuredangle\, ABB_0$ of a spherical four-bar linkage is the transmission angle. For a given four-bar, μ is a minimum when the crank and frame are in the folded position, as shown in Fig. 3.2(d). This angle will be denoted by μ_r. On the other hand, μ is a maximum when the crank and frame are in the stretched position, as shown in Fig. 3.2(b), and this angle μ will be denoted by μ_s. The less the deviation of μ_r or of μ_s from $90°$, the better the transmission quality of the linkage. Usually the optimization procedure is to select from a family of synthesized linkages the one whose $|90° - \mu_r|$ or $|\mu_s - 90°|$ is a minimum. In other words, the procedure is to minimize $|90° - \mu_r|$ or $|\mu_s - 90°|$. This task can be left to a computer and the optimum solution is found by numerical scanning (Huang, Pamidi & Soni, 1970).

The optimization problem can also be solved from a mathematical point of view, by using the method of Lagrange's multipliers (Freudenstein & Primrose, 1972). First, instead of the deviations $|90° - \mu_r|$ and $|\mu_s - 90°|$ we see that the transmission quality is just represented by $\sin \mu_r$ and $\sin \mu_s$. Applying the cosine law for sides, equation (A1.9), to $\triangle ABB_0$ shown in Fig. 3.2(d) and (b), we get

$$\Phi(a,b,c) = \frac{\cos^2 \mu_r}{\cos^2 \mu_s} = \left[\frac{\cos(f \mp a) - C_b C_c}{S_b S_c} \right]^2 \tag{8.78}$$

Maximizing $\sin \mu_r$ or $\sin \mu_s$ is equivalent to minimizing $\cos^2 \mu_r$ or $\cos^2 \mu_s$, or the function Φ.

There are two relations between the three independent variables a, b and c. Eliminating ϕ_0 from equations (8.63) and (8.66) gives

$$\Phi_1(a,c) = M^2 C_a^2 + N^2 C_c^2 - C_a^2 C_c^2 = 0 \tag{8.79}$$

where

$$\left. \begin{array}{l} M = C_f S_{\phi/2} S_{\psi/2} + C_{\phi/2} C_{\psi/2} \\ N = C_f C_{\phi/2} S_{\psi/2} - S_{\phi/2} C_{\psi/2} \end{array} \right\} \tag{8.80}$$

Applying equation (A1.9) to $\triangle B_a A_0 B_i$ and $\triangle B_a B_0 B_i$ in Fig. 2.6 and equating the sides $B_i B_a$ of both triangles gives

$$\Phi_2(a,b,c) = S_{\phi/2}^2 S_a^2 + C_{\phi/2}^2 S_c^2 - S_{\psi/2}^2 S_b^2 = 0 \tag{8.81}$$

(This equation could have been derived by eliminating ϕ_0 from equations (8.63) and (8.67), but the process would be quite complicated.)

The optimization problem is therefore to find, for given values of f, $\phi_3/2$ and $\psi_3/2$, the set of values of a, b, c which, subject to the constraints (8.79) and (8.81), will render the function Φ, representing either $\cos^2 \mu_r$ or $\cos^2 \mu_s$, an extreme value. The principle of the method of Lagrange's multipliers may be described briefly as follows. The set of values of the three independent variables a, b, c, which will render the function $\Phi(a,b,c)$ an extreme value, will also render the function

$$F(a,b,c) = \Phi + \lambda_1 \Phi_1 + \lambda_2 \Phi_2$$

an extreme value, where λ_1 and λ_2 are two unknown constant multipliers. Since, at an extreme of F, $\partial F/\partial a = \partial F/\partial b = \partial F/\partial c = 0$, which is a system of three linear equations in the two unknowns λ_1 and λ_2, we have

$$\begin{vmatrix} \dfrac{\partial \Phi}{\partial a}, & \dfrac{\partial \Phi_1}{\partial a}, & \dfrac{\partial \Phi_2}{\partial a} \\[2mm] \dfrac{\partial \Phi}{\partial b}, & \dfrac{\partial \Phi_1}{\partial b}, & \dfrac{\partial \Phi_2}{\partial b} \\[2mm] \dfrac{\partial \Phi}{\partial c}, & \dfrac{\partial \Phi_1}{\partial c}, & \dfrac{\partial \Phi_2}{\partial c} \end{vmatrix} = 0 \tag{8.82}$$

The set of required values of a, b, c and the parameter ϕ_0 for the extreme of Φ are determined by the system of equations (8.63), (8.66), (8.67) and (8.82).

In order to facilitate computation, we can simplify by taking C_a^2, C_b^2, C_c^2 as the three independent variables instead of a, b, c in the three functions Φ, Φ_1, Φ_2. In so doing, equation (8.82) becomes

$$\genfrac{}{}{0pt}{}{\Phi_{3r}(a,b,c)}{\Phi_{3s}(a,b,c)} = \begin{vmatrix} \dfrac{\partial \Phi}{\partial(C_a^2)}, & M^2 - C_c^2, & -S_{\phi/2}^2 \\[2mm] \dfrac{\partial \Phi}{\partial(C_b^2)}, & 0, & S_{\psi/2}^2 \\[2mm] \dfrac{\partial \Phi}{\partial(C_c^2)}, & N^2 - C_a^2, & -C_{\phi/2}^2 \end{vmatrix} = 0 \tag{8.83}$$

where

$$\frac{\partial \Phi}{\partial(C_a^2)} = \frac{\partial \Phi}{\partial a}\frac{da}{d(C_a^2)} = \mp \frac{1}{S_a C_a}\{\sin(f \mp a)[\cos(f \mp a) - C_b C_c]\}\frac{1}{S_b^2 S_c^2}$$

$$\frac{\partial \Phi}{\partial(C_b^2)} = \frac{\partial \Phi}{\partial b}\frac{db}{d(C_b^2)}$$
$$= -\frac{[\cos(f \mp a) - C_b C_c]}{S_b^2 C_b}\{S_b^2 C_c - [\cos(f \mp a) - C_b C_c]C_b\}\frac{1}{S_b^2 S_c^2}$$

$$\frac{\partial \Phi}{\partial(C_c^2)} = \frac{\partial \Phi}{\partial c}\frac{dc}{d(C_c^2)}$$
$$= -\frac{[\cos(f \mp a) - C_b C_c]}{S_c^2 C_c}\{S_c C_b - [\cos(f \mp a) - C_b C_c]C_c\}\frac{1}{S_b^2 S_c^2}$$

In these equations the upper signs of the double signs refer to the extreme value of $\cos^2 \mu_r$, and the lower signs to that of $\cos^2 \mu_s$. Hence the determinants in equation (8.83) are denoted correspondingly by $\Phi_{3r}(a,b,c)$ and $\Phi_{3s}(a,b,c)$. The set of required values of a, b, c and ϕ_0 for the extremes of Φ's are now determined by equations (8.63), (8.66), (8.67) and (8.83). The simplest way of solving these equations is by assuming various values of the parameter ϕ_0 within the range (8.73) or (8.77), and searching for the value of ϕ_0 at which Φ_{3r} or Φ_{3s} changes sign. This procedure can conveniently be carried out by using even a pocket personal computer. Once the minimum $\cos^2 \mu_r$ and minimum $\cos^2 \mu_s$ have been found, the ϕ_0 corresponding to the greater one is to be selected as the optimum one (see examples below).

In summary, the synthesis and optimization procedure may be stated as follows:

(1) Assign ϕ_3, ψ_3 and f, and compute ϕ_{0m} by equation (8.68).
(2) Find out within which range ϕ_3 falls, by equations (8.72) and (8.76) or Table 8.1, and determine the corresponding range of the parameter ϕ_0.
(3) Locate values of ϕ_0 at which $\cos^2 \mu_r$ and $\cos^2 \mu_s$ become minima, and select the greater one of the two. The corresponding values of dimensions a, c, b are readily determined.

Examples: Various cases of optimization of spherical crank–rockers are listed in Table 8.2. Fig. 8.26 shows the variations of $\cos \mu_r$, $\cos^2 \mu_r$, $\cos \mu_s$ and $\cos^2 \mu_s$ versus the parameter ϕ_0, for a typical case in which $\phi_3 = 170°$, $\psi_3 = 36°$ and $f = 60°$. It can be seen that, in this case, while $\cos \mu_s$ exhibits a maximum and hence $\cos^2 \mu_s$ a minimum, the value of $\cos \mu_r$ does not exhibit an extreme within the range of ϕ_0. The minimum of $\cos^2 \mu_r$ occurs where $\cos \mu_r$ passes

Fig. 8.26.

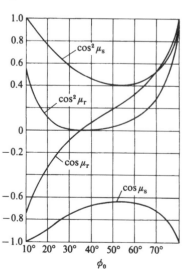

Table 8.2 Examples of optimized spherical crank–rockers

ϕ_3	ψ_3	f	ϕ_{0m}	$\phi_3/2$ is within	Range of ϕ_0	ϕ_0 for $(\cos^2 \mu_t)_{min}$	$90° - \mu_{tmax}$	ϕ_0 for $(\cos^2 \mu_s)_{min}$	$\mu_{smin} - 90°$	a	b	c
170°	36°	15°	72.576°	lower range	10°–72.576°	—	—	45.696°	3.296°	3.239°	10.807°	9.061°
170°	36°	30°	74.284°		10°–74.284°	—	—	47.303°	2.547°	6.421°	21.777°	18.106°
170°	36°	45°	77.061°		10°–77.061°	—	—	50.165°	1.314°	9.476°	33.099°	27.139°
170°	36°	60°	80.772°		10°–80.772°	—	—	54.609°	9.627°	12.311°	45.014°	36.215°
170°	36°	75°	85.193°		10°–85.193°	—	—	61.240°	7.542°	14.781°	57.864°	45.577°
170°	36°	90°	90°		10°–90°	—	—	71.354°	5.189°	16.635°	72.210°	56.226°
206°	36°	15°	72.576°	lower range	0°–72.576°	66.737°	51.114°	—	—	4.528°	16.382°	10.498°
206°	36°	30°	74.284°		0°–74.284°	70.357°	50.900°	—	—	8.839°	33.347°	20.896°
206°	36°	45°	77.061°	upper range	77.061°–154°	77.1606°	50.749°	—	—	12.621°	51.527°	30.715°
206°	36°	60°	80.772°		80.772°–154°	87.343°	51.129°	—	—	15.314°	70.342°	37.160°
206°	36°	75°	85.193°		85.193°–154°	97.644°	52.473°	—	—	16.472°	87.296°	77.730°
206°	36°	89°	89.675°		89.675°–154°	105.365°	54.360°	—	—	16.331°	101.322°	35.122°
189.614°	36°	75°	85.193°		—	—	$90° - (f - a)$ $= 32.367°$	—	$(f + a) - 90°$ $= 2.367°$	17.367°	90°	90°

through zero and is therefore identically equal to zero. Since $\cos^2 \mu_s$ is always greater than zero, its minimum is also greater than that of $\cos^2 \mu_r$. The overall minimum is therefore selected where $\cos^2 \mu_s$ becomes a minimum. The contrary is true in the examples for $\phi_3 = 206°$ and $\psi_3 = 36°$, where the parameter ϕ_0 for the minimum of $\cos^2 \mu_r$ is selected.

Note that in the last but one example, the length b is greater than $90°$. If the synthesized linkage $A_0A_1B_1B_0A_0$ is replaced by its supplementary linkage $A_0A_1B_1\bar{B}_0A_0$, it is interesting to note that μ_r of the former is just the supplementary angle $\bar{\mu}_s$ of the latter, as shown in Fig. 8.27. Consequently the four-bar with the same a and c, but with $b = 180° - 101.322° = 78.678°$ and $f = 180° - 89° = 91°$, which is supplementary to the optimal one for $\phi_3 = 206°$, $\psi_3 = 36°$, $f = 89°$, is the one whose $\bar{\mu}_s$ is a minimum of the family of supplementary linkages. In fact, if we set in the first place $\phi_3 = 206°$, $\psi_3 = -36°, f = 91°$, then we get for $\phi_0 = -(180° - 105.365°) = -74.635°$ the

Fig. 8.27. Spherical supplementary linkage $A_0AB\bar{B}_0$ of A_0ABB_0.

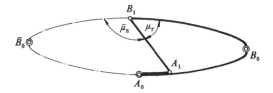

Fig. 8.28.

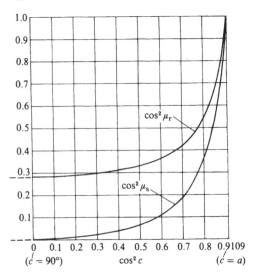

same optimal supplementary linkage. The same can also be obtained if we set $\phi_3 = 360° - 206° = 154°$, $\psi_3 = 36°$, $f = 91°$ for $\phi_0 = 74.635°$.

The last example shows the case $\phi_3 = 2(180° - \phi_{0m})$. For $\psi_3 = 36°$, $f = 75°$, the angle $\phi_{0m} = 85.193°$. As mentioned before, in this case the point R_3 in Fig. 8.24 coincides with A_{1m}, and the spherical cubic k_{B1} breaks up into three great circles. A_1 is fixed at A_{1m}, so that a is uniquely determined by $\sin^{-1}[\sin f \sin(\psi_3/2)] = 17.367°$. There are infinite choices of selecting B_1 on the extension of the great circle A_0B_{1m} beyond the point B_{1m}, or infinite choices of selecting the coupler length c within the range $a \leqslant c \leqslant 90°$. By equation (A1.2) the ratio $\cos b/\cos c = \cos B_0A_{1m} = \cos \phi_{0m}/\sin(\psi_3/2)$ is now a constant, which will be denoted by k. Equation (8.78) can now be written as

$$\frac{\cos^2 \mu_r}{\cos^2 \mu_s} = \frac{[\cos(f \mp a) - kC_c^2]^2}{(1 - k^2C_c^2)(1 - C_c^2)} \tag{8.84}$$

Equation (8.84) shows that $\cos^2 \mu_r$ (or $\cos^2 \mu_s$) is a function of $\cos^2 c$. Fig. 8.28 shows the variations of $\cos^2 \mu_r$ and $\cos^2 \mu_s$ versus $\cos^2 c$. Both curves increase monotonically with $\cos^2 c$, and both functions are minima at $\cos c = 0$ or $c = 90°$. From equation (8.84) it is evident that $\mu_{rmax} = f - a$ and $\mu_{smin} = f + a$.

For $\phi_3 = 180°$, the crank–rockers to be synthesized become *central crank-rockers* (see Fig. 2.7). It can be shown that both the $\cos \mu_r$ versus ϕ_0 and $\cos \mu_s$ versus ϕ_0 curves do not exhibit extreme values, and that $\mu_s = 180° - \mu_r$ for all values of ϕ_0. The optimization of transmission angle does not make sense for central crank–rockers.

8.5 Design of double-rockers

Four types of double-rockers can be classified. In Section 2.5.1 the Grashof double-rocker and in Section 2.5.2 three types of non-Grashof double-rockers have been introduced. Synthesis equations for coordinating prescribed rocking angles of the input and output links in their extreme positions have been given in (Chen & Chou, 1970), and those for matching a variety of design requirements have been given in (Hossne & Soni, 1979). Since the starting point of these investigations was based on the geometrical configurations of the linkage, an equation of sixth degree, or non-linear equations which resorted to iterative techniques, were involved. However, as mentioned in Section 8.1.2, even in the general four-precision-point case the locus k_{A1} of A_1 and the locus k_{B1} of B_1, both being spherical cubics, can be treated as quadratic equations. The problems of designing double-rockers ought to be considered as special cases of synthesizing function generators to match two prescribed velocity ratios. We shall therefore keep using equations (8.44), (8.45) and (8.46) (Chiang, 1986c).

Figs. 8.29(*a*), (*b*), (*c*), (*d*) show diagrammatically the four types of double-rockers together with their respective ψ–ϕ diagrams. Fig. 8.29(*a*) shows the Grashof double-rocker, and Figs. 8.29(*b*), (*c*), (*d*) show respectively non-Grashof double-rockers with internal rocking angles, external rocking angles and overlapping rocking angles. It can be seen that each ψ–ϕ diagram is a closed

Fig. 8.29. Four types of double-rockers.

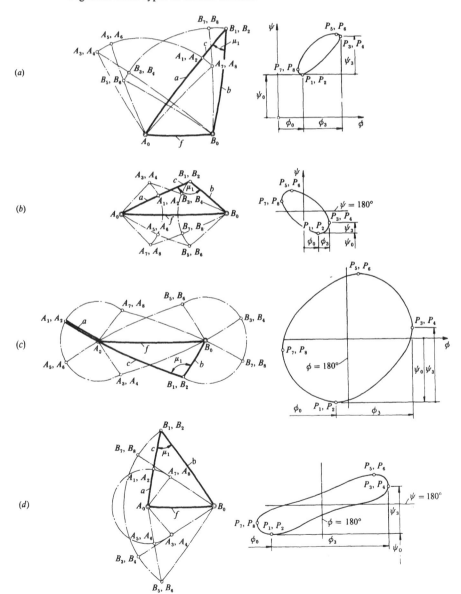

curve with four extreme points, corresponding to the four extreme positions of the two rockers. Each extreme point, representing two infinitesimally separated relative positions, is denoted by two numerals, just as in Fig. 8.12. At the extreme points, the velocity ratios are $\psi'_1 = \psi'_5 = 0$ and $1/\psi'_3 = 1/\psi'_7 = 0$. In the following we shall consider various cases of requirements imposed on the design of double-rockers.

8.5.1 The case ϕ_3, ψ_3 and f are prescribed

Setting $\psi'_1 = 0$ and $1/\psi'_3 = 0$ in equations (8.44)–(8.46), and again dividing each equation by the factor $C_{\phi 0}C_{\psi 0}$, we obtain the following three equations in the four variables $t = \tan \phi_0$, $X = \cot a/C_{\phi 0}$, $q = \tan \psi_0$, $X' = \cot b/C_{\psi 0}$:

$$S_f t X' - q + C_f t = 0 \tag{8.85}$$

$$
\begin{aligned}
&S_{ra}(C_{\psi/2}q + S_{\psi/2})X - S_{rb}(C_{\phi/2}t + S_{\phi/2})X' \\
&+ (C_{\psi/2}q + S_{\psi/2})(S_{\phi/2}t - C_{\phi/2})C_{ra} \\
&- (C_{\phi/2}t + S_{\phi/2})(S_{\psi/2}q - C_{\psi/2})C_{rb} = 0
\end{aligned}
\tag{8.86}
$$

$$
\begin{aligned}
&- S_f(C_\psi q + S_\psi)X + (C_\phi t + S_\phi)(S_\psi q - C_\psi) \\
&- C_f(C_\psi q + S_\psi)(S_\phi t - C_\phi) = 0
\end{aligned}
\tag{8.87}
$$

Note that equations (8.85) and (8.86) remain the same as the first two equations of (8.61). If, in this system of three equations, any two of the four variables are considered as two unknowns, the characteristic equation obtained by setting the determinant of the coefficients equal to zero becomes a quadratic equation between the other two variables. Thus, separating the variables q and X' from these three equations we obtain a quadratic equation relating X with t, or, noting that $X = \cot a/C_{\phi 0}$, the following quadratic equation of $\tan a$ or k_{A1}, the locus of A_1, in terms of $t = \tan \phi_0$ and $\cos \phi_0$:

$$k_{A1}: \quad E_2 \tan^2 a + E_1 \tan a + E_0 = 0 \tag{8.88}$$

where

$$
\begin{aligned}
E_2 = S_f t &\left[\left(C_{\psi/2}E_t \cot r_{a3} - \frac{S_{\phi/2}}{S_{\psi/2}} \cot r_{b3} F_t S_{\psi/2} \right)(C_{\psi/2}H_t + C_f S_{\psi/2} G_t) \right. \\
&+ \frac{S_{\phi/2}}{S_{\psi/2}} \cot r_{b3} F_t (S_\psi H_t - C_f C_\psi G_t) \left. \right] + \frac{S_{\phi/2}}{S_{\psi/2}} F_t [- C_{\psi/2}H_t \\
&- C_f S_{\psi/2} G_t + (S_{\psi/2} + C_f C_{\psi/2} t)(S_\psi H_t - C_f C_\psi G_t)]
\end{aligned}
$$

$$
\begin{aligned}
E_1 = \frac{S_f}{\cos \phi_0} &\left\{ t \left[C_{\psi/2}(C_{\psi/2}H_t + C_f S_{\psi/2} G_t) + S_f C_{\psi/2}(S_{\psi/2}E_t \cot r_{a3} \right. \right. \\
&\left. - \frac{S_{\phi/2}}{S_{\psi/2}} \cot r_{b3} F_t C_{\psi/2}) \right] - \frac{S_{\phi/2}}{S_{\psi/2}} F_t [S_{\psi/2} + C_\psi(S_{\psi/2} + C_f C_{\psi/2} t)] \left. \right\}
\end{aligned}
$$

$$E_0 = S_f^2 S_{\psi/2} C_{\psi/2} t / \cos^2 \phi_0$$

where E_t, F_t, G_t, H_t are all linear functions of t:

$$E_t = S_{\phi/2}t - C_{\phi/2}$$
$$F_t = C_{\phi/2}t + S_{\phi/2}$$
$$G_t = S_\phi t - C_\phi$$
$$H_t = C_\phi t + S_\phi$$

and $\cot r_{a3}$ and $\cot r_{b3}$ can be computed from equations (A10.1) and (A10.2).

Similarly separating the variables t and X from equations (8.85)–(8.87) yields the following quadratic equation relating b with ψ_0, or the equation of k_{B1}, the locus of B_1:

$$k_{B1}: \quad Q_2 \tan^2 b + Q_1 \tan b + Q_0 = 0 \qquad\qquad (8.89)$$

where

$$Q_2 = S_f H_q \left[C_f \cot r_{a3} F_q - M_q \left(S_{\phi/2} F_q \cot r_{a3} \right.\right.$$
$$\left.\left. - \frac{S_{\phi/2}}{S_{\psi/2}} \cot r_{b3} C_{\phi/2} E_q \right) \right]$$
$$- H_q [C_f(S_{\phi/2}G_q + C_f C_{\phi/2} H_q) + M_q(C_\phi G_q - C_f S_\phi H_q)]$$

$$Q_1 = \frac{S_f}{\cos \psi_0} \left\{ H_q \left[S_f \cot r_{a3} F_q + \frac{S_{\phi/2}}{S_{\psi/2}} C_{\phi/2} M_q - S_f S_{\phi/2} \left(\cot r_{a3} S_{\phi/2} F_q \right.\right.\right.$$
$$\left.\left.\left. - \frac{S_{\phi/2}}{S_{\psi/2}} \cot r_{b3} C_{\phi/2} E_q \right) \right] - F_q[S_{\phi/2}G_q(1 + C_\phi) + C_f C_{\phi/2} C_\phi H_q] \right\}$$

$$Q_0 = S_f^2 S_{\phi/2}^2 C_{\phi/2} H_q/(S_{\psi/2} \cos^2 \phi_0)$$

Fig. 8.30. Loci k_{A1} and k_{B1} of double-rockers for given ϕ_3, ψ_3 and f.

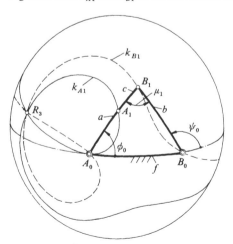

where E_q, F_q, G_q, H_q, M_q are all linear functions of q:

$$E_q = S_{\psi/2}q - C_{\psi/2}$$
$$F_q = C_{\psi/2}q + S_{\psi/2}$$
$$G_q = S_\psi q - C_\psi$$
$$H_q = C_\psi q + S_\psi$$
$$M_q = C_{\phi/2}q + C_f S_{\phi/2}$$

Fig. 8.30 shows the two cubics k_{A1} and k_{B1} for $\phi_3 = 38°$, $\psi_3 = 28°$ and $f = 52°$. Both cubics do not break up. As expected, k_{A1} passes through A_0, and k_{B1} passes through B_0 and A_0. k_{A1} is tangent to the great circle $\phi_0 = 0°$ at A_0, and k_{B1} is tangent to the great circle $\psi_0 = 180° - \psi_3$ at B_0. Moreover, k_{B1} is tangent to the great circle $\phi_0 = -\psi_3$, or $\phi_0 = 180° - \psi_3$, at A_0. Both cubics have a double point at R_3.

As in the general case of four precision-points, there are two ψ_0's corresponding to a single ϕ_0, and two ϕ_0's corresponding to a single ψ_0. Either ϕ_0 or ψ_0 may be taken as a parameter. Taking, for instance, ϕ_0 as the parameter, we can obtain two a's, hence two A_1's, for a single ϕ_0, by solving equation (8.88). For each $A_1(a, \phi_0)$, the corresponding ψ_0 is uniquely determined by equation (8.87), or

$$\tan \psi_0 = q = \frac{S_f S_\psi + \cos \phi_0 (C_\psi H_t + C_f S_\psi G_t) \tan a}{-S_f C_\psi + \cos \phi_0 (S_\psi H_t - C_f C_\psi G_t) \tan a} \tag{8.90}$$

and the corresponding link length b can then be obtained from equation (8.85) as

$$\tan b = \frac{S_f t}{\sin \psi_0 - C_f t \cos \psi_0} \tag{8.91}$$

Once $\tan \psi_0 = q$ is determined, the coupler length c can simply be computed by applying equation (A1.11) to $\triangle A_0 A_1 B_0$ (Fig. 8.30):

$$a + c = \tan^{-1} \left(\frac{S_f}{C_f \cos \phi_0 - \sin \phi_0/q} \right) \tag{8.92}$$

Example: Given $\phi_3 = 38°$, $\psi_3 = 28°$ and $f = 52°$. It is required to find the family of double-rockers.

Table 8.3 gives the dimensions of the synthesized linkages, taking ϕ_0 as the parameter. In the 'Type' column of this table, the types of the synthesized linkages are designated according to Figs. 8.29(a), (b), (c) or (d). It can be seen that most results are Grashof double-rockers. Non-Grashof double-rockers do also appear. Some of them are useless, because they cannot be turned from position P_1 to position P_3 without mechanically dismantling the joints.

The transmission angle in position P_1, $\measuredangle A_1 B_1 B_0$, is denoted by μ_1. The transmission angle μ varies from μ_1 in position P_1 to $180°$ in position P_3. It

Table 8.3 Dimensions of synthesized double-rockers for $\phi_3 = 38°$, $\psi_3 = 28°$ and $f = 52°$

ϕ_0	a	ψ_0	b	c	μ_1	Type Fig. 8.30	Remarks	a	ψ_0	b	c	μ_1	Type Fig. 8.30	Remarks
15°	9.603°	141.448°	15.679°	30.995°	131.002°	(b)		−51.286°	10.552°	−95.668°	6.528°	11.827°	(a)	
20°	11.843°	138.119°	18.969°	27.539°	123.991°	(b)		−51.825°	13.881°	−94.458°	7.454°	15.684°	(a)	
25°	13.918°	134.923°	21.972°	24.900°	117.115°	(b)		−52.296°	17.077°	−92.994°	8.358°	19.480°	(a)	
30°	15.920°	131.888°	24.863°	22.836°	110.430°	(b)		−52.670°	20.112°	−91.268°	9.235°	23.210°	(a)	
35°	17.912°	129.047°	27.762°	21.191°	103.992°	(b)		−52.913°	22.953°	−89.275°	10.081°	26.873°	(a)	
45°	22.010°	124.097°	33.888°	18.755°	92.054°	(b)		−52.857°	27.903°	−84.483°	11.652°	34.042°	(a)	
56.512°	27.002°	119.991°	41.819°	16.822°	80.276°	(b)/(a)		−51.635°	32.009°	−77.730°	13.243°	42.266°	(a)	
60°	28.544°	119.162°	44.419°	16.344°	77.176°	(a)		−50.994°	32.838°	−75.472°	13.683°	44.828°	(a)	
75°	34.832°	118.161°	56.237°	14.525°	66.288°	(a)		−47.059°	33.839°	−65.317°	15.469°	56.898°	(a)	
90°	39.630°	121.365°	67.871°	12.647°	58.285°	(a)		−42.519°	30.635°	−56.089°	17.502°	71.716°	(a)	
105°	42.556°	127.973°	77.994°	10.408°	51.094°	(a)		−39.339°	24.027°	−49.568°	20.624°	89.671°	(a)	
120°	44.205°	136.823°	86.085°	7.818°	43.160°	(a)		−39.088°	15.177°	−46.594°	26.401°	110.059°	(a)	
135°	45.332°	146.989°	92.073°	5.018°	33.888°	(a)		−44.615°	5.011°	−48.359°	39.319°	131.788°	(a)	
142°	45.835°	152°	94.159°	3.676°	29.106°	(a)		−52°	0	52°	52°	—	(a)/(c)	
145°	46.061°	154.181°	94.917°	3.098°	26.978°	(a)	use-less	−57.261°	177.819°	54.559°	60.360°	33.695°	(c)	use-less
150°	46.456°	157.849°	96.002°	2.132°	23.339°	(a)		−71.230°	174.151°	61.047°	81.503°	26.762°	(c)	
155°	46.881°	161.545°	96.864°	1.163°	19.599°	(a)		84.621°	170.458°	72.298°	62.671°	20.462°	(d)	

does not make sense, in designing this kind of double-rocker, to optimize the transmission angle, even if μ_1 is optimized.

Note that at a certain value of ϕ_0 (56.512° in the present example), the first synthesized linkage changes from a non-Grashof to a Grashof double-rocker. It is also interesting to note that at $\phi_0 = 180° - \phi_3 = 142°$, the second synthesized linkage possesses the dimensions $a = b = c = f = 52°$. However, this linkage is also useless.

8.5.2 The case involving positions $P_7(P_8)$ and $P_3(P_4)$

In these two positions, the velocity ratios satisfy the condition $d\phi/d\psi = 0$, or $1/\psi'_3 = 1/\psi'_7 = 0$. In order to avoid confusion, we denote the position $P_7(P_8)$ by $P_{1\triangle}(P_{2\triangle})$ and single out the initial and final positions from the $\psi-\phi$ diagram, as shown in Fig. 8.31. It should be noted that, for the present, ϕ_0, ψ_0, ϕ_3, ψ_3 are 'all referred to the position $P_{1\triangle}(P_{2\triangle})$. The synthesis equations can be obtained by setting $1/\psi'_1 = 1/\psi'_3 = 0$ in equations (8.44)–(8.46):

$$-S_{\psi 0}S_f \cot a - S_{\phi 0}C_{\psi 0} + C_f C_{\phi 0}S_{\psi 0} = 0 \tag{8.93}$$

$$\sin\left(\psi_0 + \frac{\psi_3}{2}\right)\sin r_{a3}\cot a - \sin\left(\phi_0 + \frac{\phi_3}{2}\right)\sin r_{b3}\cot b$$

$$= \sin\left(\psi_0 + \frac{\psi_3}{2}\right)\cos\left(\phi_0 + \frac{\phi_3}{2}\right)\cos r_{a3}$$

$$- \sin\left(\phi_0 + \frac{\phi_3}{2}\right)\cos\left(\psi_0 + \frac{\psi_3}{2}\right)\cos r_{b3} \tag{8.94}$$

$$- \sin(\psi_0 + \psi_3)S_f\cot a - \sin(\phi_0 + \phi_3)$$

$$\cdot \cos(\psi_0 + \psi_3) + C_f\cos(\phi_0 + \phi_3)\sin(\psi_0 + \psi_3) = 0 \tag{8.95}$$

Note that equation (8.94) remains the same as equation (8.45), unaltered by the values of ψ'_1 and ψ'_3. Also note that if we replace in the three equations (8.61) ϕ_0, ψ_0, a, b, ϕ_3, ψ_3, hence r_{a3} and r_{b3}, by $180° - \psi_0$, $180° - \phi_0$, b,

Fig. 8.31. $\psi-\phi$ diagram of a double-rocker, the case involving $P_7(P_8)$ and $P_3(P_4)$.

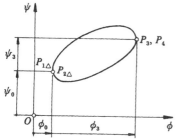

a, $-\psi_3$, $-\phi_3$, $-r_{b3}$ and $-r_{a3}$ respectively, we get equations (8.93)–(8.95). This means that in this aspect the syntheses of double-rockers and of crank–rockers are fundamentally the same. In fact, for instance, if in Fig. 8.24 the point B_1 is chosen between B_{1m} and R_3, the resulting linkage is a double-rocker, though it may not be able to coordinate the prescribed ϕ_3 and ψ_3 shown in Fig. 8.23.

On the assumption that in equations (8.93)–(8.95), ϕ_3, ψ_3 and f are given, separating t and X from these three equations gives the following equation of the locus of B_1, k_{B1}:

$$k_{B1}: \quad (C_{\psi/2}q + S_{\psi/2})[(-S_{\psi/2}C_{\phi/2} + C_f C_{\psi/2}S_{\phi/2})(1 + q^2)$$
$$- S_f S_{\phi/2}(S_{\psi/2}q - C_{\psi/2})X'] = 0 \tag{8.96}$$

Here we have used again the abbreviations $S_{\phi/2}$, $C_{\phi/2}$, $S_{\psi/2}$, $C_{\psi/2}$ for $\sin(\phi_3/2)$, $\cos(\phi_3/2)$, $\sin(\psi_3/2)$, $\cos(\psi_3/2)$. Equation (8.96) is analogous to equation (8.62), and can also be obtained from the latter by replacing the respective terms. The cubic k_{B1} consists therefore of the great circle B_0R_3 and a Thales ellipse represented by the second factor in equation (8.96). Upon substitution of the definitions of q and X' we get the following equation of this ellipse in spherical polar coordinates:

$$\tan b = \frac{-S_f S_{\phi/2}}{C_f S_{\phi/2} C_{\psi/2} - S_{\psi/2} C_{\phi/2}} \cos(\psi_0 + \psi_3/2) \tag{8.97}$$

The major axis of this Thales ellipse lies on the great circle B_0R_3.

Similarly, separating q and X' from equations (8.93)–(8.95) gives the following equation of the locus of A_1, or k_{A1}:

$$k_{A1}: \quad (C_{\phi/2}t + S_{\phi/2})\{(S_f S_\psi X - C_\psi t - C_f S_\psi)[-S_f S_\psi X$$
$$- C_\psi(C_\phi t + S_\phi) + C_f S_\psi(-S_\phi t + C_\phi)] - C_\phi t^2 - S_\phi t\} = 0 \tag{8.98}$$

Fig. 8.32. Loci k_{A1} and k_{B1} of double-rockers for given f and ϕ_3, ψ_3 in Fig. 8.31.

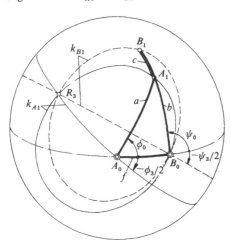

Here we have used again the abbreviations S_ϕ, C_ϕ, S_ψ and C_ψ for $\sin \phi_3$, $\cos \phi_3$, $\sin \psi_3$ and $\cos \psi_3$. Equation (8.98) is analogous to equation (8.64). The cubic k_{A1} consists of the great circle $A_0 R_3$ and a Thales ellipse with its major axis lying on the great circle $A_0 R_3$. Upon transferring the origin of the spherical polar coordinates from A_0 to B_0, this ellipse is then represented by the simple equation:

$$\tan(b - c) = -S_f \frac{S_\phi \cos(\psi_0 + \psi_3) + C_f(1 - C_\phi)\sin(\psi_0 + \psi_3)}{C_f S_\phi C_\psi - C_\phi S_\psi - S_f^2(1 - C_\phi)\cos\psi_0 \sin(\psi_0 + \psi_3)}$$

(8.99)

Fig. 8.32 shows two typical cubics k_{B1} and k_{A1} for $\phi_3 = 84°$, $\psi_3 = 62°$ and $f = 30°$.

Having found $b - c$ by equation (8.99), the length of the input link a is determined by

$$\cos a = \cos f \cos(b - c) - \sin f \sin(b - c)\cos\psi_0 \qquad (8.100)$$

and the initial position angle ϕ_0 of the input link is determined by

$$\cos \phi_0 = [\cos(b - c) - C_a C_f]/S_a S_f \qquad (8.101)$$

Equations (8.97), (8.99), (8.100) and (8.101) are the four synthesis equations for designing a spherical double-rocker when ϕ_3, ψ_3 in Fig. 8.31 and f are prescribed. The only parameter is the initial position angle ψ_0 of the output link.

For other design requirements the procedures of solution are usually quite straightforward using the above available equations. There are altogether nine variables, namely, ϕ_3, ψ_3, ϕ_0, ψ_0, $\phi_0 + \phi_3$, $\psi_0 + \psi_3$, f, a and b. The coupler length c is not to be considered as an independent variable. Any three of the four variables ϕ_0, ψ_0, f, a may be prescribed, and the fourth one is uniquely determined by equation (8.93). Taking then either $(\phi_0 + \phi_3)$ or $(\psi_0 + \psi_3)$ as a parameter, a family of infinite solutions can be obtained. Similarly any three of the four variables $\phi_0 + \phi_3$, $\psi_0 + \psi_3$, f, a may be prescribed, and the fourth one is uniquely determined by equation (8.95). In this case, taking either ϕ_0 or ψ_0 as the parameter, a family of infinite solutions can also be obtained. In all other cases the equations can always be solved without resorting to special techniques. Even in cases when both ϕ_3 and ψ_3 are not given, and four variables have been prescribed to demand a unique solution, a fifth variable can be chosen as a parameter so that it can be adjusted until a compatible solution is reached. These procedures can best be illustrated by the following numerical examples.

Example: Given $\phi_3 = 84°$, $\phi_0 = 20°$, $\psi_0 = 57°$ and $f = 50°$. It is required to determine a, ψ_3, b and c. Substituting the given values of ϕ_3, ϕ_0, ψ_0 and f into equation (8.93) gives $a = 63.5014°$. With this value of a we obtain from equation (8.95) $\psi_3 = 61.9807°$, and with this ψ_3 we obtain from equations (8.97) and (8.99) $b = 52.2296°$ and $c = 30.8239°$.

Example: Given $\phi_0 = 20°$, $(\psi_0 + \psi_3) = 119°$, $f = 50°$. It is required to find the family of infinite solutions. Since both ϕ_3 and ψ_3 are unknowns, we may take either one of them as the parameter. Assuming, for instance, $\psi_3 = 62°$, we get $\psi_0 = 119° - 62° = 57°$. From equation (8.93) we obtain $a = 63.5014°$, and from equation (8.95) we obtain $\phi_0 + \phi_3 = 104.0323°$, or $\phi_3 = 84.0323°$. With these ϕ_3, ψ_3, f and ψ_0, we can easily obtain $b = 52.2407°$ and $c = 30.8347°$.

Example: Given $a = 64°$, $b = 54°$, $f = 50°$ and $\phi_0 = 20°$. It is required to find the unique solution. From equation (8.93) we have $\psi_0 = 56.0343°$. Substituting an arbitrarily assumed value of ϕ_3 into equation (8.95), a corresponding value of ψ_3 can be obtained. A corresponding value of b can then be obtained from equation (8.97). Adjust the parameter ϕ_3 until a satisfactory value of b is reached. The results are: $\phi_3 = 88.3079°$, $\psi_3 = 65.1910°$ and $c = 32.2444°$.

8.5.3   Operating range not including dead centre positions

In order to avoid the difficulty arising from a 0° or 180° transmission angle, it has been suggested that a double-rocker may be synthesized for operation in a range between the positions $P_1(P_2)$ and $P_3(P_4)$ shown in Fig. 8.29(a), but not including the position $P_3(P_4)$ (Naganathan & Soni, 1981). For this purpose we now denote two positions P_1 and P_2 in the $\psi-\phi$ diagram as shown in Fig. 8.33. For prescribed values of f, ϕ_2 and ψ_2, the synthesis equation is again equation (8.8), in which we set $i = 2$:

$$\sin\left(\psi_0 + \frac{\psi_2}{2}\right)\sin r_{a2}\cot a - \sin\left(\phi_0 + \frac{\phi_2}{2}\right)\sin r_{b2}\cot b$$

$$= \sin\left(\psi_0 + \frac{\psi_2}{2}\right)\cos\left(\phi_0 + \frac{\phi_2}{2}\right)\cos r_{a2}$$

$$- \sin\left(\phi_0 + \frac{\phi_2}{2}\right)\cos\left(\psi_0 + \frac{\psi_2}{2}\right)\cos r_{b2} \tag{8.102}$$

Equation (8.102) contains four unknowns ϕ_0, ψ_0, a and b. There are therefore

Fig. 8.33.

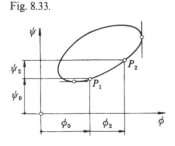

∞^3 possible solutions if any three of the four unknowns are assumed arbitrarily. Suppose a synthesized linkage in its positions P_1 and P_2 is as shown in Fig. 8.34. As the input angle ϕ increases, the transmission angle changes from a minimum value μ_1 in position P_1 to a maximum value μ_2 in position P_2. On the assumption that the transmission angle should deviate equally from both sides of 90°, we have

$$\mu_1 = 90° - \triangle \mu \quad \text{and} \quad \mu_2 = 90° + \triangle \mu \qquad (8.103)$$

Applying equation (8.51) to both configurations of the linkage gives

$$S_b S_c C_{\mu 1} = C_a C_f - C_b C_c + S_a S_f \cos \phi_0 \qquad (8.104)$$

$$S_b S_c C_{\mu 2} = C_a C_f - C_b C_c + S_a S_f \cos (\phi_0 + \phi_2) \qquad (8.105)$$

where $C_{\mu 1}$, $C_{\mu 2}$ stand respectively for $\cos \mu_1$ and $\cos \mu_2$. Since the coupler length c is involved in these equations, equation (2.5) should be taken into account, or

$$C_c = C_a C_b C_f + (S_a C_b C_{\phi 0} - C_a S_b C_{\psi 0}) S_f$$
$$+ S_a S_b (S_{\phi 0} S_{\psi 0} + C_f C_{\phi 0} C_{\psi 0}) \qquad (2.5b)$$

For a prescribed value of $\triangle \mu$, the angles μ_1 and μ_2 are known. Equations (8.102), (8.104) and (8.105) constitute a system of three equations, in the four unknowns ϕ_0, ψ_0, a, b. There are therefore ∞^1 possible solutions. This means that if any one of the four unknowns is assumed arbitrarily, the other three unknowns can be found. Assuming a value of ϕ_0, these equations may be solved by trial-and-error as follows.

Subtracting equation (8.105) from equation (8.104) and representing $S_b S_c$ by M results in

$$M = S_b S_c = \frac{S_a S_f [\cos \phi_0 - \cos (\phi_0 + \phi_2)]}{C_{\mu 1} - C_{\mu 2}} \qquad (8.106)$$

Substituting equation (8.106) back into equation (8.104) and representing $C_b C_c$

Fig. 8.34. Range not including dead centre positions.

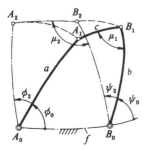

by N gives

$$N = C_b C_c = C_a C_f + S_a S_f C_{\phi 0} - M C_{\mu 1} \tag{8.107}$$

Since ϕ_0 is given, the problem is to locate the point A_1 to be sought for along the great circle inclined at an angle ϕ_0 to $A_0 B_0$. Setting a trial value of a in equations (8.106) and (8.107) results in the following quartic equation in S_b:

$$S_b^4 - (M^2 - N^2 + 1)S_b^2 + M^2 = 0 \tag{8.108}$$

which can be treated as a quadratic equation in S_b^2. Having found S_b, the coupler length is then given by

$$S_c = \frac{M}{S_b} \tag{8.109}$$

It is to be noted that both values of b and c should be real and positive, and that equations (8.106) and (8.107) are symmetrical with respect to b and c. This means that only two sets of (b, c) values can be found, and that each set can be obtained by exchanging b and c values of the other set.

The next step is to substitute one of the two b values together with the ϕ_0, a values into equation (8.102) and solve for ψ_0. The resulting equation is the following quadratic equation in $\tan(\psi_0 + \psi_2/2)$:

$$(T_1^2 - T_3^2)\tan^2\left(\psi_0 + \frac{\psi_2}{2}\right) + 2T_1 T_2 \tan\left(\psi_0 + \frac{\psi_2}{2}\right) + (T_2^2 - T_3^2) = 0$$

$$\tag{8.110}$$

where

$$\left.\begin{array}{l} T_1 = S_{ra2}\cot a - \cos\left(\phi_0 + \dfrac{\phi_2}{2}\right)C_{ra2} \\[3mm] T_2 = \sin\left(\phi_0 + \dfrac{\phi_2}{2}\right)C_{rb2} \\[3mm] T_3 = \sin\left(\phi_0 + \dfrac{\phi_2}{2}\right)S_{rb2}\cot b \end{array}\right\} \tag{8.111}$$

Finally substituting the values of ϕ_0, a, b, ψ_0 into equation (2.5b) gives the value of c. Because two ψ_0's can be obtained from equation (8.110), there are two c's corresponding to a single value of b. If the c values thus computed are the same as that computed before by equation (8.109), this set of values may be a correct solution. The following examples will clearly show the procedure.

Example: Referring to Fig. 8.34, suppose it is required to synthesize a double-rocker with $f = 50°$, $\phi_2 = 44°$, $\psi_2 = 34°$, $\mu_1 = 90° - 30° = 60°$ and $\mu_2 = 90° + 30° = 120°$. Following the above mentioned procedure, the variation of the coupler length c found by equation (8.109) as a function of a is shown in Fig. 8.35. The variations of the two corresponding values of c

Fig. 8.35.

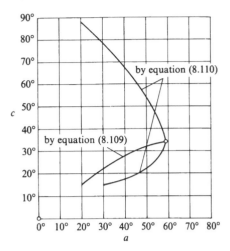

Fig. 8.36.

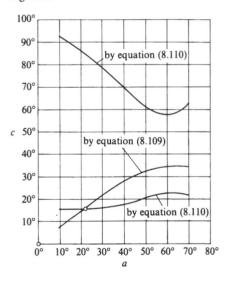

Fig. 8.37.

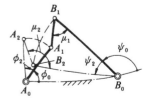

determined by the same values of a and b but through equations (8.110) and (2.5b) are also shown. The three curves intersect in one point at $a = 58.599°$. The other dimensions of the linkage are then found: $b = 59.517°$, $c = 34.258°$ and $\psi_0 = 59.019°$. The linkage is shown in Fig. 8.34. It has been found that exchanging the values of b and c does not yield real roots of equation (8.110).

It is interesting to note the fact that the three curves in Fig. 8.35 indeed intersect in one common point. This condition is also satisfied if equation (8.110) possesses a double-root, which leads to the condition

$$T_1^2 + T_2^2 - T_3^2 = 0 \qquad (8.112)$$

Since the expression of T_3 involves the rocker length b, which is to be determined by equation (8.108), the solution of the unknown a in equation (8.112) can again better be found by trial-and-error.

Example: Let it be required to synthesize a double-rocker with $f = 50°$, $\phi_2 = 42°$, $\psi_2 = 39°$, $\mu_1 = 90° - 30° = 60°$, $\mu_2 = 90° + 30° = 120°$ and $\phi_0 = 55°$. The three c-curves for the present case are shown in Fig. 8.36. Unlike in the last example, they do not intersect in a common point, but one c value obtained from equation (8.110) is identical with that computed from equation (8.109) at $a = 21.6722°$. For this a value the other dimensions of the linkage are: $b = 46.6155°$, $c = 15.7064°$ and $\psi_0 = 131.1523°$. The linkage is shown in Fig. 8.37, and is a non-Grashof double-rocker with internal rocking angles. Although equations (8.104), (8.105) and (2.5b) are all satisfied, the synthesized linkage is useless, because two dead centre positions are included between positions P_1 and P_2, as can be seen by comparing Fig. 8.37 with Fig. 2.49.

8.6   Design of drag-links

Drag-links may be synthesized according to two different kinds of requirements. The first, belonging to the case $P_1 - P_2$, deals with the rotation of the linkage from the stretched position to the folded position of the crank and frame. The second, belonging to the case $P_1 P_2 - P_3 P_4$, deals with the rotation of the linkage between two positions with unity velocity ratios. The synthesis techniques will be discussed in detail in the following sections.

8.6.1   *Design of drag-links between stretched and folded positions of crank and frame*

The two configurations of the linkage which serve as the basis of the design are shown in Fig. 8.38. In this case, $\phi_0 = \phi_2 = 180°$, and ψ_2, μ_s and μ_r are prescribed. This problem has been solved in (Soni & Harrisberger, 1967), by analogy with the planar version of this problem treated by (Hain, 1957a). Since $\mu_s = \mu_{max}$ and $\mu_r = \mu_{min}$, the transmission angle is optimized if μ_s

and μ_r deviate equally from 90°, or

$$\mu_s = 90° - \triangle \mu \quad \text{and} \quad \mu_r = 90° + \triangle \mu \tag{8.113}$$

which is equivalent to $\mu_s + \mu_r = 180°$. Note that equations (8.113) are just the conditions (8.103), if the two positions of the linkage shown in Fig. 8.38 are considered as special cases of those shown in Fig. 8.34, and $\triangle \mu$ is here given a negative value. Hence the synthesis equations developed in Section 8.5.3 may be applied in the present case, simply by setting $\phi_0 = \phi_2 = 180°$. Equations (8.102), (8.104) and (8.105) now constitute a system of three equations in the three unknowns ψ_0, a and b. The solution is uniquely determined. The solution procedure remains the same as that described in Section 8.5.3, but the equations are considerably simplified. Equation (8.106) now becomes

$$M = S_b S_c = - \frac{S_a S_f}{\cos \mu_s} \tag{8.114}$$

and equation (8.107) is reduced to

$$N = C_b C_c = C_a C_f \tag{8.115}$$

Note that equation (8.115) can also be obtained by applying the cosine law for sides, equation (A1.9), to the two triangles $\triangle B_0 A_1 B_1$ and $\triangle B_0 A_2 B_2$ shown in Fig. 8.38. This is a relationship independent of ψ_2 and μ_s. Note that it is identical with equation (2.31); the two configurations of the linkage shown in Fig. 8.38 are just the kinematic inversions of the central crank–rocker shown in Fig. 2.7. For the coefficients in equation (8.110), the following equations are valid:

$$\left. \begin{array}{l} T_1 = S_{ra2} \cot a \\ T_2 = - C_{rb2} \\ T_3 = - S_{rb2} \cot b \end{array} \right\} \tag{8.116}$$

Fig. 8.38. Drag-link between stretched and folded positions of crank and frame.

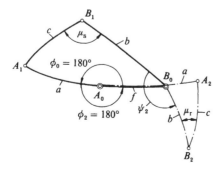

where

$$\left.\begin{array}{l} \tan r_{a2} = -S_f \tan \dfrac{\psi_2}{2} \\[2mm] \tan r_{b2} = -\dfrac{\tan f}{\cos(\psi_2/2)} \end{array}\right\} \tag{8.117}$$

Example: It is required to synthesize a drag-link according to Fig. 8.38, with $f = 45°$, $\psi_2 = 112°$ and $\mu_s = 90° + 62° = 152°$, $\mu_r = 90° - 62° = 28°$. By arbitrarily assuming a value of a in equations (8.114) and (8.115), and substituting the M and N values thus obtained into equation (8.108), two sets of (b, c) values can be found. Substituting one of the two b values together with the assumed a value into equations (8.116) and then (8.110) gives two values of ψ_0. Finally, substituting the values of a, b, ψ_0, ($\phi_0 = 180°$) into equation (2.5b), two c values can be found. There are altogether four ψ_0 values and four c values corresponding to a single a value. It has been found that one set of (b, c) values does not converge to a definite c value. The results are: $a = 69.855°$, $b = 57.522°$, $c = 63.031°$, $\psi_0 = 152.540°$.

8.6.2   Design of drag-links between positions of unity velocity ratio

Fig. 8.39 shows the ψ–ϕ diagram of a drag-link. Within one cycle of rotation of the linkage, there are two positions in which the velocity ratio equals unity, just as for a plane drag-link. Denote the former position of unity

Fig. 8.39. ψ–ϕ diagram of a drag-link with two unity velocity ratios.

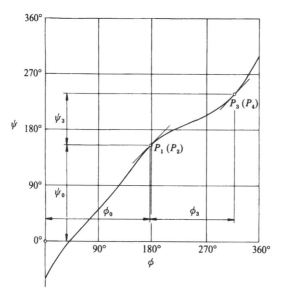

velocity ratio by $P_1(P_2)$ and the latter by $P_3(P_4)$, and the initial position angles in P_1 by ϕ_0 and ψ_0. Suppose the velocity ratio $\psi' = d\psi/d\phi < 1$ between P_1 and P_3, then $\psi' > 1$ between P_3 and $P_1 + 360°$, where $P_1 + 360°$ represents the position of the linkage turned through one complete cycle from P_1. This is the reason that the latest idea of synthesis stresses that a drag-link should be designed between two positions of unity velocity ratio to utilize the maximum capacity of a drag-link (Tsai, 1983). As shown in Fig. 8.39, if $\phi_3 > 180°$, then ϕ_3 is chosen as the working stroke, and $360° - \phi_3$ is taken as the return stroke, and vice versa. The mechanism can be used as a preconnected linkage to drive a Geneva mechanism in plane kinematics (Hain, 1957b). Similar principles can be applied in spherical kinematics (Shi, 1982, p. 46).

The $\psi-\phi$ diagrams of some spherical drag-links, however, unlike those of plane drag-links, exhibit four positions of unity velocity ratio within one cycle of rotation, as shown in Fig. 8.40. Between any two positions of unity velocity ratio, the value of ψ' fluctuates around $\psi' = 1$. This fact can also be observed from Fig. 2.33 of the well-known spherical drag-link, the Hooke's universal joint. When the two positions $P_1(P_2)$ and $P_3(P_4)$ in Fig. 8.39 approach each other indefinitely, the linkage becomes a proportional mechanism (see Section 8.2.1, and Meyer zur Capellen & Willkommen, 1974).

While the synthesis of a plane drag-link between two positions of unity velocity ratio can be treated as an inversion of a crank–rocker (Tsai, 1983)

Fig. 8.40. $\psi-\phi$ diagram of a drag-link with four unity velocity ratios.

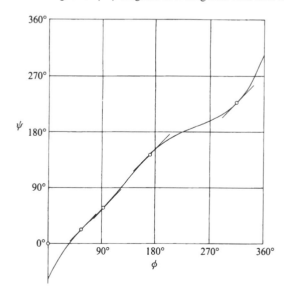

this is not the case with a spherical drag-link. However, the synthesis equations can simply be obtained by setting $\psi'_1 = \psi'_3 = 1$ in equations (8.44)–(8.46), and dividing through by $C_{\phi 0}C_{\psi 0}$:

$$-S_f qX + S_f tX' - (1 - C_f)t - (1 - C_f)q = 0 \tag{8.118}$$

$$S_{ra}(C_{\psi/2}q + S_{\psi/2})X - S_{rb}(C_{\phi/2}t + S_{\phi/2})X'$$
$$+ (C_{\psi/2}q + S_{\psi/2})(S_{\phi/2}t - C_{\phi/2})C_{ra}$$
$$- (C_{\phi/2}t + S_{\phi/2})(S_{\psi/2}q - C_{\psi/2})C_{rb} = 0 \tag{8.119}$$

$$-S_f(C_\psi q + S_\psi)X + (C_\phi t + S_\phi)S_f X' + (1 - C_f)(C_\phi t + S_\phi)(S_\psi q - C_\psi)$$
$$+ (1 - C_f)(S_\phi t - C_\phi)(C_\psi q + S_\psi) = 0 \tag{8.120}$$

where again $t = \tan\phi_0$, $X = \cot a/C_{\phi 0}$, $q = \tan\psi_0$ and $X' = \cot b/C_{\psi 0}$. Note that equation (8.119) remains the same as the second of equations (8.61). Separating q and X' from equations (8.118)–(8.120) gives the locus of A_1, in terms of $t = \tan\phi_0$ and $\cos\phi_0$:

$$k_{A1}: \quad (C_{\phi/2}t + S_{\phi/2})(F_2\tan^2 a + F_1\tan a + F_0) = 0 \tag{8.121}$$

where

$$F_2 = (1 - C_f)C_{\phi/2}C_{\phi 0}^2\left[\left\{C_\psi - C_\phi\right.\right.$$

$$\left.\left. - \tan\frac{\phi_3}{2}[(1 - C_\phi)S_\psi - C_f S_\phi(1 - C_\psi)]\right\}t^2\right.$$

$$\left. + (1 + C_f)S_\phi(S_\psi\tan\frac{\phi_3}{2} + C_\psi - 1)t\right.$$

$$\left. + (1 - C_f)\tan\frac{\phi_3}{2}\sin(\phi_3 + \psi_3) - S_\phi S_\psi + C_f(1 - C_\phi C_\psi)\right]$$

$$F_1 = S_f(S_{\phi/2}t - C_{\phi/2})C_{\phi 0}\{1 + C_\psi(C_\phi - 2) + C_f[S_\phi S_\psi - 2(1 - C_\psi)]\}$$

$$F_0 = S_f^2[\cos(\phi_3/2 - \psi_3) - C_{\phi/2}]$$

and the abbreviations are the same as those given in Section 8.4.1. The locus k_{A1} therefore breaks up into a great circle A_0R_3 and a spherical ellipse with its spherical axis lying on A_0R_3. The relative pole R_3 is a double point of k_{A1}.

On the other hand, separating t and X from equations (8.118)–(8.120) gives the locus of $B_1(b, \psi_0)$, in terms of $q = \tan\psi_0$ and $\cos\psi_0$:

$$k_{B1}: \quad (C_{\psi/2}q + S_{\psi/2})(G_2\tan^2 b + G_1\tan b + G_0) = 0 \tag{8.122}$$

where

$$G_2 = (1 - C_f)C_{\psi/2}C_{\psi 0}^2\left[\left\{C_\phi - C_\psi\right.\right.$$

$$\left.\left. + \tan\frac{\psi_3}{2}[(C_\psi - 1)S_\phi + C_f S_\psi(1 - C_\phi)]\right\}q^2\right.$$

$$+ (1 + C_f) S_\psi \left(S_\phi \tan \frac{\psi_3}{2} + C_\phi - 1 \right) q$$

$$+ (1 - C_f) \tan \frac{\psi_3}{2} \sin(\phi_3 + \psi_3) - S_\phi S_\psi + C_f(1 - C_\phi C_\psi) \Big]$$

$$G_1 = - S_f(S_{\psi/2} q - C_{\psi/2}) C_{\psi 0} \{ 1 + C_\phi(C_\psi - 2)$$

$$+ C_f[S_\phi S_\psi - 2(1 - C_\phi)] \}$$

$$G_0 = S_f^2 [\cos(\phi_3 - \psi_3/2) - C_{\psi/2}]$$

The locus k_{B1} also breaks up into a great circle, which is now $B_0 R_3$, and a spherical ellipse. The axis of the spherical ellipse lies on $B_0 R_3$, and the relative pole R_3 is also a double point of k_{B1}. Fig. 8.41 shows the two loci k_{A1} and k_{B1} for $\phi_3 = 190°$, $\psi_3 = 130°$ and $f = 20°$.

Since this is a $P_1 P_2 - P_3 P_4$ case, there are ∞^1 possible solutions. Taking ϕ_0 as a parameter, we can obtain, as usual, two a's, hence two A_1's, for a single ϕ_0, by solving the simultaneous equations (8.118) and (8.120), or

$$\tan \psi_0 = q = \frac{\triangle_q}{\triangle_B}$$

and

$$\tan b = \frac{\triangle_B}{\triangle_{x'} \cos \psi_0}$$

Fig. 8.41. Loci k_{A1} and k_{B1} of a drag-link.

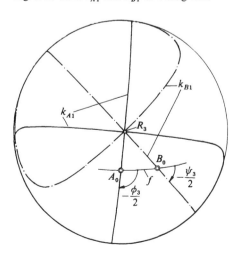

where

$$\triangle_q = \begin{vmatrix} U_3 & U_2 \\ V_3 & V_2 \end{vmatrix}, \quad \triangle_{x'} = \begin{vmatrix} U_1 & U_3 \\ V_1 & V_3 \end{vmatrix}, \quad \triangle_B = \begin{vmatrix} U_1 & U_2 \\ V_1 & V_2 \end{vmatrix}$$

$$U_1 = -S_f \frac{\cot a}{\cos \phi_0} - (1 - C_f)$$

$$U_2 = S_f \tan \phi_0$$

$$U_3 = (1 - C_f) \tan \phi_0$$

$$V_1 = -S_f C_\psi \frac{\cot a}{\cos \phi_0} + (1 - C_f)[t \sin(\phi_3 + \psi_3) - \cos(\phi_3 + \psi_3)]$$

$$V_2 = S_f(C_\phi t + S_\phi)$$

$$V_3 = S_f S_\psi \frac{\cot a}{\cos \phi_0} + (1 - C_f)[t \cos(\phi_3 + \psi_3) + \sin(\phi_3 + \psi_3)]$$

Having determined ϕ_0, a, ψ_0 and b, the coupler length c can, as usual, be obtained by means of equation (2.5b). The dimensions of the drag-link are then completely determined.

The transmission angle can again be optimized according to the same principle mentioned in Section 8.4.3 for crank–rockers. However, the location of the values of ϕ_0 for minimum $\cos^2 \mu_r$ and minimum $\cos^2 \mu_s$ will be

Fig. 8.42.

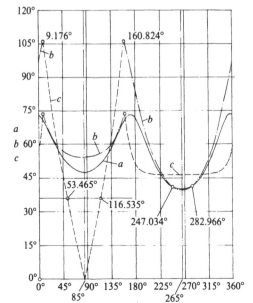

determined not by solving an algebraic equation, but simply by numerical scanning carried out by a computer. In the case shown in Fig. 8.41, when the spherical ellipse of k_{A1} encircles the point A_0, then for each value of ϕ_0, the two values of a solved from the quadratic equation of (8.121) are of opposite signs, and all A_1's may be located by running ϕ_0 from $0°$ to $180°$. In order to facilitate computation, however, we shall only take the positive a values, and let ϕ_0 run from $0°$ to $360°$. In doing so, there are only single values of b, c, $\cos^2 \mu_r$ and $\cos^2 \mu_s$ corresponding to each value of ϕ_0. The following example will illustrate the optimization procedure.

Example: It is required to design a spherical drag-link between two positions of unity velocity ratio $\psi'_1 = \psi'_3 = 1$, with $\phi_3 = 190°$, $\psi_3 = 130°$ and $f = 36°$. It is also required to optimize the transmission angle.

The variations of a, b and c as functions of ϕ_0 are shown in Fig. 8.42, and those of $\cos^2 \mu_r$ and $\cos^2 \mu_s$ are shown in Fig. 8.43, where ϕ_0 runs from $0°$ to $360°$. It can be seen that all curves are symmetrical with respect to $\phi_0 = -\phi_3/2 = -95°(= 265°)$ and $\phi_0 = 85°$. These curves show a few discontinuities:

(1) Within the ranges $0° \leqslant \phi_0 \leqslant 9.176°$ and $160.824° \leqslant \phi_0 \leqslant 360°$, supplementary linkages are to be taken in place of the linkages synthesized by the equations, in order to keep the sum of the link lengths a minimum, as mentioned in Section 3.3.

(2) Within the range $53.465° \leqslant \phi_0 \leqslant 116.535°$, the synthesized link

Fig. 8.43.

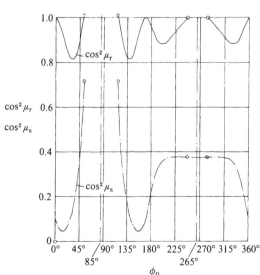

ϕ_0

length $c \leqslant f(= 36°)$, hence the linkages are not drag-links and should be rejected.

(3) Within the range $247.034° \leqslant \phi_0 \leqslant 282.966°$, the synthesized link lengths are such that $f + c \geqslant a + b$, which violates the first condition of (2.76) for a drag-link, or that the Grashof rule is not satisfied, and should be rejected.

The optimization procedure is, however, not affected by the discontinuities. The optimum transmission angle μ_r occurs at $\phi_0 = 32.845°$. The corresponding dimensions of the linkage are: $a = 59.018°$, $b = 60.170°$, $\psi_0 = 148.165°$, $c = 64.908°$ and $\mu_r = 25.443°$, $\mu_s = 67.677°$. Although the value of μ_r is not quite satisfactory, it is the best for the given angles of rotation.

9

Other spherical mechanisms

Like plane mechanisms, there are spherical mechanisms which cannot be grouped into the general four-bar linkage category as mentioned in Chapter 2. For instance, there are spherical five-bar linkages with two degrees of freedom similar to the corresponding plane five-bar linkages (Tavkhelidze & Davitashvili, 1974; Davitashvili,1983a, b), and spherical cams (Dittrich.1966a, b). In the following we shall consider some special spherical mechanisms, which contain three, five, six or eight members.

9.1   Spherical inversors

In plane kinematics there is a category of linkages called inversors, to which belong the well-known Peaucellier linkage, Perrolaz linkage and Hart linkage. The first two are eight-bar linkages and the third one is a six-bar linkage. The term *inversor* stems from the fact that, imagining the linkage shown in Fig. 9.1 is a planar Peaucellier mechanism, the product of the distances $A_0 B$ and $A_0 E$ is a constant, i.e. these two distances are in inverse proportion. If the point B is guided along a circular path with centre at B_0, then the path of E is a straight line perpendicular to the line of centres $A_0 B_0$. The spherical counterparts of these three linkages have been investigated in

Fig. 9.1. Spherical Peaucellier linkage.

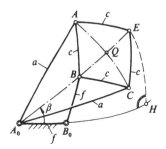

(Chen, 1968). While there are spherical inversors of the Peaucellier and Perrolaz types, the spherical counterpart of the Hart linkage does not exist, because parallelism does not exist in spherical geometry.

9.1.1   *Spherical Peaucellier linkage*

Fig. 9.1 shows this linkage. Consider first the six-bar linkage A_0CEAB isolated from the complete linkage. Let $AB = BC = CE = EA = c$, and $A_0C = A_0A = a$. The three points A_0, B, E lie obviously on a great circle. Let the middle point of BE be denoted by Q, and A_0Q and BQ by m and n respectively. We have

$$\tan\frac{A_0B}{2}\tan\frac{A_0E}{2} = \tan\frac{m-n}{2}\tan\frac{m+n}{2} = \frac{\cos n - \cos m}{\cos n + \cos m} \tag{9.1}$$

Applying equation (A1.2) to both $\triangle A_0QA$ and $\triangle BQA$, we have

$$\cos m = \frac{\cos a}{\cos QA}, \quad \cos n = \frac{\cos c}{\cos QA} \tag{9.2}$$

Substituting equations (9.2) into equation (9.1) gives

$$\tan\frac{A_0B}{2}\tan\frac{A_0E}{2} = \frac{\cos c - \cos a}{\cos c + \cos a} = \text{constant, say } K \tag{9.3}$$

Equation (9.3) means that $\tan(A_0B/2)$ and $\tan(A_0E/2)$ are in inverse proportion, hence the six-bar linkage A_0CEAB is, in a sense, an inversor.

We shall see what the path of E will be if the point B is guided along a circular path with its spherical centre at B_0, where the links $A_0B_0 = B_0B = f$. Let $\sphericalangle B_0A_0B = \beta$. Now from $\triangle A_0B_0B$, we have

$$\tan f \cos \beta = \tan\frac{A_0B}{2} = \frac{K}{\tan(A_0E/2)}$$

or

$$\tan\frac{A_0E}{2} = \frac{K}{\tan f \cos \beta} \tag{9.4}$$

Fig. 9.2. Spherical Perrolaz linkage.

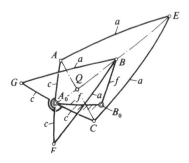

If OA_0 is taken as the direction of the $+z$-axis, and OA_0B_0 the zx-plane of a right-handed Cartesian coordinate system, upon transforming equation (9.4) by means of equation (A4.1) the path of the point $E(x, y, z)$, apart from equation (A3.1), is represented by

$$x^2 - \frac{K}{\tan f}(1+z)^2 = 0 \tag{9.5}$$

This path is obviously not a great circle, nor does it pass through the point H, the foot of the perpendicular drawn from a certain position of E to the great circle A_0B_0.

On the other hand, suppose it is required to keep the path of E along a great circle perpendicular to A_0B_0. It can be shown that the point B should then be guided along a spherical quartic. It is certainly not worth while to generate a great circle through a spherical quartic. It seems that this linkage is of rather little practical use.

9.1.2 Spherical Perrolaz linkage

This linkage is shown in Fig. 9.2, in which FA_0A and CA_0G are two single bars. Let $A_0A = A_0F = A_0C = A_0G = c$, and $AE = CE = GB = FB = a$, in the six-bar linkage isolated from the complete linkage. Also denote the intersection of A_0B and AC by Q, and A_0Q and QE by n and m respectively. We have

$$\tan\frac{A_0B}{2}\tan\frac{A_0E}{2} = \tan\frac{m-n}{2}\tan\frac{m+n}{2} = \frac{\cos n - \cos m}{\cos n + \cos m}$$

$$= \frac{\cos c - \cos a}{\cos c + \cos a} = \text{constant} \tag{9.6}$$

Equation (9.6) is identical with equation (9.3). The spherical Perrolaz linkage is therefore, in a sense, also a spherical inversor. Again, if the point B is guided along a circular path, with $B_0B = A_0B_0 = f$, the path of E is not a great circle.

9.2 Coupler-gear dwell mechanisms

Parallel to the different kinds of planar geared five-bar mechanisms, there can also be a variety of spherical geared five-bar mechanisms (Riddle, Tesar & Duffy, 1975; Lee & Akbil, 1986a, b). We are dealing here only with the essentials of such mechanisms developed in (Meyer zur Capellen & Dittrich, 1962; Meyer zur Capellen, 1963; Rath, 1960a, b; 1961). This consists of a basic four-bar, and a pair of bevel gears mounted on the axes OA and OA_0, or on OB and OB_0. The basic four-bar can either be a drag-link or a crank–rocker. The input link is, as usual, $a = A_0A$, and the output member is the bevel gear mounted on the axis OA_0 or OB_0. During the continuous rotation of the input link a, the output bevel gear may exhibit a dwell or a pilgrim-pace motion.

9.2.1   Reverted coupler-gear dwell mechanisms

Fig. 9.3(a) shows such a mechanism. Let the pair of bevel gears be denoted by z_c and z_e, of spherical pitch radii ρ_c and ρ_e respectively. The term *reverted* indicates that the output gear z_e is coaxial with the input crank a. Fig. 9.3(b) shows the angular velocity diagram, which is the plane **oac** of the angular velocity tetrahedron in Fig. 4.2(b). Note that z_c and c are one integral part. We have

$$\frac{\omega_e - \omega_{af}}{\omega_{ac}} = \frac{\sin \rho_c}{\sin \rho_e}$$

or

$$\frac{\omega_e}{\omega_{af}} = 1 - \frac{\sin \rho_c}{\sin \rho_e} \frac{\omega_{ca}}{\omega_{af}} \tag{9.7}$$

where ω_e is the angular velocity of the gear z_e, and $\omega_{ca} = -\omega_{ac}$. Differentiating equation (9.7) with respect to time, and noting that ω_{af} is a constant, we have

$$\dot{\omega}_e = -\frac{\sin \rho_c}{\sin \rho_e} \dot{\omega}_{ca} \tag{9.8}$$

The condition for a dwell of the gear z_e may be defined as, at a certain instant, both ω_e and $\dot{\omega}_e$ vanish. The vanishing of ω_e implies that the pitch point P_{ce}, the pole between c and z_e, or the point of contact of the pitch circles of the two bevel gears, coincides with the point P, the instantaneous pole of rotation of the coupler c. The vanishing of $\dot{\omega}_e$ means, according to equation (9.8), the vanishing of $\dot{\omega}_{ca}$, or the ratio ω_{ca}/ω_{af} becomes an extreme. According to that mentioned in Section 4.2.2, this condition is fulfilled whenever the collineation great circle RP is perpendicular to $B_0 B$.

Fig. 9.3. (a) Spherical coupler-gear mechanism. (b) Angular velocity diagram.

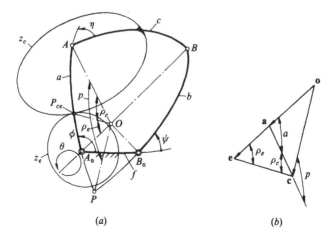

(a)   (b)

(1) Drag-link as basic four-bar

Assume the basic four-bar is a drag-link. Suppose it is required to have the dwell happening in the position $\phi = 0°$. As can be seen from Fig. 9.4(a), the point P coincides with B_0 and R with A, and $\not\prec AB_0B$ should be equal to 90°. This leads to, according to equation (A1.2), the condition for the dimensions of the drag-link:

$$\cos c = \cos b \cos (a - f) \tag{9.9}$$

As mentioned before, in order to set the pitch point P_{ce} coinciding with P,

Fig. 9.4. Coupler-gear dwell mechanisms (a) with dwell at $\phi = 0°$, (b) with dwell at $\phi = 180°$.

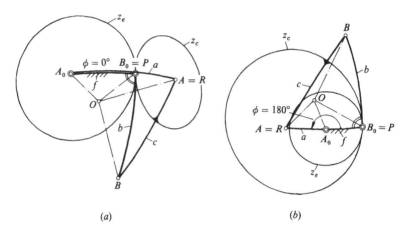

(a)   (b)

Fig. 9.5. θ–ϕ curves for a coupler-gear mechanism with $a = 60°$, $b = 70°$, $f = 30°$ and $c = 72.77°$.

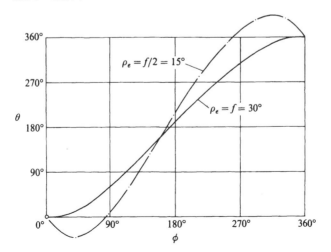

we have, as shown in Fig. 9.4(a),

$$\rho_e = f \tag{9.10}$$

Note that, if θ denotes the angle of rotation of the gear z_e from the position $\phi = 0°$, then $\omega_e = \dot{\theta}$. Also note that $\omega_{af} = \dot{\phi}$, and according to Fig. 2.3, $\omega_{ca} = -\dot{\eta}$. Integrating equation (9.7) gives

$$\triangle \theta = \triangle \phi + \frac{\sin \rho_c}{\sin \rho_e} \triangle \eta \tag{9.11}$$

where $\triangle \theta$, $\triangle \phi$ and $\triangle \eta$ are respectively the changes of θ, ϕ and η. For a given value of the parameter ϕ, the value of η can be computed from equation (2.19), and that of ω_{ca} from equation (4.14).

The solid lines in Figs. 9.5 and 9.6 show respectively the angular displacement θ and angular velocity ratio ω_e/ω_{af} for a coupler-gear dwell mechanism with $a = 60°, b = 70°, f = 30°, c = 72.77°$ (by equation (9.9)) and $\rho_e = f = 30°$. The dwell is a three-point dwell, because the θ-curve possesses a three-point contacting tangent at $\phi = 0°$.

When $\rho_e < f$, the output gear z_e exhibits a so-called *pilgrim-pace motion*, i.e. it sometimes rotates backwards. The chain lines in Figs. 9.5 and 9.6 show the corresponding curves of θ and ω_e/ω_{af} for the same basic drag-link, but with $\rho_e = f/2$.

On the other hand, suppose it is required to have the dwell happening in the position $\phi = 180°$, as shown in Fig. 9.4(b). Again P coincides with B_0 and R with A, and $\sphericalangle AB_0B$ should be equal to 90°. Hence the condition to be

Fig. 9.6. $\omega_e/\omega_{af}-\phi$ curves for the same coupler-gear mechanism as in Fig. 9.5.

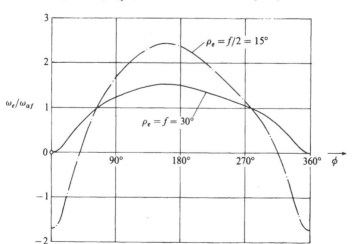

Table 9.1 *Spherical reverted coupler-gear dwell mechanisms*

	Drag-link as basic linkage		Crank–rocker as basic linkage	
Condition for link lengths	$\cos c = \cos b \cos(a-f)$	$\cos c = \cos b \cos(a+f)$	$\cos c = \cos b \cos(f-a)$	$\cos c = \cos b \cos(a+f)$
Type of gears	z_c, z_e are both external gears, $\rho_c + \rho_e = a$	z_c = internal gear, z_e = external pinion $\rho_c = -(a+\rho_e)$	z_c = external pinion, z_e = internal gear, $\rho_e = -(a+\rho_c)$	z_c = internal gear, z_e = external pinion, $\rho_c = -(a+\rho_e)$
Type of motion of z_e	$\rho_e = f$, dwell at $\phi = 0°$	$\rho_e = f$, dwell at $\phi = 180°$	$\rho_e = f$, dwell at $\phi = 0°$	$\rho_e = f$ $\begin{cases} \text{dwell at } \phi = 180° + \\ \text{possibly pilgrim-} \\ \text{pace motion.} \\ b = c = 90°, \text{5-point} \\ \text{dwell at } \phi = 180° \\ \text{under condition} \\ \text{of eqn (9.14)} \end{cases}$
	$\rho_e < f$, pilgrim-pace motion	$\rho_e < f$, pilgrim-pace motion	$|\rho_e| > f$, pilgrim-pace motion	$\rho_e > f$, pilgrim-pace motion

fulfilled by the link lengths is

$$\cos c = \cos b \cos (a + f)$$ (9.12)

In order to set the pitch point P_{ce} containing with P, as shown in Fig. 9.4(b), we have again

$$\rho_e = f$$

and z_c has to be an internal gear. The above equations are still valid, provided the spherical radius ρ_c of z_c is considered negative. Note that an internal bevel gear of half pitch-cone angle ρ may be considered as an external bevel gear of half pitch-cone angle $180° - \rho$. However, when $\rho_c > 90°$, the basic four-bar A_0ABB_0 should be replaced by its supplementary linkage $A_0\bar{A}BB_0$, so that the coupler-gear becomes an external gear. Hence there will be no ambiguity about the convention if the spherical pitch radius of an internal bevel gear is always considered negative.

For easy reference, all information for various cases is tabulated in Table 9.1.

(2) Crank–rocker as basic four-bar
Suppose the basic four-bar is a crank–rocker. Let it be required to have a dwell of the gear z_e happening at $\phi = 0°$. The condition to be fulfilled by the link lengths is again equation (9.9). The gear z_e has to be an internal gear and ρ_e is negative, to mesh with an external pinion z_c, and also $|\rho_e| = f$. When $|\rho_e| > f$, the motion of z_e becomes a pilgrim-pace motion.

Fig. 9.7. θ–ϕ curves for a coupler-gear mechanism with $a = 30°$, $b = 70°$, $f = 60°$ and $c = 90°$.

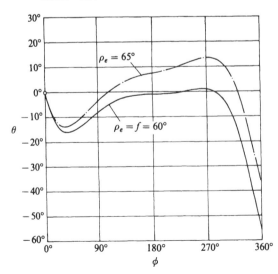

If it is required to have the dwell of z_e happening at $\phi = 180°$, the condition for the link lengths is again equation (9.12). The gear z_c has to be an internal gear (ρ_c is negative), to mesh with an external pinion z_e. The solid lines in Figs. 9.7 and 9.8 show respectively the angular displacement θ and angular velocity ratio ω_e/ω_{af} for a coupler-gear dwell mechanism with $a = 30°$, $b = 70°, f = 60°$ and $c = 90°$ (by equation (9.12)), and $\rho_e = f = 60°$. It can be seen that the motion of z_e is a dwell and pilgrim-pace motion.

When $\rho_e > f$, the output pinion z_e exhibits only a pilgrim-pace motion. The chain lines in Figs. 9.7 and 9.8 show the corresponding curves of θ and ω_e/ω_{af} for the same basic crank–rocker, but with $\rho_e = 65°$.

(3) Central oscillating cylinder as basic four-bar
If, in particular, $b = c = 90°$, the basic linkage becomes a central oscillating cylinder, as shown in Fig. 2.15(b). Considering the basic linkage as an inversion of the partial linkage A_0AB_0 of the four-bar as shown in Fig. 2.3, the angle η is given, according to equation (2.61), by

$$\cot \eta = \frac{\mu_i S_\phi}{1 - v_i C_\phi} \tag{9.13}$$

where, according to equations (2.62) and (2.63), upon inversion

$$\mu_i = \frac{\tan f}{\sin a}$$

Fig. 9.8. ω_e/ω_{af}–ϕ curves for the same coupler-gear mechanism as in Fig. 9.7.

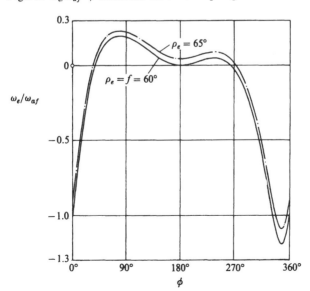

and

$$v_i = \frac{\tan f}{\tan a}$$

If, in this particular case, $\rho_e = f$ and $\rho_c = -(a + f)$, equation (9.7) can be written as

$$\omega_e = \omega_{af} - \frac{\sin(a + f)}{\sin f} \cdot \dot{\eta} \tag{9.7a}$$

Successive differentiations of equation (9.7a) with respect to time give

$$\dot{\omega}_e = -\frac{\sin(a + f)}{\sin f} \ddot{\eta}, \quad \ddot{\omega}_e = -\frac{\sin(a + f)}{\sin f} \dddot{\eta}, \quad \dddot{\omega}_e = -\frac{\sin(a + f)}{\sin f} \ddddot{\eta}$$

It can be shown that the derivatives $\omega_e = \dot{\omega}_e = \ddot{\omega}_e = 0$ at $\phi = 180°$ for any combination of a and f ($a \leqslant f$). In other words, there is always a dwell of z_e at $\phi = 180°$. However, $\dddot{\eta}$, and hence $\dddot{\omega}_e$, vanishes, as derived by successive differentiations of equation (9.13), only if the following condition is satisfied:

$$2 \sin a \tan^2 f - \cos a \tan f + \sin a = 0 \tag{9.14}$$

Equation (9.14) is a quadratic equation in $\tan f$ if a is considered as a parameter. This relationship is shown as the solid curve in Fig. 9.9 where, instead of f, the factor $1 - \sin(a + f)/\sin f$ is plotted as a function of a. For (a, f) values outside this solid curve, the ω_e/ω_{af} curve looks somewhat like the solid line shown in Fig. 9.8, but symmetrical with respect to the line $\phi = 180°$. This means that, besides the position $\phi = 180°$, ω_e passes two more

Fig. 9.9. Factor $1-\sin(a + f)/\sin f$ as a function of a for a coupler-gear dwell mechanism with $b = c = 90°$.

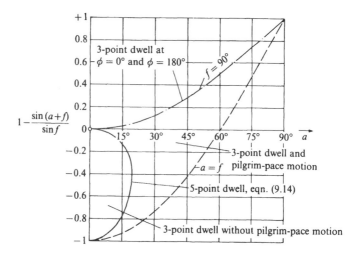

times through zero, hence the motion of the pinion z_e is a rest at $\phi = 180°$ and a pilgrim-pace motion. For (a, f) values on this solid curve, the four zero positions of ω_e shrink into one single point at $\phi = 180°$, hence a five-point dwell there. For (a, f) values inside this curve, the two extra zero positions of the ω_e curve disappear, hence the motion of z_e is a rest at $\phi = 180°$ without pilgrim-pace motion. In Fig. 9.9, the area is further limited by two curves: $f = 90°$ and $a = f$. On the curve $f = 90°$, the pinion z_e exhibits also a dwell at $\phi = 0°$ and $\phi = 180°$.

9.2.2 Non-reverted coupler-gear dwell mechanisms

The term *non-reverted* refers to the arrangement that a pair of bevel gears, similar to those shown in Fig. 9.3(*a*), are mounted on the axes OB and OB_0. The output gear, which is coaxial with b, is not coaxial with the input link a. In order to explain more clearly the function of the non-reverted coupler-gear mechanisms, it is expedient to make use of the arrangement of Fig. 9.3(*a*), but assuming the link b to be the input link, and ψ the input angle. θ is still the output angle, and $\dot{\psi} = d\psi/dt$ is considered a constant. We now have

$$\frac{d\theta}{d\psi} = \frac{d\theta}{d\phi} \frac{d\phi}{d\psi} \tag{9.15}$$

and also

$$\frac{d^2\theta}{d\psi^2} = \frac{d^2\theta}{d\phi^2} \left(\frac{d\phi}{d\psi}\right)^2 + \frac{d\theta}{d\phi} \frac{d^2\phi}{d\psi^2} \tag{9.16}$$

Note that in each case listed in Table 9.1 wherever z_e exhibits a dwell, $\omega_e = (d\theta/d\phi)\dot{\phi} = 0$, and $\dot{\omega}_e$, as defined there, is $\dot{\omega}_e = (d^2\theta/d\phi^2)\dot{\phi}^2 = 0$. This means that, in all these cases, according to equations (9.15) and (9.16), $d\theta/d\phi = d^2\theta/d\phi^2 = 0$. Therefore the gear z_e also exhibits a dwell if b is taken as the input link, rotating with a constant angular velocity.

9.3 Spherical crank-gear dwell mechanisms

This is a kind of mechanism derived from planar three-gear mechanisms. The following is the essential part of the work done in (Meyer zur Capellen & von der Osten-Sacken, 1968). Fig. 9.10(*a*) shows a typical such mechanism. It consists, like the previously mentioned spherical coupler-gear dwell mechanisms, of a basic four-bar, but with two pairs of bevel gears mounted on axes OA, OB and OB_0. The gear on axis OA, or z_a, is fixed to the link a. The gear mounted on axis OB, or z_m, meshes with z_a and a gear z_n mounted on axis OB_0. For the gear train z_a-z_m, there can be three types of gears, namely, (*a*) both z_a and z_m are external gears, (*b*) z_a = external pinion, z_m = internal gear, and (*c*) z_a = internal gear, z_m = external pinion. Similarly there can also be three types of gears for the gear train z_m–z_n. There are therefore altogether $3 \times 3 = 9$ different possible combinations of the gears, provided that the gear z_m is allowed to be used, at the same time, both as an external and an internal gear.

(1) Angular velocity of output gear z_n

Fig. 9.10(*b*) shows the angular velocity diagram of the mechanism in Fig. 9.10(*a*), and is an extension of the angular velocity tetrahedron as shown in Fig. 4.2(*b*). Let the spherical pitch radii of the gears z_a, z_m and z_n be denoted

Fig. 9.10. (*a*) Spherical crank-gear mechanism. (*b*) Angular velocity diagram.

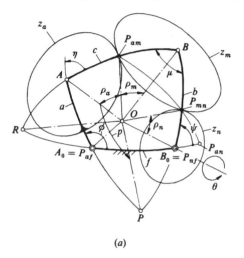

(*a*)

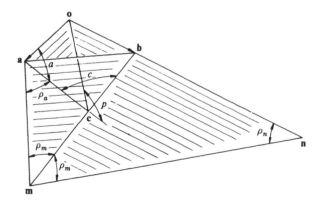

(*b*)

respectively by ρ_a, ρ_m and ρ_n. We have then, from $\triangle$ **acm**,

$$\frac{\omega_{ac}}{\omega_{cm}} = \frac{\sin \rho_m}{\sin \rho_a}$$

or

$$\omega_{cm} = \frac{\sin \rho_a}{\sin \rho_m} \omega_{ac} \qquad (9.17)$$

Also from the $\triangle$ **mbn**, we have

$$\frac{\omega_{cm} + \omega_{bc}}{\omega_{nb}} = \frac{\sin \rho_n}{\sin \rho_m}$$

or, by equation (9.17),

$$\omega_{nb} = \frac{\sin \rho_m}{\sin \rho_n} (\omega_{cm} + \omega_{bc}) = \frac{\sin \rho_m}{\sin \rho_n} \left(\frac{\sin \rho_a}{\sin \rho_m} \omega_{ac} + \omega_{bc} \right)$$

The angular velocity of the output gear z_n is therefore

$$\omega_n = \omega_{bf} + \omega_{nb} = \omega_{bf} + \omega_{ac} \frac{\sin \rho_a}{\sin \rho_n} + \omega_{bc} \frac{\sin \rho_m}{\sin \rho_n} \qquad (9.18)$$

The spherical radii ρ_a, ρ_m and ρ_n are subject to the conditions

$$\rho_a + \rho_m = c$$

and

$$\rho_m + \rho_n = b$$

or other conditions if one of the two gears is an internal gear. The above equations are still valid provided that the spherical pitch radius of an internal gear is considered as negative. In equation (9.18) the angular velocities $\omega_{bf}, \omega_{ac} = -\omega_{ca}$ and $\omega_{bc} = -\omega_{cb}$ can be computed by means of equations (4.11), (4.14) and (4.15) respectively.

(2) Angle of rotation of output gear z_n
Again let the angle of rotation of the output gear z_n be denoted by θ. The angles η and μ are defined as shown in Fig. 2.3. Integration of equation (9.18) gives

$$\triangle \theta = \triangle \psi + \triangle \eta \frac{\sin \rho_a}{\sin \rho_n} + \triangle \mu \frac{\sin \rho_m}{\sin \rho_n} \qquad (9.19)$$

where $\triangle \theta$, $\triangle \eta$ and $\triangle \mu$ are the respective algebraic changes of θ, η and μ.

(3) Dead centre positions
A dead centre position of the mechanism, i.e. one in which $\omega_n = 0$, is reached when the relative pole P_{an} coincides with A_0. This condition is fulfilled if the basic four-bar is itself in a dead centre position and at the same time the

relative pole P_{am} also coincides with A_0. This is the case if $\rho_a = a$ for the gear z_a, which meshes with an external gear z_m in the inner dead centre position or with an internal gear z_m in the outer dead centre position.

Although the cases mentioned above are sufficient, they are not necessary for the occurrence of $\omega_n = 0$.

(4) Dwell positions

A three-point dwell of the output gear z_n may again be defined as, at a certain instant, $\omega_n = \dot{\omega}_n = 0$. The design of a general crank-gear dwell mechanism is quite a complicated problem. However, we shall consider a simplified case in which the following assumptions are made: $b = c = 90°$ and $\rho_a = \rho_m = \rho_n = 45°$. The basic four-bar then becomes a central oscillating cylinder, as shown in Figs. 2.15(b),(c), and all three gears are external gears of equal size. This mechanism is shown in Fig. 9.11. The angular velocity of z_n, according to equation (9.18), is

$$\omega_n = \omega_{bf} + \omega_{ac} + \omega_{bc} \tag{9.20}$$

The three terms in equation (9.20) can be expressed in terms of the great circle arc $h = AB_0$. Since in the present case, Fig. 9.11, $\psi = 90° - \psi_s$, equation (2.3) can be written as, with the abbreviations $S_h = \sin h$, $C_h = \cos h$,

$$C_\psi = \frac{S_\phi}{S_h} S_a \tag{9.21}$$

Fig. 9.11. Spherical crank-gear mechanism with $b = c = 90°$, and $\rho_a = \rho_m = \rho_n = 45°$

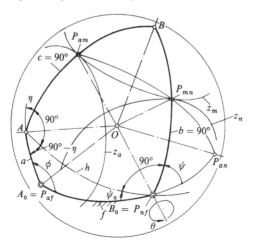

Differentiating equation (9.21) with respect to time gives

$$\omega_{bf} = \dot{\psi} = \frac{S_a S_f}{S_h^2(C_a - C_f C_h)}(S_a S_f C_h S_\phi^2 - S_h^2 C_\phi)\omega_{af} \qquad (9.22)$$

Similarly we have

$$\omega_{ac} = \dot{\eta} = \frac{S_a S_f}{S_h^2(C_f - C_a C_h)}(S_a S_f C_h S_\phi^2 - S_h^2 C_\phi)\omega_{af} \qquad (9.23)$$

Now because $h = \sphericalangle B_0 BA$, therefore $\omega_{bc} = \dot{h}$. Differentiating equation (2.2) with respect to time gives

$$\omega_{bc} = \dot{h} = \frac{S_a S_f S_\phi}{S_h}\omega_{af} \qquad (9.24)$$

Fig. 9.12. Spherical crank-gear dwell mechanism with the same dimensions as in Fig. 9.11, but $f = 90°$, $a = 39.66°$ in position $\phi = 301.51°$.

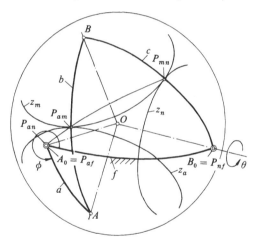

Fig. 9.13. $\omega_n/\omega_{af}-\phi$ curve for a crank-gear dwell mechanism with $b = c = f = 90°$ and $a = 39.66°$.

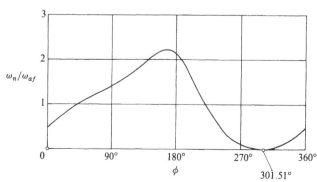

Substituting equations (9.22), (9.23) and (9.24) into equation (9.20), and rearranging, we obtain finally

$$\omega_n = \left[C_f + \frac{S_a S_f}{\sin h} S_\phi + \frac{(1 - \cos h)(C_a - C_f \cos h)}{\sin^2 h} \right] \omega_{af} \qquad (9.25)$$

where h has to be determined by equation (2.2). Differentiating equation (9.25) with respect to time, we can get an expression of $\dot\omega_n$, for a constant ω_{af}, which includes the three unknowns a, f and ϕ. For a given value of, say, f, the simultaneous equations $\omega_n = 0$ and $\dot\omega_n = 0$ can be solved for the two unknowns a and ϕ. As an example, assuming $f = 90°$, the solution is $a = 39.66°$ and $\phi = 301.51°$. Fig. 9.12 shows this mechanism in the dwell position. Note that the relative pole P_{an}, which is the intersection of the two great circles $P_{am}P_{mn}$ and $P_{af}P_{nf}$, coincides with $A_0 (= P_{af})$, hence $\omega_n = 0$. Fig. 9.13 shows the corresponding $\omega_n/\omega_{af}-\phi$ diagram of this mechanism, which shows that $\omega_n = \dot\omega_n = 0$ at $\phi = 301.51°$.

9.4   Spherical Geneva mechanisms

Like a planar Geneva mechanism, the spherical Geneva mechanism may also be considered as a series of central oscillating cylinders, as shown in Fig. 2.15(c), operating intermittently. Fig. 9.14 shows a four-slot spherical

Fig. 9.14. Spherical Geneva mechanism.

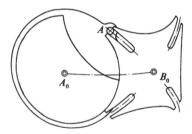

Fig. 9.15. Spherical central oscillating cylinder in dead centre position.

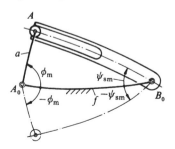

Geneva mechanism. The following discussions are mainly due to the investigations of (Meyer zur Capellen, 1961).

Fig. 9.15 shows a single spherical central oscillating cylinder in its dead centre position, i.e. the crank A_0A is perpendicular to the *centre-line* great circle AB_0. Let this crank angle be denoted by ϕ_m, and the corresponding

Fig. 9.16. ψ_s, ψ' and ψ'' as functions of ϕ for a four-slot Geneva mechanism with $f = 60°$.

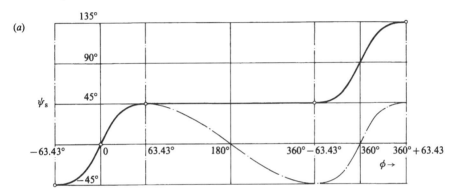

(a)

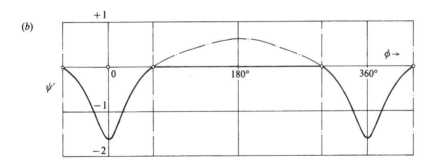

(b)

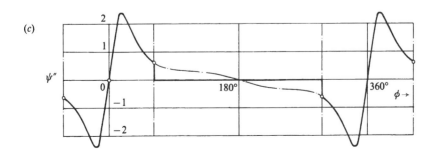

(c)

oscillating cylinder angle by ψ_{sm} which is also $\psi_{s\,max}$. The displacement equation is simply equation (2.61), or

$$\tan\psi_s = \frac{\mu S_\phi}{1 - \nu C_\phi} \qquad [(2.61)]$$

with μ and ν as defined in equations (2.62) and (2.63). The values of ϕ_m and ψ_{sm} are, respectively, according to equations (A1.6) and (A1.1), given by

$$\cos\phi_m = \nu = \frac{\tan a}{\tan f} \qquad (9.26)$$

and

$$\sin\psi_{sm} = \frac{\sin a}{\sin f} \qquad (9.27)$$

Eliminating a from the above two equations gives the following relation between ϕ_m and ψ_{sm}, or, according to equation (A1.5),

$$\tan\phi_m \tan\psi_{sm} = \frac{1}{\cos f} \qquad (9.28)$$

For a Geneva mechanism the angle ψ_{sm} is determined by the number of slots z, or

$$\psi_{sm} = \frac{360°}{2z} = \frac{180°}{z} \qquad (9.29)$$

The lengths a and f are therefore coupled by equation (9.27).

The output angle ψ_s and the differential coefficients ψ', ψ'' and ψ''' of a spherical central oscillating cylinder have been given by equations (2.60)–(2.68). Figs. 9.16(a),(b),(c) show, respectively, the variations of ψ_s, ψ' and ψ'' as functions of ϕ for a spherical Geneva mechanism with $z = 4$ (or $\psi_{sm} = 45°$) and $f = 60°$. It can be seen that, at $\phi = \pm\phi_m = \pm 63.43°$, there is an abrupt change of the angular accelerations of the output link b (represented by ψ''). However, in these positions, the absolute value of the angular acceleration of the output link is not a maximum. The maximum absolute angular acceleration of b can easily be determined by using even a pocket personal computer to locate the position where ψ''' changes sign.

The ratio w of the switching time to rest time is given by

$$w = \frac{2\phi_m}{360° - 2\phi_m} = \frac{\phi_m}{180° - \phi_m} \qquad (9.30)$$

where ϕ_m has to be determined by equations (9.29) and (9.28).

The spherical Geneva mechanism may also be driven by a spherical drag-link as in the planar case (Shi, 1982).

9.5   Coupling of a plane antiparallelogram linkage and a spherical central oscillating cylinder or a spherical central Whitworth mechanism

It is possible to link together a plane mechanism and a spherical mechanism, to obtain a special proportional mechanism, simply by coupling the output shaft of one mechanism with the input shaft of the other. Using the output motion of a wobble-plate to drive a reciprocating piston was suggested as early as 1929 (Müller, 1929). The following investigation is due to (Meyer zur Capellen & Schreiber, 1971). Let the plane mechanism be preconnected to the spherical mechanism, hence the former may be called the driving linkage, and the latter the driven linkage.

(1) The driving linkage

Fig. 9.17 shows a plane antiparallelogram linkage $D_0 D^* A^* A_0$ with $D_0 A_0 = D^* A^* = f_p$, $D_0 D^* = A_0 A^* = a_p$. The input angle is denoted by θ and the output angle by ϕ. Let $\sphericalangle D^* D_0 A^* = \sphericalangle A_0 A^* D_0 = \beta$. We have

$$\phi = \theta + 2\beta \tag{9.31}$$

Let $\lambda = f_p/a_p$. It is well known that, for a plane oscillating cylinder $D^* A^* D_0$,

$$\tan \beta = \frac{\lambda \sin \phi}{1 + \lambda \cos \phi} \tag{9.32}$$

Eliminating β between equations (9.31) and (9.32) gives

$$\sin \phi = \frac{(1 - \lambda^2) \sin \theta}{N_\theta} \tag{9.33}$$

and

$$\cos \phi = \frac{(1 + \lambda^2) \cos \theta - 2\lambda}{N_\theta} \tag{9.34}$$

where

$$N_\theta = 1 + \lambda^2 - 2\lambda \cos \theta = (\lambda - \cos \theta)^2 + \sin^2 \theta$$

Fig. 9.17. Plane antiparallelogram linkage.

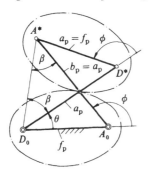

The velocity ratio of this mechanism is, differentiating equations (9.31) and (9.32),

$$i_p = \frac{d\phi}{d\theta} = \frac{1 - \lambda^2}{N_\theta} \tag{9.35}$$

Further differentiation of equation (9.35) gives

$$i_p'' = \frac{d^2\phi}{d\theta^2} = -\frac{2\lambda(1 - \lambda^2)}{N_\theta^2}\sin\theta \tag{9.36}$$

It is well known that the fixed and moving polodes of an antiparallelogram linkage are two equal ellipses and the motion of the coupler relative to the fixed link is equivalent to the epicyclic rolling of one ellipse on the other, as represented by the chain lines in Fig. 9.17, which is a plane version of Fig. 6.6. It can be shown that if, in the parallelogram linkage, $a_p < f_p$, the motion equations similar to those derived above can also be obtained, but the two ellipses are attached respectively to the input and output links, then they will rotate, contrary to as shown in Fig. 9.17, in opposite senses.

There are two alternatives of the driving linkage, namely, (a) the plane coupler-gear mechanism similar to that mentioned in Section 9.2.1, with a central oscillating cylinder as the basic four-bar, and (b) the elliptical oscillating cylinder as mentioned in Section 2.4.6(1). Both plane mechanisms may, under certain conditions of the link dimensions, exhibit the same law of motion as that of the antiparallelogram linkage. Details of these conditions can be found in (Meyer zur Capellen & Schreiber, 1972).

(2) The driven linkage
The well-known spherical central oscillating cylinder as shown in Figs. 2.15(b)

Fig. 9.18. Spherical central oscillating cylinder.

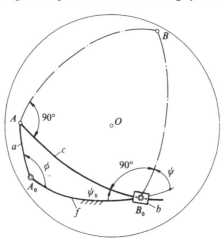

or (c), or the spherical central Whitworth mechanism as shown in Fig. 2.25(a), (b) is taken as the driven linkage, the motion equations of which have been given as equations (2.59)–(2.68). However, in order to avoid confusion, we denote here $i_s = d\psi_s/d\phi$, $i'_s = d^2\psi_s/d\phi^2$, etc. For reasons of clarity this linkage is shown once more in Fig. 9.18, in order to show that its axis OA_0 and crank angle ϕ are identical with those of the driving linkage shown in Fig. 9.17.

(3) The plane–spherical linkage assembly as a proportional mechanism
If now the plane driving linkage and the spherical driven linkage are assembled together, the displacement equation, i.e. the relation between the output angle ψ_s and the input angle θ, can be found by substituting equations (9.33) and (9.34) into equation (2.61), or

$$\tan \psi_s = \frac{\mu_z S_\theta}{1 - v_z C_\theta} \tag{9.37}$$

where

$$\mu_z = (1 - \lambda^2)\tan a/Z$$
$$v_z = [(1 + \lambda^2)\tan a \cos f + 2\lambda \sin f]/Z$$
$$Z = (1 + \lambda^2)\sin f + 2\lambda \tan a \cos f$$

It is interesting to note that equation (9.37) is exactly of the same form as equation (2.61). This reveals that the linkage assembly, like a single spherical central Whitworth mechanism, can be used as a proportional mechanism. Because $\lambda \leqslant 1$, hence μ_z and v_z are always positive, just as μ and v are positive in equation (2.61). Consequently a proportional mechanism exists at $\theta = 180°$,

Fig. 9.19. Equation (9.38), f–a diagrams for $\lambda = $ constant.

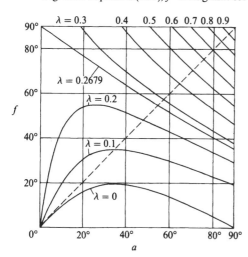

similar to that mentioned in Section 2.4.3, provided that μ_z and v_z, in place of μ and v respectively, satisfy equation (2.77), the condition for $d^3\psi_s/d\theta^3 = 0$, or

$$2(\mu_z^2 - v_z^2) - v_z + 1 = 0$$

After lengthy arithmetics, the above equation becomes

$$\frac{2\lambda}{(1-\lambda)^2} - \frac{2\tan^2 a \tan^2 f + \tan^2 f - \tan a \tan f}{(\tan a + \tan f)^2} = 0 \qquad (9.38)$$

Alternatively, one can also arrive at the above equation by means of the velocity ratio i_z of the whole linkage assembly and its derivative (Meyer zur Capellen & Schreiber, 1971). We now have

$$i_z = \frac{d\psi_s}{d\theta} = \frac{d\phi}{d\theta}\frac{d\psi_s}{d\phi} = i_p i_s$$

$$i_z' = \frac{d^2\psi_s}{d\theta^2} = i_p' i_s + i_p^2 \frac{d^2\psi_s}{d\phi^2} = i_p' i_s + i_p^2 i_s' \qquad (9.39)$$

Substituting equations (9.35) and (9.36) for i_p and i_p', and equations (2.65) and (2.66) for i_s and i_s' into equation (9.39), and demanding that the equation $i_z' = 0$ should have a triple root at $\theta = 180°$, we can get equation (9.38).

Equation (9.38) represents the condition put forward for the three independent parameters λ, a and f, to ensure a stationary velocity ratio at $\theta = 180°$. Fig. 9.19 shows the family of curves $\lambda = $ constant in the f–a diagram. Some special cases will be considered.

(a) Wobble-plate as the driven linkage. In this case, $f = 90°$. The λ-values are given by the intersection points of the λ-curves with the horizontal line $f = 90°$. Positive values of a exist only for $\lambda \geq 2 - \sqrt{3} = 0.2679$.

(b) Hooke's universal joint as the driven linkage. In this case, $a = 90°$. The λ-values are given by the intersection points of the λ-curves with the vertical line $a = 90°$. In particular, for $\lambda = 2 - \sqrt{3} = 0.2679$, $\tan^2 f = 1/2$, or $f = 35.264°$.

(c) $\lambda = 0$. In this case, $\phi = \theta$, and the driving linkage is nothing but a rigid crank. The linkage assembly becomes simply a central Whitworth mechanism, and its characteristics as a proportional mechanism have already been discussed in Section 2.4.3.

9.6   Spherical six-bar linkages

As in plane kinematics, there are two basic types of six-bar linkages in spherical kinematics, namely, the Watt's and Stephenson's types. A number of interesting examples can be read in (Duditza, 1968b). In the following we shall only mention two special cases.

9.6.1 Watt's type six-bar linkages

The plane analogue of a Watt's type six-bar linkage is shown in Fig. 9.20, the two four-bar linkages being connected in series. In spherical mechanisms there can be a variety of combinations of the two linkages A_0ABB_0 and $C_0(=B_0)CDD_0$. For instance, either linkage can be a wobble-plate or a Hooke's joint. In fact the couplings of two Hooke's joints mentioned in Sections 2.4.7 and 2.4.8 are just special cases of the present case. Consequently it can be seen that the two linkages need not be on the same unit sphere. The transmission characteristics of each combination can be derived by using equations in Chapter 1.

The variation possibilities as well as the analysis and design of such linkages can be found in (Kunad, 1968; Kunad, Goetze & Gismann, 1974; Shi, 1982). It is to be noted that, for classification purposes, each individual spherical

Fig. 9.20. Plane analogue of Watt's type six-bar linkage.

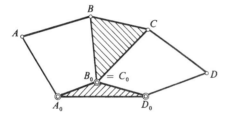

Fig. 9.21. (a) Plane analogue of Stephenson's type six-bar linkage. (b) Spherical Stephenson's type linkage, with A_0ABB_0 as a Hooke's joint.

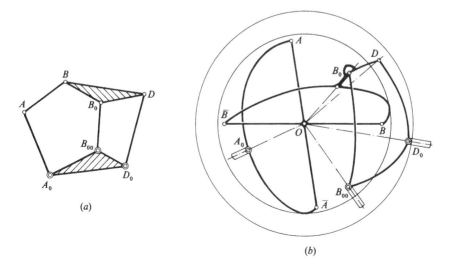

(a)

(b)

linkage has to be reduced to the one with minimum sum of link lengths, as mentioned in Section 3.3.

9.6.2   Stephenson's type six-bar linkages

The plane analogue of a Stephenson's type six-bar linkage is shown in Fig. 9.21(*a*). A spherical six-bar linkage corresponding to this is shown in Fig. 9.21(*b*), in which the linkage A_0ABB_0 is a Hooke's joint, but with the joint B_0 not fixed. The output motion of the Hooke's joint is driving the coupler B_0D of the four-bar $B_{00}B_0DD_0$, which can be a drag-link, or a Grashof double-rocker.

10

Harmonic analysis of spherical four-bar linkages

While there are numerous investigations on harmonic analysis of plane four-bar linkages, those specifically dealing with the harmonic analysis of spherical four-bars are comparatively few. However, it seems that the existing investigations are sufficient to enable us to understand the behaviour of a spherical four-bar linkage.

10.1   Harmonic analysis of the output angle

Parallel to the investigation of (Freudenstein, 1959) on harmonic analysis of plane four-bars, Yang has developed the following study on spherical four-bar mechanisms (Yang, 1962). Referring to Fig. 2.3, the output angle is

$$\psi = 180° - (\psi_s + \psi_u)$$

The harmonic analysis of ψ can therefore be dealt with in two parts, ψ_s and ψ_u.

(1) The part ψ_s

For the partial linkage, the central oscillating cylinder A_0AB_0, we have, according to equation (2.61),

$$\psi_s = \tan^{-1}\frac{\mu_s S_\phi}{1 - v_s C_\phi} \tag{2.61a}$$

where $\mu_s^\dagger = \tan a/\sin f$ and $v_s = \tan a/\tan f$, as defined before. It is evident that, from Fig. 2.3, ψ_s is an odd function of ϕ, therefore its Fourier series expansion is of the form

$$\psi_s = \sum_{m=1}^{\infty} b_m \sin m\phi \tag{10.1}$$

---

† The symbol μ_s is used here in place of μ as defined in equation (2.62), to avoid confusion with the angle $\mu = \sphericalangle ABB_0$.

where

$$b_m = \frac{1}{\pi} \int_{-\pi}^{\pi} \psi_s \sin m\phi \, d\phi$$

Integrating by parts,

$$b_m = \frac{1}{m\pi} \int_{-\pi}^{\pi} \frac{d\psi_s}{d\phi} \cos m\phi \, d\phi \tag{10.2}$$

The expression of $d\psi_s/d\phi$ is obtained by differentiating equation (2.61a)

$$\frac{d\psi_s}{d\phi} = \frac{\mu_s(C_\phi - v_s)}{1 - 2v_s C_\phi + \mu_s^2 S_\phi^2 + v_s^2 C_\phi^2} \tag{10.3}$$

Because of the disparity between the constants μ_s and v_s, equation (10.3) cannot be expanded directly into a simple series as in the plane four-bar case (Freudenstein, 1959). Now by introducing the complex variable

$$z = e^{i\phi}, \quad \text{with } i = \sqrt{-1}$$

and hence

$$\sin \phi = \frac{z - z^{-1}}{2i}, \quad \cos \phi = \frac{z + z^{-1}}{2}$$

equation (10.3) can be written in terms of z:

$$\frac{d\psi_s}{d\phi} = -\frac{z}{2}\left[\frac{1}{z + \kappa_1} - \frac{1}{z + 1/\kappa_1} + \frac{1}{z - \kappa_2} - \frac{1}{z - 1/\kappa_2} \right] \tag{10.4}$$

where $\kappa_1 = \tan(a/2)\tan(f/2)$, $\kappa_2 = \tan(f/2)/\tan(a/2)$. We note two different expansions of the function $(z - \kappa)^{-1}$, namely,

the Taylor series expansion for

$$|\kappa| > 1 : (z - \kappa)^{-1} = -\sum_{n=1}^{\infty} \kappa^{-n} z^{n-1} \tag{10.5}$$

and the Laurent series expansion for

$$|\kappa| < 1 : (z - \kappa)^{-1} = \sum_{n=1}^{\infty} \kappa^{n-1} z^{-n} \tag{10.6}$$

Since a and f are always positive and not greater than $180°$, there are four cases to be distinguished:

$$\text{Case 1}: \kappa_1 = \tan\frac{a}{2}\tan\frac{f}{2} < 1, \kappa_2 < 1, f < a;$$

$$b_m = -\frac{1}{m}[(-\kappa_1)^m + \kappa_2^m]$$

$$\text{Case 2}: \kappa_1 = \tan\frac{a}{2}\tan\frac{f}{2} < 1, \kappa_2 > 1, f > a;$$

$$b_m = -\frac{1}{m}[(-\kappa_1)^m - (\kappa_2)^{-m}]$$

Case 3: $\kappa_1 = \tan\frac{a}{2}\tan\frac{f}{2} > 1, \kappa_2 < 1, f < a;$ (10.7)

$$b_m = -\frac{1}{m}[-(-\kappa_1)^{-m} + \kappa_2^m]$$

Case 4: $\kappa_1 = \tan\frac{a}{2}\tan\frac{f}{2} > 1, \kappa_2 > 1, f > a;$

$$b_m = -\frac{1}{m}[-(-\kappa_1)^{-m} - (\kappa_2)^{-m}]$$

where the coefficients b_m's are obtained as follows. Taking, for instance, case 2, $\kappa_1 < 1$ and $\kappa_2 > 1$, equation (10.4) can be expanded by means of equations (10.5) and (10.6):

$$\frac{d\psi_s}{d\phi} = -\frac{1}{2}\left\{ \sum_{n=1}^{\infty} [(-\kappa_1)^{n-1}z^{-(n-1)} \right.$$

$$\left. + (-\kappa_1)^n z^n - \kappa_2^{-n}z^n - \kappa_2^{-(n-1)}z^{-(n-1)}] \right\}$$ (10.8)

Substituting equation (10.8) into equation (10.2), and recalling the definite integral

$$\int_{-\pi}^{\pi} z^{\pm n} \cos m\phi \, d\phi = \begin{cases} \pi, \text{ if } m = n \\ 0, \text{ if } m \neq n \end{cases}$$ (10.9)

we obtain

$$b_m = -\frac{1}{2m\pi}[\pi(-\kappa_1)^m + \pi(-\kappa_1)^m - \pi\kappa_2^{-m} - \pi\kappa_2^{-m}]$$

$$= -\frac{1}{m}[(-\kappa_1)^m - \kappa_2^{-m}]$$

as given in equations (10.7). Coefficients b_m for the other three cases can be obtained in a similar way.

(2) The part ψ_u
Similar to equation (2.61a, p. 335), the angle ψ_u can be expressed in terms of the transmission angle $\mu = \sphericalangle B_0BA$ from $\triangle B_0BA$:

$$\psi_u = \tan^{-1}\frac{\mu_c S_\mu}{1 - v_c C_\mu}$$ (10.10)

where $\mu_c = \tan c/\sin b$ and $v_c = \tan c/\tan b$, and S_μ, C_μ stand respectively for $\sin \mu$ and $\cos \mu$. The angle μ is related to the input angle ϕ by applying equation

(A1.9) to $\triangle BAB_0$, and comparing with equation (2.2),

$$C_\mu = \lambda_1 + \lambda_2 C_\phi \tag{10.11}$$

where

$$\left.\begin{array}{l} \lambda_1 = \dfrac{C_a C_f - C_b C_c}{S_b S_c} \\[4mm] \lambda_2 = \dfrac{S_a S_f}{S_b S_c} \end{array}\right\} \tag{10.12}$$

Also, from Fig. 2.3, it can be seen that ψ_u is an even function of ϕ, therefore its Fourier series expansion is of the form

$$\psi_u = \sum_{m=0}^{\infty} a_m \cos m\phi \tag{10.13}$$

where

$$a_0 = \frac{1}{2\pi} \int_{-\pi}^{\pi} \psi_u \, d\phi \tag{10.14}$$

and

$$a_{m(m \neq 0)} = \frac{1}{\pi} \int_{-\pi}^{\pi} \psi_u \cos m\phi \, d\phi$$

Integrating by parts,

$$a_{m(m \neq 0)} = -\frac{1}{m\pi} \int_{-\pi}^{\pi} \frac{d\psi_u}{d\phi} \sin m\phi \, d\phi \tag{10.15}$$

The derivative $d\psi_u/d\phi$ is, taking equation (10.12) into consideration,

$$\frac{d\psi_u}{d\phi} = \frac{d\psi_u}{d\mu} \frac{d\mu}{d\phi} = \frac{d\psi_u}{d\mu} \frac{S_\phi}{S_\mu} = F_\phi G_\phi \tag{10.16}$$

where

$$F_\phi = \lambda_2 \sin\phi \frac{d\psi_u}{d\mu} \tag{10.17}$$

and

$$G_\phi = [1 - (\lambda_1 + \lambda_2 C_\phi)^2]^{-1/2} \tag{10.18}$$

The function F_ϕ is obtained as follows. Differentiating equation (10.10) with respect to ϕ, and then expressing the function F_ϕ in terms of $z = e^{i\phi}$, we get

$$\begin{aligned} F_\phi &= \lambda_2 S_\phi \frac{d\psi_u}{d\mu} = \frac{\lambda_2 \mu_c (C_\mu - v_c) S_\phi}{1 - 2v_c C_\mu + \mu_c^2 S_\mu^2 + v_c^2 C_\mu^2} \\[3mm] &= \frac{i}{2}\left[-2\frac{\cot c}{\sin b} + \frac{\cot b}{\sin c} z \left(\frac{1}{z + \kappa_1} + \frac{1}{z + 1/\kappa_1} - \frac{1}{z - \kappa_2} - \frac{1}{z - 1/\kappa_2} \right) \right. \\[2mm] &\quad \left. + \frac{\cot c}{\sin b} z \left(\frac{1}{z + \kappa_1} + \frac{1}{z + 1/\kappa_1} + \frac{1}{z - \kappa_2} + \frac{1}{z - 1/\kappa_2} \right) \right] \end{aligned} \tag{10.19}$$

The partial fractions in equation (10.19) are of the same pattern as those in equation (10.4), hence we have, again according to equations (10.5) and (10.6),

$$F_\phi = -\frac{i}{2}\frac{\cot c}{\sin b} - \frac{i}{2}\sum_{n=1}^{\infty}[D_n z^n - D_{n-1}z^{-(n-1)}] \qquad (10.20)$$

where

$$D_n = \frac{\cot b}{\sin c}(s_1^n - s_2^n) + \frac{\cot c}{\sin b}(s_1^n + s_2^n) \qquad (10.21)$$

$$s_1 = \begin{cases} -\kappa_1, & \text{if } \kappa_1 < 1 \\ -\kappa_1^{-1}, & \text{if } \kappa_1 > 1 \end{cases}$$

and

$$s_2 = \begin{cases} \kappa_2, & \text{if } \kappa_2 < 1 \\ \kappa_2^{-1}, & \text{if } \kappa_2 > 1 \end{cases}$$

Equation (10.20) can be reduced to the form

$$
\begin{aligned}
F_\phi &= -\frac{i}{2}\left(\frac{\cot c}{\sin b} + D_0\right) - \frac{i}{2}\sum_{n=1}^{\infty}D_n(z^n - z^{-n}) \\
&= -\frac{i}{2}\left(\frac{\cot c}{\sin b} + D_0\right) + \sum_{n=1}^{\infty}D_n \sin n\phi
\end{aligned} \qquad (10.22)
$$

Since G_ϕ in equation (10.18) is an even function of ϕ, hence when the two constant terms of F_ϕ in equation (10.22) are multiplied by G_ϕ and substituted into equation (10.15), the definite integral vanishes. Consequently F_ϕ may be simplified in advance, or

$$F_\phi = \sum_{n=1}^{\infty}D_n \sin n\phi \qquad (10.23)$$

The Fourier series expansion of G_ϕ is a cosine series which may be written as

$$G_\phi = \sum_{j=0}^{\infty}H_j \cos j\phi \qquad (10.24)$$

Substituting equations (10.23) and (10.24) into equation (10.16) gives

$$\frac{d\psi_u}{d\phi} = \sum_{j=0}^{\infty}\sum_{n=1}^{\infty}H_j D_n \sin n\phi \cos j\phi \qquad (10.25)$$

Substituting equation (10.25) into equation (10.15) and noting that

$$\int_{-\pi}^{\pi}\sin \alpha\phi \sin \beta\phi \, d\phi = \begin{cases} \pi, & \text{if } \alpha = \beta \\ 0, & \text{if } \alpha \neq \beta \end{cases}$$

we obtain finally

$$a_m \ (m \neq 0) = -\frac{1}{m\pi}\int_{-\pi}^{\pi}\sum_{j=0}^{\infty}\sum_{n=1}^{\infty}H_j D_n \sin n\phi \cos j\phi \sin m\phi \, d\phi$$

$$= -\frac{1}{2m\pi} \int_{-\pi}^{\pi} \sum_{j=0}^{\infty} \sum_{n=1}^{\infty} H_j D_n [\sin{(n+j)\phi}$$
$$+ \sin{(n-j)\phi}] \sin{m\phi}\, d\phi$$

$$= -\frac{1}{2m} \left(2H_0 D_m + \sum_{j=1}^{m-1} H_j D_{m-j} \right.$$
$$\left. + \sum_{j=1}^{\infty} H_j D_{m+j} - \sum_{n=1}^{\infty} H_{m+n} D_n \right)$$

$$= -\frac{1}{2m} \left[2H_0 D_m + \sum_{j=1}^{m-1} H_{m-j} D_j \right.$$
$$\left. + \sum_{j=1}^{\infty} (H_j D_{m+j} - H_{m+j} D_j) \right] \tag{10.26}$$

(3) Complete Fourier coefficients of $\psi_s + \psi_u$

Combining equations (10.1) and (10.13), we get

$$180° - \psi = \psi_s + \psi_u = a_0 + \sum_{m=1}^{\infty} (a_m \cos{m\phi} + b_m \sin{m\phi}) \tag{10.27}$$

where a_0, a_m and b_m are given respectively by equations (10.14), (10.26) and (10.7). It is to be noted that, in equation (10.26), the second term applies only for $m \geqslant 2$. For $m = 1$, this term should be omitted. D_n's are defined in equation (10.21) and H_j's, for the special case $\lambda_1 = 0$, as computed in (Freudenstein, 1959), are

$$\left. \begin{aligned}
H_0 &= 1 + \tfrac{1}{4}\lambda_2^2 + \tfrac{9}{64}\lambda_2^4 + \tfrac{25}{256}\lambda_2^6 + \left(\tfrac{35}{128}\right)^2 \lambda_2^8 + \cdots \\
H_2 &= \tfrac{1}{4}\lambda_2^2 + \tfrac{3}{16}\lambda_2^4 + \tfrac{75}{512}\lambda_2^6 + \tfrac{(35)(56)}{(128)^2}\lambda_2^8 + \cdots \\
H_4 &= \tfrac{3}{64}\lambda_2^4 + \tfrac{15}{256}\lambda_2^6 + \tfrac{(35)(28)}{(128)^2}\lambda_2^8 + \cdots \\
H_6 &= \tfrac{5}{512}\lambda_2^6 + \tfrac{35}{(16)(128)}\lambda_2^8 + \cdots \\
H_8 &= \tfrac{35}{(128)^2}\lambda_2^8 + \cdots
\end{aligned} \right\} \tag{10.28}$$

Equation (10.27) may also be written as

$$\psi_s + \psi_u = a_0 + \sum_{m=1}^{\infty} c_m \sin{(m\phi + \phi_m)} \tag{10.29}$$

where

$$c_m = (a_m^2 + b_m^2)^{1/2}$$

and

$$\phi_m = \tan^{-1}\left(\frac{b_m}{a_m}\right)$$

c_m is the amplitude and ϕ_m is the phase angle of the mth harmonic of $\psi_s + \psi_u = 180° - \psi$.

(4) Maximum pressure angle and range of output angle as design parameters
The pressure angle is defined, referring to Fig. 2.3, as the complement of the transmission angle μ, or $|90° - \mu|$. The pressure angle becomes a maximum when $\phi = 0°$ or $\phi = 180°$, and will be denoted by σ_x. From equation (10.11) we have

$$\sigma_x = |\sin^{-1}(\lambda_1 \pm \lambda_2)| \tag{10.30}$$

The range of the output angle ψ of a spherical crank–rocker was denoted by $\triangle \psi$ in Fig. 2.6. It is given by equations (2.27a) and (2.25a) as

$$\triangle \psi = \psi_i - \psi_a = \cos^{-1}\frac{C_f C_b - \cos(c-a)}{S_f S_b} - \cos^{-1}\frac{C_f C_b - \cos(c+a)}{S_f S_b}$$
$$\tag{10.31}$$

Either σ_x or $\triangle \psi$, or both, can be taken as the design parameters, in determining the harmonic analysis of a spherical four-bar, as will be shown in the two special cases mentioned below.

(5) Special cases
Two special cases, the wobble-plate and the central slider–crank, will be considered. The relations between the link lengths and σ_x and/or $\triangle \psi$ in each case are shown in Table 10.1. It can be seen that, for a wobble-plate, the only link length that can freely be assigned is $a = \sigma_x = \triangle \psi/2$. In the case of a spherical central slider–crank, a is determined by $\triangle \psi$ and c is determined by both $\triangle \psi$ and σ_x. The value λ_1 in these two cases vanishes identically, thus causing not only an attenuation of the portion of the cosine series contributed by the function G_ϕ (equation (10.18)), but also a reduction of the maximum pressure angle σ_x (equation (10.30)). Expressions for a_m, b_m and c_m are also listed. The value of c_m serves as an indication of the magnitude of the amplitude of the mth harmonic of the output angle.
Example: Assume $\sigma_x = 30°$ as a reasonable maximum pressure angle in both cases. This determines the amplitude c_m's of the wobble-plate, as shown in the lower portion of Table 10.1. For the central slider–crank, a further parameter $\triangle \psi$ is needed. For comparison purposes, this is selected as $\triangle \psi = 42.9414°$, the same as the value of $\triangle \psi$ for a plane crank–rocker, which possesses the link proportions $a_p/f_p = 0.26795$ and $b_p/f_p = c_p/f_p = 0.732164$ to satisfy the conditions $b_p = c_p$ and $2b_p^2 = 1 + a_p^2$ (to ensure that $|90° - \mu_{min}| = |\mu_{max} - 90°|$) (Freudenstein & Mohan, 1961). The numerical results reveal, according to (Yang, 1962), the following facts:

    (a) The first harmonic amplitude of the wobble-plate is about 140 per cent and the third and fifth are close to 200 per cent of the corresponding harmonic amplitudes of the plane crank–rocker, but

Table 10.1 *Fourier coefficients of output angle for certain mechanisms*

	Wobble-plate	Spherical central slider–crank	Plane crank–rocker
a	σ_x	$\triangle\psi/2$	
b	$\pi/2$	$\pi/2$	
c	$\pi/2$	$\sin^{-1}\left(\sin\dfrac{\triangle\psi}{2}\middle/\sin\sigma_x\right)$	
f	$\pi/2$	$\pi/2$	
σ_x	a	$\sin^{-1}\dfrac{\sin a}{\sin c}$	
$\triangle\psi$	$2\sigma_x$	$2a$	
a_0	$\pi/2$	eqn (10.14)	
a_m	0	eqn (10.26), $(m=\text{even})$ $0, (m=\text{odd})$	
b_m	$0, (m=\text{even})$ $\dfrac{2}{m}\left(\tan\dfrac{\sigma_x}{2}\right)^m, (m=\text{odd})$	$0, (m=\text{even})$ $\dfrac{2}{m}\left(\tan\dfrac{\triangle\psi}{4}\right)^m,$ $(m=\text{odd})$	
c_m	$0, (m=\text{even})$ $\dfrac{2}{m}\left(\tan\dfrac{\sigma_x}{2}\right)^m, (m=\text{odd})$	$|a_m|, (m=\text{even})$ $|b_m|, (m=\text{odd})$	
Examples	$\sigma_x=30°$	$\sigma_x=30°$ $\triangle\psi=42.9414°$	$\sigma_x=30°$ $\triangle\psi=42.9414°$
Link lengths	$a=30°$	$a=21.4707°$ $c=47.0586°$	$f_p=1$ $a_p=0.26795$ $b_p=c_p=0.732164$
c_1	0.535898	0.379182	0.372423
c_2	0	0.035874	0.035898
c_3	0.012825	0.004543	0.007071
c_4	0	0.001288	0.001289
c_5	0.000552	0.000098	0.000292
c_6	0	0.000054	0.000062

the range of the former is 60°, in comparison with the range of 42.9° of the latter.

(*b*) The first and second harmonic amplitudes of the spherical central slider–crank and those of the plane crank–rocker are very close. However, the third harmonic amplitude of the former is significantly lower than that of the latter.

From the foregoing it seems that, from the point of view of harmonic analysis, no discriminative preference can yet be decided between a wobble-plate and a plane crank–rocker. However, as far as maximum pressure angle and range of output angle are concerned, it seems that the spherical central slider–crank is favoured for high speed applications.

(6) The Hooke's universal joint
For a Hooke's universal joint, the above equations cannot be applied directly, because the function ψ_s, which changes from π to $-\pi$, should be treated as a discontinuous function of ϕ over the range $0 \leqslant \phi = 2\pi$. The Fourier coefficients b_m have to be found by piecewise integration. In the next section, we shall see how these coefficients can be obtained in an alternative way (see equation (10.35)).

10.2   Harmonic analysis of the velocity ratio of special spherical four-bar linkages

According to the works of Meyer zur Capellen and his coworkers, the Fourier coefficients of the velocity ratio of some special spherical four-bars can be derived in a rather easy way, as will be shown in the following.

10.2.1   *The Hooke's universal joint (Meyer zur Capellen, 1958a)*

It has been shown in equations (2.81), (2.96) and (2.97) that the velocity ratio of a Hooke's universal joint is

$$\psi' = \frac{C_f}{1 - S_f^2 C_\phi^2} \qquad [(2.81)]$$

$$= \frac{1 - \lambda_p^2}{1 - 2\lambda_p \cos 2\phi + \lambda_p^2} = 1 - 2i_p \qquad [(2.96)], [(2.97)]$$

where λ_p is the bar ratio of the plane indicatrix, a plane oscillating cylinder, of the Hooke's universal joint, as defined in equation (2.95), $\lambda_p = (1 - C_f)/(1 + C_f) = \tan^2(f/2)$, and i_p is the velocity ratio of this plane oscillating cylinder as given in equation (2.93), i.e.

$$i_p = -\frac{\lambda_p(\cos \theta_p - \lambda_p)}{1 - 2\lambda_p \cos \theta_p + \lambda_p^2} \qquad [(2.93)]$$

Now the Fourier series expansion of a function of the form (2.93) is readily available, or

$$i_p = -\lambda_p(\cos \theta_p + \lambda_p \cos 2\theta_p + \lambda_p^2 \cos 3\theta_p + \cdots) \qquad (10.32)$$

Therefore

$$\psi' = \frac{C_f}{1 - S_f^2 C_\phi^2} = 1 + 2\lambda_p \cos 2\phi + 2\lambda_p^2 \cos 4\phi + 2\lambda_p^3 \cos 6\phi + \cdots \qquad (10.33)$$

Equation (10.33) can be verified numerically by assuming, for instance, $\phi = 180°$, and checking that the slope of the $\psi-\phi$ curve as shown in Fig. 2.32 is slightly greater than 1.

Integrating equation (10.33) with respect to ϕ gives

$$\psi = (\phi - 90°) + \lambda_p \sin 2\phi + \tfrac{1}{2}\lambda_p^2 \sin 4\phi + \tfrac{1}{3}\lambda_p^3 \sin 6\phi + \cdots \tag{10.34}$$

Expanding ϕ into a Fourier series, equation (10.34) can then be written as

$$\psi = -90° + 2\sin\phi + \tfrac{2}{3}\sin 3\phi + \tfrac{2}{5}\sin 5\phi + \cdots$$
$$+ (\lambda_p - 1)\sin 2\phi + \left(\frac{\lambda_p^2}{2} - \frac{1}{2}\right)\sin 4\phi + \left(\frac{\lambda_p^3}{3} - \frac{1}{3}\right)\sin 6\phi + \cdots \tag{10.35}$$

Differentiating equation (10.33) with respect to ϕ gives

$$\psi'' = -2(2\lambda_p \cos 2\phi + 4\lambda_p^2 \sin 4\phi + 6\lambda_p^3 \sin 6\phi + \cdots)$$

10.2.2   The wobble-plate (Meyer zur Capellen, 1958a)

The velocity ratio of a wobble-plate has been given in equation (2.54), and is, noting that in Fig. 2.13 $\phi = 90° + \theta$,

$$\psi' = -\frac{S_a C_\phi C_a}{1 - S_a^2 C_\phi^2} \tag{10.36}$$

Using equation (10.33) as a formula, we can expand equation (10.36) into

$$\psi' = -S_a C_\phi (1 + 2\lambda_p' \cos 2\phi + 2\lambda_p'^2 \cos 4\phi + 2\lambda_p'^3 \cos 6\phi + \cdots) \tag{10.37}$$

where $\lambda_p' = (1 - C_a)/(1 + C_a) = \tan^2(a/2)$. Using also the recursion formula

$$2\cos\phi \cos 2n\phi = \cos(2n + 1)\phi + \cos(2n - 1)\phi$$

we obtain the following Fourier series for ψ':

$$\psi' = -2(\eta \cos\phi + \eta^3 \cos 3\phi + \eta^5 \cos 5\phi + \cdots) \tag{10.38}$$

where $\eta = \sqrt{\lambda_p'} = \tan(a/2)$. Integrating equation (10.38) gives

$$\psi = 180° - 2(\eta \sin\phi + \tfrac{1}{3}\eta^3 \sin 3\phi + \tfrac{1}{5}\eta^5 \sin 5\phi + \cdots) \tag{10.39}$$

The Fourier series for the part $\psi_s + \psi_u$ in equation (10.39) is exactly the same as that derived by (Yang, 1962) (see Table 10.1).

Differentiating equation (10.38) with respect to ϕ gives

$$\psi'' = 2(\eta \sin\phi + 3\eta^3 \sin 3\phi + 5\eta^5 \sin 5\phi + \cdots)$$

An alternative method of finding the Fourier coefficients of the velocity ratio of a spherical central slider–crank through repeatedly using equation (10.38) can be read in (Meyer zur Capellen & Rath, 1960).

10.3   Harmonic analysis of rotation energy of a spherical central oscillating cylinder or a spherical central Whitworth mechanism

As a final item of the harmonic analysis, we shall study the work of Meyer zur Capellen and Thünker on the harmonic analysis of the rotation energy of certain spherical mechanisms (Meyer zur Capellen & Thünker, 1975a, b). The basic idea of this investigation is to consider the output angle of a spherical central oscillating cylinder as a superposition of the output angles of two plane oscillating cylinders, hence the velocity ratio is a superposition of the velocity ratios of the two corresponding plane linkages. Since the rotation energy of the spherical linkage can be expressed in terms of the square of the velocity ratio, and the Fourier coefficients of the velocity ratio of a plane oscillating cylinder are well known and simple, therefore the Fourier coefficients of the rotation energy of the spherical oscillating cylinder can be obtained in closed forms. A similar procedure applies to the spherical central Whitworth mechanism.

10.3.1   Spherical central oscillating cylinder

A typical such linkage was shown in Fig. 9.18. The output angle is $\psi = 90° - \psi_s$, hence, as usual, the angle ψ_s may sometimes be taken as the output angle instead of ψ. It was given in equation (2.61) that

$$\tan \psi_s = \frac{\mu S_\phi}{1 - \nu C_\phi} \qquad [(2.61)]$$

with $\mu = \tan a/\sin f$ and $\nu = \tan a/\tan f$ as defined in equations (2.62) and (2.63). Let ψ_s be the sum of two angles ψ_{s1} and ψ_{s2}:

$$\psi_s = \psi_{s1} + \psi_{s2} \qquad (10.40)$$

Fig. 10.1. Sum of output angles of two plane linkages $\psi_{s1} + \psi_{s2} = \psi_s$.

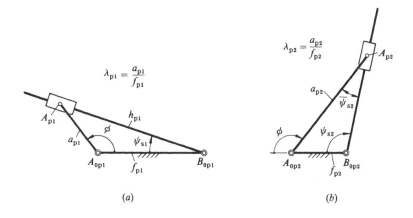

(a)   (b)

where ψ_{s1} and ψ_{s2} are the output angles of two plane oscillating cylinders with bar ratios λ_{p1} and λ_{p2} respectively. A typical plane oscillating cylinder was shown in Fig. 2.38. It is well known that

$$\tan \psi_{s1} = \frac{\lambda_{p1} S_\phi}{1 - \lambda_{p1} C_\phi} \quad \text{and} \quad \tan \psi_{s2} = \frac{\lambda_{p2} S_\phi}{1 + \lambda_{p2} C_\phi} \tag{10.41}$$

provided that the input angles ϕ of the two plane linkages are arranged as shown in Figs. 10.1(a) and (b), with ϕ counted in opposite senses. Note that the input angle ϕ in equations (2.61) and (10.41) remains the same. Substituting equations (10.41) into the trigonometric identity

$$\tan \psi_s = \frac{\tan \psi_{s1} + \tan \psi_{s2}}{1 - \tan \psi_{s1} \tan \psi_{s2}}$$

and solving for λ_{p1} and λ_{p2}, we get

$$\left.\begin{array}{l} \lambda_{p1} = \tan\dfrac{a}{2}\tan\dfrac{f}{2} \\[2ex] \lambda_{p2} = \tan\dfrac{a}{2}\bigg/ \tan\dfrac{f}{2} \end{array}\right\} \tag{10.42}$$

The kinematic meaning of equations (10.42) is this: In the original spherical oscillating cylinder, there are two independent parameters a and f. These two parameters are transferred to the two independent bar ratios λ_{p1} and λ_{p2}, each belonging to an individual plane oscillating cylinder.

The velocity ratio is now, from equation (10.40),

$$\psi_s' = \psi_{s1}' + \psi_{s2}' \tag{10.43}$$

In the spherical oscillating cylinder, let the moment of inertia of the link a with respect to the axis OA_0 be denoted by Θ_a, and that of link b with respect to the axis OB_0 by Θ_b. Furthermore, it is assumed that the moment of inertia of the coupler c is negligible. The constructive form of the linkage should be somewhat like that shown in Fig. 2.15(b), rather than Fig. 2.15(c). The total rotation energy is then

$$E = \tfrac{1}{2}(\Theta_a \omega_{af}^2 + \Theta_b \omega_{bf}^2) = \frac{\omega_{af}^2}{2}(\Theta_a + \psi_s'^2 \Theta_b) \tag{10.44}$$

In equation (10.44), the only variable is $\psi_s'^2$. In other words, the kinetic energy depends only on $\psi_s'^2$. The harmonic analysis of the rotation energy is therefore reduced to that of $\psi_s'^2$ only. Squaring both sides of equation (10.43) results in

$$\psi_s'^2 = \psi_{s1}'^2 + \psi_{s2}'^2 + 2\psi_{s1}'\psi_{s2}' \tag{10.45}$$

The problem is therefore reduced to finding the Fourier coefficients of the three terms $\psi_{s1}'^2, \psi_{s2}'^2$ and $2\psi_{s1}'\psi_{s2}'$.

(1) The parts $\psi_{s1}'^2$ and $\psi_{s2}'^2$

The velocity ratio ψ_{s1}' (or ψ_{s2}') is a function of ϕ and λ_{p1} (or λ_{p2}), and is

$$\psi_{s1}' = \frac{\lambda_{p1}(\cos\phi - \lambda_{p1})}{1 - 2\lambda_{p1}\cos\phi + \lambda_{p1}^2}, \quad \text{(or)} \quad \psi_{s2}' = \frac{\lambda_{p2}(\cos\phi + \lambda_{p2})}{1 + 2\lambda_{p2}\cos\phi + \lambda_{p2}^2}$$

$$(10.46)$$

Consider first ψ_{s1}' only. Referring to Fig. 10.1(a), let the origin point of a complex coordinate system be taken at A_0, and $A_0B_0 = f_{p1}$ be the positive direction of the real axis. We then have

$$h_{p1}\,e^{-i\psi_{s1}} = f_{p1} - a_{p1}\,e^{i\phi}$$

or

$$\left(\frac{h_{p1}}{f_{p1}}\right)e^{-i\psi_{s1}} = 1 - \lambda_{p1}\,e^{i\phi} \tag{10.47}$$

where a_{p1} is the length of the crank of the plane oscillating cylinder shown in Fig. 10.1(a), and h_{p1} is the magnitude of the length $A_{p1}B_{0p1}$. Taking logarithms of both sides of equation (10.47) yields

$$\ln Q - i\psi_{s1} = \ln(1 - \lambda_{p1}\,e^{i\phi}) \tag{10.48}$$

where $Q = h_{p1}/f_{p1}$. Differentiating equation (10.48) with respect to ϕ, we get

$$\frac{Q'}{Q} - i\psi_{s1}' = \frac{-i\lambda_{p1}\,e^{i\phi}}{1 - \lambda_{p1}\,e^{i\phi}} \tag{10.49}$$

where $Q' = dQ/d\phi$. Expanding the factor $(1 - \lambda_{p1}\,e^{i\phi})^{-1}$ into a power series, which is justified for $\lambda_{p1} < 1$, and separating real and imaginary parts, we can rewrite equation (10.49) in the following forms:

$$\psi_{s1}' = \lambda_{p1}\cos\phi + \lambda_{p1}^2\cos 2\phi + \lambda_{p1}^3\cos 3\phi + \cdots \tag{10.50}$$

and

$$\frac{Q'}{Q} = \lambda_{p1}\sin\phi + \lambda_{p1}^2\sin 2\phi + \lambda_{p1}^3\sin 3\phi + \cdots \tag{10.51}$$

Note that equation (10.50) is identical with equation (10.32), where a counterclockwise sense of rotation was considered as positive.

Similarly we have

$$\psi_{s2}' = \lambda_{p2}\cos\phi - \lambda_{p2}^2\cos 2\phi + \lambda_{p2}^3\cos 3\phi - \cdots \tag{10.52}$$

Let $N = 1 - 2\lambda_{p1}\cos\phi + \lambda_{p1}^2$, which is the denominator of the expression for ψ_{s1}' in equations (10.46). It can be seen that $N = (h_{p1}/f_{p1})^2 = Q^2$. Hence

$$\frac{Q'}{Q} = \frac{\lambda_{p1}\sin\phi}{N} = \lambda_{p1}\sin\phi + \lambda_{p1}^2\sin 2\phi + \lambda_{p1}^3\sin 3\phi + \cdots \tag{10.53}$$

Differentiating equation (10.53) with respect to ϕ, we get

$$\lambda_{p1}\frac{(1+\lambda_{p1}^2)\cos\phi - 2\lambda_{p1}}{N^2} = \lambda_{p1}\cos\phi + 2\lambda_{p1}^2\cos 2\phi$$

$$+ 3\lambda_{p1}^3\cos 3\phi + \cdots \qquad (10.54)$$

Squaring the expression for ψ_{s1}' in equation (10.46), it can be shown that

$$\psi_{s1}'^2 = \frac{1}{4}\left[1 + \left(\frac{1+\lambda_{p1}^2}{1-\lambda_{p1}^2} - 2\right)(1+2\psi_{s1}') + 2\lambda_{p1}\frac{(1+\lambda_{p1}^2)\cos\phi - 2\lambda_{p1}}{N^2}\right]$$

$$(10.55)$$

or, by substituting equations (10.50) and (10.54) into equation (10.55),

$$\psi_{s1}'^2 = A_0 + \sum_{m=1}^{\infty} A_m\cos m\phi$$

where

$$A_0 = \frac{\lambda_{p1}^2}{2(1-\lambda_{p1}^2)}$$

$$A_m = \frac{\lambda_{p1}^m}{2}\left(m - \frac{1-3\lambda_{p1}^2}{1-\lambda_{p1}^2}\right)$$

Similarly it can be shown that the Fourier series expansion of $\psi_{s2}'^2$ is

$$\psi_{s2}'^2 = G_0 + \sum_{m=1}^{\infty} G_m\cos m\phi$$

where

$$\left. \begin{array}{l} G_0 = \dfrac{\lambda_{p2}^2}{2(1-\lambda_{p2}^2)} \\[3mm] G_m = \dfrac{(-1)^m}{2}\lambda_{p2}^m\left(m - \dfrac{1-3\lambda_{p2}^2}{1-\lambda_{p2}^2}\right) \end{array} \right\} \qquad (10.56)$$

(2) The part $2\psi_{s1}'\psi_{s2}'$

It can be shown that the following identity is valid:

$$2\psi_{s1}'\psi_{s2}' = \frac{\lambda_{p1}\lambda_{p2}}{1+\lambda_{p1}\lambda_{p2}} + \frac{1}{(\lambda_{p1}+\lambda_{p2})(1+\lambda_{p1}\lambda_{p2})}$$

$$\cdot[\lambda_{p2}(1+2\lambda_{p1}\lambda_{p2}+\lambda_{p1}^2)\psi_{s1}' - \lambda_{p1}(1+2\lambda_{p1}\lambda_{p2}+\lambda_{p2}^2)\psi_{s2}'] \quad (10.57)$$

Equation (10.57) shows that the term $2\psi_{s1}'\psi_{s2}'$ contains only linear terms of ψ_{s1}' and ψ_{s2}', and can therefore be expanded into a Fourier series, by substituting equations (10.50) and (10.52).

10.3.2   Spherical central Whitworth mechanism

In this case, $a > f$. While λ_{p1} remains smaller than 1, λ_{p2} is greater than 1. The Fourier coefficients involving ψ_{s2}' derived in last section are no longer valid. However, we may write

$$\psi'_{s2} = \frac{\lambda_{p2}(\cos\phi + \lambda_{p2})}{1 + 2\lambda_{p2}\cos\phi + \lambda_{p2}^2}$$

$$= 1 - \frac{\bar{\lambda}_{p2}(\cos\phi + \bar{\lambda}_{p2})}{1 + 2\bar{\lambda}_{p2}\cos\phi + \bar{\lambda}_{p2}^2} = 1 - \bar{\psi}'_{s2} \qquad (10.58)$$

where the angle $\bar{\psi}_{s2} = \measuredangle\, B_0 A A_0$ as shown in Fig. 10.1(b), and $\bar{\lambda}_{p2} = 1/\lambda_{p2} = \tan(f/2)/\tan(a/2) < 1$. Using equation (10.52) as a formula, we obtain

$$\psi'_{s2} = 1 - \bar{\lambda}_{p2}\cos\phi + \bar{\lambda}_{p2}^2\cos 2\phi - \bar{\lambda}_{p2}^3\cos 3\phi + \cdots \qquad (10.59)$$

(1) The part ψ'^2_{s2}

We now have

$$\psi'^2_{s2} = (1 - \bar{\psi}'_{s2})^2 = 1 - 2\bar{\psi}'_{s2} + \bar{\psi}'^2_{s2} \qquad (10.60)$$

In equation (10.60) the Fourier coefficients of $\bar{\psi}'_{s2}$ and $\bar{\psi}'^2_{s2}$ can be obtained, according to equations (10.52) and (10.56), simply by replacing λ_{p2} by $\bar{\lambda}_{p2}$. The result is

$$\psi'^2_{s2} = L_0 + \sum_{m=1}^{\infty} L_m \cos m\phi$$

where

$$L_0 = \frac{2 - \bar{\lambda}_{p2}^2}{2(1 - \bar{\lambda}_{p2}^2)}$$

$$L_m = \frac{(-1)^m}{2}\,\bar{\lambda}_{p2}^m\left(m + \frac{3 - \bar{\lambda}_{p2}^2}{1 - \bar{\lambda}_{p2}^2}\right)$$

(2) The part $2\psi'_{s1}\psi'_{s2}$

We now have

$$2\psi'_{s1}\psi'_{s2} = 2\psi'_{s1} - 2\psi'_{s1}\bar{\psi}'_{s2} \qquad (10.61)$$

The term $2\psi'_{s1}\bar{\psi}'_{s2}$ in equation (10.61) can be obtained from equation (10.57) by replacing λ_{p2} by $\bar{\lambda}_{p2}$. The result is

$$2\psi'_{s1}\psi'_{s2} = -\frac{\lambda_{p1}\bar{\lambda}_{p2}}{1 + \lambda_{p1}\bar{\lambda}_{p2}} + \frac{1}{(\lambda_{p1} + \bar{\lambda}_{p2})(1 + \lambda_{p1}\bar{\lambda}_{p2})}$$

$$\cdot\{[2\lambda_{p1} + \bar{\lambda}_{p2}(1 + \lambda_{p1}^2)]\psi'_{s1} + \lambda_{p1}(1 + 2\lambda_{p1}\bar{\lambda}_{p2} + \bar{\lambda}_{p2}^2)\psi'_{s2}\}$$

APPENDIX 1

Spherical trigonometry

A1.1 Fundamental equations of a right spherical triangle – Napier's rules

A spherical triangle may have one, two or three right angles. Since spherical triangles having two or three right angles can be solved by inspection, we shall be concerned only with right spherical triangles having one right angle.

Fig. A1.1 shows a right spherical triangle. The right angle is denoted by C, and the other two angles by A and B. The three sides opposite to A, B, C are denoted by a, b, c respectively. Deleting the right angle C, we have the five

Fig. A1.1. Right spherical triangle.

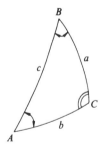

Fig. A1.2.

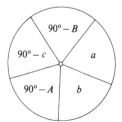

quantities A, b, a, B, c around the right triangle. Arranging the five parts in a circular form, but replacing the three quantities A, c, B by their respective complementary parts as shown in Fig. A1.2, the two Napier's rules are:

(1) The sine of any middle part is equal to the product of the cosines of the opposite parts.
(2) The sine of any middle part is equal to the product of the tangents of the adjacent parts.

According to Napier's rule (1) we have:

$$\left. \begin{array}{l} \sin a = \sin c \sin A \\ \sin b = \sin c \sin B \end{array} \right\} \tag{A1.1}$$

$$\cos c = \cos a \cos b \tag{A1.2}$$

$$\left. \begin{array}{l} \cos A = \cos a \sin B \\ \cos B = \cos b \sin A \end{array} \right\} \tag{A1.3}$$

and according to Napier's rule (2) we have:

$$\left. \begin{array}{l} \tan B \sin a = \tan b \\ \tan A \sin b = \tan a \end{array} \right\} \tag{A1.4}$$

$$\left. \begin{array}{l} \tan A \cos c = \cot B \\ \tan B \cos c = \cot A \end{array} \right\} \tag{A1.5}$$

$$\left. \begin{array}{l} \tan c \cos A = \tan b \\ \tan c \cos B = \tan a \end{array} \right\} \tag{A1.6}$$

A1.2 Fundamental equations of a general spherical triangle

Fig. A1.3 shows a general spherical triangle, with the three angles denoted by A, B, C, and the three respective opposite sides by a, b, c. The three heights are denoted by h_a, h_b, h_c.

Fig. A1.3. General spherical triangle.

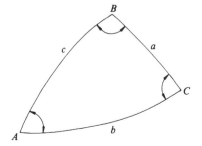

The sine law:

$$\frac{\sin A}{\sin a} = \frac{\sin B}{\sin b} = \frac{\sin C}{\sin c} = \frac{\bar{s}}{\sin a \sin b \sin c} \tag{A1.7}$$

where

$$\bar{s} = \sin a \sin h_a = \sin b \sin h_b = \sin c \sin h_c \tag{A1.8}$$

The cosine law for sides:

$$\cos a = \cos b \cos c + \sin b \sin c \cos A \tag{A1.9}$$

The cosine law for angles:

$$\cos A = -\cos B \cos C + \sin B \sin C \cos a \tag{A1.10}$$

The cotangent law including four successive parts a, C, b, A:

$$\cos b \cos C = \sin b \cot a - \sin C \cot A \tag{A1.11}$$

The two laws including five successive parts b, A, c, B, a, and B, a, C, b, A:

$$\sin b \cos c \cos A = \sin c \cos b - \sin a \cos B \tag{A1.12}$$

$$\sin B \cos C \cos a = -\sin C \cos B + \sin A \cos b \tag{A1.13}$$

The four Napier's analogies:

$$\frac{\sin \frac{1}{2}(A - B)}{\sin \frac{1}{2}(A + B)} = \frac{\tan \frac{1}{2}(a - b)}{\tan \frac{1}{2}c} \tag{A1.14}$$

$$\frac{\cos \frac{1}{2}(A - B)}{\cos \frac{1}{2}(A + B)} = \frac{\tan \frac{1}{2}(a + b)}{\tan \frac{1}{2}c} \tag{A1.15}$$

$$\frac{\sin \frac{1}{2}(a - b)}{\sin \frac{1}{2}(a + b)} = \frac{\tan \frac{1}{2}(A - B)}{\cot \frac{1}{2}C} \tag{A1.16}$$

$$\frac{\cos \frac{1}{2}(a - b)}{\cos \frac{1}{2}(a + b)} = \frac{\tan \frac{1}{2}(A + B)}{\cot \frac{1}{2}C} \tag{A1.17}$$

A1.3   Equations of a spherical ellipse

A spherical ellipse may be defined as the locus of a point, on the unit sphere, the sum of whose spherical distances from two foci F and F' remains a constant. If this constant sum is $2a_s$, and the spherical distance FF' is $2e_s$, the equation of the spherical ellipse in a position as shown in Fig. A1.4, where the end of the spherical major axis is on the x-axis and the major axis lies on the xy-plane, is

$$2\cos 2a_s(\cos 2a_s - \cos 2e_s)y^2 - \sin^2 2a_s z^2$$
$$- 2\sin 2a_s(\cos 2a_s - \cos 2e_s)xy = 0 \tag{A1.18}$$

The spherical major axis is $2a_s$. If the spherical minor axis is $2b_s$, then because of equation (A1.2), $\cos a_s = \cos b_s \cos e_s$, equation (A1.18) becomes

$$\cos 2a_s \sin^2 b_s y^2 + \sin^2 a_s \cos^2 b_s z^2 - \sin 2a_s \sin^2 b_s xy = 0 \tag{A1.19}$$

In the special case that the spherical major axis $2a_s$ subtends constantly a right angle at any point on the ellipse, the equation of the spherical ellipse is simplified, because $\cos 2e_s = (1 + \cos^2 2a_s)/(2\cos 2a_s)$, to

$$y^2 + z^2 - \tan 2a_s \cdot xy = 0 \qquad (A1.20)$$

Such a spherical ellipse may be called, by analogy with plane geometry, a Thales ellipse. If the coordinates (x, y, z) are transformed into spherical polar coordinates (p, θ) by means of equations (A4.3), the Thales ellipse is represented by

$$\tan p = \tan 2a_s \cos \theta \qquad (A1.21)$$

Equation (A1.21) can easily be conceived by considering the spherical triangle $\triangle ABC$ as shown in Fig. A1.1. If AB is kept fixed, the locus of C is a Thales ellipse, as either one of equations (A1.6) is identical with equation (A1.21).

The gnomonic projection of a Thales ellipse onto a plane tangent to the sphere at the end of the major axis is a circle with diameter $\tan 2a_s$.

It is to be noted that the equation of a spherical ellipse is identical with that of a spherical hyperbola. This is because if a spherical ellipse, Fig. A1.4, is viewed in a direction normal to the plane QOz, the two ellipses, the original one and its antipode, will appear as a spherical hyperbola.

Fig. A1.4. Spherical ellipse.

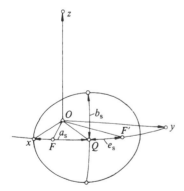

APPENDIX 2

Fundamentals of matrix algebra

A2.1 Rotation of a coordinate system

Consider first a vector $\mathbf{r}$ lying in the $y_1 z_1$-plane of a right-handed reference coordinate system $x_1 y_1 z_1$, Fig. A2.1. The vector $\mathbf{r}$ is thus represented by its three components along the x_1, y_1 and z_1 axes in terms of the respective unit vectors $\mathbf{i}_1, \mathbf{j}_1, \mathbf{k}_1$ as follows:

$$\mathbf{r} = 0\mathbf{j}_1 + y_1\mathbf{j}_1 + z_1\mathbf{k}_1 = \begin{bmatrix} 0 \\ y_1 \\ z_1 \end{bmatrix} \begin{matrix} (\mathbf{i}_1) \\ (\mathbf{j}_1) \\ (\mathbf{k}_1) \end{matrix} \tag{A2.1}$$

Suppose the whole coordinate system is rotated about its x_1-axis through a positive angle α, to reach the position of a second coordinate system $x_a y_a z_a$. The same vector $\mathbf{r}$ is then represented in the $x_a y_a z_a$-system of unit vectors

Fig. A2.1. Rotation of coordinate system.

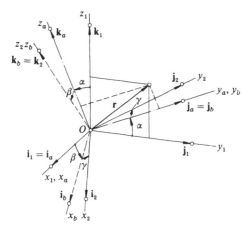

$\mathbf{i}_a, \mathbf{j}_a, \mathbf{k}_a$, and we have

$$\mathbf{r} = 0\mathbf{i}_a + y_a\mathbf{j}_a + z_a\mathbf{k}_a = \begin{bmatrix} 0 \\ y_a \\ z_a \end{bmatrix} \begin{matrix} (\mathbf{i}_a) \\ (\mathbf{j}_a) \\ (\mathbf{k}_a) \end{matrix} \tag{A2.2}$$

The relations between the coordinates x_a, y_a, z_a and x_1, y_1, z_1 are the following system of linear equations:

$$\left. \begin{matrix} x_a = 1 \cdot x_1 + \quad 0 \cdot y_1 + \quad 0 \cdot z_1 \\ y_a = 0 \cdot x_1 + \cos \alpha \cdot y_1 + \sin \alpha \cdot z_1 \\ z_a = 0 \cdot x_1 - \sin \alpha \cdot y_1 + \cos \alpha \cdot z_1 \end{matrix} \right\} \tag{A2.3}$$

Equations (A2.3) represent a case of general rotation of the $x_1 y_1 z_1$-system about the x_1-axis, in which the vector $\mathbf{r}$ may have a finite x_1-component which remains unchanged by the rotation. Equation (A2.3) may be written in a matrix form as follows:

$$\begin{bmatrix} x_a \\ y_a \\ z_a \end{bmatrix} = \begin{bmatrix} 1 & 0 & 0 \\ 0 & \cos \alpha & \sin \alpha \\ 0 & -\sin \alpha & \cos \alpha \end{bmatrix} \begin{bmatrix} x_1 \\ y_1 \\ z_1 \end{bmatrix} \tag{A2.4}$$

or, symbolically,

$$\begin{bmatrix} x_a \\ y_a \\ z_a \end{bmatrix} = \mathbb{X}_\alpha \begin{bmatrix} x_1 \\ y_1 \\ z_1 \end{bmatrix} \tag{A2.5}$$

The vector components (x_a, y_a, z_a) and (x_1, y_1, z_1) are considered as column matrices and

$$\mathbb{X}_\alpha = \begin{bmatrix} 1 & 0 & 0 \\ 0 & \cos \alpha & \sin \alpha \\ 0 & -\sin \alpha & \cos \alpha \end{bmatrix} \tag{A2.6}$$

is the 3×3 coordinate transformation matrix of the $x_1 y_1 z_1$-system about the x_1-axis. Equation (A2.5) implies that applying the matrix $\mathbb{X}_\alpha$ to the column

matrix $\begin{bmatrix} x_1 \\ y_1 \\ z_1 \end{bmatrix}$ transforms it into $\begin{bmatrix} x_a \\ y_a \\ z_a \end{bmatrix}$.

The application of one matrix upon another matrix follows the same rule as that for the multiplication of determinants.

If the $x_a y_a z_a$-system is further rotated about the y_a-axis through a positive angle β, to reach a coordinate system $x_b y_b z_b$, with unit vectors $\mathbf{i}_b, \mathbf{j}_b, \mathbf{k}_b$, the same vector $\mathbf{r}$ is then represented in the $x_b y_b z_b$-system as

$$\mathbf{r} = x_b\mathbf{i}_b + y_b\mathbf{j}_b + z_b\mathbf{k}_b = \begin{bmatrix} x_b \\ y_b \\ z_b \end{bmatrix} \begin{matrix} (\mathbf{i}_b) \\ (\mathbf{j}_b) \\ (\mathbf{k}_b) \end{matrix}$$

and we have

$$\begin{bmatrix} x_b \\ y_b \\ z_b \end{bmatrix} = \mathbb{Y}_\beta \begin{bmatrix} x_a \\ y_a \\ z_a \end{bmatrix} \tag{A2.7}$$

where the transformation matrix

$$\mathbb{Y}_\beta = \begin{bmatrix} \cos\beta & 0 & -\sin\beta \\ 0 & 1 & 0 \\ \sin\beta & 0 & \cos\beta \end{bmatrix} \tag{A2.8}$$

Still further rotation of the $x_b y_b z_b$ coordinate system about the z_b-axis through a positive angle γ brings it to a coordinate system $x_2 y_2 z_2$, with unit vectors i_2, j_2, k_2. The same vector r is represented in the $x_2 y_2 z_2$-system as

$$r = x_2 i_2 + y_2 j_2 + z_2 k_2 = \begin{bmatrix} x_2 \\ y_2 \\ z_2 \end{bmatrix} \begin{matrix} (i_2) \\ (j_2) \\ (k_2) \end{matrix}$$

and we have

$$\begin{bmatrix} x_2 \\ y_2 \\ z_2 \end{bmatrix} = \mathbb{Z}_\gamma \begin{bmatrix} x_b \\ y_b \\ z_b \end{bmatrix} \tag{A2.9}$$

where the transformation matrix

$$\mathbb{Z}_\gamma = \begin{bmatrix} \cos\gamma & \sin\gamma & 0 \\ -\sin\gamma & \cos\gamma & 0 \\ 0 & 0 & 1 \end{bmatrix} \tag{A2.10}$$

Combining equations (A2.9), (A2.7) and (A2.5) we may write

$$\begin{bmatrix} x_2 \\ y_2 \\ z_2 \end{bmatrix} = \mathbb{Z}_\gamma \mathbb{Y}_\beta \mathbb{X}_\alpha \begin{bmatrix} x_1 \\ y_1 \\ z_1 \end{bmatrix} = \mathbb{M}_{12} \begin{bmatrix} x_1 \\ y_1 \\ z_1 \end{bmatrix}$$

where $\mathbb{M}_{12}$ is the resultant transformation matrix of all three rotations, and

$$\mathbb{M}_{12} = \mathbb{Z}_\gamma \mathbb{Y}_\beta \mathbb{X}_\alpha = \begin{bmatrix} C_\beta C_\gamma & C_\alpha S_\gamma + S_\alpha S_\beta C_\gamma & S_\alpha S_\gamma - C_\alpha S_\beta C_\gamma \\ -C_\beta S_\gamma & C_\alpha C_\gamma - S_\alpha S_\beta S_\gamma & S_\alpha C_\gamma + C_\alpha S_\beta S_\gamma \\ S_\beta & -S_\alpha C_\beta & C_\alpha C_\beta \end{bmatrix} \tag{A2.11}$$

with the abbreviations $S_\alpha = \sin\alpha$, $C_\alpha = \cos\alpha$, etc.

The multiplication of matrices is associative, e.g.

$$\mathbb{Z}_\gamma \mathbb{Y}_\beta \mathbb{X}_\alpha = \mathbb{Z}_\gamma (\mathbb{Y}_\beta \mathbb{X}_\alpha) = (\mathbb{Z}_\gamma \mathbb{Y}_\beta) \mathbb{X}_\alpha \tag{A2.12}$$

The multiplication of matrices is, in general, not commutative, e.g.

$$\mathbb{Y}_\beta \mathbb{X}_\alpha \neq \mathbb{X}_\alpha \mathbb{Y}_\beta \tag{A2.13}$$

Fig. A2.2. Eulerian angles.

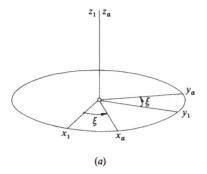

(a)

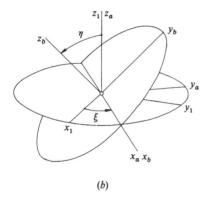

(b)

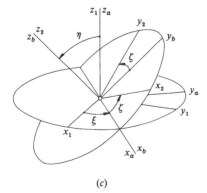

(c)

A2.2   Eulerian angles

The rotation of a coordinate system with a fixed origin from its initial position $x_1 y_1 z_1$ to an arbitrary final position $x_2 y_2 z_2$ can be considered as three rotations through the so-called Eulerian angles $\xi, \eta, \zeta,$[†] as shown in Figs. A2.2(a), (b), (c). Here the three transformation matrices are:

$$\mathbb{Z}_\xi = \begin{bmatrix} \cos\xi & \sin\xi & 0 \\ -\sin\xi & \cos\xi & 0 \\ 0 & 0 & 1 \end{bmatrix} \tag{A2.14}$$

$$\mathbb{X}_\eta = \begin{bmatrix} 1 & 0 & 0 \\ 0 & \cos\eta & \sin\eta \\ 0 & -\sin\eta & \cos\eta \end{bmatrix} \tag{A2.15}$$

$$\mathbb{Z}_\zeta = \begin{bmatrix} \cos\zeta & \sin\zeta & 0 \\ -\sin\zeta & \cos\zeta & 0 \\ 0 & 0 & 1 \end{bmatrix} \tag{A2.16}$$

The resultant transformation matrix is then

$$\mathbb{M}_{12} = \mathbb{Z}_\zeta \mathbb{X}_\eta \mathbb{Z}_\xi = \begin{bmatrix} m_{11} & m_{12} & m_{13} \\ m_{21} & m_{22} & m_{23} \\ m_{31} & m_{32} & m_{33} \end{bmatrix}$$

$$= \begin{bmatrix} C_\xi C_\zeta - S_\xi C_\eta S_\zeta & S_\xi C_\zeta + C_\xi C_\eta S_\zeta & S_\eta S_\zeta \\ -C_\xi S_\zeta - S_\xi C_\eta C_\zeta & -S_\xi S_\zeta + C_\xi C_\eta C_\zeta & S_\eta C_\zeta \\ S_\xi S_\eta & -C_\xi S_\eta & C_\eta \end{bmatrix} \tag{A2.17}$$

with the abbreviations $S_\xi = \sin\xi$, $C_\xi = \cos\xi$, etc.

A2.3   Orthogonal matrices

All transformation matrices encountered in spherical kinematics and, in particular, the 3×3 transformation matrices appearing in this book, are orthogonal matrices. Observation of any one of the 3×3 transformation matrices, for instance the matrix in equation (A2.14), shows that if each row is considered as three components of a vector, the magnitude of each row vector is unity. Thus

$$(\cos\phi)^2 + (\sin\phi)^2 = 1$$

and

$$(-\sin\phi)^2 + (\cos\phi)^2 = 1$$

The same is true for each column vector, i.e. if each column is considered as three components of a vector, the magnitude of each column is unity. The

---

[†] The conventional notations for Eulerian angles are ϕ, θ, ψ. In order to avoid confusion with the notations used for input and output angles, the present notations are used here instead.

scalar product of two row vectors or of two column vectors is zero. Thus,

$$(\cos\phi)(-\sin\phi) + (\sin\phi)(\cos\phi) = 0$$

hence the name *orthogonal matrix*.

The necessary and sufficient condition that a matrix is orthogonal is that its row vectors, or column vectors, are orthogonal unit vectors. This applies, certainly, to a more complicated matrix such as the matrix in equation (A2.17), which, being the product of a series of orthogonal matrices, is also an orthogonal matrix.

The matrix formed by interchanging the rows and columns of a given matrix is called the transpose of the original matrix. Thus, if a given matrix is

$$\mathbb{A} = \begin{bmatrix} a_{11} & a_{12} & a_{13} \\ a_{21} & a_{22} & a_{23} \\ a_{31} & a_{32} & a_{33} \end{bmatrix} \tag{A2.18}$$

its transpose, denoted as $\mathbf{A}^T$, is

$$\mathbb{A}^T = \begin{bmatrix} a_{11} & a_{21} & a_{31} \\ a_{12} & a_{22} & a_{32} \\ a_{13} & a_{23} & a_{33} \end{bmatrix} \tag{A2.19}$$

Because of the properties of orthogonal matrices, it follows that, when $\mathbb{A}$ is an orthogonal matrix,

$$\mathbb{A}^T\mathbb{A} = \begin{bmatrix} 1 & 0 & 0 \\ 0 & 1 & 0 \\ 0 & 0 & 1 \end{bmatrix} = \mathbb{I} \tag{A2.20}$$

where the matrix in equation (A2.20) is called a unit matrix, and is denoted by $\mathbb{I}$. The transpose of an orthogonal matrix is therefore equal to its reciprocal, denoted by $\mathbb{A}^{-1}$, or

$$\mathbb{A}^T = \mathbb{A}^{-1} \tag{A2.21}$$

A2.4   Single rotation of a body

Suppose in Fig. A2.1 the coordinate system $x_1 y_1 z_1$ is kept fixed, while the vector $\mathbf{r}$ is rotated about the x_1-axis through an angle of $(-\alpha)$, i.e. a clockwise angular displacement α. It appears that equations (A2.3) are valid for the new components x_a, y_a, z_a of $\mathbf{r}$, expressed in the unit vectors $\mathbf{i}_1, \mathbf{j}_1, \mathbf{k}_1$ of the original coordinate system $x_1 y_1 z_1$. On the other hand, if we want to rotate the vector $\mathbf{r}$ about the x_1-axis through a positive angle $(+\alpha)$ to a new position, we simply apply the same matrix in equation (A2.6) to the components of $\mathbf{r}$, but replacing α by $(-\alpha)$, to get the components of the rotated vector.

For the sake of clarity, let us consider a fixed coordinate system xyz, as shown in Fig. A2.3, with its three unit vectors $\mathbf{i}, \mathbf{j}, \mathbf{k}$. A vector $\mathbf{r}_1$ is to be rotated through a positive angle $(+\alpha)$ about the x-axis to reach the position $\mathbf{r}_2$. Both vectors are expressed in their respective components along the xyz-axes, as

$$\mathbf{r}_1 = x_1\mathbf{i} + y_1\mathbf{j} + z_1\mathbf{k} \quad \text{and} \quad \mathbf{r}_2 = x_2\mathbf{i} + y_2\mathbf{j} + z_2\mathbf{k}$$

We then have

$$\begin{bmatrix} x_2 \\ y_2 \\ z_2 \end{bmatrix} = \begin{bmatrix} 1 & 0 & 0 \\ 0 & \cos\alpha & -\sin\alpha \\ 0 & \sin\alpha & \cos\alpha \end{bmatrix} \begin{bmatrix} x_1 \\ y_1 \\ z_1 \end{bmatrix} = \mathbb{X}_{(-\alpha)} \begin{bmatrix} x_1 \\ y_1 \\ z_1 \end{bmatrix} \tag{A2.22}$$

Comparison of equation (A2.22) with equation (A2.6) shows that the matrix $\mathbb{X}_{(-\alpha)}$ is the transpose of $\mathbb{X}_\alpha$, and hence the reciprocal of $\mathbb{X}_\alpha$, i.e.

$$\mathbb{X}_{(-\alpha)} = \mathbb{X}_\alpha^T = \mathbb{X}_\alpha^{-1} \tag{A2.23}$$

Note that, referring to Fig. A2.3, the matrix $\mathbb{X}_\alpha$ is the one which, when applied to the components (x_2, y_2, z_2) of $\mathbf{r}_2$, transforms them back to the components (x_1, y_1, z_1) of $\mathbf{r}_1$. The above mentioned concept applies to the position vector

Fig. A2.3.

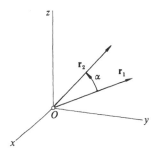

Fig. A2.4. Rotation of a vector.

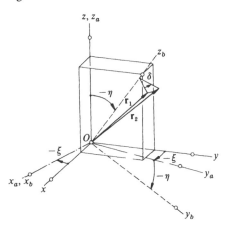

of any point on a moving body. The words *rotation of a vector* and *rotation of a body* are in general equivalent.

We distinguish therefore the rotation of a coordinate system relative to a fixed body from the rotation of a body relative to a fixed coordinate system. For the former we call the corresponding matrix a *transformation matrix*, and for the latter a *displacement matrix*. From the foregoing we conclude that a displacement matrix is the reciprocal of the corresponding transformation matrix.

We now proceed to find the matrix for rotating a given vector $\mathbf{r}_1$ to a position $\mathbf{r}_2$ through an angle δ about an inclined axis z_b, whose direction cosines l_x, l_y, l_z with respect to a reference coordinate system xyz of unit vectors $\mathbf{i}, \mathbf{j}, \mathbf{k}$ are also given, Fig. A2.4. Before applying to $\mathbf{r}_1$ a displacement matrix of the simple form such as that in equation (A2.22), the vector $\mathbf{r}_1$ has to be expressed in terms of components of a coordinate system which contains the z_b-axis. Now the position of the z_b-axis can be reached by rotating the xyz-system through two Eulerian angles $-\xi$ and $-\eta$ to a position of the $x_b y_b z_b$-system. The vector $\mathbf{r}_1$ is thus expressed in both the xyz and $x_b y_b z_b$-systems as

$$\mathbf{r}_1 = x_1\mathbf{i} + y_1\mathbf{j} + z_1\mathbf{k} = x_{1b}\mathbf{i}_b + y_{1b}\mathbf{j}_b + z_{1b}\mathbf{k}_b$$

where $\mathbf{i}_b, \mathbf{j}_b, \mathbf{k}_b$ are the three unit vectors of the $x_b y_b z_b$-system. According to equation (A2.17), the components (x_{1b}, y_{1b}, z_{1b}) are

$$\begin{bmatrix} x_{1b} \\ y_{1b} \\ z_{1b} \end{bmatrix} = \mathbb{X}_{(-\xi)}\mathbb{Z}_{(-\eta)} \begin{bmatrix} x_1 \\ y_1 \\ z_1 \end{bmatrix} = \mathbb{B} \begin{bmatrix} x_1 \\ y_1 \\ z_1 \end{bmatrix} \tag{A2.24}$$

where $\mathbb{B} = \mathbb{X}_{(-\xi)}\mathbb{Z}_{(-\eta)}$, whose elements can be found by replacing ξ, η, ζ by $-\xi, -\eta, 0$ respectively in equation (A2.17). Now because

$$z_{1b} = m_{31}x_1 + m_{32}y_1 + m_{33}z_1$$

and on the other hand

$$z_{1b} = l_x x_1 + l_y y_1 + l_z z_1$$

therefore

$$l_x = m_{31} = \sin\eta\sin\xi \tag{A2.25}$$
$$l_y = m_{32} = \sin\eta\cos\xi \tag{A2.26}$$
$$l_z = m_{33} = \cos\eta \tag{A2.27}$$

We then have, according to equation (A2.14),

$$\begin{bmatrix} x_{2b} \\ y_{2b} \\ z_{2b} \end{bmatrix} = \mathbb{Z}_{(-\delta)} \begin{bmatrix} x_{1b} \\ y_{1b} \\ z_{1b} \end{bmatrix} \tag{A2.28}$$

where

$$\mathbb{Z}_{(-\delta)} = \begin{bmatrix} \cos\delta & -\sin\delta & 0 \\ \sin\delta & \cos\delta & 0 \\ 0 & 0 & 1 \end{bmatrix} \qquad \text{(A2.29)}$$

Let the components of $\mathbf{r}_2$ expressed in the xyz-system and the $x_b y_b z_b$-system be respectively

$$\mathbf{r}_2 = x_2\mathbf{i} + y_2\mathbf{j} + z_2\mathbf{k} = x_{2b}\mathbf{i}_b + y_{2b}\mathbf{j}_b + z_{2b}\mathbf{k}_b$$

Consequently, we have

$$\begin{bmatrix} x_2 \\ y_2 \\ z_2 \end{bmatrix} = \mathbb{B}^{-1}\begin{bmatrix} x_{2b} \\ y_{2b} \\ z_{2b} \end{bmatrix} = \mathbb{B}^{\mathrm{T}}\begin{bmatrix} x_{2b} \\ y_{2b} \\ z_{2b} \end{bmatrix} \qquad \text{(A2.30)}$$

Combining equations (A2.30), (A2.28) and (A2.24) results in

$$\begin{bmatrix} x_2 \\ y_2 \\ z_2 \end{bmatrix} = \mathbb{B}^{\mathrm{T}}\mathbb{Z}_{(-\delta)}\mathbb{B}\begin{bmatrix} x_1 \\ y_1 \\ z_1 \end{bmatrix} = \mathbb{D}_{12}\begin{bmatrix} x_1 \\ y_1 \\ z_1 \end{bmatrix} \qquad \text{(A2.31)}$$

where the matrix

$$\mathbb{D}_{12} = \mathbb{B}^{\mathrm{T}}\mathbb{Z}_{(-\delta)}\mathbb{B} \qquad \text{(A2.32)}$$

is the displacement matrix for rotating a vector $\mathbf{r}_1$ about an axis z_b through an angle δ. Multiplication of the three matrices in equation (A2.32) and taking equations (A2.25), (A2.26) and (A2.27) into consideration yields finally the elements of the displacement matrix

$$\mathbb{D}_{12} = \begin{bmatrix} d_{11} & d_{12} & d_{13} \\ d_{21} & d_{22} & d_{23} \\ d_{31} & d_{32} & d_{33} \end{bmatrix} \qquad \text{(A2.33)}$$

where

$$\left.\begin{aligned} &d_{11} = l_x^2\,\mathrm{vers}\,\delta + \cos\delta, \qquad d_{12} = l_x l_y\,\mathrm{vers}\,\delta - l_z\sin\delta, \\ &d_{13} = l_x l_z\,\mathrm{vers}\,\delta + l_y\sin\delta, \\ &d_{21} = l_x l_y\,\mathrm{vers}\,\delta + l_z\sin\delta, \qquad d_{22} = l_y^2\,\mathrm{vers}\,\delta + \cos\delta, \\ &d_{23} = l_y l_z\,\mathrm{vers}\,\delta - l_x\sin\delta \\ &d_{31} = l_x l_z\,\mathrm{vers}\,\delta - l_y\sin\delta, \qquad d_{32} = l_y l_z\,\mathrm{vers}\,\delta + l_x\sin\delta. \\ &d_{33} = l_z^2\,\mathrm{vers}\,\delta + \cos\delta \end{aligned}\right\} \qquad \text{(A2.34)}$$

The matrix $\mathbb{D}_{12}$, being a product of orthogonal matrices, remains an orthogonal matrix. Equations (A2.34) are identical with equation (3) in (Suh & Radcliffe, 1967) which was derived from a vector equation.

A2.5   Successive rotations of a body

If a body is rotated successively about the axes of a fixed coordinate system xyz, from its initial position 1 to a final position 2, it is required to find the displacement matrix $\mathbb{D}_{12}$ which, when applied to the coordinates of

A_1 of a point A of the body in its initial position 1, transforms them to the coordinates of A_2 of the same point A of the body in its final position 2. Let the coordinates of A_1 and A_2 with respect to a fixed coordinate system xyz be denoted by $A_1(x_{A1}, y_{A1}, z_{A1})$ and $A_2(x_{A2}, y_{A2}, z_{A2})$ respectively. The displacement matrix $\mathbb{D}_{12}$ is defined by

$$\begin{bmatrix} x_{A2} \\ y_{A2} \\ z_{A2} \end{bmatrix} = \mathbb{D}_{12} \begin{bmatrix} x_{A1} \\ y_{A1} \\ z_{A1} \end{bmatrix} \tag{A2.35}$$

Following what we have described in the upper part of Section A2.4, a displacement matrix is equal to the reciprocal of the corresponding transformation matrix. Thus, if $\mathbb{M}_{12}$ is the corresponding transformation matrix, i.e. when the body is fixed and the coordinate system is rotated from the relative position 1 to the relative position 2, then

$$\mathbb{D}_{12} = \mathbb{M}_{12}^{-1} = \mathbb{M}_{12}^{T} \tag{A2.36}$$

Therefore if a body is displaced by three successive rotations about the three axes of a fixed xyz-system corresponding to the transformation matrix in equation (A2.11), then

$$\mathbb{D}_{12} = \mathbb{M}_{12}^{T} = \begin{bmatrix} C_\beta C_\gamma & -C_\beta S_\gamma & S_\beta \\ C_\alpha S_\gamma + S_\alpha S_\beta C_\gamma & C_\alpha C_\gamma - S_\alpha S_\beta S_\gamma & -S_\alpha C_\beta \\ S_\alpha S_\gamma - C_\alpha S_\beta C_\gamma & S_\alpha C_\gamma + C_\alpha S_\beta S_\gamma & C_\alpha C_\beta \end{bmatrix} \tag{A2.37}$$

However, because

$$\mathbb{M}_{12}^{T} = \mathbb{M}_{12}^{-1} = (\mathbb{Z}_\gamma \mathbb{Y}_\beta \mathbb{X}_\alpha)^{-1} = \mathbb{X}_\alpha^{-1} \mathbb{Y}_\beta^{-1} \mathbb{Z}_\gamma^{-1} \tag{A2.38}$$

care should be taken that the body is displaced in the order of rotating about the axes z, y and x through respective angles γ, β and α. If a certain displacement of the body is to be considered as rotations in the order about the axes x, y and z through respective angles α, β and γ, the correct displacement matrix is

$$\mathbb{D}_{12} = \begin{bmatrix} C_\beta C_\gamma & -C_\alpha S_\gamma + S_\alpha S_\beta C_\gamma & S_\alpha S_\gamma + C_\alpha S_\beta C_\gamma \\ C_\beta S_\gamma & C_\alpha C_\gamma + S_\alpha S_\beta S_\gamma & -S_\alpha C_\gamma + C_\alpha S_\beta S_\gamma \\ -S_\beta & S_\alpha C_\beta & C_\alpha C_\beta \end{bmatrix} \tag{A2.39}$$

Similarly if a body is displaced by three successive rotations through three Eulerian angles corresponding to the transformation matrix in equation (A2.17), the displacement matrix is

$$\mathbb{D}_{12} = \begin{bmatrix} C_\xi C_\zeta - S_\xi C_\eta S_\zeta & -C_\xi S_\zeta - S_\xi C_\eta C_\zeta & S_\xi S_\eta \\ S_\xi C_\zeta + C_\xi C_\eta S_\zeta & -S_\xi S_\zeta + C_\xi C_\eta C_\zeta & -C_\xi S_\eta \\ S_\eta S_\zeta & S_\eta C_\zeta & C_\eta \end{bmatrix}$$

Again, because

$$\mathbb{M}_{12}^{T} = \mathbb{M}_{12}^{-1} = (\mathbb{Z}_\zeta \mathbb{X}_\eta \mathbb{Z}_\xi)^{-1} = \mathbb{Z}_\xi^{-1} \mathbb{X}_\eta^{-1} \mathbb{Z}_\zeta^{-1} \tag{A2.40}$$

the body is displaced in the order of rotating about the axes z, x and z through respective angles ζ, η and ξ. If the body is considered to be displaced in the order of rotating about the axes z, x and z through respective angles ξ, η and ζ, the correct displacement matrix is

$$\mathbb{D}_{12} = \begin{bmatrix} C_\xi C_\zeta - S_\xi C_\eta S_\zeta & -S_\xi C_\zeta - C_\xi C_\eta S_\zeta & S_\eta S_\zeta \\ C_\xi S_\zeta + S_\xi C_\eta C_\zeta & -S_\xi S_\zeta + C_\xi C_\eta C_\zeta & -S_\eta C_\zeta \\ S_\xi S_\eta & C_\xi S_\eta & C_\eta \end{bmatrix} \quad \text{(A2.41)}$$

Note that in this book no reference is made to any coordinate system embedded in the moving body. In a displacement matrix all axes of rotation are fixed in space.

A2.6   Displacement matrix transformed by a transformation matrix

Let $\mathbb{D}_{12}$ be a displacement matrix as defined in equation (A2.35), i.e. when $\mathbb{D}_{12}$ is applied to the coordinates of a point A_1, displacing these to the coordinates of a point A_2,

$$\mathbb{D}_{12} \begin{bmatrix} x_{A1} \\ y_{A1} \\ z_{A1} \end{bmatrix} = \begin{bmatrix} x_{A2} \\ y_{A2} \\ z_{A2} \end{bmatrix} \quad \text{(A2.42)}$$

Now suppose the coordinate system is rotated by a transformation matrix $\mathbb{M}$ which transforms the coordinates of A_1 to the coordinates of the same point A_1, but with respect to a new coordinate system $x'y'z'$. In other words,

$$\mathbb{M} \begin{bmatrix} x_{A1} \\ y_{A1} \\ z_{A1} \end{bmatrix} = \begin{bmatrix} x'_{A1} \\ y'_{A1} \\ z'_{A1} \end{bmatrix} \quad \text{and} \quad \mathbb{M} \begin{bmatrix} x_{A2} \\ y_{A2} \\ z_{A2} \end{bmatrix} = \begin{bmatrix} x'_{A2} \\ y'_{A2} \\ z'_{A2} \end{bmatrix} \quad \text{(A2.43)}$$

From the last two equations (A2.43), we have by definition

$$\begin{bmatrix} x_{A1} \\ y_{A1} \\ z_{A1} \end{bmatrix} = \mathbb{M}^{-1} \begin{bmatrix} x'_{A1} \\ y'_{A1} \\ z'_{A1} \end{bmatrix} \quad \text{and} \quad \begin{bmatrix} x_{A2} \\ y_{A2} \\ z_{A2} \end{bmatrix} = \mathbb{M}^{-1} \begin{bmatrix} x'_{A2} \\ y'_{A2} \\ z'_{A2} \end{bmatrix} \quad \text{(A2.44)}$$

Substituting equations (A2.44) into equation (A2.42), we obtain

$$\mathbb{D}_{12} \mathbb{M}^{-1} \begin{bmatrix} x'_{A1} \\ y'_{A1} \\ z'_{A1} \end{bmatrix} = \mathbb{M}^{-1} \begin{bmatrix} x'_{A2} \\ y'_{A2} \\ z'_{A2} \end{bmatrix} \quad \text{(A2.45)}$$

Multiplying both sides of equation (A2.45) by the matrix $\mathbb{M}$ gives

$$\mathbb{M} \mathbb{D}_{12} \mathbb{M}^{-1} \begin{bmatrix} x'_{A1} \\ y'_{A1} \\ z'_{A1} \end{bmatrix} = \begin{bmatrix} x'_{A2} \\ y'_{A2} \\ z'_{A2} \end{bmatrix} \quad \text{(A2.46)}$$

From equation (A2.46) it can be seen that the new displacement matrix is $\mathbb{M} \mathbb{D}_{12} \mathbb{M}^{-1}$, which, when applied to the coordinates of A'_1, displaces them to the coordinates of A'_2. We can therefore write the new displacement matrix as

$$\mathbb{D}'_{12} = \mathbb{M} \mathbb{D}_{12} \mathbb{M}^{-1} \quad \text{(A2.47)}$$

APPENDIX 3

Useful vector equations in spherical geometry

Equations of surfaces are given as functions of the coordinates (x, y, z) of a point on the surface with respect to a reference rectangular coordinate system xyz with its origin at the centre of a unit sphere. The position vector of a point on the surface is written as $\mathbf{r} = x\mathbf{i} + y\mathbf{j} + z\mathbf{k}$, where $\mathbf{i}, \mathbf{j}, \mathbf{k}$ are the respective unit vectors along the axes x, y, z. The equation of the unit sphere is then

$$x^2 + y^2 + z^2 = 1 \tag{A3.1}$$

or its equivalent

$$\left(\frac{x}{z}\right)^2 + \left(\frac{y}{z}\right)^2 + 1 = \frac{1}{z^2} \tag{A3.1a}$$

The position vectors of two points A and B are written as

$$\overrightarrow{OA} = \mathbf{r}_A = x_A\mathbf{i} + y_A\mathbf{j} + z_A\mathbf{k}, \quad \overrightarrow{OB} = \mathbf{r}_B = x_B\mathbf{i} + y_B\mathbf{j} + z_B\mathbf{k}$$

A3.1   The spherical distance AB

The spherical distance between two points A and B, or the angle $\sphericalangle AOB$, is given by the scalar product of $\mathbf{r}_A$ and $\mathbf{r}_B$:

$$\cos \sphericalangle AOB = \mathbf{r}_A \cdot \mathbf{r}_B = (x_A\mathbf{i} + y_A\mathbf{j} + z_A\mathbf{k}) \cdot (x_B\mathbf{i} + y_B\mathbf{j} + z_B\mathbf{k})$$
$$= x_A x_B + y_A y_B + z_A z_B \tag{A3.2}$$

A3.2   The perpendicular bisector of the line (great circle) AB

For a point (x, y, z) which is equally distant from A and B,

$$x_A x + y_A y + z_A z = x_B x + y_B y + z_B z$$

or

$$(x_B - x_A)x + (y_B - y_A)y + (z_B - z_A)z = 0 \tag{A3.3}$$

which is the equation of the plane perpendicular to the vector $\mathbf{r}_A - \mathbf{r}_B$. Equation (A3.3), together with equation (A3.1), represents the perpendicular bisector of AB.

A3.3   The great circle passing through points A and B

The vector (not necessarily a unit vector) normal to the plane containing $\mathbf{r}_A$ and $\mathbf{r}_B$ is given by $\mathbf{r}_A \times \mathbf{r}_B$. Hence the equation of the plane containing $\mathbf{r}_A$ and $\mathbf{r}_B$ is given by $\mathbf{r} \cdot (\mathbf{r}_A \times \mathbf{r}_B) = 0$, or

$$(x\mathbf{i} + y\mathbf{j} + z\mathbf{k}) \cdot \begin{vmatrix} \mathbf{i} & \mathbf{j} & \mathbf{k} \\ x_A & y_A & z_A \\ x_B & y_B & z_B \end{vmatrix} = 0$$

which is equivalent to

$$\begin{vmatrix} x & y & z \\ x_A & y_A & z_A \\ x_B & y_B & z_B \end{vmatrix} = 0 \tag{A3.4}$$

Equation (A3.4), together with equation (A3.1), represents the great circle passing through A and B.

APPENDIX 4

Equations of transformation of coordinates

A4.1 **Transformation between spherical polar coordinates and right-handed Cartesian coordinates**

Fig. A4.1 (a) shows a point A on the surface of the unit sphere. Let the coordinates of A with respect to a right-handed Cartesian coordinate system O-xyz be (x, y, z), and its spherical polar coordinates be (p, θ), where θ is positive when measured counterclockwise from the zx-plane. The transformation equations from (p, θ) to (x, y, z) are:

$$
\left.
\begin{aligned}
\cos p &= z \\
\sin^2 p &= x^2 + y^2 \\
\tan^2 p &= \frac{x^2 + y^2}{z^2} \\
\sin \theta &= \frac{y}{\sqrt{(x^2 + y^2)}} \\
\cos \theta &= \frac{x}{\sqrt{(x^2 + y^2)}} \\
\tan \theta &= \frac{y}{x}
\end{aligned}
\right\}
\tag{A4.1}
$$

The equations to transform from (x, y, z) to (p, θ) are

$$
\left.
\begin{aligned}
x &= \sin p \cos \theta \\
y &= \sin p \sin \theta \\
z &= \cos p
\end{aligned}
\right\}
\tag{A4.2}
$$

When the origin of the spherical polar coordinates is taken at $(1, 0, 0)$, and θ is measured from the xy-plane as shown in Fig. A4.1(b), the above equations are still valid provided that x, y, z are replaced respectively by y, z, x. In particular the equations for transforming from (x, y, z) to (p, θ) are

Fig. A4.1. $(a),(b)$ Spherical polar coordinates.

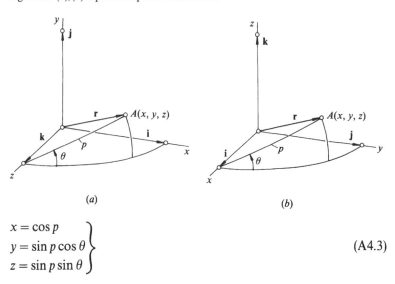

(a) (b)

$$\left.\begin{array}{l} x = \cos p \\ y = \sin p \cos \theta \\ z = \sin p \sin \theta \end{array}\right\} \tag{A4.3}$$

A4.2   Transformations between spherical rectangular coordinates and spherical polar coordinates, and between those and right-handed Cartesian coordinates

Let the location of a point A on the surface of a unit sphere be denoted by its spherical rectangular coordinates (u, v) with respect to an origin P, as shown in Fig. A4.2. It is understood that to reach the location of A

Fig. A4.2. Gnomonic projection of a point A onto a tangent plane at P.

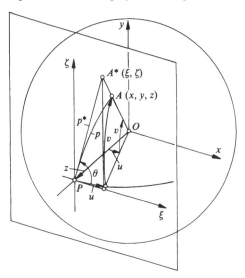

from P the sequence $u \to v$ must be followed. Let the spherical polar coordinates of the point A be (p, θ), where the angle θ is measured counterclockwise from the spherical polar great circle on which u is measured. We have then, according to equations (A1.2) and (A1.4),

$$\left.\begin{array}{l} \cos p = \cos u \cos v \\ \tan \theta = \tan v / \sin u \end{array}\right\} \tag{A4.4}$$

and according to equations (A1.1) and (A1.6), we have

$$\left.\begin{array}{l} \sin v = \sin p \sin \theta \\ \tan u = \cos \theta \tan p \end{array}\right\} \tag{A4.5}$$

From equations (A4.2) and (A4.5), (A4.4), we get

$$\left.\begin{array}{l} x = \sin u \cos v \\ y = \sin v \\ z = \cos u \cos v \end{array}\right\} \tag{A4.6}$$

Therefore

$$\left.\begin{array}{l} \tan u = \dfrac{x}{z} \\[2mm] \sin v = y \end{array}\right\} \tag{A4.7}$$

A4.3   Transformation between spherical polar coordinates and plane polar coordinates of gnomonic projection

Suppose the point A is projected from the sphere centre O onto a plane tangent to the unit sphere at the point P. The projected point A^* of A is known as the gnomonic projection of A. The spherical polar coordinates (p, θ) of A have to be transformed into the plane polar coordinates (p^*, θ) of A^*. It is clear that the angle θ is not altered by the projection. The relation between p^* and p is

$$p^* = \tan p \tag{A4.8}$$

A4.4   Transformation between spherical polar coordinates and plane rectangular coordinates of gnomonic projection

Let the plane rectangular coordinates of a point A with respect to the origin P be denoted by (ξ, ζ), where the ξ-axis is in the plane of the great circle of u, as shown in Fig. A4.2. The relations between (ξ, ζ) and (p, θ) are

$$\left.\begin{array}{l} \xi = p^* \cos \theta = \tan p \cos \theta \\ \zeta = p^* \sin \theta = \tan p \sin \theta \end{array}\right\} \tag{A4.9}$$

and

$$\left.\begin{array}{l} \tan^2 p = p^{*2} = \xi^2 + \zeta^2 \\[2mm] \tan \theta = \dfrac{\zeta}{\xi} \end{array}\right\} \tag{A4.10}$$

A4.5   Transformations between plane rectangular coordinates of gnomonic projection and right-handed Cartesian coordinates, and between those and spherical rectangular coordinates

In Fig. A4.2 let the coordinates of the point A on the spherical surface with respect to a right-handed Cartesian coordinate system $O\text{-}xyz$ be (x, y, z), as shown in Fig. A4.1(a). Let the ξ, ζ-axes be parallel to the x, y-axes respectively. Then the relations between the coordinates (ξ, ζ) of A^* and (x, y, z) of A, are, comparing equations (A4.2) with equations (A4.9):

$$\left. \begin{aligned} \xi &= \frac{x}{z} \\ \zeta &= \frac{y}{z} \end{aligned} \right\} \tag{A4.11}$$

Equations (A4.11) are identical with the well-known transformation equations used for homogeneous coordinates. A homogeneous equation of a curve on the spherical surface can therefore easily be transformed into an equation of its gnomonic projection by means of equation (A4.11).

Substituting equations (A4.6) and (A4.7) into equations (A4.11) gives

$$\left. \begin{aligned} \xi &= \tan u \\ \zeta &= \frac{\tan v}{\cos u} \end{aligned} \right\} \tag{A4.12}$$

From the last equations we obtain

$$\left. \begin{aligned} \tan u &= \xi \\ \tan v &= \frac{\zeta}{\sqrt{(1 + \xi^2)}} \end{aligned} \right\} \tag{A4.13}$$

and the consequent relations

$$\left. \begin{aligned} \frac{1}{\cos u} &= \sqrt{(1 + \xi^2)} \\ \frac{1}{\cos v} &= \sqrt{\left(\frac{1 + \xi^2 + \zeta^2}{1 + \xi^2} \right)} \end{aligned} \right\} \tag{A4.14}$$

A4.6   Transformation between the position angle of a spherical crank and that of its gnomonic projection

In Fig. A4.3, $A_0 A$ is a spherical crank, and the crank axis is OA_0. With respect to an origin point R, the spherical rectangular coordinates of A_0 are $(e, 0)$, and those of A are (u, v), where the spherical distances are $e = RA_0$, $u = RG$ and $v = GA$. Let the spherical crank length $A_0 A$ be represented by a. The gnomonic projections of A_0, G and A on a plane tangent to the unit sphere at R are denoted by A_0^*, G^* and A^* respectively. The position angle of A_0A with respect to the great circle of u is ϕ. The gnomonic projection of the angle ϕ is denoted by ϕ^*. We have then, according to equations (A1.6) and (A1.4):

$$\left.\begin{array}{l} \tan(u - e) = \cos\phi\tan a \\ \tan v = \sin(u - e)\tan\phi \end{array}\right\} \tag{A4.15}$$

The linear distances $A_0^*G^*$ and G^*A^* on the tangent plane are:

$$\left.\begin{array}{l} A_0^*G^* = \tan u - \tan e \\ G^*A^* = \tan v\,\dfrac{OG^*}{OR} = \dfrac{\tan v}{\cos u} \end{array}\right\} \tag{A4.16}$$

Dividing G^*A^* by $A_0^*G^*$, and taking equations (A4.15) into consideration, we obtain

$$\tan\phi^* = \cos e\tan\phi \tag{A4.17}$$

Fig. A4.3. Gnomonic projection of a crank A_0A onto a tangent plane at R.

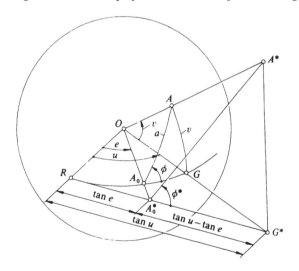

APPENDIX 5

Coefficients in equations (4.45) and (4.49)

$L_{42} = -\sin^2 a \sin^4 f$

$L_{32} = 2 \sin a \sin^3 f (\cos c \cos b - 2 \cos a \cos f)$

$L_{31} = 2 \sin a \cos a \sin^3 f$

$L_{22} = \sin^2 f (\sin^2 a \cos^2 b - 5 \cos^2 a \cos^2 f$
$\qquad + \cos^2 a \cos^2 b \sin^2 f - \cos^2 a \sin^2 b \cos^2 f$
$\qquad - \cos^2 c + 6 \cos a \cos c \cos b \cos f + 2 \sin^2 b)$

$L_{21} = 2 \sin^2 f (-2 \cos a \cos c \cos b + 2 \cos^2 a \cos f - \sin^2 a \cos f)$

$L_{20} = \sin^2 f (\cos^2 c - \cos^2 a)$

$L_{12} = 2 \sin f (\cos a \cos b \cos f - \cos c)[\sin a \cos b + \cot a \cos c \cos f$
$\qquad - \cos a \cot a \cos b (\cos^2 f - \sin^2 f)]$
$\qquad + 4 \sin a \cos a \sin^2 b \sin f \cos f (1 + \cot^2 a \sin^2 f)$

$L_{11} = 2 \sin f (\cos a \cos b \cos f - \cos c)[\cot a (\cos a \cos b \cos f - \cos c)$
$\qquad - 2 \sin a \cos b \cos f] - 2 \sin a \cos a \sin^2 b \sin f$
$\qquad \cdot (2 \cos^2 f + \cot^2 a \sin^2 f + 1)$

$L_{10} = 2 \sin a \sin f (\cos a \cos f - \cos c \cos b)$

$L_{02} = (1 + \cot^2 a \sin^2 f)[(\cos a \cos b \cos f - \cos c)^2$
$\qquad - \sin^2 a \sin^2 b (1 + \cot^2 a \sin^2 f)]$

$L_{01} = 2 \cos f [\sin^2 a \sin^2 b (1 + \cot^2 a \sin^2 f)$
$\qquad - (\cos a \cos b \cos f - \cos c)^2]$

$L_{00} = \cos^2 f (\cos^2 c - \sin^2 a) + \cos b (\cos b - 2 \cos a \cos c \cos f)$

$M_{10} = 4 U_4^3 - V_6^2$

$M_9 \; = 12 U_4^2 U_3 + 2 V_6 V_5$

$M_8 \; = 12 U_4 (U_4 U_2 + U_3^2) - (V_5^2 + 2 V_6 V_4)$

$M_7 \; = 4 (U_3^3 + 3 U_4^2 U_1 + 6 U_4 U_3 U_2) + 2 (V_6 V_3 + V_5 V_4)$

$M_6 \; = 12 (U_4^2 U_0 + U_3^2 U_2 + U_4 U_2^2) + 24 U_4 U_3 U_1$
$\qquad - V_4^2 - 2 (V_6 V_2 + V_5 V_3)$

$$M_5 = 12U_3(U_3U_1 + U_2^2) + 24U_4(U_3U_0 + U_2U_1)$$
$$+ 2(V_6V_1 + V_5V_2 + V_4V_3)$$
$$M_4 = 4U_2^3 + 12(U_3^2U_0 + U_4U_1^2) + 24U_2(U_4U_0 + U_3U_1)$$
$$- V_3^2 - 2(V_6V_0 + V_5V_1 + V_4V_2)$$
$$M_3 = 12U_1(U_2^2 + U_3U_1) + 24U_0(U_4U_1 + U_3U_2)$$
$$+ 2(V_5V_0 + V_4V_1 + V_3V_2)$$
$$M_2 = 12(U_2^2U_0 + U_2U_1^2 + U_4U_0^2) + 24U_3U_1U_0$$
$$- V_2^2 - 2(V_4V_0 + V_3V_1)$$
$$M_1 = 4U_1^3 + 12U_3U_0^2 + 24U_2U_1U_0 + 2(V_3V_0 + V_2V_1)$$
$$M_0 = 12U_0(U_1^2 + U_2U_0) - V_1^2 - 2V_2V_0$$

where

$$U_4 = 12U_{41} - 3U_{42} + U_{43}$$
$$U_3 = 12U_{31} - 3U_{32} - U_{33}$$
$$U_2 = 12U_{21} - 3U_{22} + U_{23}$$
$$U_1 = -3U_{12} - U_{13}$$
$$U_0 = U_{03}$$

where

$$U_{41} = L_{42}L_{02}$$
$$U_{42} = L_{32}L_{12}$$
$$U_{43} = L_{22}^2$$
$$U_{31} = L_{42}L_{01}$$
$$U_{32} = L_{32}L_{11} + L_{31}L_{12}$$
$$U_{33} = 2L_{22}L_{21}$$
$$U_{21} = L_{42}L_{00}$$
$$U_{22} = L_{32}L_{10} + L_{31}L_{11}$$
$$U_{23} = L_{21}^2 + 2L_{22}L_{20}$$
$$U_{12} = L_{31}L_{10}$$
$$U_{13} = 2L_{21}L_{20}$$
$$U_{03} = L_{20}^2$$

and

$$V_6 = 72V_{61} + 9V_{62} - 27(V_{63} + V_{64}) - 2V_{65}$$
$$V_5 = 72V_{51} + 9V_{52} - 27(V_{53} + V_{54}) - 2V_{55}$$
$$V_4 = 72V_{41} + 9V_{42} - 27(V_{43} + V_{44}) - 2V_{45}$$
$$V_3 = 72V_{31} + 9V_{32} - 27(V_{33} + V_{34}) - 2V_{35}$$
$$V_2 = 72V_{21} + 9V_{22} - 27(V_{23} + V_{24}) - 2V_{25}$$
$$V_1 = 9V_{12} - 2V_{15}$$
$$V_0 = -2V_{05}$$

where

$$V_{61} = L_{42}L_{22}L_{02}$$
$$V_{62} = L_{32}L_{22}L_{12}$$
$$V_{63} = L_{42}L_{12}^2$$
$$V_{64} = L_{32}^2 L_{02}$$
$$V_{65} = L_{22}^3$$
$$V_{51} = L_{42}(-L_{22}L_{01} - L_{21}L_{02})$$
$$V_{52} = L_{32}(-L_{22}L_{11} - L_{21}L_{12}) - L_{31}L_{22}L_{12}$$
$$V_{53} = -2L_{42}L_{12}L_{11}$$
$$V_{54} = -L_{32}(2L_{31}L_{02} + L_{32}L_{01})$$
$$V_{55} = -3L_{22}^2 L_{21}$$
$$V_{41} = L_{42}(L_{22}L_{00} + L_{20}L_{02} + L_{21}L_{01})$$
$$V_{42} = L_{32}(L_{22}L_{10} + L_{20}L_{12} + L_{21}L_{11}) + L_{31}(L_{.} L_{11} + L_{21}L_{12})$$
$$V_{43} = L_{42}(L_{11}^2 + 2L_{12}L_{10})$$
$$V_{44} = L_{31}^2 L_{02} + L_{32}(2L_{31}L_{01} + L_{32}L_{00})$$
$$V_{45} = 3L_{22}(L_{21}^2 + L_{22}L_{20})$$
$$V_{31} = L_{42}(-L_{21}L_{00} - L_{20}L_{01})$$
$$V_{32} = L_{32}(-L_{21}L_{10} - L_{20}L_{11}) - L_{31}(L_{22}L_{10} + L_{20}L_{12} + L_{21}L_{11})$$
$$V_{33} = -2L_{42}L_{11}L_{10}$$
$$V_{34} = -L_{31}(2L_{32}L_{00} + L_{31}L_{01})$$
$$V_{35} = -L_{21}(L_{21}^2 + 6L_{22}L_{20})$$
$$V_{21} = L_{42}L_{20}L_{00}$$
$$V_{22} = L_{32}L_{20}L_{10} + L_{31}(L_{21}L_{10} + L_{20}L_{11})$$
$$V_{23} = L_{42}L_{10}^2$$
$$V_{24} = L_{31}^2 L_{00}$$
$$V_{25} = 3L_{20}(L_{22}L_{20} + L_{21}^2)$$
$$V_{12} = -L_{31}L_{20}L_{10}$$
$$V_{15} = -3L_{21}L_{20}^2$$
$$V_{05} = L_{20}^3$$

APPENDIX 6

Coefficients in equations of R_{M90}-curve, R_{90}^1-curve, circle-point curve and centre-point curve

In equation (6.91), the equation of the R_{M90}-curve,

$$R_{M90}: \quad N_2 \tan^2 p_0 + N_1 \tan p_0 + N_0 = 0$$

the coefficients are:

$$\left. \begin{aligned}
N_2 &= n_1 S_{\theta 0}^3 + n_2 S_{\theta 0}^2 C_{\theta 0} + n_3 S_{\theta 0} C_{\theta 0}^2 + n_4 C_{\theta 0}^3 \\
N_1 &= n_7 S_{\theta 0}^2 + n_8 S_{\theta 0} C_{\theta 0} + n_9 C_{\theta 0}^2 \\
N_0 &= n_5 S_{\theta 0} + n_6 C_{\theta 0}
\end{aligned} \right\} \tag{A6.1}$$

where, also in equation (6.90a), with the second expression for each coefficient if step (1) is carried out,

$$\left. \begin{aligned}
n_1 &= d_{212}d_{233} \quad = S_{\gamma 12}d_{233} \\
n_2 &= d_{212}d_{133} \quad = S_{\gamma 12}d_{133} \\
n_3 &= -d_{122}d_{233} = S_{\gamma 12}d_{233} \\
n_4 &= -d_{122}d_{133} = S_{\gamma 12}d_{133} \\
n_5 &= -d_{212}d_{323} + (d_{222} - 1)d_{313} = -S_{\gamma 12}d_{323} - V_{\gamma 12}d_{313} \\
n_6 &= d_{122}d_{313} - (d_{112} - 1)d_{323} = -S_{\gamma 12}d_{313} + V_{\gamma 12}d_{323} \\
n_7 &= d_{212}[(d_{333} - 1) - (d_{223} - 1)] + (d_{222} - 1)d_{213} \\
&= S_{\gamma 12}[(d_{333} - 1) - (d_{223} - 1)] - V_{\gamma 12}d_{213} \\
n_8 &= -d_{212}d_{123} + d_{122}d_{213} - (d_{222} - 1)(d_{333} - d_{113}) \\
&\quad - (d_{112} - 1)[(d_{223} - 1) - (d_{333} - 1)] \\
&= -S_{\gamma 12}(d_{213} + d_{123}) + V_{\gamma 12}[(d_{223} - 1) - (d_{113} - 1)] \\
n_9 &= -d_{122}[(d_{333} - 1) - (d_{113} - 1)] - (d_{112} - 1)d_{123} \\
&= S_{\gamma 12}[(d_{333} - 1) - (d_{113} - 1)] + V_{\gamma 12}d_{123}
\end{aligned} \right\} \tag{A6.2}$$

In equation (6.94), the equation of the R_{90}^1-curve,

$$R_{90}^1: \quad C_2 \tan^2 p_{A1} + C_1 \tan p_{A1} + C_0 = 0$$

the coefficients are:

$$C_2 = c_1 S_{\theta A1}^3 + c_2 S_{\theta A1}^2 C_{\theta A1} + c_3 S_{\theta A1} C_{\theta A1}^2 + c_4 C_{\theta A1}^3$$
$$C_1 = c_7 S_{\theta A1}^2 + c_8 S_{\theta A1} C_{\theta A1} + c_9 C_{\theta A1}^2 \qquad\qquad (A6.3)$$
$$C_0 = c_5 S_{\theta A1} + c_6 C_{\theta A1}$$

where, also in equation (6.93a), with the second expression for each coefficient if step (1) is carried out,

$$c_1 = -d_{122}d_{323} = S_{\gamma 12}d_{323}$$
$$c_2 = -d_{122}d_{313} = S_{\gamma 12}d_{313}$$
$$c_3 = d_{212}d_{323} \quad = S_{\gamma 12}d_{323}$$
$$c_4 = d_{212}d_{313} \quad = S_{\gamma 12}d_{313}$$
$$c_5 = d_{122}d_{233} - (d_{222} - 1)d_{133} = -S_{\gamma 12}d_{233} + V_{\gamma 12}d_{133}$$
$$c_6 = -d_{212}d_{133} + (d_{112} - 1)d_{233} = -S_{\gamma 12}d_{133} - V_{\gamma 12}d_{233}$$
$$c_7 = -d_{122}[(d_{333} - 1) - (d_{223} - 1)] - d_{123}(d_{222} - 1)$$
$$\quad = S_{\gamma 12}[(d_{333} - 1) - (d_{223} - 1)] + V_{\gamma 12}d_{123}$$
$$c_8 = (d_{112} - 1)[(d_{223} - 1) - (d_{333} - 1)] + (d_{222} - 1)$$
$$\quad \cdot [(d_{333} - 1) - (d_{113} - 1)] + d_{122}d_{213} - d_{212}d_{123}$$
$$\quad = -V_{\gamma 12}[(d_{223} - 1) - (d_{113} - 1)] - S_{\gamma 12}(d_{123} + d_{213})$$
$$c_9 = d_{212}[(d_{333} - 1) - (d_{113} - 1)] + (d_{112} - 1)d_{213}$$
$$\quad = S_{\gamma 12}[(d_{333} - 1) - (d_{113} - 1)] - V_{\gamma 12}d_{213}$$

$$\qquad\qquad (A6.4)$$

In order to save space, the determinant in the equation of the circle-point curve k_1, equation (6.118), may be written in a form containing only one row, as follows:

$$\begin{vmatrix} G_2 & S_2 & T_2 \\ G_3 & S_3 & T_3 \\ G_4 & S_4 & T_4 \end{vmatrix} = |G_i, S_i, T_i| = 0, \quad i = 2, 3, 4$$

According to equations (6.53)–(6.55), this equation becomes

$$|(d_{11i} - 1)x_{A1} + d_{12i}y_{A1} + d_{13i}z_{A1}, d_{21i}x_{A1} + (d_{22i} - 1)y_{A1} + d_{23i}z_{A1},$$
$$d_{31i}x_{A1} + d_{32i}y_{A1} + (d_{33i} - 1)z_{A1}| = 0$$

Expansion of this determinant results in the homogeneous cubic equation (6.118a) in x_{A1}, y_{A1}, z_{A1}. The coefficients are:

$$d_1 = |d_{12i}, (d_{22i} - 1), d_{32i}|$$
$$d_2 = |(d_{11i} - 1), (d_{22i} - 1), d_{32i}| + |d_{12i}, d_{21i}, d_{32i}|$$
$$\quad + |d_{12i}, (d_{22i} - 1), d_{31i}|$$
$$d_3 = |(d_{11i} - 1), d_{21i}, d_{32i}| + |(d_{11i} - 1), (d_{22i} - 1), d_{31i}|$$
$$\quad + |d_{12i}, d_{21i}, d_{31i}|$$
$$d_4 = |(d_{11i} - 1), d_{21i}, d_{31i}|$$

$$d_5 = |d_{12i}, d_{23i}, (d_{33i} - 1)| + |d_{13i}, (d_{22i} - 1), (d_{33i} - 1)|$$
$$+ |d_{13i}, d_{23i}, d_{32i}|$$
$$d_6 = |(d_{11i} - 1), d_{23i}, (d_{33i} - 1)| + |d_{13i}, d_{21i}, (d_{33i} - 1)|$$
$$+ |d_{13i}, d_{23i}, d_{31i}|$$
$$d_7 = |d_{12i}, (d_{22i} - 1), (d_{33i} - 1)| + |d_{12i}, d_{23i}, d_{32i}|$$
$$+ |d_{13i}, (d_{22i} - 1), d_{32i}| \qquad\qquad\qquad (A6.5)$$
$$d_8 = |(d_{11i} - 1), (d_{22i} - 1), (d_{33i} - 1)| + |(d_{11i} - 1), d_{23i}, d_{32i}|$$
$$+ |d_{12i}, d_{21i}, (d_{33i} - 1)| + |d_{12i}, d_{23i}, d_{31i}|$$
$$+ |d_{13i}, d_{21i}, d_{32i}| + |d_{13i}, (d_{22i} - 1), d_{31i}|$$
$$d_9 = |(d_{11i} - 1), d_{21i}, (d_{33i} - 1)| + |(d_{11i} - 1), d_{23i}, d_{31i}|$$
$$+ |d_{13i}, d_{21i}, d_{31i}|$$

After transforming into spherical polar coordinates by means of equations (A4.2), equation (6.118a) becomes equation (6.119):

$$k_1: \quad D_2 \tan^2 p_{A1} + D_1 \tan p_{A1} + D_0 = 0$$

where the coefficients are:

$$D_2 = d_1 S_{\theta A1}^3 + d_2 S_{\theta A1}^2 C_{\theta A1} + d_3 S_{\theta A1} C_{\theta A1}^2 + d_4 C_{\theta A1}^3$$
$$D_1 = d_7 S_{\theta A1}^2 + d_8 S_{\theta A1} C_{\theta A1} + d_9 C_{\theta A1}^2 \qquad\qquad (A6.6)$$
$$D_0 = d_5 S_{\theta A1} + d_6 C_{\theta A1}$$

with the notation $S_{\theta A1} = \sin \theta_{A1}, C_{\theta A1} = \cos \theta_{A1}$.

Similarly the equation of the centre-point curve k_m, equation (6.121), can also be written as

$$\begin{vmatrix} L_2 & Q_2 & H_2 \\ L_3 & Q_3 & H_3 \\ L_4 & Q_4 & H_4 \end{vmatrix} = |L_i, Q_i, H_i| = 0, \quad i = 2, 3, 4$$

or, according to equations (6.59)–(6.61), this equation becomes

$$|(d_{11i} - 1)x_0 + d_{21i}y_0 + d_{31i}z_0, d_{12i}x_0 + (d_{22i} - 1)y_0 + d_{32i}z_0,$$
$$d_{13i}x_0 + d_{23i}y_0 + (d_{33i} - 1)z_0| = 0$$

Expansion of this determinant results in the homogeneous cubic equation (6.121a) in x_0, y_0, z_0. The coefficients are:

$$m_1 = |d_{21i}, (d_{22i} - 1), d_{23i}|$$
$$m_2 = |(d_{11i} - 1), (d_{22i} - 1), d_{23i}| + |d_{21i}, d_{12i}, d_{23i}|$$
$$+ |d_{21i}, (d_{22i} - 1), d_{13i}|$$
$$m_3 = |(d_{11i} - 1), d_{12i}, d_{23i}| + |(d_{11i} - 1), (d_{22i} - 1), d_{13i}|$$
$$+ |d_{21i}, d_{12i}, d_{13i}|$$
$$m_4 = |(d_{11i} - 1), d_{12i}, d_{13i}|$$

$$m_5 = |d_{21i}, d_{32i}, (d_{33i} - 1)| + |d_{31i}, (d_{22i} - 1), (d_{33i} - 1)|$$
$$\quad + |d_{31i}, d_{32i}, d_{23i}|$$
$$m_6 = |(d_{11i} - 1), d_{32i}, (d_{33i} - 1)| + |d_{31i}, d_{12i}, (d_{33i} - 1)|$$
$$\quad + |d_{31i}, d_{32i}, d_{13i}|$$
$$m_7 = |d_{21i}, (d_{22i} - 1), (d_{33i} - 1)| + |d_{21i}, d_{32i}, d_{23i}|$$
$$\quad + |d_{31i}, (d_{22i} - 1), d_{23i}|$$
$$m_8 = |(d_{11i} - 1), (d_{22i} - 1), (d_{33i} - 1)| + |(d_{11i} - 1), d_{32i}, d_{23i}|$$
$$\quad + |d_{21i}, d_{12i}, (d_{33i} - 1)| + |d_{21i}, d_{32i}, d_{13i}| + |d_{31i}, d_{12i}, d_{23i}|$$
$$\quad + |d_{31i}, (d_{22i} - 1), d_{13i}|$$
$$m_9 = |(d_{11i} - 1), d_{12i}, (d_{33i} - 1)| + |(d_{11i} - 1), d_{32i}, d_{13i}|$$
$$\quad + |d_{31i}, d_{12i}, d_{13i}|$$

$$(A6.7)$$

After transforming into spherical polar coordinates by means of equations (A4.2) equation (6.121a) becomes equation (6.122):

$$k_m: \quad M_2 \tan^2 p_0 + M_1 \tan p_0 + M_0 = 0$$

where the coefficients are:

$$M_2 = m_1 S_{\theta 0}^3 + m_2 S_{\theta 0}^2 C_{\theta 0} + m_3 S_{\theta 0} C_{\theta 0}^2 + m_4 C_{\theta 0}^3$$
$$M_1 = m_7 S_{\theta 0}^2 + m_8 S_{\theta 0} C_{\theta 0} + m_9 C_{\theta 0}^2 \qquad (A6.8)$$
$$M_0 = m_5 S_{\theta 0} + m_6 C_{\theta 0}$$

with the notation $S_{\theta 0} = \sin \theta_0$, $C_{\theta 0} = \cos \theta_0$.

For the case $P_1 P_2 P_3 - P_4$ mentioned in Section 6.11.1(3), the coefficients in equations (A6.5), after neglecting higher orders and dividing through by a common factor $d\gamma^3$, should be replaced respectively by

$$d_1^* = -\Theta(d_{224} - 1) + d_{324}$$
$$d_2^* = -\Theta(d_{124} + d_{214}) + d_{314}$$
$$d_3^* = -\Theta(d_{114} - 1) + d_{324}$$
$$d_4^* = d_{314}$$
$$d_5^* = -\Theta(d_{334} - 1)$$
$$d_6^* = 0 \qquad (A6.9)$$
$$d_7^* = -\Theta(d_{234} + d_{324}) + (d_{334} - 1)$$
$$d_8^* = -\Theta(d_{134} + d_{314})$$
$$d_9^* = d_{334} - 1$$

where $\Theta = -ds/d\gamma$. Similarly the coefficients in equations (A6.7) should be replaced respectively by

$$m_1^* = -\Theta(d_{224} - 1) - d_{234}$$
$$m_2^* = -\Theta(d_{124} + d_{214}) - d_{134}$$
$$m_3^* = -\Theta(d_{114} - 1) - d_{234}$$

$$m_4^* = -d_{134}$$
$$m_5^* = -\Theta(d_{334} - 1)$$
$$m_6^* = 0$$
$$m_7^* = -\Theta(d_{234} + d_{324}) - (d_{334} - 1)$$
$$m_8^* = -\Theta(d_{134} + d_{314})$$
$$m_9^* = -(d_{334} - 1)$$

(A6.10)

APPENDIX 7

Coefficients in equation (6.127)

In equation (6.125),

$$\begin{vmatrix} M_2/C_{\theta 0}^3 & M_0/C_{\theta 0} \\ N_2/C_{\theta 0}^3 & N_0/C_{\theta 0} \end{vmatrix}^2 + \begin{vmatrix} M_2/C_{\theta 0}^3 & M_1/C_{\theta 0}^2 \\ N_2/C_{\theta 0}^3 & N_1/C_{\theta 0}^2 \end{vmatrix} \begin{vmatrix} M_0/C_{\theta 0} & M_1/C_{\theta 0}^2 \\ N_0/C_{\theta 0} & N_1/C_{\theta 0}^2 \end{vmatrix} = 0$$

the elements $M_2/C_{\theta 0}^3, M_1/C_{\theta 0}^2, M_0/C_{\theta 0}$, according to equations (A6.8), are

$$\left. \begin{aligned} M_2/C_{\theta 0}^3 &= m_1\tau^3 + m_2\tau^2 + m_3\tau + m_4 \\ M_1/C_{\theta 0}^2 &= m_7\tau^2 + m_8\tau + m_9 \\ M_0/C_{\theta 0} &= m_5\tau + m_6 \end{aligned} \right\} \qquad (A7.1)$$

where $\tau = \tan\theta_0$, and the coefficients $m_1, m_2, \ldots, m_9$ are already given in equations (A6.7). The elements $N_2/C_{\theta 0}^3, N_1/C_{\theta 0}^2, N_0/C_{\theta 0}$, according to equations (A6.1), are

$$\left. \begin{aligned} N_2/C_{\theta 0}^3 &= n_1\tau^3 + n_2\tau^2 + n_3\tau + n_4 \\ N_1/C_{\theta 0}^2 &= n_7\tau^2 + n_8\tau + n_9 \\ N_0/C_{\theta 0} &= n_5\tau + n_6 \end{aligned} \right\} \qquad (A7.2)$$

where the coefficients $n_1, n_2, \ldots, n_9$ are already given in equations (A6.2). Denoting

$$\Phi_{ij} = \begin{vmatrix} m_i & m_j \\ n_i & n_j \end{vmatrix} = m_i n_j - m_j n_i,$$

26 2×2 determinants may be evaluated according to the following scheme:

Subscript	5	6	7	8	9
1	Φ_{15}	Φ_{16}	Φ_{17}	Φ_{18}	Φ_{19}
2	Φ_{25}	Φ_{26}	Φ_{27}	Φ_{28}	Φ_{29}
3	Φ_{35}	Φ_{36}	Φ_{37}	Φ_{38}	Φ_{39}
4	Φ_{45}	Φ_{46}	Φ_{47}	Φ_{48}	Φ_{49}
5	—	—	Φ_{57}	Φ_{58}	Φ_{59}
6	—	—	Φ_{67}	Φ_{68}	Φ_{69}

The following notations are used for sums of determinants:

$$\Omega_1 = \Phi_{16} + \Phi_{25}$$
$$\Omega_2 = \Phi_{18} + \Phi_{27}$$
$$\Omega_3 = \Phi_{26} + \Phi_{35}$$
$$\Omega_4 = \Phi_{36} + \Phi_{45}$$
$$\Omega_5 = \Phi_{39} + \Phi_{48}$$
$$\Omega_6 = \Phi_{58} + \Phi_{67}$$
$$\Omega_7 = \Phi_{59} + \Phi_{68}$$
$$\Omega_8 = \Phi_{19} + \Phi_{28} + \Phi_{37}$$
$$\Omega_9 = \Phi_{29} + \Phi_{38} + \Phi_{47}$$

The coefficients in equation (6.127) are, denoting $\tan(-\gamma_{12}/2)$ by τ_1:

$$
\left.
\begin{aligned}
g_8 &= \Phi_{15}^2 + \Phi_{17}\Phi_{57} \\
g_{05} &= g_8\tau_1 + g_7 \\
g_{04} &= g_8\tau_1^2 + g_7\tau_1 + g_6 \\
g_{03} &= g_8\tau_1^3 + g_7\tau_1^2 + g_6\tau_1 + g_5 \\
g_{02} &= g_8\tau_1^4 + g_7\tau_1^3 + g_6\tau_1^2 + g_5\tau_1 + g_4 \\
g_{01} &= g_8\tau_1^5 + g_7\tau_1^4 + g_6\tau_1^3 + g_5\tau_1^2 + g_4\tau_1 + g_3 \\
g_{00} &= g_8\tau_1^6 + g_7\tau_1^5 + g_6\tau_1^4 + g_5\tau_1^3 + g_4\tau_1^2 + g_3\tau_1 + g_2
\end{aligned}
\right\} \tag{A7.3}
$$

where, also in equation (6.126),

$$
\left.
\begin{aligned}
g_8 &= \Phi_{15}^2 + \Phi_{17}\Phi_{57} \\
g_7 &= 2\Phi_{15}\Omega_1 + \Phi_{17}\Omega_6 + \Phi_{57}\Omega_2 \\
g_6 &= \Omega_1^2 + 2\Phi_{15}\Omega_3 + \Phi_{17}\Omega_7 + \Omega_2\Omega_6 + \Phi_{57}\Omega_8 \\
g_5 &= 2\Phi_{15}\Omega_4 + 2\Omega_1\Omega_3 + \Phi_{17}\Phi_{69} + \Omega_2\Omega_7 + \Omega_6\Omega_8 + \Phi_{57}\Omega_9 \\
g_4 &= \Omega_3^2 + 2\Phi_{15}\Phi_{46} + 2\Omega_1\Omega_4 + \Phi_{69}\Omega_2 + \Omega_7\Omega_8 + \Omega_6\Omega_9 + \Phi_{57}\Omega_5 \\
g_3 &= 2\Phi_{46}\Omega_1 + 2\Omega_3\Omega_4 + \Phi_{69}\Omega_8 + \Omega_7\Omega_9 + \Omega_5\Omega_6 + \Phi_{49}\Phi_{57} \\
g_2 &= \Omega_4^2 + 2\Phi_{46}\Omega_3 + \Phi_{69}\Omega_9 + \Omega_5\Omega_7 + \Phi_{49}\Omega_6 \\
g_1 &= 2\Phi_{46}\Omega_4 + \Phi_{69}\Omega_5 + \Phi_{49}\Omega_7
\end{aligned}
\right\}
$$

$$\tag{A7.4}$$

As a cross check of the correctness of the coefficients thus computed, the following two conditions should be satisfied:

$$
\left.
\begin{aligned}
\Phi_{46}^2 + \Phi_{49}\Phi_{69} &= 0 \\
g_8\tau_1^7 + g_7\tau_1^6 + g_6\tau_1^5 + g_5\tau_1^4 + g_4\tau_1^3 + g_3\tau_1^2 + g_2\tau_1 + g_1 &= 0
\end{aligned}
\right\} \tag{A7.5}
$$

Expanding equation (6.128) by means of equations (A7.1) and (A7.2) gives the value of $\tan p_0$ corresponding to each real root τ_0 of equation (6.127):

$$\tan p_0 = -\frac{\Phi_{15}\tau_0^4 + \Omega_1\tau_0^3 + \Omega_3\tau_0^2 + \Omega_4\tau_0 + \Phi_{46}}{\cos\theta_0(\Phi_{17}\tau_0^5 + \Omega_2\tau_0^4 + \Omega_8\tau_0^3 + \Omega_9\tau_0^2 + \Omega_5\tau_0 + \Phi_{49})}$$

(A7.6)

It should be noted that, in spite of the correctness of equation (A7.6), the computation of either its numerator or denominator often involves the subtraction of two nearly equal numbers, and the significant figures may hence be lost, thus resulting in an erroneous value of $\tan p_0$. A safe way is by substituting each value of θ_0 ($= \tan^{-1}\tau_0$) back into equations (A6.8) and (A6.1) to work out the coefficients $M_0, M_1, M_2; N_0, N_1, N_2$ of equations (6.122) and (6.91) and finding the two roots of each quadratic equation. The value of $\tan p_0$ that is identical in both quadratic equations is the correct one.

APPENDIX 8

Coefficients in equation of k_{A0}-curve

A8.1 **Transformation matrix** $\mathbb{M}_Q$

Referring to Fig. 7.7, suppose the coordinates of $E_1(x_1, y_1, z_1)$, $E_2(x_2, y_2, z_2)$ and the angle $\phi_2 (= \phi_{12})$ are given. The coordinates (x_Q, y_Q, z_Q) of Q as mentioned in Section 7.3.2 can be found as follows:

$$\cos E_1 E_2 = x_1 x_2 + y_1 y_2 + z_1 z_2$$

$$\sin QE_1 = \sin QE_2 = \sqrt{\left(\frac{1 - \cos E_1 E_2}{1 - \cos \phi_2}\right)}, \quad 0 \leqslant QE_1 = QE_2 \leqslant 90°$$

Let

$$\left.\begin{aligned}
\Delta &= x_2 y_1 - x_1 y_2 \\
\Delta_1 &= z_2 x_1 - z_1 x_2 \\
\Delta_2 &= z_2 y_1 - z_1 y_2 \\
q_2 &= \Delta^2 + \Delta_1^2 + \Delta_2^2 \\
q_1 &= 2\cos QE_1 [(x_2 - x_1)\Delta_1 + (y_2 - y_1)\Delta_2] \\
q_0 &= \cos^2 QE_1 [(y_2 - y_1)^2 + (x_2 - x_1)^2] - \Delta^2
\end{aligned}\right\}$$

Solve the following quadratic equation for z_Q:

$$q_2 z_Q^2 + q_1 z_Q + q_0 = 0 \tag{A8.1}$$

and then compute

$$\left.\begin{aligned}
x_Q &= [-(y_2 - y_1)\cos QE_1 - z_Q \Delta_2]/\Delta \\
y_Q &= [(x_2 - x_1)\cos QE_1 + z_Q \Delta_1]/\Delta
\end{aligned}\right\} \tag{A8.2}$$

There are two sets of solutions corresponding to the two roots of equation (A8.1). The correct one is the one that satisfies the following equations:

$$\left.\begin{aligned}
(x_Q^2 V_{\phi 2} + C_{\phi 2})x_1 + (x_Q y_Q V_{\phi 2} - z_Q S_{\phi 2})y_1 + (x_Q z_Q V_{\phi 2} + y_Q S_{\phi 2})z_1 &= x_2 \\
(x_Q y_Q V_{\phi 2} + z_Q S_{\phi 2})x_1 + (y_Q^2 V_{\phi 2} + C_{\phi 2})y_1 + (y_Q z_Q V_{\phi 2} - x_Q S_{\phi 2})z_1 &= y_2 \\
(x_Q z_Q V_{\phi 2} - y_Q S_{\phi 2})x_1 + (y_Q z_Q V_{\phi 2} + x_Q S_{\phi 2})y_1 + (z_Q^2 V_{\phi 2} + C_{\phi 2})z_1 &= z_2
\end{aligned}\right\}$$

$$\tag{A8.3}$$

Equations (A8.3) are obtained by applying equations (A2.34) to the present case. According to equations (A4.7), the spherical rectangular coordinates of Q are

$$u_Q = \tan^{-1} \frac{x_Q}{z_Q}, \qquad -90° \leqslant u_Q \leqslant 90°$$

$$v_Q = \sin^{-1} y_Q, \qquad -90° \leqslant v_Q \leqslant 90°$$

For brevity use the symbols $S_u = \sin u_Q$, $C_v = \cos v_Q$, etc. The angle χ, negative as shown in Fig. 7.7, is computed from

$$\tan \chi = (C_u x_1 - S_u z_1)/(S_u S_v x_1 - C_v y_1 + C_u S_v z_1), \qquad -90° \leqslant \chi \leqslant 90°$$

The coordinate system is rotated from the original xyz position about the y, x and z axes through respective angles u_Q, $-v_Q$ and χ, to the position $x'y'z'$. The transformation matrix is then

$$\mathbb{M}_Q = \begin{bmatrix} C_\chi & S_\chi & 0 \\ -S_\chi & C_\chi & 0 \\ 0 & 0 & 1 \end{bmatrix} \begin{bmatrix} 1 & 0 & 0 \\ 0 & C_v & -S_v \\ 0 & S_v & C_v \end{bmatrix} \begin{bmatrix} C_u & 0 & -S_u \\ 0 & 1 & 0 \\ S_u & 0 & C_u \end{bmatrix}$$

Multiplication of these three matrices results in the final form of $\mathbb{M}_Q$ in equation (7.32).

A8.2   Coefficients in equation (7.30)

Upon substitution of equations (7.27) into equation (7.29), each one of the nine elements contains six terms in the variables x_0, y_0, z_0. Expanding this determinant results in 216 terms, each term being a 3×3 determinant containing only single term elements. These are reduced to the following expression containing only third and lower degree terms in the variables x_0, y_0, z_0, with constant coefficients:

$$\left. \begin{aligned} &k_{31}x_0^3 + k_{32}y_0^3 + k_{33}z_0^3 + k_{34}x_0^2 y_0 + k_{35}x_0^2 z_0 + k_{36}y_0^2 z_0 + k_{37}y_0^2 x_0 \\ &+ k_{38}z_0^2 x_0 + k_{39}z_0^2 y_0 + k_{30}x_0 y_0 z_0 + k_{21}x_0^2 + k_{22}y_0^2 + k_{23}z_0^2 \\ &+ k_{24}x_0 y_0 + k_{25}y_0 z_0 + k_{26}x_0 z_0 + k_{11}x_0 + k_{12}y_0 + k_{13}z_0 + k_0 = 0 \end{aligned} \right\}$$

$$(A8.4)$$

where

$$k_{31} = |V_{\phi i}x_i, S_{\phi i}z_i, C_{\phi i}z_i - z_1| + |V_{\phi i}x_i, C_{\phi i}y_i - y_1, -S_{\phi i}y_i|, \quad i = 2, 3, 4$$

$$k_{32} = |-S_{\phi i}z_i, V_{\phi i}y_i, C_{\phi i}z_i - z_1| + |C_{\phi i}x_i - x_1, V_{\phi i}y_i, S_{\phi i}x_i|$$

$$k_{33} = |S_{\phi i}y_i, C_{\phi i}y_i - y_1, V_{\phi i}z_i| + |C_{\phi i}x_i - x_1, -S_{\phi i}x_i, V_{\phi i}z_i|$$

$$k_{34} = |V_{\phi i}x_i, C_{\phi i}y_i - y_1, S_{\phi i}x_i| + |V_{\phi i}y_i, S_{\phi i}z_i, C_{\phi i}z_i - z_1|$$

$$+ |V_{\phi i}y_i, C_{\phi i}y_i - y_1, -S_{\phi i}y_i| + |C_{\phi i}x_i - x_1, V_{\phi i}x_i, -S_{\phi i}y_i|$$

$$k_{35} = |V_{\phi i}x_i, -S_{\phi i}x_i, C_{\phi i}z_i - z_1| + |V_{\phi i}z_i, S_{\phi i}z_i, C_{\phi i}z_i - z_1|$$
$$+ |V_{\phi i}z_i, C_{\phi i}y_i - y_1, -S_{\phi i}y_i| + |C_{\phi i}x_i - x_1, S_{\phi i}z_i, V_{\phi i}x_i|$$

$$k_{36} = |S_{\phi i}y_i, V_{\phi i}y_i, C_{\phi i}z_i - z_1| + |-S_{\phi i}z_i, V_{\phi i}z_i, C_{\phi i}z_i - z_1|$$
$$+ |C_{\phi i}x_i - x_1, V_{\phi i}z_i, S_{\phi i}x_i| + |-S_{\phi i}z_i, C_{\phi i}y_i - y_1, V_{\phi i}y_i|$$

$$k_{37} = |C_{\phi i}x_i - x_1, V_{\phi i}y_i, -S_{\phi i}y_i| + |-S_{\phi i}z_i, V_{\phi i}x_i, C_{\phi i}z_i - z_1|$$
$$+ |C_{\phi i}x_i - x_1, V_{\phi i}x_i, S_{\phi i}x_i| + |V_{\phi i}y_i, C_{\phi i}y_i - y_1, S_{\phi i}x_i|$$

$$k_{38} = |C_{\phi i}x_i - x_1, S_{\phi i}z_i, V_{\phi i}z_i| + |S_{\phi i}y_i, C_{\phi i}y_i - y_1, V_{\phi i}x_i|$$
$$+ |C_{\phi i}x_i - x_1, -S_{\phi i}x_i, V_{\phi i}x_i| + |V_{\phi i}z_i, -S_{\phi i}x_i, C_{\phi i}z_i - z_1|$$

$$k_{39} = |-S_{\phi i}z_i, C_{\phi i}y_i - y_1, V_{\phi i}z_i| + |S_{\phi i}y_i, C_{\phi i}y_i - y_1, V_{\phi i}y_i|$$
$$+ |C_{\phi i}x_i - x_1, -S_{\phi i}x_i, V_{\phi i}y_i| + |S_{\phi i}y_i, V_{\phi i}z_i, C_{\phi i}z_i - z_1|$$

$$k_{30} = |V_{\phi i}y_i, -S_{\phi i}x_i, C_{\phi i}z_i - z_1| + |V_{\phi i}z_i, C_{\phi i}y_i - y_1, S_{\phi i}x_i|$$
$$+ |C_{\phi i}x_i - x_1, V_{\phi i}z_i, -S_{\phi i}y_i| + |S_{\phi i}y_i, V_{\phi i}x_i, C_{\phi i}z_i - z_1|$$
$$+ |-S_{\phi i}z_i, C_{\phi i}y_i - y_1, V_{\phi i}x_i| + |C_{\phi i}x_i - x_1, S_{\phi i}z_i, V_{\phi i}y_i|$$

$$k_{21} = |V_{\phi i}x_i, C_{\phi i}y_i - y_1, C_{\phi i}z_i - z_1| + |C_{\phi i}x_i - x_1, S_{\phi i}z_i, -S_{\phi i}y_i|$$
$$+ |S_{\phi i}y_i, S_{\phi i}z_i, V_{\phi i}x_i|$$

$$k_{22} = |C_{\phi i}x_i - x_1, V_{\phi i}y_i, C_{\phi i}z_i - z_1| + |-S_{\phi i}z_i, C_{\phi i}y_i - y_1, S_{\phi i}x_i|$$
$$+ |V_{\phi i}y_i, S_{\phi i}z_i, S_{\phi i}x_i|$$

$$k_{23} = |C_{\phi i}x_i - x_1, C_{\phi i}y_i - y_1, V_{\phi i}z_i| + |S_{\phi i}y_i, -S_{\phi i}x_i, C_{\phi i}z_i - z_1|$$
$$+ |S_{\phi i}y_i, V_{\phi i}z_i, S_{\phi i}x_i|$$

$$k_{24} = |V_{\phi i}y_i, C_{\phi i}y_i - y_1, C_{\phi i}z_i - z_1| + |-S_{\phi i}z_i, C_{\phi i}y_i - y_1, -S_{\phi i}y_i|$$
$$+ |C_{\phi i}x_i - x_1, V_{\phi i}x_i, C_{\phi i}z_i - z_1| + |C_{\phi i}x_i - x_1, S_{\phi i}z_i, S_{\phi i}x_i|$$
$$+ |V_{\phi i}x_i, S_{\phi i}z_i, S_{\phi i}x_i| + |V_{\phi i}y_i, S_{\phi i}z_i, -S_{\phi i}y_i|$$

$$k_{25} = |C_{\phi i}x_i - x_1, V_{\phi i}z_i, C_{\phi i}z_i - z_1| + |-S_{\phi i}z_i, -S_{\phi i}x_i, C_{\phi i}z_i - z_1|$$
$$+ |C_{\phi i}x_i - x_1, C_{\phi i}y_i - y_1, V_{\phi i}y_i|$$
$$+ |S_{\phi i}y_i, C_{\phi i}y_i - y_1, S_{\phi i}x_i| + |S_{\phi i}y_i, V_{\phi i}y_i, S_{\phi i}x_i|$$
$$+ |-S_{\phi i}z_i, V_{\phi i}z_i, S_{\phi i}x_i|$$

$$k_{26} = |C_{\phi i}x_i - x_1, C_{\phi i}y_i - y_1, V_{\phi i}x_i| + |C_{\phi i}x_i - x_1, -S_{\phi i}x_i, -S_{\phi i}y_i|$$
$$+ |V_{\phi i}z_i, C_{\phi i}y_i - y_1, C_{\phi i}z_i - z_1| + |S_{\phi i}y_i, S_{\phi i}z_i, C_{\phi i}z_i - z_1|$$
$$+ |V_{\phi i}x_i, S_{\phi i}x_i, S_{\phi i}y_i| + |V_{\phi i}z_i, S_{\phi i}z_i, -S_{\phi i}y_i|$$

$$k_{11} = |C_{\phi i}x_i - x_1, S_{\phi i}z_i, C_{\phi i}z_i - z_1| + |C_{\phi i}x_i - x_1, C_{\phi i}y_i - y_1, -S_{\phi i}y_i|$$

$$k_{12} = |-S_{\phi i}z_i, C_{\phi i}y_i - y_1, C_{\phi i}z_i - z_1| + |C_{\phi i}x_i - x_1, C_{\phi i}y_i - y_1, S_{\phi i}x_i|$$

$$k_{13} = |S_{\phi i}y_i, C_{\phi i}y_i - y_1, C_{\phi i}z_i - z_1| + |C_{\phi i}x_i - x_1, -S_{\phi i}x_i, C_{\phi i}z_i - z_1|$$

$$k_0 = |C_{\phi i}x_i - x_1, C_{\phi i}y_i - y_1, C_{\phi i}z_i - z_1|$$

After transforming x_0, y_0, z_0 into spherical polar coordinates (p_0, θ_0) by means of equations (A4.2), equation (A8.4) becomes

$$L_3 t^3 + L_2 t^2 + L_1 t + L_0 = -(H_2 t^2 + H_1 t + H_0)\frac{1}{\cos p_0} \tag{A8.5}$$

where

$$L_3 = k_{31}C_\theta^3 + k_{34}C_\theta^2 S_\theta + k_{37}C_\theta S_\theta^2 + k_{32}S_\theta^3 + k_{11}C_\theta + k_{12}S_\theta$$
$$L_2 = k_{35}C_\theta^2 + k_{30}C_\theta S_\theta + k_{36}S_\theta^2 + k_{13}$$
$$L_1 = (k_{38} + k_{11})C_\theta + (k_{39} + k_{12})S_\theta$$
$$L_0 = k_{33} + k_{13}$$
$$H_2 = k_{21}C_\theta^2 + k_{24}C_\theta S_\theta + k_{22}S_\theta^2 + k_0$$
$$H_1 = k_{26}C_\theta + k_{25}S_\theta$$
$$H_0 = k_{23} + k_0$$

and

$$t = \tan p_0$$

with the abbreviations $S_\theta = \sin\theta_0$ and $C_\theta = \cos\theta_0$.

Note that $1/\cos p_0 = \sqrt{(1 + t^2)}$. Squaring equation (A8.5) once gives finally equation (7.30) of the k_{40}-curve, where

$$q_{06} = L_3^2 - H_2^2$$
$$q_{05} = 2(L_3 L_2 - H_2 H_1)$$
$$q_{04} = L_2^2 + 2L_3 L_1 - H_1^2 - 2H_2 H_0 - H_2^2$$
$$q_{03} = 2(L_3 L_0 + L_2 L_1 - H_1 H_0 - H_2 H_1)$$
$$q_{02} = L_1^2 + 2L_2 L_0 - H_0^2 - 2H_2 H_0 - H_1^2$$
$$q_{01} = 2(L_1 L_0 - H_1 H_0)$$
$$q_{00} = L_0^2 - H_0^2$$

APPENDIX 9

Synthesis equations for function generators – finitely separated relative positions

A9.1 **Four precision-points** $P_1-P_2-P_3-P_4$

Three crank rotation pairs ϕ_2, ψ_2; ϕ_3, ψ_3; ϕ_4, ψ_4 are to be coordinated. Compute first by equations (8.4) and (8.5):

$$\cot r_{ai} = -\frac{\sin\dfrac{\phi_i}{2}\cot\dfrac{\psi_i}{2} - \cos f \cos\dfrac{\phi_i}{2}}{\sin f} \qquad [(8.4)]$$

$$\cot r_{bi} = -\frac{-\sin\dfrac{\psi_i}{2}\cot\dfrac{\phi_i}{2} + \cos f \cos\dfrac{\psi_i}{2}}{\sin f} \qquad [(8.5)]$$

Since an arctangent function can only give a value of the argument within the range $-90°$ to $+90°$, care should be taken that both r_{ai} and r_{bi} thus found are referred to the same R_i, or to the same antipode of R_i.

Let

$$
\left.
\begin{array}{ll}
s_{1i} = \sin r_{ai} & s_{2i} = \cos r_{ai} \\[4pt]
s_{3i} = \sin r_{bi} & s_{4i} = \cos r_{bi} \\[4pt]
s_{5i} = \sin\dfrac{\phi_i}{2} & s_{6i} = \cos\dfrac{\phi_i}{2} \quad i = 2,3,4 \\[4pt]
s_{7i} = \sin\dfrac{\psi_i}{2} & s_{8i} = \cos\dfrac{\psi_i}{2} \\[4pt]
t = \tan\phi_0 \\[4pt]
q = \tan\psi_0
\end{array}
\right\} \qquad \text{(A9.1)}
$$

If the first column of the determinant in equation (8.9) is divided by $\cos\psi_0$, the second column by $\cos\phi_0$ and the third column by $\cos\phi_0\cos\psi_0$, expanding this determinant then results in the quadratic equation (8.10) in the unknown

q, with t as a parameter,

$$a_2q^2 + a_1q + a_0 = 0 \qquad [(8.10)]$$

where

$$\left.\begin{array}{l} a_2 = u_1t^2 + u_2t + u_3 \\ a_1 = u_7t^2 + u_8t + u_9 \\ a_0 = u_4t^2 + u_5t + u_6 \end{array}\right\} \qquad (A9.2)$$

The nine u's in equations (A9.2) are all 3×3 determinants. For brevity each determinant will be written in a single representative row with subscript i. We use the notations

$$c_{18i} = s_{1i}s_{8i}, \quad c_{258i} = s_{2i}s_{5i}s_{8i}, \text{ etc.}$$

for further simplicity. The nine determinants are

$$\left.\begin{array}{l} u_1 = |c_{18i},\ c_{36i},\ c_{258i} - c_{467i}| \\ u_2 = |c_{18i},\ c_{36i},\ -c_{268i} - c_{457i}| + |c_{18i},\ c_{35i},\ c_{258i} - c_{467i}| \\ u_3 = |c_{18i},\ c_{35i},\ -c_{268i} - c_{457i}| \\ u_4 = |c_{17i},\ c_{36i},\ c_{257i} + c_{468i}| \\ u_5 = |c_{17i},\ c_{36i},\ -c_{267i} + c_{458i}| + |c_{17i},\ c_{35i},\ c_{257i} + c_{468i}| \\ u_6 = |c_{17i},\ c_{35i},\ -c_{267i} + c_{458i}| \\ u_7 = |c_{18i},\ c_{36i},\ c_{257i} + c_{468i}| + |c_{17i},\ c_{36i},\ c_{258i} - c_{467i}| \\ u_8 = |c_{18i},\ c_{36i},\ -c_{267i} + c_{458i}| + |c_{18i},\ c_{35i},\ c_{257i} + c_{468i}| \\ \qquad + |c_{17i},\ c_{36i},\ -c_{268i} - c_{457i}| + |c_{17i},\ c_{35i},\ c_{258i} - c_{467i}| \\ u_9 = |c_{18i},\ c_{35i},\ -c_{267i} + c_{458i}| + |c_{17i},\ c_{35i},\ -c_{268i} - c_{457i}| \end{array}\right\}$$

$$(A9.3)$$

For each assumed value of ϕ_0, there are two roots of equation (8.10). For each real root q_0 we have

$$\psi_0 = \tan^{-1} q_0$$

Lengths of driving and driven cranks:

$$a = \tan^{-1}\frac{\delta}{\delta_a \cos\phi_0} \qquad (A9.4)$$

$$b = \tan^{-1}\frac{\delta}{\delta_b \cos\psi_0} \qquad (A9.5)$$

where

$$\left.\begin{array}{l} \delta = (w_1t_0 + w_2)q_0 + (w_3t_0 + w_4) \\ \delta_a = (w_5t_0^2 + w_6t_0 + w_7)q_0 + (w_8t_0^2 + w_9t_0 + w_{10}) \\ \delta_b = (w_{11}q_0^2 + w_{12}q_0 + w_{13})t_0 + (w_{14}q_0^2 + w_{15}q_0 + w_{16}) \end{array}\right\} \qquad (A9.6)$$

$$w_1 = |c_{18i}, \; c_{36i}, \; 1|$$

$$w_2 = |c_{18i}, \; c_{35i}, \; 1|$$

$$w_3 = |c_{17i}, \; c_{36i}, \; 1|$$

$$w_4 = |c_{17i}, \; c_{35i}, \; 1|$$

$$w_5 = |c_{258i} - c_{467i}, \; c_{36i}, \; 1|$$

$$w_6 = |c_{258i} - c_{467i}, \; c_{35i}, \; 1| + |-c_{268i} - c_{457i}, \; c_{36i}, \; 1|$$

$$w_7 = |-c_{268i} - c_{457i}, \; c_{35i}, \; 1|$$

$$w_8 = |c_{257i} + c_{468i}, \; c_{36i}, \; 1|$$

$$w_9 = |c_{257i} + c_{468i}, \; c_{35i}, \; 1| + |-c_{267i} + c_{458i}, \; c_{36i}, \; 1|$$

$$w_{10} = |-c_{267i} + c_{458i}, \; c_{35i}, \; 1|$$

$$w_{11} = |c_{18i}, \; -c_{258i} + c_{467i}, \; 1|$$

$$w_{12} = |c_{18i}, \; -c_{257i} - c_{468i}, \; 1| + |c_{17i}, \; -c_{258i} + c_{467i}, \; 1|$$

$$w_{13} = |c_{17i}, \; -c_{257i} - c_{468i}, \; 1|$$

$$w_{14} = |c_{18i}, \; c_{268i} + c_{457i}, \; 1|$$

$$w_{15} = |c_{18i}, \; c_{267i} - c_{458i}, \; 1| + |c_{17i}, \; c_{268i} + c_{457i}, \; 1|$$

$$w_{16} = |c_{17i}, \; c_{267i} - c_{458i}, \; 1|$$

(A9.7)

Length of coupler:

$$c = \cos^{-1}\,[\cos f \cos a \cos b$$
$$+ \sin f\,(\sin a \cos b \cos \phi_0 - \cos a \sin b \cos \psi_0)$$
$$+ \sin a \sin b\,(\sin \phi_0 \sin \psi_0 + \cos f \cos \phi_0 \cos \psi_0)]$$

(A9.8)

A9.2.   Five precision-points P_1–P_2–P_3–P_4–P_5

This is treated as a combination of cases $(P_1$–P_2–P_3–$P_4)$ and $(P_1$–P_2–P_3–$P_5)$.

Four crank rotation pairs ϕ_2, ψ_2; ϕ_3, ψ_3; ϕ_4, ψ_4; ϕ_5, ψ_5 are to be coordinated.

Equations (A9.3) remain unchanged for the evaluation of $u_1, u_2, \dots, u_9$ for $i = 2, 3, 4$. For $i = 2, 3, 5$ the coefficients of equation (8.11) corresponding to equations (A9.2), are

$$b_2 = v_1 t^2 + v_2 t + v_3$$
$$b_1 = v_7 t^2 + v_8 t + v_9$$
$$b_0 = v_4 t^2 + v_5 t + v_6$$

(A9.9)

The values of $v_1, v_2, \dots, v_9$ may be evaluated by using equations (A9.3), e.g.

$$v_1 = |c_{18i}, \; c_{36i}, \; c_{258i} - c_{467i}| \quad i = 2, 3, 5$$

etc. Denoting

$$\triangle_{ij} = \begin{bmatrix} u_i & u_j \\ v_i & v_j \end{bmatrix} = u_i v_j - u_j v_i$$

we may evaluate 27 determinants according to the following scheme:

Subscript	4	5	6	7	8	9
1	$\triangle_{14}$	$\triangle_{15}$	$\triangle_{16}$	$\triangle_{17}$	$\triangle_{18}$	$\triangle_{19}$
2	$\triangle_{24}$	$\triangle_{25}$	$\triangle_{26}$	$\triangle_{27}$	$\triangle_{28}$	$\triangle_{29}$
3	$\triangle_{34}$	$\triangle_{35}$	$\triangle_{36}$	$\triangle_{37}$	$\triangle_{38}$	$\triangle_{39}$
4	—	—	—	$\triangle_{47}$	$\triangle_{48}$	$\triangle_{49}$
5	—	—	—	$\triangle_{57}$	$\triangle_{58}$	$\triangle_{59}$
6	—	—	—	$\triangle_{67}$	$\triangle_{68}$	$\triangle_{69}$

The following notations are used for the sums of determinants:

$$\Lambda_1 = \triangle_{15} + \triangle_{24}$$
$$\Lambda_2 = \triangle_{18} + \triangle_{27}$$
$$\Lambda_3 = \triangle_{26} + \triangle_{35}$$
$$\Lambda_4 = \triangle_{29} + \triangle_{38}$$
$$\Lambda_5 = \triangle_{48} + \triangle_{57}$$
$$\Lambda_6 = \triangle_{59} + \triangle_{68}$$
$$\Lambda_7 = \triangle_{16} + \triangle_{25} + \triangle_{34}$$
$$\Lambda_8 = \triangle_{19} + \triangle_{28} + \triangle_{37}$$
$$\Lambda_9 = \triangle_{49} + \triangle_{58} + \triangle_{67}$$

The first six coefficients of equation (8.13) are:

$$f_8 = \triangle_{14}^2 + \triangle_{17}\triangle_{47}$$
$$f_7 = 2\triangle_{14}\Lambda_1 + \triangle_{17}\Lambda_5 + \triangle_{47}\Lambda_2$$
$$f_6 = \Lambda_1^2 + 2\triangle_{14}\Lambda_7 + \triangle_{17}\Lambda_9 + \Lambda_2\Lambda_5 + \triangle_{47}\Lambda_8$$
$$f_5 = 2(\triangle_{14}\Lambda_3 + \Lambda_1\Lambda_7) + \triangle_{17}\Lambda_6 + \Lambda_2\Lambda_9 + \Lambda_5\Lambda_8 + \triangle_{47}\Lambda_4$$
$$f_4 = \Lambda_7^2 + 2(\triangle_{14}\triangle_{36} + \Lambda_1\Lambda_3) + \triangle_{17}\triangle_{69} + \Lambda_2\Lambda_6 + \Lambda_8\Lambda_9$$
$$+ \Lambda_4\Lambda_5 + \triangle_{39}\triangle_{47}$$
$$f_3 = 2(\triangle_{36}\Lambda_1 + \Lambda_3\Lambda_7) + \triangle_{69}\Lambda_2 + \Lambda_6\Lambda_8 + \Lambda_4\Lambda_9 + \triangle_{39}\Lambda_5$$

$$(A9.10)$$

Denote the three known roots of equation (8.13) by

$$t_1 = -\tan\frac{\phi_2}{2}$$

$$t_2 = -\tan\frac{\phi_3}{2}$$

$$t_3 = -\tan\frac{\phi_2 + \phi_3}{2}$$

and let

$$g_1 = t_1 + t_2 + t_3$$
$$g_2 = t_1 t_2 + t_2 t_3 + t_3 t_1$$
$$g_3 = t_1 t_2 t_3$$

The coefficients of equation (8.14) are

$$f_{40} = g_1 f_8 + f_7$$
$$f_{30} = (g_1^2 - g_2) f_8 + g_1 f_7 + f_6$$
$$f_{20} = [g_1(g_1^2 - 2g_2) + g_3] f_8 + (g_1^2 - g_2) f_7 + g_1 f_6 + f_5$$
$$f_{10} = [g_1(g_1^3 - 3g_1 g_2 + 2g_3) + g_2^2] f_8 + [g_1(g_1^2 - 2g_2) + g_3] f_7$$
$$\qquad + (g_1^2 - g_2) f_6 + g_1 f_5 + f_4$$
$$f_{00} = [g_1(g_1^4 - 4g_1^2 g_2 + 3g_1 g_3 + 3g_2^2) - 2g_2 g_3] f_8$$
$$\qquad + [g_1(g_1^3 - 3g_1 g_2 + 2g_3) + g_2^2] f_7$$
$$\qquad + [g_1(g_1^2 - 2g_2) + g_3] f_6 + (g_1^2 - g_2) f_5 + g_1 f_4 + f_3$$

The values q_0 of q corresponding to each real root t_0 of equation (8.14) is found by expanding equation (8.15):

$$q_0 = -\frac{\triangle_{14} t_0^4 + \Lambda_1 t_0^3 + \Lambda_7 t_0^2 + \Lambda_3 t_0 + \triangle_{36}}{\triangle_{17} t_0^4 + \Lambda_2 t_0^3 + \Lambda_8 t_0^2 + \Lambda_4 t_0 + \triangle_{39}} \qquad (A9.11)$$

The starting crank angles are then determined by

$$\phi_0 = \tan^{-1} t_0$$

and

$$\psi_0 = \tan^{-1} q_0$$

For the calculation of the lengths of the driving and driven cranks and that of the coupler, equations (A9.4)–(A9.8) apply.

Synthesis equations for function generators – case $P_1 P_2 - P_3 P_4$

One crank rotation pair ϕ_3, ψ_3 is to be coordinated, and two prescribed velocity ratios ψ'_1 and ψ'_3 in positions P_1 and P_3 respectively are to be matched. Link length f and angle ϕ_0 are given.

Compute first

$$\cot r_{a3} = -\frac{\sin\frac{\phi_3}{2}\cot\frac{\psi_3}{2} - \cos f \cos\frac{\phi_3}{2}}{\sin f} \tag{A10.1}$$

and

$$\cot r_{b3} = -\frac{-\sin\frac{\psi_3}{2}\cot\frac{\phi_3}{2} + \cos f \cos\frac{\psi_3}{2}}{\sin f} \tag{A10.2}$$

Care should be taken that r_{a3} and r_{b3} thus found are both referred to the same point R_3, or to its antipode.

Let

$$c_1 = \sin r_{a3}$$
$$c_2 = \cos r_{a3}$$
$$c_3 = \sin r_{b3}$$
$$c_4 = \cos r_{b3}$$
$$c_5 = \sin\frac{\phi_3}{2}$$
$$c_6 = \cos\frac{\phi_3}{2}$$
$$c_7 = \sin\frac{\psi_3}{2}$$
$$c_8 = \cos\frac{\psi_3}{2}$$

$$c_u = \cos \psi_3$$
$$c_v = \sin \psi_3$$
$$c_x = \cos \phi_3$$
$$c_y = \sin \phi_3$$
$$t = \tan \phi_0$$
$$q = \tan \psi_0$$

and use the notations for the products:

$$c_{12} = c_1 c_2, \quad c_{123} = c_1 c_2 c_3, \quad c_{ux} = c_u c_x, \quad \text{etc.}$$

If the first column of the determinant in equation (8.47) is divided by $\cos \psi_0$, the second column by $\cos \phi_0$, and the third column by $\cos \phi_0 \cos \psi_0$, equation (8.47) may be written in the following form, the whole determinant being represented by a single row with subscript i:

$$|e_{1i}q + e_{2i}, \quad e_{3i}t + e_{4i}, \quad (e_{5i}t + e_{6i})q + (e_{7i}t + e_{8i})| = 0, \quad i = 1, 2, 3$$

$$(A10.3)$$

where

$$e_{11} = -\psi_1' S_f$$
$$e_{21} = 0$$
$$e_{31} = S_f$$
$$e_{41} = 0$$
$$e_{51} = 0$$
$$e_{61} = 1 - \psi_1' C_f$$
$$e_{71} = \psi_1' - C_f$$
$$e_{81} = 0$$
$$e_{12} = c_{18}$$
$$e_{22} = c_{17}$$
$$e_{32} = -c_{36}$$
$$e_{42} = -c_{35}$$
$$e_{52} = -c_{258} + c_{467}$$
$$e_{62} = c_{268} + c_{457}$$
$$e_{72} = -c_{257} - c_{468}$$
$$e_{82} = c_{267} - c_{458}$$
$$e_{13} = -\psi_3' c_u S_f$$
$$e_{23} = -\psi_3' c_v S_f$$
$$e_{33} = c_x S_f$$
$$e_{43} = c_y S_f$$
$$e_{53} = c_{uy}(\psi_3' C_f - 1) - c_{vx}(\psi_3' - C_f)$$

$$e_{63} = c_{ux}(1 - \psi'_3 C_f) - c_{vy}(\psi'_3 - C_f)$$
$$e_{73} = c_{vy}(\psi'_3 C_f - 1) + c_{ux}(\psi'_3 - C_f)$$
$$e_{83} = -c_{vx}(\psi'_3 C_f - 1) + c_{uy}(\psi'_3 - C_f)$$

Expansion of equation (A10.3) results in the quadratic equation (8.48) in the unknown $q = \tan \psi_0$ with $t = \tan \phi_0$ as a parameter:

$$a_2 q^2 + a_1 q + a_0 = 0 \qquad\qquad [(8.48)]$$

where

$$a_2 = u_1 t^2 + u_2 t + u_3$$
$$a_1 = u_7 t^2 + u_8 t + u_9$$
$$a_0 = u_4 t^2 + u_5 t + u_6$$

The nine u's are all 3×3 determinants, and are:

$$u_1 = |e_{1i}, e_{3i}, e_{5i}|$$
$$u_2 = |e_{1i}, e_{3i}, e_{6i}| + |e_{1i}, e_{4i}, e_{5i}|$$
$$u_3 = |e_{1i}, e_{4i}, e_{6i}|$$
$$u_4 = |e_{2i}, e_{3i}, e_{7i}|$$
$$u_5 = |e_{2i}, e_{3i}, e_{8i}| + |e_{2i}, e_{4i}, e_{7i}|$$
$$u_6 = |e_{2i}, e_{4i}, e_{8i}|$$
$$u_7 = |e_{1i}, e_{3i}, e_{7i}| + |e_{2i}, e_{3i}, e_{5i}|$$
$$u_8 = |e_{1i}, e_{3i}, e_{8i}| + |e_{1i}, e_{4i}, e_{7i}| + |e_{2i}, e_{3i}, e_{6i}| + |e_{2i}, e_{4i}, e_{5i}|$$
$$u_9 = |e_{1i}, e_{4i}, e_{8i}| + |e_{2i}, e_{4i}, e_{6i}|$$

For each assumed value of ϕ_0, there are two roots of equation (8.48). For each real root q_0 we have

$$\psi_0 = \tan^{-1} q_0$$

Lengths of driving and driven cranks:

$$a = \tan^{-1} \frac{\delta}{\delta_a \cos \phi_0} \qquad\qquad (A10.4)$$

$$b = \tan^{-1} \frac{\delta}{\delta_b \cos \psi_0} \qquad\qquad (A10.5)$$

where

$$\delta = (w_1 t_0 + w_2)q_0 + (w_3 t_0 + w_4)$$
$$\delta_a = (w_5 t_0^2 + w_6 t_0 + w_7)q_0 + (w_8 t_0^2 + w_9 t_0 + w_{10})$$
$$\delta_b = (w_{11} q_0^2 + w_{12} q_0 + w_{13})t_0 + (w_{14} q_0^2 + w_{15} q_0 + w_{16})$$
$$w_1 = |e_{1i}, e_{3i}, 1|$$
$$w_2 = |e_{1i}, e_{4i}, 1|$$
$$w_3 = |e_{2i}, e_{3i}, 1|$$
$$w_4 = |e_{2i}, e_{4i}, 1|$$

$$w_5 = |e_{5i}, e_{3i}, 1|$$
$$w_6 = |e_{5i}, e_{4i}, 1| + |e_{6i}, e_{3i}, 1|$$
$$w_7 = |e_{6i}, e_{4i}, 1|$$
$$w_8 = |e_{7i}, e_{3i}, 1|$$
$$w_9 = |e_{7i}, e_{4i}, 1| + |e_{8i}, e_{3i}, 1|$$
$$w_{10} = |e_{8i}, e_{4i}, 1|$$
$$w_{11} = |e_{1i}, e_{5i}, 1|$$
$$w_{12} = |e_{1i}, e_{7i}, 1| + |e_{2i}, e_{5i}, 1|$$
$$w_{13} = |e_{2i}, e_{7i}, 1|$$
$$w_{14} = |e_{1i}, e_{6i}, 1|$$
$$w_{15} = |e_{1i}, e_{8i}, 1| + |e_{2i}, e_{6i}, 1|$$
$$w_{16} = |e_{2i}, e_{8i}, 1|$$

The length of the coupler c is determined by equation (A9.8).

REFERENCES

Alt, H. (1921). Zur Synthese der ebenen Mechanismen. *Zeitschrift für angewandte Mathematik und Mechanik* **1**, 373–98.

Alt, H. (1932a). Zur Geometre der Koppelrastgetriebe. *Ingenieur-Archiv* **3**, 394–411.

Alt, H. (1932b). Der Übertragungswinkel und seine Bedeutung für das Konstruieren periodischer Getriebe. *Werkstattstechnik* **26**, 61–4.

Angeles, J. (1986). Optimierung ebener, sphärischer und räumlicher Getriebe zur approximierten Lagenzuordnung. *Mechanism and Machine Theory* **21**, 187–97.

Austin, T. C., Denavit, J.,& Hartenberg, R. S. (1965). Analysis of Errors in the Double Hooke Joint. *Trans, ASME, Journal of Engineering for Industry* **87B**,251-7.

Bagci, C. (1971). Static force and torque analysis using 3 × 3 screw matrix, and transmission criteria for space mechanisms. *Trans. ASME, Journal of Engineering for Industry* **93B**, 90–101.

Bagci, C. (1973). Design of spherical crank–rocker mechanism with optimum transmission. *Trans. ASME, Journal of Engineering for Industry* **95B**, 577–83.

Bagci, C. (1984). Geometric methods for the synthesis of spherical mechanisms for the generation of functions, paths and rigid body positions using conformal projections. *Mechanism and Machine Theory* **19**, 113–27.

Bagci, C. & Parekh, K.C. (1971). Minimum error synthesis of the spherical four-bar and Watt's type spherical six-bar mechanism for function generation. In *Proceedings of the Third World Congress on Theory of Machines and Mechanisms*, Vol. C, 1–18. Kupari, Yugoslavia.

Ball, Sir R.S. (1900). *A Treatise on Theory of Screws*, Section 10. Cambridge University Press, Cambridge.

Beyer, R. (1953). *Kinematische Getriebesynthese*. Springer-Verlag, Berlin.

Beyer, R. (1958). Space mechanisms. In *Transactions of the Fifth Conference on Mechanisms*, 141–63. The Penton Publishing Co., Cleveland, Ohio.

Beyer, R. (1963). *Technische Raumkinematik*. Springer, Berlin/Göttingen/Heidelberg.

Bisshopp, K.E. (1969). Note on spherical motion. *Journal of Mechanisms* **4**, 159–66.

Blaschke, W. (1948). *Zur Bewegungsgeometrie auf der Kugel*. Sitz. Ber. Heidelberger Akad. Wiss.

Blaschke, W. (1950). *Einführung in die Differentialgeometrie*. Springer, Berlin/Göttingen/ Heidelberg.

Bottema, O. (1961). On the instantaneous invariants of the motion of a rigid plane system. In *Proceedings of the International Conference of Mechanisms*, 159–64, Yale University. Shoe String Press, New Haven, New England.

Bottema, O. (1965). Acceleration axes in spherical kinematics. *Trans. ASME, Journal of Engineering for Industry* **87B**, 150–4.

Bottema, O. & Roth, B. (1979). *Theoretical Kinematics.* North-Holland, Amsterdam.

Bruewitsch, N.G. (1937). Kinematics of spherical 4-bar linkages (in Russian). *Westnik Inzenerow i Technikow* **8**, 465–8.

Chen, F.Y. (1968). *On a Class of Spherical Linkages*. ASME Paper No. 68-Mech-43.

Chen, F.Y. (1975). On closed form synthesis equations of the spherical crank–rocker mechanism. In *Proceedings of the Fourth World Congress on Mechanism and Machine Theory*, 707–710. Newcastle upon Tyne, England.

Chen, F.Y. & Chou, P.H. (1970). *Dimensional Synthesis of the Spherical Double-Rocker Mechanism*. ASME Paper No. 70-Mech-81.

Chen, J.S. & Chiang, C.H. (1983). Fourth order synthesis of spherical 4-bar function generators. *Mechanism and Machine Theory* 18, 451–6.

Chiang, C.H. (1970). Simplified graphical acceleration analysis of four-bar linkages. *Journal of Mechanisms* 5, 549–62.

Chiang, C.H. (1971). Einfache Verfahren zur Ruckermittlung eines Gelenkvierecks und zur Maßsynthese des Funktionsgetriebes. *Feinwerktechnik* 75, 306–13.

Chiang, C.H. (1976). Synthesis of spherical four-bar function generators by means of three relative poles. *Mechanism and Machine Theory* 11, 285–94.

Chiang, C.H. (1983). Synthesis of spherical four-bar function generators to match two prescribed velocity ratios. *Trans. ASME, Journal of Mechanisms, Transmissions and Automation in Design* 105, 631–6.

Chiang, C.H. (1984a). On the classification of spherical four-bar linkages. *Mechanism and Machine Theory* 19, 283–7.

Chiang, C.H. (1984b). Angular velocity RCCC-linkage of a spherical four-bar linkage. *Mechanism and Machine Theory* 19, 277–81.

Chiang, C.H. (1986a). Synthesis of spherical four-bar path generators. *Mechanism and Machine Theory* 21, 135–43.

Chiang, C.H. (1986b). Design of spherical and planar crank–rockers and double-rockers as function generators–I. Crank–rockers. *Mechanism and Machine Theory* 21, 287–96.

Chiang, C.H. (1986c). Design of spherical and planar crank–rockers and double-rockers as function generators–II. Double–rockers. *Mechanism and Machine Theory* 21, 297–305.

Chiang, C.H. & Chen, J.S. (1983). On some kinematic relations between a spherical four-bar linkage and its gnomonic projection. In *Proceedings of the Sixth World Congress on Theory of Machines and Mechanisms*, Vol. 1, 350–3. Wiley Eastern, New Delhi.

Chiang, C.H. & Chung, T.T. (1980). *Analytical Synthesis of Four-Bar Function Generators to Match Prescribed Differential Coefficients*. ASME Paper No. 80-DET-33.

Crossley, F.R.E. (1955). 3-D mechanisms. *Machine Design*, Vol. 27, No. 8, August, 175–9.

Davitashvili, N.S. (1983a). Designing five-link hinged mechanisms taking into account the angle drive. *Mechanism and Machine Theory* 18, 481–9.

Davitashvili, N.S. (1983b). Investigation and designing of spherical and plane five-link bar mechanisms. In *Proceedings of the Sixth World Congress on Theory of Machines and Mechanisms*, Vol. 1, 354–7. Wiley Eastern, New Delhi.

Denavit, J. (1965). Discussion on paper of Bottema (1965). *Trans. ASME, Journal of Engineering for Industry* 87B, 153–4.

Denavit, J. & Hartenberg, R.S. (1960). Approximate synthesis of spatial linkages. *Journal of Applied Mechanics* 27, 201–6.

Di Benedetto, A., Francesco, O. & Pennestri, E. (1983). Synthesis of the spherical four-bar linkage for prescribed instantaneous angular velocities. In *Proceedings of the Eighth Oklahoma State University Applied Mechanisms Conference*, 65-1–65-6. Saint Louis, Missouri.

Dijksman, E.A. (1976). *Motion Geometry of Mechanisms*. Cambridge University Press, Cambridge.

Dittrich, G. (1964). *Über die momentane Bewegungsgeometrie eines sphärisch bewegten starren Systems*. Gerd Wasmund, Köln, West Germany.

Dittrich, G. (1965). Analyse und Anwendungen der Krümmungseigenschaften der Bahnkegel sphärischer Getriebe. In *Proceedings of the International Conference on Mechanism and Machine Theory* at Varna, Bulgaria 1, 79–91.

Dittrich, G. (1966a). Systematik sphärischer Kurvengetriebe. *Ind.-Anz.* 88,Nr.23,459-63.

Dittrich, G. (1966b). Konstruktion und Herstellung sphärischer Kurvengetriebe. *Konstruktion* 18, 421-6.

Dittrich, G. (1967). Die Totlagen der sphärischen Schubkurbel. *Ind.-Anz.* Nr. 34, 715.

Dittrich, G. (1970). Vergleich von ebenen, sphärischen und räumlichen Getrieben. *VDI-Berichte* Nr. 140, 25–34, VDI-Verlag, Düsseldorf.

Dittrich, G. & Sommer, J. (1969). Gelenkwellen–Kinematik, Übertragungsfähigkeit, Anwendungen. *Ind.-Anz.* 91, 1684-6.

Dittrich, G. & Zakel, H. (1975). Sphärische Koppelkurven und ihre Anwendung. In *Proceedings of the Fourth World Congress on Theory of Machines and Machinisms*, 939-44. Newcastle upon Tyne, England.

Dittrich, G. & Zakel, H. (1981). Krümmungseigenschaften sphärischer Bahnkurven im Hinblick auf ihre Anwendungen. *Forschungsberichte des Landes Nordrhein-Westfalen*, Nr. 3086. Westdeutscher Verlag, Leverkusen, West Germany.

Dobrovolskii, V.V. (1940). Theory of relative motion in spherical mechanisms (in Russian). *Izv. Akad. Nauk. Otd. Tekh. Nauk.*, 33–46.

Dobrovolskii, V.V. (1943). Synthesis of spherical mechanisms (in Russian). *Akad. Nauk. SSSR. Trudy Sem. Teorii Masin i Mechanizmov*, 5–20.

Dobrovolskii, V.V. (1944). On spherical coupler curves (in Russian). *Prikl. Math. Mekh.*, VIII, 475–7.

Dobrovolskii, V.V. (1945). On Burmester's points in spherical motion (in Russian). *Prikladnaia Mathemetika i Mekhanikz., Akad. Nauk. SSSR.*, Vol. 9, 489–91.

Dobrovolskii, V.V. (1947a). *Theory of Spherical Mechanisms* (in Russian). Moscow.

Dobrovolskii, V.V. (1947b). Spherical Representation of three dimensional four-bar linkages (in Russian). *Trudy Sem. Teoril Masin i Mehanizmov, Akad. Nauk. SSR*, Vol. 2, 111–26.

Dobrovolskii, V.V. (1947c). The method of spherical representation in the theory of spatial mechanisms (in Russian). *Trudy Sem. Teorii Masin i Mehanizmov, Akad. Nauk. SSSR.*, Vol. 3, No. 11, 5–37.

Dobrovolskii, V.V. (1952). The construction of the relative positions of the links of spatial seven-bar linkages by the method of spherical representation (in Russian). *Trudy Sem. Teorii Masin i Mehanizmov, Akad. Nauk. SSSR.* Vol. 12, No. 47, 52–62.

Dowler, H.J., Duffy, J. & Tesar, D. (1976). A generalized study of three multiply separated positions in spherical kinematics. *Mechanism and Machine Theory* 11, 395–410.

Dowler, H.J., Duffy, J. & Tesar, D. (1978). A generalized study of four and five multiply separated positions in spherical kinematics–II. *Mechanism and Machine Theory* 13, 409–35.

Duditza, Fl. (1968a). Polykardangetriebe. *Maschinenmarkt* 74, Nr. 63, 1254–60.

Duditza, Fl. (1968b). Über Sphärische Sechsgliedrige Getriebe. *Grundl. Landtechn.* 18, 146–50.

Duditza, Fl. (1969). Zur strukturellen Ordnung der Kardangelenkgetriebe. *Maschinenmarkt* 75, 321-9.

Duditza, Fl. & Dittrich, G. (1969). Die Bedingungen für die Umlauffähigkeit sphärischer viergliedriger Kurbelgetriebe. *Ind.-Anz.* 91, 1687–90.

Filemon, E. (1971). In addition to the Burmester theory. In *Proceedings of the Third World Congress on Theory of Machines and Mechanisms*, Vol. D, 63–78. Kupari, Yugoslavia.

Freudenstein, F. (1955). Approximate synthesis of four-bar linkages. *Trans. ASME* 77, 853–61.

Freudenstein, F. (1956). On the maximum and minimum velocities and the accelerations in four-link mechanisms. *Trans. ASME* 78, 779–87.

Freudenstein, F. (1959). Harmonic analysis of crank-and-rocker mechanisms with application. *Trans. ASME, Journal of Applied Mechanics* **26**, 673–5.

Freudenstein, F. (1965a). Higher path-curvature analysis in plane kinematics. *Trans. ASME, Journal of Engineering for Industry* **87B**, 184–90.

Freudenstein, F. (1965b). On the determination of the type of spherical four-link mechanisms (in Russian). *Contemporary Problems in the Theory of Machines and Mechanisms*, Academy of Sciences of the USSR, 193–6.

Freudenstein, F. & Mohan, K. (1961). When linkages need harmonic analysis. *Product Engineering*, March 6, 47–50.

Freudenstein, F. & Primrose, E.J.F. (1972). The classical transmission-angle problem. In *Conference on Mechanisms*, 105–10. The Institution of Mechanical Engineers, London.

Freudenstein, F. & Sandor, G.N. (1961). On the Burmester points of a plane. *Trans. ASME, Journal of Applied Mechanics* **28**, 41–9. (Discussions 473–4.)

Funabashi, H. & Freudenstein, F. (1979). Performance criteria for high-speed crank-and-rocker linkages, Part II: Spherical crank-and-rocker linkages. *Trans. ASME, Journal of Mechanical Design* **101**, 26–31.

Garnier, R. (1956). Cours de cinématique. Tome II. Gauthier–Villars, Paris.

Gilmartin, M.J. & Duffy, J. (1972). Type and mobility analysis of the spherical four-link mechanism. In *Conference on Mechanisms*, 90–7. The Institution of Mechanical Engineers, London.

Grashof, F. (1883). *Theoretische Maschinenlehre*, p. 117. Berlin.

Gupta, K.C. (1986). Rotatability considerations for spherical four-bar linkages with applications to robot wrist design. *Trans. ASME, Journal of Mechanisms, Transmissions and Automation in Design* **108**, 387–91.

Hackmüller, E. (1938). Zur Konstruktion der Burmesterschen Punkte. *Maschinenbau, RM-AfG* **6**, 648–9.

Hain, K. (1957a). Übertragungsgünstigste unsymmetrische Doppelkurbel-Getriebe. *VDI-Forschungsheft* **461**, 23–5.

Hain, K. (1957b). How to apply drag-link mechanisms in the synthesis of mechanisms. In *Trans. Fourth Conference on Mechanisms*, 66–75. West Lafayette, Indiana.

Hartenberg, R.S. & Denavit, J. (1964). *Kinematic Synthesis of Linkages*, p. 356. McGraw-Hill, New York.

Hein, G. (1959). Analytische und zeichnerische Unterlagen für zwei und drei Lagen eines sphärisch bewegten Getriebegliedes als Hilfsmittel zur Synthese sphärischer Kurbelgetriebe. *Forsch. Ing.-Wes.* **25**, 92–6, 115–26.

Hossne G., A.J.G. & Soni, A.H. (1979). Design of spherical double-rocker linkages. In *Proceedings of the Sixth Oklahoma State University Applied Mechanism Conference* XX-1–XX-6. Denver, Colorado.

Huang, M., Pamidi, P.R. & Soni, A.H. (1970). Design of a spherical four-link crank–rocker mechanism. *Journal of Mechanisms* **5**, 5–10.

Huang, M. & Soni, A.H. (1969). Design of spherical and spatial four-link crank–rocker mechanisms with or without passive constraint. In *Proceedings of the Oklahoma State University Applied Mechanism Conference*, 22.1–22.5. Tulsa, Oklahoma.

Johnson, H.L. (1965). *Path Generation in Space*. ASME Paper No. 65-WA/MD-13.

Kamphuis, H.J. (1969). Application of spherical instantaneous kinematics to the spherical slider-crank mechanism. *Journal of Mechanisms* **4**, 43–56.

Keator, F.W. & Crossley, F.R.E. (1955). Analyzing dimensional and velocity characteristics of 3-D mechanisms. *Machine Design*, Vol. 27, 204–9.

Keler, M. (1970). Analyse und Synthese räumlicher, sphärischer und ebener Getriebe in dual-komplexer Darstellung. *Feinwerktechnik* **74**, 341–51.

400 *References*

Kraus, R. (1952). Wertigkeitsbilanz und ihre Anwendung auf eine Geradführung für Meßgeräte. *Feinwerktechnik* **56**, 57–63.

Kraus, R. (1954). *Getriebelehre*, Vol. 1, Section 42. VEB Verlag Technik, Berlin.

Kreyszig, E. (1959). *Differential Geometry*. Toronto University Press, Toronto.

Kunad, G. (1968). Systematik und Kinematik gekoppelter sphärischer Getriebe. *Maschinenbautechnik (Getriebetechnik)* **17**, 491–2.

Kunad, G., Goetze, R. & Gismann, J. (1974). Rechnergestützte Analyse und Synthese von räumlichen Übertragungsgetrieben (3R-3R Getriebe). *Maschinenbautechnik* **23**, 318–21.

Lakshminarayana, K. (1972). On the synthesis of the spherical four-bar. *Mechanism and Machine Theory* **7**, 63–9.

Lee, T.W. & Akbil, E. (1986a, b). Kinematic synthesis of spherical two-gear drives with prescribed entire-motion characteristics: unlimited crank rotations and optimum transmission. *Trans. ASME, Journal of Mechanisms, Transmissions and Automation in Design* **108**, (a) part 1: theory. 46–52, (b) part 2: applications. 53–9.

Lowen, G. (1967). A graphical method for the determination of angular accelerations in four-linked spatial mechanisms. *Journal of Mechanisms* **2**, 475–82.

Luck, K. (1975). Synthese allgemein räumlicher und sphärische Koppelgetriebe unter Einbeziehung der Computertechnik. *Wiss. Z. der Technischen Universität Dresden* **24**, 1051–62.

Luck, K. & Modler, K.-H. (1974). Analytische Behandlung des Totlagen-Problems bei ebenen, sphärischen und räumlichen Viergelenkgetrieben. *Mechanism and Machine Theory* **9**, 27–35.

McCarthy, J.M. & Ravani, B. (1986). Differential kinematics of spherical and spatial motions using kinematic mapping. *Trans. ASME Journal of Applied Mechanics* **53**, 15–22.

McLarnan, C.W. (1968). On linkage synthesis with minimum error. *Journal of Mechanisms* **3**, 101–5.

Meyer zur Capellen, W. (1958a). Das Kreuzgelenk als periodische Getriebe. *Werkstatt und Betrieb* **91**, 435–44.

Meyer zur Capellen, W. (1958b). Über elliptischer Kurbelschleifen. *Werkstatt und Betrieb* **91**, 723–9.

Meyer zur Capellen, W. (1960). Die Extrema der Übersetzungen in ebenen und sphärischen Kurbeltrieben. *Ingenieur-Archiv* **27**, 352–64.

Meyer zur Capellen, W. (1961). Sphärische Maltesergetriebe. *Techn. Mitteil.* **54**, 239–44.

Meyer zur Capellen, W. (1962). Der sphärische Doppelschieber als kinematische Umkehrung des Kreuzgelenks. *Ind.-Anz.* **84**, 1591–5.

Meyer zur Capellen, W. (1963). Ebene und sphärische Koppelrädertriebe als Rastgetriebe. *Ind.-Anz.* **85**, 2063–7.

Meyer zur Capellen, W. (1965a). Die Kopplung zweier Kreuzgelenke. *Ind.-Anz.* **87**, 111–15.

Meyer zur Capellen, W. (1965b). Die Kopplung zweier Kreuzgelenke. *Ind.-Anz.* **87**, 433–5.

Meyer zur Capellen, W. (1971). Spärische Viergelenkgetriebe mit zeitweise linearem Abtriebsgesetz. In *Proceedings of the Third World Congress on Theory of Machines and Mechanisms*, Vol. B, 115–26. Kupari, Yugoslavia.

Meyer zur Capellen, W. (1976). Über Verzweigungslagen bei sphärischen Viergelenktrieben. *Mechanism and Machine Theory* **11**, 277–84.

Meyer zur Capellen, W. (1983a). Die sphärischen Analoga zu den ρ-Kurven von H. Alt. *Mechanism and Machine Theory* **18**, 73–83.

Meyer zur Capellen, W. (1983b). Die Krümmungsfläche der sphärischen Kinematik. *Mechanism and Machine Theory* **18**, 243–8.

Meyer zur Capellen, W. (1983c). Nomogramme für die Krümmung sphärischer und ebener Bahnkurven. *Mechanism and Machine Theory* **18**, 249–54.

Meyer zur Capellen, W. & Dittrich, G. (1962). Sphärische Umlaufrastgetriebe. *Ind.-Anz.* **84**, Nr. 26, 471–7.

Meyer zur Capellen, W. & Dittrich, G. (1966). The instantaneous distribution of acceleration of a spherically moving system. *Journal of Mechanisms* **1**, 23–42.

Meyer zur Capellen, W. & Dittrich, G. (1967). Umlaufende sphärische Kurbelschleife mit stationärem Übersetzungsverhältnis. *Ind.-Anz.* **89**, 1701–3.

Meyer zur Capellen, W., Dittrich, G. & Janssen, B. (1966). Systematik und Kinematik ebener und sphärische Viergelenkgetriebe. *Forschungsberichte des Landes Nordrhein-Westfalen*, Nr. 1611. Westdeutscher Verlag, Köln und Opladen, West Germany.

Meyer zur Capellen, W. & Ernst von der Osten-Sacken. (1968). Systematik und Kinematik ebener und sphärischer Kurbelrädertriebe. *Forschungsberichte des Landes Nordrhein-Westfalen*, Nr. 1901. Westdeutscher Verlag, Köln und Opladen, West Germany.

Meyer zur Capellen, W. & Rath, W. (1960). Kinematik der sphärischen Schubkurbel. *Forschungsberichte des Landes Nordrhein-Westfalen*, Nr. 873. Westdeutscher Verlag, Köln und Opladen, West Germany.

Meyer zur Capellen, W. & Schreiber, E. (1971). Die Kopplung elliptischer Zahnräder mit der sphärischen Kurbelschleife. In *Proceedings of the Third World Congress on Theory of Machines and Mechanisms*, Vol. F, 393–403. Kupari, Yugoslavia.

Meyer zur Capellen, W. & Schreiber, E. (1972). Kopplung von ebene und räumlichen Getrieben: Elliptische Zahnräder und sphärische Kurbelschleife. *Klepzig Fachberichte* **80**, 267–74.

Meyer zur Capellen, W. & Thünker, N. (1975a). Die Harmonischen der Bewegungsenergie sphärischer Kubelschleifen. *Mechanism and Machine Theory* **10**, 139–46.

Meyer zur Capellen, W. & Thünker, N. (1975b). Die kinetische Energie der ebenen Kurbelschleifen und ihre Harmonische Analyse. *Mechanism and Machine Theory* **10**, 147–54.

Meyer zur Capellen, W. & Werner, M. (1975). Konjugierte Stellungen bei sphärischen Viergelenkgetrieben und die zugehörigen speziellen Koppelkurven. *Mechanism and Machine Theory* **10**, 421–30.

Meyer zur Capellen, W. & Willkommen, W.W. (1974). Sphärische Viergelenkgetriebe als Proportionalgetriebe. *Forschungsberichte des Landes Nordrhein-Westfalen*, Nr. 2386. Westdeutscher Verlag, Köln und Opladen, West Germany.

Meyer zur Capellen, W. et al. (1970). Die Extrema der Abtriebsbeschleunigungen in sphärischen periodischen Getrieben. *Ind.-Anz.* **92**, 1263–7.

Modler, K.-H. (1972). Reihenfolge der homologen Punkte. *Maschinenbautechnik* **21**, 258–65.

Müller, F.O. (1929). Beschleunigungsverhältnisse beim sphärischen Kurbeltrieb und verwandten Mechanism. *VDI-Z.* **73**, 117–25.

Müller, H.R. (1962). *Sphärische Kinematik*. VEB-Verlag der Wissenschaften, Berlin.

Müller, R. (1892). Über die Bewegung eines starren ebenen Systems durch fünf unendlich benachbarte Lagen. *Zeitschrift für Mathematik und Physik* **37**, 129–50.

Müller, R. (1903). Über einige Kurven, die mit der Theorie des ebenen Gelenkvierecks in Zusammenhang stehen. *Zeitschrift für Mathematik und Physik* **48**, 224–48.

Müller, R. (1932). *Einführung in die Theoretische Kinematik*. Springer, Berlin.

Naganathan, G. & Soni, A.H. (1981). Design of spherical double-rocker mechanisms. In *Proceedings of the Seventh Oklahoma State University Applied Mechanisms Conference*, XXXI-1–XXXI-4, Kansas City, Missouri.

Osman, M.O.M., Dukkipati, R.V. & Osman, M. (1983). Synthesis of a spherical four-bar linkage for a limited variation in the velocity ratio. In *Proceedings of the Sixth World Congress on Theory of Machines and Mechanisms*. Vol. 1, 250–3. Wiley Eastern, New Delhi.

Pamidi, P.R. (1976). On extreme velocity ratios in spherical four-link mechanisms. *Trans. ASME, Journal of Engineering for Industry* **98B**, 1260–5.

Pamidi, P.R. & Soni, A.H. (1969). How to design a spherical four-link mechanism for a prescribed extreme velocity ratio. In *Proceedings of the Oklahoma State University Applied Mechanisms Conference*, 23-1–23-4. Tulsa, Oklahoma.

Pottmann, H. (1985). Zur Konstruktion der sphärischen Wendekurve. *Mechanism and Machine Theory* **20**, 77–9.

Primrose, E.J.F. & Freudenstein, F. (1969). Spatial motion I – point paths of mechanisms with four or fewer links. *Trans. ASME, Journal of Engineering for Industry* **91B**, 103–14.

Rao, A.V.M., Sandor, G.N., Kohli, D. & Soni, A.H. (1973). Closed form synthesis of spatial function generating mechanism for the maximum number of precision points. *Trans. ASME, Journal of Engineering for Industry* **95B**, 725–36.

Rao, S.S. & Ambeker, A.G. (1974). Optimum design of spherical 4-R function generating mechanisms. *Mechanism and Machine Theory* **9**, 405–10.

Rath, W. (1960a). Rückkehrende sphärische Koppelrädergetriebe. *Klepzig Fachberichte* **68**, 141–6.

Rath, W. (1960b). Sphärische Koppelrädergetriebe, Steg des Rädertriebes ist das Abtriebsglied der sphärischen Viergelenkkette. *Klepzig Fachberichte* **68**, 274–83.

Rath, W. (1961). Die sphärischen Koppelrädertriebe und ihre Bedeutung als neue Getriebe-kombenation in Wissenschaft und Praxis. *Industrie-Anzeiger* **83**, 108–14.

Ravani, B. & Roth, B. (1984). Mapping of spatial kinematics. *Trans. ASME Journal of Mechanisms, Transmissions and Automation in Design* **106**, 341–7.

Reinholtz, C.F., Sandor, G.N. & Duffy, J. (1986). Branching analysis of spherical *RRRR* and spatial *RCCC* mechanisms. *Trans. ASME, Journal of Mechanisms, Transmissions and Automation in Design* **108**, 481–6.

Reuleaux, F. (1876). *The Kinematics of Machinery.* English edn, translated by A.B.W. Kennedy, p. 327. Dover, New York.

Riddle, D.L., Tesar, D. & Duffy, J. (1975). Kinematic synthesis of geared spherical five-bar mechanisms for function generation. *Trans. ASME, Journal of Engineering for Industry* **97B**, 723–30.

Roth, B. (1967). Finite position theory applied to mechanism synthesis. *Trans. ASME Journal of Applied Mechanics* **34**, 599–605.

Sarkisharn, Y.L. (1982). *Approximate Synthesis of Mechanisms* (in Russian), p. 151. Hayka, Moscow.

Sasskii, K.F. (1960). Some problems in the calculation of spherical hinged mechanisms (in Russian). *Trud. Inst. Mash.*, XX, **78**, 10–19.

Savage, M. & Hall, A.S. (1970). Unique description of all spherical four-bar linkages. *Trans. ASME, Journal of Engineering for Industry* **92B**, 559–66.

Schoenflies, A. (1886). *Geometrie der Bewegung in synthetischer Darstellung.* Teubner, Leipzig.

Schöpke, H. (1968). Gelenkwellen. *Antriebstechnik* **7**, Nr. 4, 123–9.

Shi, Zechang. (1982). Maßsynthese von Getriebekombinationen aus ebenen oder sphärischen Doppelkurbeln und anderen Getrieben zur Verwirklichung bereichsweise vorgegebener Übersetzungsverhältnisse. *Fotodruck J. Mainz*, Aachen, West Germany.

Shigley, J.E. & Uicker, J.J. (1980). *Theory of Machines and Mechanisms*, p. 362. McGraw-Hill, New York.

Shoup, T.E. & Pelan, B.J. (1971). Design of four-bar mechanisms for optimum transmission angle and optimum structural error. In *Proceedings of the Second Oklahoma State University Applied Mechanism Conference*, 4-1–4-9, Stillwater, Oklahoma.

Sieber, H. (1959). Analytische und graphische Verfahren zur Statik und Dynamik räumlicher Kurbelgetriebe. *Konstruktion* **11**, 333–44.

Sodhi, R. & Shoup, T.E. (1982). Axodes for the four-revolute spherical mechanism. *Mechanism and Machine Theory* **17**, 173–8.

Sodhi, R.S. & Shoup, T.E. (1983). Design of four revolute spherical function generator by curve matching. In *Proceedings of the Sixth World Congress on Theory of Mechines and Mechanisms*, Vol. 1, 102–5. Wiley Eastern, New Delhi.

Sodhi, R.S., Wilhelm, A.J. & Shoup, T.E. (1985) Design of a four-revolute spherical function generator with transmission effectiveness by curve matching. *Mechanism and Machine Theory* **20**, 577–85.

Soni, A.H. (1970). Discussion on paper of Savage & Hall (1970). *Trans. ASME, Journal of Engineering for Industry* **92B**, 563–6.

Soni, A.H. & Dukkipati, R.V. (1975). How to design spherical four-bar with optimum transmission angle and optimum structural error. In *Proceedings of the Fourth Oklahoma State University Applied Mechanism Conference*, 17-1–17-8. Chicago, Illinois.

Soni, A.H. & Hamid, S.(1972), *Synthesis of Spherical Six-Link Mechanisms for Path Generation*. ASME Paper No.72-Mech-83.

Soni, A.H. & Harrisberger, L. (1967). The design of spherical drag-link mechanism. *Trans. ASME, Journal of Engineering for Industry* **89B**, 177–81.

Soni, A.H. & Huang, M. (1971). Synthesis of four-link space mechanisms via extension of point-position-reduction technique. *Trans. ASME, Journal of Engineering for Industry* **93B**, 85–9.

Sridhar, B.N. & Torfason, L.E. (1970a). *Optimization of Spherical Four-Bar Path Generators*. ASME Paper No. 70-Mech-46.

Sridhar, B.N. & Torfason, L.E. (1970b). *Spherical Linkage Synthesis Using Stereographic Projection*. ASME Paper No. 70-Mech-71.

Streit, Don A. & Soni, A.H. (1979). Design of spherical and an RCCC space crank–rocker mechanism with unit time ratio. In *Proceedings of the Sixth Oklahoma State University Applied Mechanism Conference*, XIX-1–XIX-4. Denver, Colorado.

Struik. D.J. (1950). *Lectures on Classical Differential Geometry*. Addison-Wesley, Cambridge, Massachusetts.

Suh, C.H. (1970). Design of spatial linkages to replace gears. *Journal of Mechanisms* **5**, 217–37.

Suh, C.H. & Radcliffe, C.W. (1967). Synthesis of spherical linkages with use of the displacement matrix. *Trans. ASME, Journal of Engineering for Industry* **89B**, 215–22.

Sutherland, G. & Roth, B. (1973). A transmission index for spatial mechanisms. *Trans. ASME, Journal of Engineering for Industry* **95B**, 589–97.

Tavkhelidze, D.S. (1971). A study of kinematics and dynamics of four-link spherical mechanisms, using Euler's angles. *Journal of Mechanisms* **6**, 505–15.

Tavkhelidze, D.S. & Davitashvili, N.S. (1974). Kinematic analysis of five-link spherical mechanisms. *Mechanism and Machine Theory* **9**, 181–90.

Tavkhelidze, D.S., Davitashvili, N.S. & Demurishvili, N.V. (1979). The determination of technological error in spherical 4-link hinged mechanism. *Mechanism and Machine Theory* **14**, 43–59.

Tawchelidse, D.S. (1968). Neue sphärische und räumliche Getriebe. *Antriebstechnik* **7**, 459–61.

Tesar, D. (1967). The generalized concept of three multiply separated positions in coplanar motion. *Journal of Mechanisms* **2**, 461–74.

Ting,K.-L. & Soni, A.H. (1983). Instantaneous Kinematics of a Plane in Spherical Motion. *Trans, ASME, Journal of Mechanisms, Transmissions and Automation in Design* **105**,561-6.

404   *References*

Tölke, J. (1975). Erzeugungsmöglichkeiten der sphärischen Kreispunktkurve. *Mechanism and Machine Theory* **10**, 207–15.

Tsai, L.W. (1983). Design of drag-link mechanisms with minimax transmission angle deviation. *Trans. ASME, Journal of Mechanisms, Transmission and Automation in Design* **105**, 686–91.

Uhing, J. (1957). Einfache Raumgetriebe für ungleichförmige Dreh- und Schwingbewegung. *Konstruktion* **9**, 18–21.

Veldkamp, G.R. (1967a). Canonical systems and instantaneous invariants in spatial kinematics. *Journal of Mechanisms* **2**, 329–88.

Veldkamp, G.R. (1967b). An approach to spherical kinematics using tools suggested by plane kinematics. *Journal of Mechanisms* **2**, 437–50.

Veldkamp, G.R. (1969). On the spherical oscillating cylinder mechanism. *Trans. ASME, Journal of Engineering for Industry* **91B**, 143–6.

Verma, P.P. & Bussel, W.H. (1970). *The Use of a Planar Mechanism Synthesis to Produce a Spherical Path Generator Linkage*. ASME paper No. 70-Mech-51.

Waldron, K.J. & Strong, R.T. (1978). Improved solutions of the branch and order problems of Burmester linkage synthesis. *Mechanism and Machine Theory* **13**, 199–207.

Wills, A.P. (1931). *Vector and Tensor Analysis*, p. 57. Prentice-Hall, New York.

Wörle, H. (1962). Untersuchungen über Koppelkurven viergliedriger räumlicher Kurbelgetriebe. *Konstruktion* **14**, 390–2.

Yang, A.T. (1962). Harmonic analysis of spherical four-bar mechanisms. *Trans. ASME, Journal of Applied Mechanics* **29**, 683–8.

Yang, A.T. (1965). Static force and torque analysis of spherical four-bar mechanisms. *Trans. ASME, Journal of Engineering for Industry* **87B**, 221–7.

Yang, A.T. & Roth, B. (1973). The higher order path curvature in spherical kinematics. *Trans. ASME, Journal of Engineering for Industry* **95B**, 612–16.

Yuan, M.S.C. & Freudenstein, F. (1971). Kinematic analysis of spatial mechanisms by means of screw coordinates. Part 1 – Screw coordinates. *Trans. ASME, Journal of Engineering for Industry* **93B**, 61–6.

Yuan, M.S.C., Freudenstein, F. & Woo, L.S. (1971). Kinematic analysis of spatial mechanisms by means of screw coordinates. Part 2 – Analysis of spatial mechanisms. *Trans. ASME, Journal of Engineering for Industry* **93B**, 67–73.

Zimmerman, J.R. (1967). Four-precision-point synthesis of the spherical four-bar function generator. *Journal of Mechanisms* **2**, 133–9.

NAME INDEX

SUBJECT INDEX